HOW TO USE THIS BOOK

We recommend very strongly that, for this guide to be used most effectively for the identification of fungus species, pages 24-46 are read carefully. A knowledge of the anatomy of fungi, and the associated technical terms, is indispensable for a correct reading of the texts in the Directory (pp. 47-226).

The Directory includes over 1,350 species of fungi, representative of all major groups. The majority of these are the large basidiomycetes commonly called mushrooms and toadstools, and a very high proportion of European species is included. The commoner large ascomycetes (cup and flask fungi) are also described, together with sufficient common representatives of other fungal groups to enable the overall scope of the fungal kingdom to be appreciated.

The brief introductions to each family or other group outline the common characteristics of the appearance and biology of the species within it, and, although in most cases this information is applicable to non-European species, the main aim has been to encapsulate details about the species occurring within the geographic area covered by the book.

At the end of the accounts of agaric families only, a list of the approximate number of British genera and species is given. Genera given in round brackets are not included in the book. In other groups only an approximation is given, partly because the information is often not known with certainty, and also because family and other hierarchical limits themselves are under constant revision.

In each species account, the scientific name appears at the beginning of the entry, followed by the English vernacular name for those few species that have acquired one (*see p. 14*), e.g.

Amanita muscaria **Fly Agaric**

Some of the key features for identification of the species then follow, mainly to help distinguish it from species that may appear similar in the illustrations, e.g.

Overall size, habit, smell, habitat

The descriptions are based on details given in standard reference works, supplemented by the examination of fresh specimens, herbarium specimens, or details taken from field notebooks. Where the required facts were lacking or unclear from all of these sources, no hesitation has been made in inserting a question-mark. Indeed, it is hoped that this will encourage collectors to make their own observations.

Each illustration represents a typical specimen, but it should not be forgotten that very young or very old specimens will vary from these, and that atypical examples can occur, especially when growing in slightly unusual habitats or out of season.

Where it has been necessary to describe colours (of the flesh, for instance) that are not apparent from the illustrations, it has *not* been assumed that readers will all have access to standard colour-charts; so comparison with everyday objects has been made.

The categories used in the detailed accounts of individual species vary slightly between groups. Some fungi, for instance, have no stem, and others no gills; but the variations from the norm (represented by large basidiomycetes) are fairly self-evident.

In order to present as much information as possible about each fungal species, some of the details have been very slightly abbreviated, as explained below.

The following descriptive categories or key-words are all used at least once in the Directory, and definitions or guidance on their meaning and application can be found on the pages indicated. Dimensions used for each category are given where appropriate.

ACERVULUS (ACERVULI), cm, *see p. 44.*

AECIOSPORE, μm, *see p. 234.*

AECIUM (AECIA), cm, *see p. 234.*

APLANOSPORE, μm, *see p. 230.*

APOTHECIUM (APOTHECIA), cm, *see p. 42.*

ASCOSPORE, μm, *see p. 235.*

Some common ascospore shapes are illustrated here:

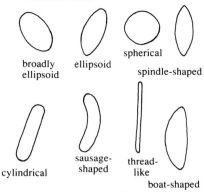

broadly ellipsoid

ellipsoid

spherical

spindle-shaped

cylindrical

sausage-shaped

thread-like

boat-shaped

ASCUS (ASCI), μm, *see p. 42.*

BASIDIOSPORE, μm, *see p. 231.*

Some common basidiospore shapes are illustrated here:

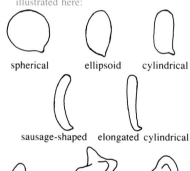

spherical

ellipsoid

cylindrical

sausage-shaped   elongated cylindrical

irregularly star-shaped

bullet-shaped

angular

BASIDIUM (BASIDIA), μm, *see p. 232.*

CAP: The range in diameter of the cap in centimetres is given as the average of at least two measurements, e.g.

5-9

Cap colour (where it changes markedly during growth, or for some other reason cannot be shown adequately in the illustration), shape, change in shape during development, surface texture, and marginal features are described as ex-

plained on *pp. 30-32.* e.g.

at first convex and broadly umbonate, then flatter and markedly depressed, finely downy with margin inrolled

CAPILLITIUM (CAPILLITIA), *see p. 193.*

CHLAMYDOSPORE, μm, *see Glossary.*

CLEISTOTHECIUM (CLEISTOTHECIA), cm, *see p. 42.*

CONIDIOPHORE, μm, *see Glossary.*

CONIDIUM (CONIDIA), μm, *see p. 230.*

CYSTIDIUM (CYSTIDIA), μm, *see p. 37.*

FLESH: The colour, colour change (especially after bruising), texture and relative firmness of the flesh are described (*see pp. 31-32*), e.g.

soft, rather fibrous in stem, white, sometimes red-tinged when cut

In some instances the response of the flesh to a chemical test is given (*see p. 36*), e.g.

Schaeffer+.

FOLDS, *see p. 299.*

FRUIT BODY, cm, *see p. 298.*

GALL, cm, *see Glossary.*

GILL: Gills are described mainly in relation to their colour, their relative closeness, and their method of attachment to the stem (*see pp. 32-33*), e.g.

white, then buff, variable, often branched, very crowded, decurrent

GLEBA, *see Glossary.*

HABIT, *see p. 28.*

The habit, habitat and season of occurrence (especially in Britain) are indicated, e.g.

In large groups, often in rings. On soil, among grass in pastures, parkland, roadsides, not usually with trees. Late summer-autumn.

HAIRS, μm, *see p. 43*

HYPHAL SYSTEM, *see p. 40*

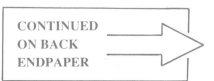

CONTINUED ON BACK ENDPAPER

Collins

New Generation Guide

TO THE

FUNGI

OF BRITAIN AND EUROPE

The Introduction explains what fungi are and discusses the evidence for their ancient aquatic origin and possible derivation from algae. The major differences between fungi and other living organisms are described together with the special features used in fungal classification. The unique techniques required for the collection, examination and identification of fungi are given in considerable and careful detail.

Armed with this understanding of what fungi are and how scientists classify and identify them, the reader is ready to use the Directory, in which the commonest and most important mushrooms and toadstools of Britain and Europe are set out in systematic order, together with common representatives of most other fungal groups. The illustrations of each species may be used in conjunction with the information in the text to identify fungi that are found and collected. Only after putting a name to a fungus is it really possible to take an interest in it, and many details of the fungus's status, habitat, structure and reproduction are given in handy reference form.

The third and longest part of the book considers each stage of the many and varied life cycles to be found among the fungi. It is an account of survival, of the advantages and disadvantages in the various types of spore, in the many ways that they are discharged, dispersed, germinate and grow to produce fungal colonies in a wide range of habitats and environments. It describes how fungi feed, often at the expense of other organisms and how they adapt or succumb to the multiplicity of threats to their existence and self-perpetuation. Whether it is read as a story, or dipped into, it explains what we see fungi doing, and the often hidden reasons why they are doing it.

Overleaf: Probably every habitat in the world has its fungal components, playing their part in the life or death of the plants and animals around them. Many are hidden, unseen, microscopic; others are large and obvious, at least for a short period of their annual cycle. Although the woodland habitat shown reveals only seven species of large and obvious mushrooms, toadstools or bracket fungi, there may be a hundred other species living obscurely on the leaves, bark, or wood, or in the soil.

Collins

New Generation Guide

TO THE

FUNGI

OF BRITAIN AND EUROPE

Stefan Buczacki

GENERAL EDITOR

David Attenborough

ILLUSTRATED BY

John Wilkinson

COLLINS
8 Grafton Street, London W1

First published 1989
ISBN 0 00 219448 1 Paperback
ISBN 0 00 219449 X Hardback

Text copyright © 1989 by Stefan Buczacki

Illustrations copyright © 1989 by John Wilkinson

William Collins Sons & Co. Ltd
London Glasgow Sydney Auckland Toronto Johannesburg

Typeset by Qualitext Typesetting, Abingdon, Oxon

Colour and black-and-white reproduction
by Alpha Reprographics Ltd, Perivale

Made and printed in Great Britain
by William Collins Sons & Co. Ltd, Glasgow

Dr Stefan Buczacki is well-known to millions of radio listeners in Britain for his weekly contributions to BBC Radio 4's 'Gardeners' Question Time'; but his interests in gardening are paralleled by those in natural history. After taking a first-class degree in Botany, and a doctorate in Forestry, he spent many years in research on the fungi that cause plant diseases, and achieved international recognition in this field. He has served on the Council of the British Mycological Society, and on the management committees of other leading scientific bodies, but left research in 1984 to concentrate full-time on broadcasting, writing and photography.

Also in the New Generation guide series

Collins New Generation Guide to the
Birds of Britain and Europe
by Christopher Perrins

Collins New Generation Guide to the
Wild Flowers of Britain and Northern Europe
by Alastair Fitter

CONTENTS

FOREWORD

Sir David Attenborough

Identifying fungi can be a matter of life and death, if a collector has cookery in mind, although the number of truly lethal species to be found in Europe is often somewhat exaggerated. It is no exaggeration, however, to say that identification beyond the requirements of the kitchen can in many instances be exceedingly difficult. Indeed, this book may be the first field guide, outside technical texts, that enables a reader to do so across the whole range of groups of European fungi.

The fungi, which change their shape and colour so swiftly during their often brief appearances, require a knowledge of their microstructure if their relationships and therefore their classification are to be properly understood. The Directory section describing the species is therefore preceded by one which outlines the evolution of fungi and describes the methods of collecting them, and the microscopic and chemical procedures necessary for discovering their diagnostic characters.

But the act of successfully attaching a name to a fungus, triumphant though it may well be in many instances, should not mark the end of a naturalist's curiosity about a mushroom or a toadstool, a rust or a bracket fungus.

Many more questions will spring to mind about these strange organisms that appear in our countryside, and even in our houses, so suddenly, mysteriously and briefly, apparently from nowhere. How do they spread? What is their relationship with the plants beside which they grow? In what form do they survive when they are no longer visible to the naked eye above ground?

The answers to such questions can only come from an understanding of the biology of fungi. This subject, therefore, forms the last section of the guide. In it, the often complex life-histories of typical fungi are followed, from the dissemination of their microscopic spores to the dramatic appearance of a fruiting body and its equally sudden dissolution. Examples are provided using species found in the Directory, so that particularly interesting features of a fungus encountered in the field are not missed.

Previous New Generation Guides, with their three inter-related sections, have aimed to provide a deeper understanding of animals and plants than that given by any other field guides. No group of organisms is in greater need of this treatment than the fungi – which, arguably, are neither.

PREFACE

Dr Stefan Buczacki

Mycology, the study of fungi, has been called the Cinderella of the natural history world. Certainly there are some among its subjects that could readily pass as pumpkins, but then there are those equally reminiscent of umbrellas, shelf brackets, frog-spawn and organ pipes. Fungi have always fascinated mankind while at the same time appearing slightly mysterious and slightly worrying. Their frequent (although by no means invariable) appearance in dark and damp places is part of the mystique, as is their unpredictable and ephemeral nature; here today, yet gone tomorrow for a year or more, is a quite normal happening. And the knowledge that the group includes some of the most exquisite of gastronomic treasures and some of the natural world's most potent toxins has not helped to remove the aura of mysticism.

For centuries, we have been content to describe, list, catalogue and collect, but only in very recent times has there been the inclination and insight to explain fungal biology. Even today, popular guide books to fungi are leagues behind their botanical and zoological counterparts in the information offered on the biology and behaviour of the organisms they cover. They illustrate, and sometimes help in naming, but very little else. This book is an attempt to put right that omission in that it not only illustrates and names but also places fungi in the overall scheme of life, and explains what is known of their relationship with each other and with other inhabitants of our planet's ecosystems. I am greatly indebted to Crispin Fisher, David Attenborough and Collins for enabling me to do this; and indebted too for what Crispin modestly calls his professional ignorance of the subject. He has taken the attitude that if he can be made to understand mycology, anyone can; an attitude of immeasurable assistance to me as author but one that does a gross injustice to his own, most alert biological mind.

Many people have contributed over the years to my own mycological education and none more so than my first mycological mentor, Dr John Manners, a fine and understanding teacher to whom I owe a great debt. More specifically, I am deeply grateful to Dr Roy Watling, recently President of the British Mycological Society, who read much of my text and made many helpful suggestions. It is a pleasure also to express my appreciation to Malcolm Clark and Bert Brand, two modern representatives of Britain's long tradition of fine amateur field mycologists, who made comments on specific parts of the book. In thanking these colleagues, I must nonetheless dissociate them from any errors of fact that may remain and for which I take responsibility. But I must thank one person above all: when Crispin Fisher first asked me to write the book, I agreed on the one condition that John Wilkinson would illustrate it. He has accepted the most astonishing array of reference material and the most irritating of requested changes without complaint. This book would be much the poorer without his beautiful paintings.

Part 1: What is a fungus?

Fungus is a word with which everyone is familiar but asked to provide a definition most people would offer something including at least one of three other words – mushroom, toadstool and mould. As will be explained shortly, all three of these are imprecise and all three conjure up images that in fact represent only a small part of fungus biology. The word fungus itself is of uncertain etymology; the Oxford English Dictionary suggests an origin in the Greek *sphonggis,* a sponge, and although there is room for individual variance it is now general practice in English to pronounce the word with a soft 'g'. A more ancient word for fungi in general is *mycetes* and the study of fungi has been known since the mid-nineteenth century as mycology. The root *myc-,* originating also in the Greek with *mykes,* a term apparently applied somewhat irregularly to certain species, occurs widely in fungal terminology (as witness *-mycete* as a taxonomic Class ending and *mycelium,* a fungal growth, which will be found repeatedly throughout the book). Today, we can define a fungus with some precision as a parasitic or non-parasitic organism, feeding heterotrophically (requiring carbohydrates from an outside source, rather than being able to make their own by photosynthesis), reproducing by sexual or asexual spores and usually forming hyphae. (Reference to the glossary will give brief elucidation of any among these terms that is unfamiliar: they will be greatly amplified in due course.) Mushrooms and toadstools are the names applied to the large fruit bodies of some species (often generally called agarics) among the group of fungi known as the basidiomycetes, and to a lesser extent of some of the group called ascomycetes too. The two terms have no precise meaning, and even the common assumption that mushrooms are edible and toadstools inedible or poisonous does not hold true. The English language is indeed unusual in having two separate words at all (or three, if fungus is included); in French and German, for instance, *champignon* and *Pilz* serve quite adequately. The word mushroom originates in the Old French *mousseron,* through *mousse,* meaning moss and can be traced in the Old High German *mos.* The origin of the word toadstool has baffled even the most enquiring lexicographer and one authority has summarised it admirably in saying that 'the superficial derivation of toadstool is as apparent as the association of toads with agarics is obscure'. The word mould is applied to fungal growth in damp places and derives from the Anglo-Saxon *molde.* Further comments on some of the names currently used in English for particular types of fungi are given on p. 14.

The conspicuous yet ephemeral nature of the large species of fungi, such as those to which we now apply the terms mushroom and toadstool, has attracted man's attention since ancient times; Pliny (AD 23–79) appears to have been the first to describe them, and his account summarised beautifully so much of what passed for understanding for many centuries: 'Among the most wonderful things is the fact that anything can spring up and live without a root', he wrote, suggesting that a fundamental difference from plants had already been recognised. He continued 'These things are called truffles (*tubera*); they are surrounded on all sides by earth . . . they are a kind of earthy concretion . . . There are two kinds: one is sandy and injures the teeth, the other without any foreign matter'. From Pliny's time almost to the present, men have argued and debated the nature of fungi. They were for hundreds of years not even generally recognised as living things, and the ponderous progress of elucidation is exemplified by the remarks of

the German herbalist Jerome Bock who, writing some 1,500 years after Pliny, could only comment that they were 'neither herbs, nor roots, nor flowers, nor seeds, but merely the superfluous moisture of earth, of trees, or rotten wood, and of other rotting things'.

But gradually a little light began to shine on the dark world of the fungus, and by 1583 at least one observer, the Italian Cesalpino, had decided to countenance at least the possibility that they were a type of living being – an organism. He remarked 'Some plants have no seed . . . and spring from decaying substances . . . they are a sort of intermediate existence between plants and inanimate nature'. Although a few years later Cesalpino's compatriot della Porta (see p. 227) observed spores, and later still yet a third Italian, Micheli, actually demonstrated the development of fungi from them, it was to be many more years before their status as organisms became accepted generally. But even this advance was only the end of the beginning, for the conundrum of where in the overall scheme of life they should be placed has continued and, even now, is not finally resolved.

No less an eighteenth-century figure than Baron Otto von Münchausen typified in his writings the belief that fungi were related in some manner to the microscopic forms of animal life generally referred to as *animalcules* or *infusoria*. Linnaeus, with whom Münchausen corresponded, reacted to his views by creating a new animal genus to accommodate some of the forms he described. And in what, with hindsight, was one of the most wonderfully appropriate gestures in the history of taxonomy, Linnaeus named the new genus *Chaos*. The merits of placing fungi with animals created an interesting and lively debate, one not helped by the observations made by various authorities of those fungi that parasitise insects and emerge subsequently from their bodies. A spirited but inevitably futile argument ensued on the likelihood or otherwise of vegetables changing into animals

and vice versa. Slowly, however, fungi gravitated towards the plant rather than the animal kingdom, a progress associated principally with the erroneous analogy drawn between spores and seeds (see p. 227). So for the past 200 years or so, mycology has been a branch of botany rather than of zoology.

But ask a school-child or educated adult today to explain in what way living things are subdivided, and the chances are high that they will still proffer two categories or kingdoms, plants and animals. This view has its basis, as does most modern classification, with Linnaeus who in 1751 set down his 'three kingdoms of nature' of which one, *Lapides* or stones was inanimate and two, *Vegetabilia* and *Animalia*, living. Nonetheless, other more complex systems have been propounded at various times and the most seminal was that of the German Haeckel who around one hundred years ago put forward a four-kingdom scheme in which Fungi, together with Algae and Lichens, were placed in one of the two sub-divisions of the Kingdom Metaphyta that also included plants. From Haeckel's scheme, others have evolved and one of the most widely accepted at the present time is that of the American Whittaker, who published a five-kingdom classification in 1949. Whittaker, in common with other modern authors, accords the fungi a separate kingdom largely on the basis of the way they obtain nourishment, which is different from that of plants and of animals (see p. 258). In the light of such classifications and modern knowledge, it is pertinent to examine more closely the relationship of fungi with other life forms, and to consider the important matter of how they evolved.

FOSSIL EVIDENCE AND THE POSSIBLE ORIGIN OF FUNGI

The evolutionist seeking evidence for the origin of species, turns as much as anywhere to the fossil record. Here he sees, frozen in the time capsules of geological strata, the life forms of ages past, and can chart the organisms that inhabited the earth an almost unimaginable number of years ago. Although the very oldest fossils may be difficult to interpret, the specialist in almost every group of organisms can point to a time in the past when the foundations of his interest were laid. The ornithologist knows that birds first appeared some 150 million years ago in the Jurassic period; the pteridologist can see fossil ferns in Upper Devonian rocks around 350 million years old; the entomologist can chart insects back at least to the Devonian and possibly the earlier Silurian, while the student of sponges can know with some degree of certainty that his chosen animals were present in the Cambrian, over 500 million years distant. The mycologist, however, can mostly just grope in the dark and share his ignorance with the devotees of jelly fish and soft-bodied worms (although even they can find casts recording where such animals last laid their bodies). For fungi are soft-bodied too, not readily given to the processes of fossilisation: with few exceptions, the fossil record of the fungi is one of tantalising glimpses and involves speculation based on a very limited range of structures.

Although so-called fossil fungi have been described since the early nineteenth century, most of the older reports are now discounted and the putative fungal remains explained as coral, animal burrows or even fish fragments. Nonetheless, among the abundant plant remains of the Carboniferous coal forests were found some indisputably fossil micro-fungi growing in the leaves and stems of the swamp ferns and horsetails. Their relative paucity was explained by the

fact that even today fungi do not occur on such forms nearly as abundantly as they do on flowering plants. Thus it was possible to state with some confidence that fungi had been present on the earth, occupying a similar ecological niche to that occupied by many today, about 350 million years ago. Subsequently many perfectly preserved fossils of fungi attributable to modern genera were found on the leaves of flowering plants dating from some 50 million years ago, and there is every reason to suppose that fungi adapted to this group when it first evolved, presumably from coniferous progenitors, some 50 million years earlier.

But the study of fossil fungi was set back upon its heels, as was that of fossil botany, by the astonishing discoveries of fossil plants made in the early years of this century at Rhynie in Scotland. Here a marsh or bog of the Middle Devonian age, some 370 million years old, was perfectly preserved in chert rock. The plants unearthed at Rhynie were almost all unlike any seen before; although they had higher plant-like conducting tissues, they were spore-bearing and simply branched. And when their stems and rhizomes were examined microscopically, they contained quite distinct fungal mycelium. To try to assign these fungi to modern groups has been merely to provide fodder for futile argument, yet there are grounds for considering at least some to have been parasitic in living tissue or even to have displayed the apparently sophisticated symbiotic relationship called a mycorrhiza (see p. 267).

Fungal presence on earth had thus been pushed back a very long way, but it may go back a great deal further. Even more ancient rocks, from North America and South Africa especially, contain evidence for the existence of bacteria, and of blue-green algae or other 'filamen-

Reconstruction of original Devonian vegetated landscape at Rhynie. At bottom left can be seen the tuber-like structure of *Horneophyton* in which fossil evidence of fungal growth was found.

tous' life forms, as long ago as two or even three thousand million years. Whatever the validity of these claims, there is now no doubt that fungi are a very old group indeed and, from whatever group of organisms they evolved, they did so a very long time ago.

The oldest positive fungal remains were associated with aquatic or marsh plants; indeed, it is scarcely plausible to consider so fragile and aqueous a structure as the fungal hypha to have originated anywhere other than in water. But as what? To answer this meaningfully, it is important to look rather more closely at the essential features of fungi and see how other organisms compare with them.

As has been mentioned, in modern classification fungi are separated from animals principally on the basis of their mode of nutrition: animals eat, fungi absorb. Plants are different too in that they photosynthesise, a quite distinct nutritional process in which solar energy is trapped and used to bring about the formation of nutrient substances from the raw materials of atmospheric carbon dioxide and water. No fungus can photosynthesise and there is no evidence from fossils that they ever could. Thus far, therefore, fungi seem uniquely distinct. If comparisons are extended beyond nutrition, however, some similarities to other organisms are apparent, even without entering into biological and biochemical complexities. Remove the ability to photosynthesise from

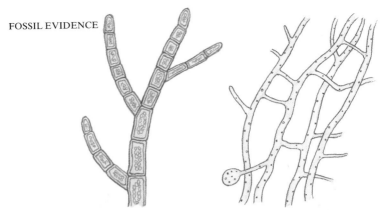

Microscopic comparison of a filamentous alga (left) and the mycelium of an Oomycete fungus.

some filamentous algae and there would remain an organism more closely resembling some fungi than any other yet discovered. The reproductive structures, the presence of free-swimming spores with two propulsion organs, the filamentous form, the aquatic habitat and the presence of the most un-animal-like substance cellulose in their make up, place one group of fungi especially, the Oomycetes, firmly on an evolutionary road from an alga-like ancestor.

But the Oomycetes or watermoulds are alone among the major groups of fungi in containing cellulose in their cells walls; other groups have chitin, which is a widespread structural material among animals, instead. Indeed the Oomycetes are significantly different from most fungi in other important though more technical ways too, and there are good grounds for considering them to have evolved differently. If they have an algal origin, what of the remainder, the major groups that contain mushrooms, toadstools and all other macro- and most micro-fungi?

Working from the universal presence of the structural material chitin, the functioning of important biochemical reactions and some features of the genetic material, a scheme has been proposed that indicates an evolutionary line encompassing all other modern fungi from an ancestral aquatic type obtaining its nutrition by 'eating' rather than absorbing, having free-swimming spores with two propulsion organs, and containing chitin not cellulose. No such organism is known, but among modern fungi the type is best matched by the Plasmodiophoromycetes, a small, soil or water-inhabiting group of organisms

Highly magnified microscopic view of a plasmodiophoromycete fungus, showing its 'eating' method of parasitising its host.

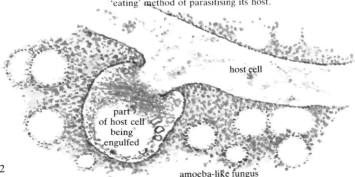

host cell

part of host cell being engulfed

amoeba-like fungus

parasitic on plants, on algae and on some Oomycetes. In this group, and in this group alone, forms exist which appear to have some vestiges of an amoeba-like ability to ingest or 'eat' nutrients as well as absorbing them. Their wholly parasitic life style, existing entirely within the cells of their hosts, may have significance too in indicating the survival of an ancient habit. For fungi have colonised dry land, and today they have adapted

A putative phylogenetic tree for the fungi

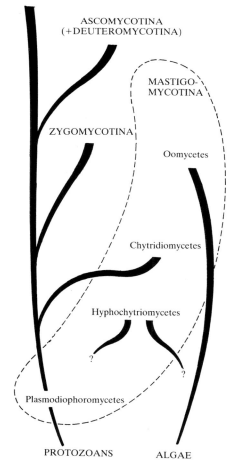

BASIDIOMYCOTINA

ASCOMYCOTINA
(+DEUTEROMYCOTINA)

MASTIGO-
MYCOTINA

ZYGOMYCOTINA

Oomycetes

Chytridiomycetes

Hyphochytriomycetes

?

Plasmodiophoromycetes

PROTOZOANS   ALGAE

even to desert environments, although access to a water supply remains essential. How then did they escape from their aqueous prison?

Perhaps the plants of the Rhynie marsh and the life style of the Plasmodiophoromycetes contain clues, and perhaps the popular theories about the relative evolutionary advancement of parasitic and non-parasitic modes of existence need revision, at least in relation to fungi. For it has long been thought that parasitism (especially that displayed by the Plasmodiophoromycetes, called obligate parasitism and involving total dependence upon a living source of food – see p. 259) is a fairly recent development, a sophisticated adaptation to provide an organism with a continuing nutrient supply for as long as its host plant or animal remains alive. Yet, as plants colonised dry land, what better way for the fungi to do the same than to come inside them, protected by their tissues from the dessicating effects of the primaeval atmosphere? At various times in evolutionary history, non-parasitic forms may subsequently have arisen, quite possibly through increasing ability to continue to feed on their hosts' tissues as they ultimately succumbed, leading to a natural progression to feeding on other organic matter in the soil beneath.

But before progressing to the present-day ordering of fungi in more detail, one very important point must be emphasised. The evolutionary line suggested on the left will always be speculative for it is based, unlike evolutionary charts for almost all other organisms, solely on living forms. It presupposes that some extant forms are ancient and is created in ignorance of any types of fungi that have arisen and died out in the past. To speculate on the prehistory of reptiles without knowing of the existence of dinosaurs would be a reasonable zoological analogy.

13

THE NAMING AND CLASSIFICATION OF FUNGI

Living organisms are given names and are classified into groups. Fungi are no exception, but it will perhaps come as no surprise, in the light of the comments made so far, that neither in nomenclature nor in classification are matters quite as simple as might be wished. It is now fairly generally understood that the colloquial names applied locally to organisms in particular geographical or linguistic regions (known as vernacular names) are of little value in other regions; hence students of the various groups use internationally accepted scientific names (based on Latin or Greek, or a combination thereof), but usually with vernacular names too. In a botanical guide, names such as creeping buttercup or sea plantain will be found, therefore, alongside their scientific counterparts, *Ranunculus repens* and *Plantago maritima*. Almost all the species of plants, mammals, birds and other groups of large and conspicuous organisms are sufficiently familiar to have vernacular names. This is true of relatively few fungi, however, and even common and widespread groups like the toadstool genus *Mycena* have never been graced with English names. The only English names given in this book therefore are those widely and generally used; certainly no attempt has been made to invent one from the scientific name.

The scientific system of naming organisms used today is a binomial or two-name system derived from that created by the Swedish biologist Linnaeus, to whom reference has already been made. The binomial of each organism does more than signify its uniqueness, however, for it also attempts to indicate the relationship of it to other similar forms. While each group of effectively identical individuals is called a species, designated by the second of the two names, the larger groups to which similar species are considered to belong are called genera (singular genus) and it is the genera that contribute the first name in familiar manner. Hence, the fungus genus *Agaricus* includes, among others, the species *Agaricus campestris, Agaricus macrosporus* and

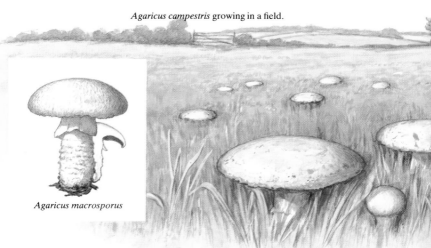

Agaricus campestris growing in a field.

Agaricus macrosporus

Agaricus bernardii. The specific or trivial name often attempts to give some information about the organism – *campestris* signifies a fungus of the fields and *macrosporus* one with large spores, for example, although sometimes, as in *bernardii* it does no more than recognise an individual, like Bernard, who may or may not have played some part in its study.

One group of fungi has presented taxonomists over the years with a unique conundrum and still causes some confusion today. In the past a large number of fungi were collected, studied, scientifically described and named that appeared to be possessed of only one method of reproduction, sexual or asexual, but not both. Those forms with asexual reproduction alone were called imperfect fungi or deuteromycetes. Subsequently, increased study demonstrated that many such fungi were after all capable of sexual reproduction, given appropriate environmental conditions; such discoveries are still being made today. Almost invariably, it was revealed that the sexual reproduction is of the form characteristic of the Sub-Division Ascomycotina; and in many instances it was discovered that the sexually reproducing form was already known and had quite separately been described and named as

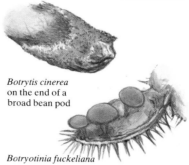

Botrytis cinerea on the end of a broad bean pod

Botryotinia fuckeliana on the husk of a sweet chestnut

an ascomycete with a sexual, but no *asexual,* reproductive system. Thus the untenable situation occurred of one fungus placed in two quite separate Classes, and therefore with two names. By international agreement, the name of the ascomycete sexually-reproducing stage is retained and the other discarded, although in a few instances (where the asexual form is much more commonly found, and especially where it is economically more important, as a plant pathogen for instance) its deuteromycete name is used. For example, the common grey mould fungus, so familiar to gardeners and growers, is still called *Botrytis cinerea* even though it is known to be merely the asexual stage of the ascomycete *Botryotinia fuckeliana.* For once, we must live with the 'untenable situation'.

The hierarchy above the genus in most classifications is the Family, but it has been a curious feature of fungal classification in the past, certainly in popular texts, that this has almost been ignored and a jump made one step further to the Order. An attempt to rectify this is made here in the hope that field mycologists will begin to think more, as botanists and ornithologists do, in terms of families and not simply of isolated genera. To reinforce this approach, the only key given (pp. 45–46) is largely a key to families and the fungi are arranged strictly in family sequence. Names of families always have the ending -aceae. Names of Orders end in -ales and above them in the taxonomic

Agaricus bernardii

hierarchy are the Sub-Class, ending in -mycetidae, the Class, ending in -mycetes, and the Sub-Division, ending in -cotina. (Intermediate and sub-categories for many of these groupings exist but are not generally used in this book.)

The scientific names of some particularly well-known fungi have a long ancestry; modern generic names like *Boletus* and *Tuber* date back to the Roman names for particular species, although not necessarily those to which they are applied today. Similarly ancient names occur in other disciplines within natural history too and, to rationalise matters for each discipline, by international agreement a year has been designated before which any name used is considered invalid today. For plants and fungi, that year is 1753, the date of publication of Linnaeus's seminal *Species Plantarum*.

Mention has been made of the word *Boletus* as an ancient fungal name; *Agaricus* is another and *Polyporus* a third and, almost alone among fungal generic names, they have given rise to vernacular versions in bolete, agaric and polypore. As these terms are still widely used, a comment on them is needed.

Although *Boletus* in the past meant primarily a fungus now called *Amanita caesarea,* the name bolete is applied today, as in this book, to mean any fungus belonging to the family Boletaceae (which in fact has no close relationship to *Amanita caesarea*).

Agaricus was the name once used for a huge genus that included very many fungi of the type that we would now recognise as of the umbrella-shaped mushroom or toadstool form and, although these are now spread across many dozens of different genera (all still in the order Agaricales, but with few in the family Agaricaceae, and even fewer in *Agaricus* itself), the vernacular version agaric is still usefully used to mean any gill-bearing fungus of this Order. It has even spawned an adjective, agaricoid, to mean 'of superficially agaric form but belonging to some other group'.

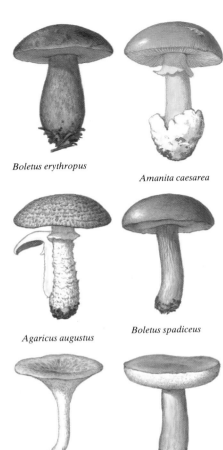

Boletus erythropus

Amanita caesarea

Agaricus augustus

Boletus spadiceus

Polyporus lentus

Gyroporus castaneus

The word polypore is now applied to any fungus belonging to the Basidiomycotina (apart from the stalked, toadstool-like boletes,) that discharges its spores through pores and not from gills. The actual genus *Polyporus* which once embraced many of these fungi is now greatly reduced in size, and numerous species have been redeployed across many genera and many families (see pp. 174–184).

As with flowering plants, the

16

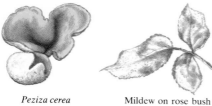

Peziza cerea

Mildew on rose bush
Sphaerotheca pannosa

Field Mushroom
Agaricus campestris

Rose Rust
Phragmidium tuberculatum

The mushroom cultivated for sale in shops
is *Agaricus bisporus.*

Commercial mushroom
soup is usually made
from *Boletus edulis.*

modern classification of fungi accords the greatest weight to those characters considered least likely to be affected or distorted by variations in the environment in which they grow, and to those which might conceivably have some bearing on the genetic relatedness of the organisms. The characters are those associated with sexual reproduction and, like the binomial system of nomenclature, their use derives principally from Linnaeus whose famed 'sexual system' ordered the plant kingdom largely on the basis of flower structure. (Thus it is that the sweet pea finds itself in the same family as the laburnum, and the familiar garden weed groundsel is in the same genus as some very large African trees.) Superficially, the cup fungus *Peziza* seems not too dissimilar from some mushrooms and toadstools; yet *Peziza* is in fact deemed a much closer relative of the mildew on the rose bush, while the supermarket mushroom is improbably allied with rose rust. The basis of this alignment is the type of spore produced as a result of sexual reproduction and the manner of its development. Below the level of the taxonomic Class, more detailed characters of spores and spore-bearing structures are used to subdivide the fungi further. The major types of spore and their formation will be described later, and details of the characters assigned to Order, Family and genus are given in the Directory section. However, a simple outline classification of the great groups of fungi is given here, with a listing of those Classes, Orders and Families represented in the book.

Before outlining this classification, certain additional points must be made. Other than at the very broadest levels, there is no universally accepted classification of fungi and above the taxonomic level of genus, as has been mentioned already, the category of Family has sometimes been all but disregarded. No two standard texts adopt the same classification system, and the system will even be found to vary (and particular fungal species to flit from genus to genus) in different

17

editions of the same book. Mycology has its fair share of lumpers and splitters too: those who favour a few large, and those who favour many small genera. Take the boletes, for instance: at one time, virtually all stalked toadstools with pores were placed in the genus *Boletus*. Now, in Britain, they are divided between *Aureoboletus, Boletinus, Boletus, Gyroporus, Leccinum, Porphyrellus, Strobilomyces, Suillus, Tylopilus* and *Uloporus*, whilst in European texts, further subdivision and additional names will be found in *Chalciporus, Gyrodon, Pulveroboletus, Xerocomus* and others. In one sense, this is not too bad a thing, as it does at least indicate that mycology is alive and well and that matters are under constant investigation and study. Nonetheless, it can be extremely confusing to experienced and inexperienced students alike, and in this book an attempt has been made to follow a median path. Names have been chosen that may not always be the latest proposed, but which it is hoped are those with which most readers will be most familiar, that have proved durable and that in most cases are still used in Britain in records published of official collecting expeditions (forays).

The names of species of the major groups and family delimitations used here are based primarily on:

Cannon, Hawksworth & Sherwood-Pike (1985) *The British Ascomycotina*

Corner (1967) *A Monograph of Clavaria and Allied Genera*

Demoulin & Marriott (1980) *Key to the Gasteromycetes of Great Britain*

Dennis, Orton & Hora (1960) *New Check List of British Agarics and Boleti*

Henderson, Orton & Watling (1970 –) *British Fungus Flora: Agarics and Boleti*

Pegler (1973) *The Polypores*
Names of groups less comprehensively covered are based on currently accepted British authorities. No attempt is made to provide lists of all

alternative names for every species but synonyms are given especially where the chosen names differ from the above sources and also where they differ from:

Christiansen (1959 – 60) *Danish Resupinate Fungi*

Eriksson & Ryvarden (1973 – 84) *The Corticiaceae of North Europe*

Donk (1964) *Families of Aphyllophorales*

Moser (1978) *Die Röhrlinge und Blätterpilze*

Ryvarden (1976 – 78) *Polyporaceae of North Europe*

The arrangement of families of agarics is based on spore print colour (see p. 35) which, although no longer considered an important taxonomic criterion, remains the most useful character for the amateur mycologist for whom this book is primarily written. Within agaric families, the species groupings are based largely on Moser (*op. cit.*), as his is the most widely used system, presents very comprehensive keys and is available in both German and English.

Aureoboletus cramesinus

Boletinus cavipes

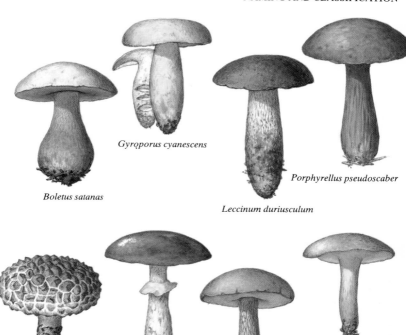

Gyroporus cyanescens

Porphyrellus pseudoscaber

Boletus satanas

Leccinum duriusculum

Uloporus lividus
(=Gyrodon lividus)

Suillus luteus

Tylopilus felleus

Strobilomyces floccopus

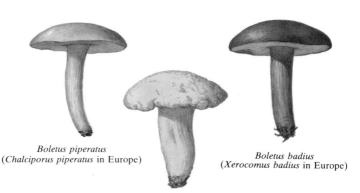

Boletus piperatus
(Chalciporus piperatus in Europe)

Boletus badius
(Xerocomus badius in Europe)

Pulveroboletus lignicola

19

THE CLASSIFICATION OF FUNGI INDICATING THE GROUPS COVERED IN THIS BOOK

Unlike birds, mammals and flowering plants, there are special difficulties in preparing definitive national lists of fungi, and no-one can say precisely how many species occur in a particular area. Partly this is because, being ephemeral, they are easily missed or overlooked, but also because the separation of many species requires painstaking microscopical study for which many collectors may have neither time nor inclination. It is also found that in some groups (which experts excuse by calling them 'critical'), the actual limits of individual species are not universally agreed – experts cannot decide where one species ends and another begins. For instance, a particular collection of morphologically similar toadstools may have spherical spores ranging in size from 5 to 20 μm in diameter, with a tendency for there to be rather fewer individuals with spores around 12–15 μm in diameter. Is this to be interpreted as two species, with spore sizes ranging from 5–12 and 15–20 μm respectively, or is it to be considered one unusually variable species? Differences of view will arise. And it should never be forgotten that, no matter how much it may attempt to reveal underlying natural and 'real' relationships, all classification is inherently artificial – species and other taxonomic categories are creations of man, for organisms do not classify themselves. So it is not possible to give an accurate figure for the number of different fungi that exist in total, and world estimates range upwards from 5,000 genera and 100,000 species. There may well be more species of fungi than of flowering plants in the world. Moreover, no two experts would agree on the most common 1,000 or 1,500 species in any area; careful analysis of British and European collecting records has been made in the selection of the larger or macro-fungi presented in this book. A few rare but particularly interesting species, or rare species that are the sole representatives of important genera, are also included. The selection of micro-species is superficial, but sufficient to include common representatives of all major groups and to give meaningful illustration to the accounts of fungal biology.

In the classified list that follows, the figure beside the name of a family refers to the page in the Directory section on which that family begins.

KINGDOM FUNGI

DIVISION
Myxomycota

(This group is considered here to be restricted to slime moulds and related organisms, and is not covered by this book).

DIVISION
Eumycota

Sub-Division
Basidiomycotina

Class Hymenomycetes

Order Agaricales

FAMILY
Boletaceae 47
Gomphidiaceae 53
Amanitaceae 54
Lepiotaceae 57
Tricholomataceae 60
Hygrophoraceae 88
Russulaceae 94
Pleurotaceae 111
Pluteaceae 112
Entolomataceae 115
Cortinariaceae 120
Bolbitiaceae 142
Paxillaceae 145
Agaricaceae 145
Strophariaceae 149
Coprinaceae 151

Order Aphyllophorales

FAMILY
Auriscalpiaceae 160
Cantharellaceae 161
Clavariaceae 162
Coniophoraceae 165
Corticiaceae 165
Gomphaceae 172
Hydnaceae 173
Hymenochaetaceae 174
Fistulinaceae 176
Ganodermataceae 177
Polyporaceae 177
Schizophyllaceae 184
Cyphellaceae 184
Sparassidaceae 185
Stereaceae 185
Thelephoraceae 187

Order Exobasidiales

FAMILY
Exobasidiaceae 189

Order Dacrymycetales

FAMILY
Dacrymycetaceae 189

Order Tremellales

FAMILY
Tremellaceae 190

Order Auriculariales

FAMILY
Auriculariaceae 191

Class Gasteromycetes

Order Sclerodermatales

FAMILY
Sclerodermataceae 192
Astraeaceae 192
Sphaerobolaceae 193

Order Melanogastrales

FAMILY
Melanogastraceae 193

Order Tulostomatales

FAMILY
Tulostomataceae 193

Order Lycoperdales

FAMILY
Geastraceae 193
Lycoperdaceae 195

Order Nidulariales

FAMILY
Nidulariaceae 197

Order Phallales

FAMILY
Hysterangiaceae 198
Phallaceae 198
Clathraceae 198

Order Hymenogastrales

FAMILY
Rhizopogonaceae 199

Class Teliomycetes

Order Ustilaginales

FAMILY
Ustilaginaceae 199
Tilletiaceae 200

Order Uredinales

FAMILY
Pucciniaceae 201
Melampsoraceae 202

Sub-Division
Ascomycotina

Class 'Euascomycetes'

Order Taphrinales

FAMILY
Protomycetaceae 204
Taphrinaceae 204

Class 'Plectomycetes'

Order Elaphomycetales

FAMILY
Elaphomycetaceae 204

Order Erysiphales

FAMILY
Erysiphaceae 205

Class 'Pyrenomycetes'

Order Clavicipitales

FAMILY
Clavicipitaceae 205

Order Hypocreales

FAMILY
Hypocreaceae 206

Order Ophiostomatales

FAMILY
Ophiostomataceae 206

Order Diatrypales

FAMILY
Diatrypaceae 206

Order Diaporthales

FAMILY
Valsaceae 206

Order Sphaeriales

FAMILY
Xylariaceae 207
Sordariaceae 208

Class 'Discomycetes'

Order Rhytismatales

FAMILY
Rhytismataceae 208

Order Helotiales

FAMILY
Geoglossaceae 209
Orbiliaceae 209
Dermateaceae 209
Hyaloscyphaceae 210
Sclerotiniaceae 212
Helotiaceae 213

Order Pezizales

FAMILY
Morchellaceae 215
Helvellaceae 216
Pezizaceae 217
Tuberaceae 219
Terfeziaceae 219
Ascobolaceae 219
Sarcosomataceae 220
Humariaceae 220

Class 'Loculoascomycetes'

Order Dothideales

FAMILY

Sub-Division

Class 'Hyphomycetes'

Class 'Coelomycetes'

Sub-Division
Zygomycotina

Class Zygomycetes

Order Mucorales

FAMILY

Order Entomophthorales

FAMILY

Sub-Division
Mastigomycotina

Class Oomycetes

Order Peronosporales

FAMILY

Class Chytridiomycetes

Order Chytridiales

FAMILY

Class Plasmodiophoromycetes

Order Plasmodiophorales

FAMILY

COLLECTION, STUDY AND IDENTIFICATION OF FUNGI

Unlike the study of birds, mammals and to some extent plants and other large wild organisms, the study and identification of fungi inevitably entails the collection of specimens, because relatively few species can be named accurately in the field, other than by the most experienced collector. Even then, it is almost always necessary to pick fruit bodies for close inspection. Most, however, require microscopic examination and sometimes simple chemical tests too, either to verify an identification based on superficial characters, or indeed to identify them at all.

Enthusiasts should have no misgivings about collecting specimens provided it is carried out sensibly. While it is understandably and rightly illegal to uproot a plant, and unwise and also sometimes illegal to pick its flowers, no such restrictions apply to fungi. This is because the fruit bodies that are the objects of attention are merely the outward manifestations of very extensive but invisible growth in soil, bark or other substance on which the fruit body appears. This growth is quite unaffected by the removal of the fruit bodies – which explains, of course, why gardeners experience so much frustration when regular removal of toadstools from their lawns makes no difference to their continued appearance, year after year. As fungal fruit bodies are reproductive structures, bearing spores, there will clearly be some effect on the numbers of spores available to start new colonies elsewhere if the entire fruit bodies are removed; but the

spore does not have the same relative importance vis à vis the invisible growth in the soil as the seed does to the root system of a flowering plant.

Nonetheless, over-collection is always wasteful: two or three fruit bodies of each species should be adequate for identification, and perhaps five or six if material is to be preserved as part of a permanent collection. It is very unlikely that the time available to the average amateur collector will permit the examination and identification of more than about six, or at the most ten, unknown species from each collecting expedition. To take home samples of more than this is also wasteful, especially as the main autumn collecting period lasts long enough for perhaps a dozen trips to be made.

The identification of fungi is not inherently any more difficult than the identification of other organisms; but it requires a degree of patience, and there are a number of unique factors of which the collector should be aware. Perhaps the major problem lies with the ephemeral nature of most fungal fruit bodies and their fairly irregular appearance from season to season. In many instances (especially with agarics), there are only a few weeks each season in which to practise identification, and some species

may only be seen once every few years, even in the same locality. Beginners can take comfort from the fact that even experienced field mycologists have to re-learn a great deal each autumn. Only the professional or very serious amateur with access to a fungal herbarium has year-round availability of material for study. The factors to be considered in the identification of fungi will be enumerated shortly; but the first priority is a list of the basic equipment needed for their collection and examination. This list relates essentially to the macro-fungi that will be most collectors' primary interest; no account will be given of the artificial culture techniques necessary to study many microfungi.

COLLECTING EQUIPMENT

For removing specimens from their natural growing position, a range of appliances will be helpful, most of which can be obtained at a garden centre. A hand trowel, a smaller trowel-like tool or 'widger' (such as those sold for use with house plants), a pair of secateurs (preferably of anvil pattern), a sharp knife and, if possible, a small saw should enable most situations to be dealt with. Immediately on collection, each specimen should be laid out quite separately (bracken or leaves can make useful partitions) in a suitable carrier for return to 'base'; and there really is no better carrier than a Sussex trug of traditional pattern.

A notebook with several pencils is essential (even though some mycologists now use pocket tape-recorders) and a loose-leaved pattern with a waterproof cover will enable the information to be filed permanently later. An assortment of lined and plain pages will facilitate the making of both notes and sketches. Water-colour pencils are very useful for making notes of the colour of fresh specimens. Each collection of specimens should be accorded an individual number and jewellers' tags, on which the appropriate number is written, can usefully be attached to the specimens themselves. If the fungi are to form part of a permanent collection (see below), the tags need never be removed but can be dried with the specimens. To carry fungi home safely, rigid containers are needed; *never* put fungi into a plastic bag, as they will rapidly lose all semblance of anything mycological and be useless for further study. Small tubes, and small plastic boxes with tight fitting lids such as those used for storing food in deep-freezers, are good: several will fit into a haversack-style bag. On returning home, the tubes and boxes can be placed in a refrigerator (*not* a deep-freezer) to keep the specimens fresh for a few days – although the importance of examining fungi promptly (especially for the production of spore prints – see p. 35), and of drying them promptly for long-term storage, cannot be overstressed: several features of significance for identification can change quite rapidly after they have been picked.

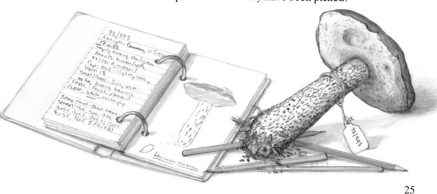

EXAMINATION EQUIPMENT

Although a hand-lens magnifying 10 times is as invaluable an item of mycological field equipment as it is for the botanist or entomologist, a microscope is essential for any other than the most cursory examination of fungi. It need not be a sophisticated or expensive microscope if its only function is as an aid to identification (rather than detailed academic study). A basic 'student' microscope, giving a magnification of about 150 times, will be adequate for inspecting the shape and overall form of spores and spore-bearing structures, although for examination of the surface details of spores an oil-immersion objective is of enormous help. A basic student microscope can be obtained for about £50 at the time of going to press. Since the size of spores and other bodies are such important criteria, a micrometer eye-piece permitting measurements to be made quickly and accurately is an almost obligatory adjunct. A camera lucida attachment, which projects an image of the field of view onto a sheet of paper at the side of the microscope, is a great aid to accurate drawing of spores and other microscopic features; but it is by no means essential.

A small range of chemical reagents will be necessary for use with particular groups of fungi which produce characteristic colour changes when the chemicals are applied to them; either as macroscopic reactions, visible to the naked eye, or as microscopic effects, to be seen under the microscope. These reagents are indicated on p. 36 where the details of the various tests are given.

Gummed labels, a few simple dissecting needles, scalpels, microscope slides and cover glasses, an accurate ruler and dividers for measuring complete the fairly basic inventory.

Spores seen through a microscope fitted with a measuring scale

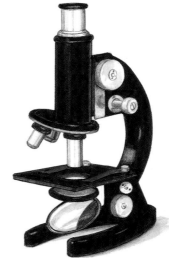

A 'student' microscope

dividers

cover glasses

scalpel

slide labels

slides

ruler

dissecting needles

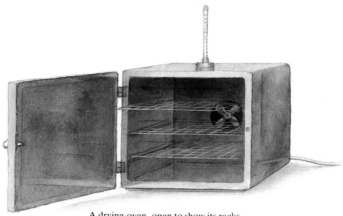

A drying-oven, open to show its racks

PERMANENT STORAGE OF SPECIMENS

For long-term storage of fungal specimens (and remember always to preserve specimens that appear unusual or uncommon), careful preparation is needed. This is very difficult to achieve satisfactorily without a well ventilated drying oven, preferably incorporating a circulatory fan. Within the oven fresh specimens should be laid out carefully and separately on wire shelves or racks. A suitable oven can be purchased from companies supplying science equipment to schools. A temperature of 60°C for about 48 hours will dry most types of small or medium sized mushroom and toadstool, although it may be necessary to cut large fruit bodies into sections and dry them for a week or so.

Nonetheless, fungal characters do change dramatically on drying and the end product may bear little or no resemblance to the beautiful structure collected in the woodland glade. So it is essential to record such evanescent characters as colour, smell, shape and size before drying, although spores and most other features of microscopic interest retain their form well and can be examined at leisure after small pieces of dried tissue have been macerated in ammoniacal solutions,

warm water, Melzer's reagent (p. 36), methylene blue or cotton blue (p. 38). But for some fungi, such as those in the genera *Russula* and *Lactarius,* features like spore print colour, smell (and, in a very few instances, taste) are of such overwhelming importance as aids to identification that accurate naming of dried specimens without detailed notes on the fresh material is often impossible. Dried fungi are best kept in stout paper packets, or cardboard boxes for large specimens, and stored in a dry, fairly warm place, with crystals of naphthalene or other insect repellent scattered among the specimens to deter insects and mites and those moulds that would feed upon their larger and more august brethren.

A few types of basidiomycete macro-fungi, such as the jelly-like members of the family Dacrymycetaceae do not dry satisfactorily; although they can be preserved in alcohol, formaldehyde or other liquid, the results are not very satisfactory. Most types of ascomycete, apart from a few terrestrial species are much less fleshy than most large basidiomycetes and will dry very adequately in the air at room temperature. Leaf-inhabiting fungi are best preserved by drying the leaves in the conventional way in a flower press and mounting them on sheets of stout paper.

TECHNIQUES OF COLLECTION AND EXAMINATION IN THE FIELD

The first rule in collecting fungi is to make as many notes and to collect as much information as possible while in the field; so many features of a specimen can change in a few hours, and it is not always possible to return to the same spot to record some previously overlooked but vital fact, such as the type of tree beneath which the collection was made. The relevant pages of the note-book should contain, therefore, the date and weather conditions, the precise locality, the nature of the habitat (woodland, marsh, golf-course, recently-dug roadside verge or stable sand-dune, for instance), the substance on which the fungus is growing (its substrate), the nature of the local vegetation (especially the species of tree or plant on which, or close to which, the specimen is grow-

ing: take a leaf or other sample if the species cannot be identified on the spot), and note the presence too of any other types of fungi growing close by.

Note the relationship of the fruit bodies one to the other. This is especially important with agarics which may occur as *solitary* individuals, or attached to each other in various ways in *tufts* or *clumps,* or in a manner termed *trooping* (groups of isolated individuals close together but not attached). Ascomycetes and other types of fungi on twigs and leaves may also occur as single fruit bodies or grouped together with a common surrounding tissue; a hand lens and some experience will be needed to be certain of the various forms of these.

Remove the specimens carefully from the substrate, noting especially if the stem base displays the feature known as rooting (being inserted deeply into the material, rather like a

Fungus on old plaster

Fungus on tree branch

Fungus on soil

Fungus on rotting timber

Agarics trooping

A solitary agaric   Agarics in a tuft

carrot). Whenever possible, try to take at least one immature fruit body, but remember that without some fully ripened ones identification will usually be impossible. It is much better to place only one type of fungus in each container for bringing home; many agarics look remarkably similar, especially when seen apart from their habitat, and trying to relate members of a mixed collection to one species can cause nightmares of frustration. The need not to mix collections is even more important when collecting fungi to eat: an inedible or poisonous species can *very* easily be tossed into the pan along with the edible ones.

Make a special record of any features that are immediately obvious and striking (a hairy cap, a smell of almonds or a bright orange colour, for example) and those characters that change on handling – a colour change like bruising where the tissues have been touched, or a suddenly apparent aroma perhaps.

Single fruit body on a twig

A group of fruit bodies on a twig

EXAMINATION AT HOME

Under slightly more leisurely circumstances, it is possible to begin a systematic examination of the specimens. While numerous macroscopic features of the fruit bodies and microscopic details of their structure can be recorded, not all are needed to identify every fungus, and each individual species description within the Directory section uses only a proportion of them therefore. The placing of a specimen in its major grouping can be achieved with the aid of the first part of the key (p. 45) but thereafter, the following are the major features that may need to be taken into account in assigning species to the various Orders, Families and genera. The basis of this account is the identification of agarics, for these will comprise the bulk of the harvest from most collecting expeditions. Additional and different features needed for other groups are described on p. 38 onwards.

Rooting and non-rooting fungi

29

CRITERIA USED FOR IDENTIFYING AGARICS

Macroscopic features

CAP

Dimensions The *diameter* to be used is the average measured in centimetres across at least two diameters of a mature cap. *Height,* which is used normally only with markedly conical or bell-shaped caps, is the average in centimetres of at least two heights measured from the apex to the cap edge.

Cap diameter and height vary considerably with general growing conditions and while there are obviously large and obviously small types of agaric, size alone is hardly ever a criterion for determining the limits of a species; the size ranges given in species descriptions should never be considered as excluding the existence of some particularly large or small individuals.

Colour This can vary greatly as the cap matures and opens, and is sometimes variable from one part of the cap to another as well. It also changes in some species when the cap is wet, and this phenomenon can aid identification in certain groups. The commonest cap colours among fungi are shades of brown, yellow and orange; but they can range from white and greys through pink and red to black. Blue and mauve are uncommon, and green is very rare. Although technically, and for the greatest accuracy, it is best to describe colours in relation to standard colour charts, most of these are expensive, difficult to obtain and time-consuming to use. Coloured sketches or colour descriptions related to everyday objects are more practical and the latter have been largely adopted in this book.

Shape It is in cap shape that there is the greatest difference between the mature and the immature individual, and this difference should be noted. The description of cap shape usually used in species descriptions relates to the mature form. Six main types are recognised:
   campanulate or bell-shaped
   conic or cone-like
   convex (or in its extreme form, *domed*) with the appearance of an upturned bowl.
   flat
   parabolic
   uplifted, where the entire cap is depressed into a bowl-like form with uplifted margins.
   The presence and form of any central bump or depression should also be noted. A cap with some form of central bump is called *umbonate;* one with a depression *depressed;* a very deep depression giving the cap the appearance of a funnel is found quite commonly and is very characteristic of some genera; a depression in the cap with a small bump or pimple in the centre is quite common, too, and such caps are called *umbilicate.*

CAP SHAPES

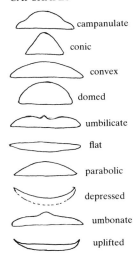

campanulate

conic

convex

domed

umbilicate

flat

parabolic

depressed

umbonate

uplifted

Surface characters There are many different cap surface features, often very characteristic of particular groups, but only the commonest and most important need be considered. Note if the surface is *shiny, dull* or *silky,* if it is *dry* or *moist, sticky, glutinous, oily* or *gelatinous.* The surface texture varies widely too, but the most important types to note are *smooth* and *split* or *cracked,* with a covering that may range from *micaceous* (glistening with tiny mica-like particles), *powdery, granular* and *scaly* to more or less *hairy* or *woolly.*

Marginal characters The margin of the cap may differ significantly from the remainder in colour or surface texture. The actual edge may be either perfectly smooth (*entire*) or more or less *wavy, split* or *eroded.* There are often small *radial lines* around the circumference associated with the gill attachment; but some caps are lined radially as a separate marginal feature.

Flesh characters These are very important for the identification of many species and should be noted carefully. Thickness (from cap upper surface to under surface where the gills emerge) both in the centre and at the margin may be measured in millimetres for record purposes but is usually mentioned in species descriptions only if it is significantly thick or thin. Colour is an important feature, especially any changes in it when the flesh is cut or broken. Some such changes occur almost immediately; others take some minutes to become apparent. Smell is important, too, and is best experienced by holding a piece of broken cap to the face in cupped hands. It can be described by reference to familiar everyday objects like flour, aniseed or radish; such highly individual expressions as 'reminiscent of old elevator oil' which occurs in an American fungus guidebook should, however, be avoided. But sometimes it defies precise description and can only be said to be pleasant or unpleasant, mushroomy or earthy. For a very few groups of

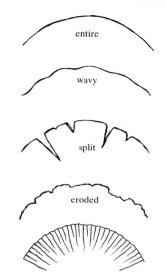

radial lines associated with gill attachment

radial lines as a separate feature

MARGINAL CHARACTERS

agarics, flesh taste is an important feature in identification; **but it is important to stress that tasting a fungus is not the same as eating it.** A small piece of the cap flesh should be chewed on the tip of the tongue, the sensation (hot and peppery for instance) noted, **and the fragments then spat out.** It should also be said that taste is never the first criterion to

Measuring thickness of cap

use when identifying an unknown species; **it must be employed only when** the fungus has been fairly positively placed in a particular family, or in a genus like *Russula*, within which individual species descriptions mention taste as an important diagnostic feature. In a few genera such as *Lactarius* and *Mycena*, the presence of fluid exuding from cut or broken flesh is an important feature. The colour of this fluid should be noted, together with any changes it makes on exposure to the air; this exposure and colour change is best achieved by touching the fluid drops onto a white handkerchief. The consistency of the flesh should also be recorded, noting for instance if it is crumbly, rubbery or brittle.

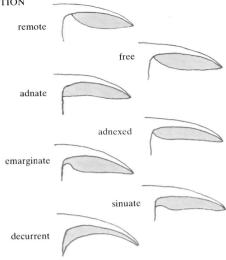

GILLS

Certain features of the gills are important in the identification of all gilled fungi. Of greatest significance is the manner by which the gills are attached to the stem; there are six major types of attachment, with a degree of intergrading between some of them. The specimen must be cut longitudinally to determine gill attachment.

Free gills do not actually make contact with the stem: when viewed from below, a circular gap is apparent around the top of the stem where the cap underside can be seen. When this gap is very wide and the gills end a considerable distance from the stem, they are said to be *remote. Adnate gills* are attached to the stem squarely, their entire width making contact, whereas *adnexed gills* and *emarginate gills* are only attached to the stem for a small or a large proportion of their width respectively. *Sinuate gills* appear to be notched at the lower edge where they meet the stem. *Decurrent gills* arch downwards at the inner edge and appear to run down, gradually merging with the stem.

Gill width is sometimes used as a distinguishing feature, as is the thickness from face to face of each individual gill. The spacing of gills is an expression of their appearance when seen from beneath the cap, and

METHODS OF GILL ATTACHMENT

ranges from *crowded* (where the gills are very close together), through *close* to *distant* (where they are very wide apart). Some species possess *lamellulae* between the gills; these are shorter gills that do not extend entirely from margin to stem.

The appearance of the gill margin (its lower edge) is especially important in some genera. It may be described as *wavy* in the same way as the edge of the cap itself; but quite commonly gills are found that appear toothed (*serrate*) or minutely ragged (*fimbriate*). Sometimes the gill edge is of different colour to the remainder of the gill and is then said to be *marginate*. Overall gill colour, especially the difference between immature and mature gills, is very important in some groups. Surface features of gills are not as important in identification as are surface features of the cap; but in a few groups relative waxiness, covering with powder or pubescence (minute hairiness, like the surface of a peach) is used as a diagnostic criterion.

Finally, reference must be made to the deliquescence or self-liquefying of the gills which turn into a black, ink-like liquid and which is characteristic of many species in the genus *Coprinus*.

SPACING OF GILLS
(with intermediate lamellulae)

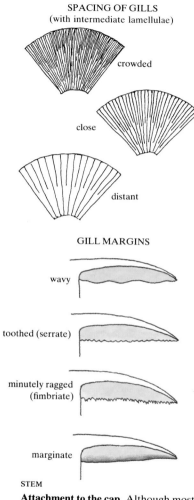

crowded

close

distant

GILL MARGINS

wavy

toothed (serrate)

minutely ragged
(fimbriate)

marginate

from the substrate to the point of its attachment to the gills (which may be some distance from the cap surface if the gills are markedly decurrent). The diameter of the stem is often expressed in guide-books, but it is a fairly variable character and difficult to measure accurately; a general note of a stout or markedly thin stem (taking width in relation to length), and of any tendency to taper either towards the apex or towards the base, is often of more use. Its shape in transverse section should be noted if it is other than *circular*: some species have markedly *flattened* or *grooved* stems, for instance, and it is important to observe if it is *solid* in section, *hollow*, or *stuffed* (apparently with a central hollow filled with cottony

ATTACHMENTS OF STEM TO CAP

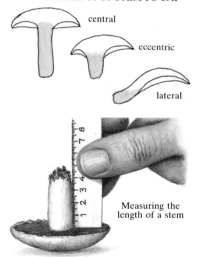

central

eccentric

lateral

Measuring the
length of a stem

STEM

Attachment to the cap Although most agarics have the stem attached *centrally* to the cap, some are slightly *eccentric* and a few, which appear superficially bracket-like, have it attached *laterally*. A very few are *stemless* and have a fruit body form more commonly associated with other groups of fungi (see p. 160).

Dimensions The length of the stem is measured from its point of emergence

SECTIONS THROUGH STEMS

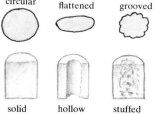

circular flattened grooved

solid hollow stuffed

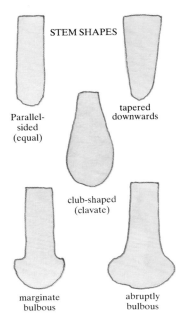

STEM SHAPES

Parallel-sided (equal)

tapered downwards

club-shaped (clavate)

marginate bulbous

abruptly bulbous

The presence or absence of veils are very important features that have manifestations on the stem and, to some extent, on the cap too. Veils are more or less filmy sheets of tissue produced on the fruit bodies of some agaric species. They are of two types, partial veils and universal veils. A *partial veil* covers the gills of an agaric fruit body as it emerges from the substrate, stretching from the cap edge to the stem. As the cap grows and expands, this veil tears in one of two main ways. An *arachnoid* (spider or cobweb-like) veil splits radially leaving fibrils on the cap edge and sometimes adhering across the gills too. By contrast, a *membranous* veil tears concentrically around the cap, sometimes leaving flaps of tissue conspicuously on the cap edge and, more importantly, a ring of tissue (called the annulus or ring) on the stem itself. In many fungi the ring is barely detectable, but in others it forms a very obvious feature, important in identification. The ring may take several forms: if it joins only loosely to the stem, it is called *movable*, if more tightly adhering *attached*. If it is on the upper part of the stem, a ring is called *superior*; if on the lower half *inferior*. A ring with a cotton wool-like roll of tissue on the underside is referred to as *double*.

The manifestations of a *universal veil* are somewhat different. Universal veils are not formed by all agarics, but when present they envelop the entire developing 'button' and, as the fruit body expands and matures, fragments of the veil remain as flakes on the cap surface, often in contrasting colour to the remainder of the cap. More significantly, however, the veil remains enveloping the base of the stem as a structure called a *volva*, the presence of which is highly characteristic of certain genera. The volva takes one of two main forms: when its tissues adhere closely to the stem base, it is called *adherent* and its surface may be loose and scaly, powdery or, sometimes, marked with characteristic concentric zones. When the volva envelops the stem base like a loose

tissue). Looked at externally or from a longitudinal section, many agarics can be seen to have *parallel-sided* stems but some are *tapered downwards* (most species with rooting stems taper downwards into the 'root') while others are markedly club-shaped (*clavate*) with a highly pronounced taper upwards, or even bulbous (with a pronounced swelling at the base like an onion). Some bulbous forms have a marked margin around the upper edge of the bulb: *marginate bulbous*. Those that swell very abruptly at the base are called *abruptly bulbous*.

Many of the cap flesh characters like colour, taste and smell, and some of the surface textural features of the cap, are applicable to the stem too. It is particularly important to note any differences in colour, texture or surface features that are restricted to the extreme apex or base. Other features to note on the stem surface are the various degrees of wrinkling or grooving mentioned above, while the flesh is often much tougher than that of the cap and can be cartilaginous, chalky, corky, fibrous, leathery or even woody, in addition to the possibilities referred to already.

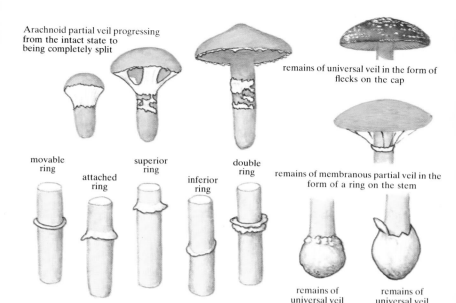

Arachnoid partial veil progressing from the intact state to being completely split

remains of universal veil in the form of flecks on the cap

movable ring

attached ring

superior ring

inferior ring

double ring

remains of membranous partial veil in the form of a ring on the stem

remains of universal veil with adherent volva at base of stem

remains of universal veil with free volva at base of stem

bag, it is said to be *free* and its tissues may then vary from very fragile to fairly tough and membranous.

SPORE PRINT

Reference has already been made to the spore print, and it is one of the basic features employed in the identification and (to a lesser extent nowadays) in the classification of agarics. It must be stressed that the colour of the mature gills may not always give an indication of the colour of the spore print; some fungi with dark coloured gills produce white or colourless spores and consequently a white print. To produce a spore print, use a fresh, mature, but not over-ripe fruit body. The freshness must be stressed, for it is often difficult to obtain a print from specimens that have been kept in a refrigerator or allowed to dry out slightly. It is an operation, therefore, that should be started immediately on returning home after a foray. Cut the cap from the stem at the apex and place it gills downwards onto a piece of smooth, stiff, white paper or card. Cover the cap with an inverted jar or similar cover and leave it undisturbed.

Depending on the state of cap maturity, it may need to be left for anything between half an hour and twenty-four hours. The spores will by then have been discharged from the gills as described later (p. 237) and have produced a pattern on the card; this is the spore print and for most identification purposes the colour of the pattern on the paper, when dry, can be used. For critical genera like *Russula*, scrape the spores into a small heap with a microscope slide cover glass, flatten the heap gently with the cover-glass and assess the colour of this mass of spores in daylight. Take the card to a window during the daytime; do not use evening light in autumn, nor artificial light, which can give confusing colours.

In some agaric genera, most notably *Russula,* subtle variations in spore print colour are very important in the identification of individual species and to facilitate this, carefully produced colour charts are provided on the end papers of the book with which the spore print colours should be matched.

Chemical tests on the fruit body

The identification of some species in some genera is aided by a gross colour change that occurs when chemical reagent is applied to the tissues. The following are the most useful of these tests, and reference is made to them in the Directory. It should be appreciated that each is only of value for particular groups and must only be used to aid diagnosis when they are referred to specifically in the species descriptions. All of the reagents should be prepared freshly, certainly each season; and sulphovanillin is best made up anew each time it is needed. **Some of the chemicals, especially chloral hydrate and the concentrated mineral acids, are very dangerous.** Special permission may be needed before they can be purchased. All should be stored and used with respect, and none allowed to be used by children.

IRON SALTS TEST

Apply a few drops of a fresh aqueous solution of 10% (weight in g: volume in ml.) ferric chloride or ferrous sulphate to the stem and observe any colour change. If it is possible to obtain a large crystal of ferrous sulphate, this can be rubbed directly on the stem for rapid identification of certain species of *Russula* in the field. It can be kept fresh when not in use by placing it in a corked tube containing a wad of cotton wool moistened with dilute ammonium sulphate.

MELZER'S TEST

Prepare Melzer's reagent by adding 1.5g iodine, 5g potassium iodide and 100g chloral hydrate to 100ml of water. Warm carefully (do not boil) and stir thoroughly. When added to tissues or spores (especially white spores) en masse, a colour change to very dark blue is called an *amyloid response;* a change to red-brown is a *pseudo-amyloid response;* no change is *non-amyloid.*

The same reagent is also used for microscopic tests (see next column).

SCHAEFFER'S TEST

Apply a streak across the cap of *Agaricus* species with a glass rod dipped in pure aniline and cross this with another rod dipped in concentrated nitric acid. A flame red colour at the point of intersection gives Schaeffer +; no red colour gives Schaeffer −.

SULPHO-VANILLIN TEST

Add 8 ml concentrated sulphuric acid to 3 ml water and dissolve 1g pure vanillin in this. A characteristic colour change occurs in some groups when this is applied to the stem. Clear away immediately after use as the reagent is highly corrosive.

MISCELLANEOUS REAGENT TESTS

In certain groups, application of one of the following reagents to cap or stem gives a characteristic colour reaction:

10–40% aqueous solutions of potassium or sodium hydroxide (KOH or NaOH)
10% and 75% aqueous ammonia
40% aqueous formaldehyde (formalin)
Dilute or concentrated solutions of hydrochloric, nitric or sulphuric acids
2% aqueous phenol

Microscopic features

Spores Spore shape, spore dimensions and any spore ornamentation are the most important microscopic characters in the identification of agarics. Mount a very small scraping from a spore print on a microscope slide. If the spores are coloured, mount them in water; if white or colourless, use Melzer's reagent which will give an immediate indication of an amyloid or pseudoamyloid response (see above).

Spores vary enormously in shape. Sometimes the shape is geometrically symmetrical, and then a description like spherical, ovoid or ellipsoid has an immediate meaning. Or apparently so. But when one well-known fungus guide-book includes for spore shapes the terms ovoid, oval, ovate, egg-

shaped, elliptic, elliptical, ellipsoid and ellipsoidal, that neither the Collins English dictionary nor ninety-nine out of a hundred readers could differentiate, only confusion ensues. Quite often, moreover, the shape is complexly irregular and, although equally complex names have been devised for them, it is much simpler in many instances to relate them to familiar objects – pear shaped, spindle shaped or pip shaped, for instance, the suffix sub- indicating that the spore shapes do not correspond perfectly. The commonest spore shapes are illustrated on the end-papers and reference should be made to these drawings when reading the species descriptions in the Directory.

Spore dimensions are similarly straightforward to record if the spore has a regular shape, but potentially very difficult to make if it is irregular. For normal purposes the diameter of spherical spores and the shortest and longest dimensions for other shaped spores are used. Always measure at least five, and preferably ten spores of each collection of fresh material (25 of dried material) and calculate a mean value. As with fruit body dimensions, individual spores will be found occasionally that exceed the quoted ranges; but in general spore size is a good and important diagnostic feature. Measurements of all microscopic dimensions are made to the nearest half of a micrometre, indicated by the Greek letter μ followed by m. One micrometre (1 μm) is one thousandth of a millimetre. Microscope eye-piece micrometers should be calibrated with reference to a standard calibrated slide.

Colour and ornamentation Spore colour as seen under the microscope is rarely a significant feature in the indentification of agarics; but in many genera the spores have characteristic surface ornamentation in the forms of tiny bumps, spines or ridges and furrows which are used extensively as diagnostic features. As for spore shape, complex names have been devised for many of these patterns; some of those found most frequently

are illustrated on the end-papers and reference should be made to these drawings. Although such ornamentation can usually be seen under the low-power magnification of the microscope, an oil-immersion objective giving much higher magnification will be found very helpful.

BASIDIAL AND CYSTIDIAL CHARACTERS
In very few agaric genera will it be necessary to resort to detailed examination of the spore-bearing basidia; but in a few groups it may be important to check the numbers of spores on each basidium. This is done most conveniently by mounting a small fragment of mature gill tissue dry on a slide with no cover glass and examining it quickly. By adjustment of the microscope illumination, it is usually possible to see if the basidia bear the usual four spores or a different number. (When mounted in water or other liquid, the spores are easily dislodged and it is difficult to appreciate the three-dimensional structure of the basidium).

spores on a basidium

types of cystidia

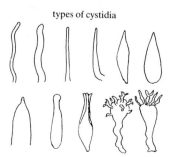

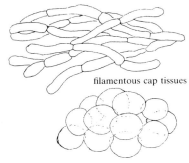

filamentous cap tissues

cellular cap tissues

Of greater overall importance for identification are the features of the non-spore-bearing structures that occur among the basidia on the gill edge and/or the gill surface face (and, to some extent, elsewhere too). Some of these are believed to be immature or aborted basidia, and are called basidioles. More important, however, are the sterile structures called cystidia. Their presence, size, form and surface ornamentation and encrusting are highly characteristic of some groups; the appearance of some of the most common is illustrated on p. 37. To examine cystidia, mount a very small piece of gill tissue, including a portion of the margin, in water on a slide. Place a cover glass over the top and then tap it gently (a rubber mounted on the end of a pencil is ideal for this). This will cause the cells to separate, when they can readily be examined. Few other types of fruit body tissue need to be examined microscopically, and the characteristics of these are important only for the identification of certain groups. A thin tangential slice may be removed from the surface of the cap with a scalpel and mounted in water. Examination of the edge of this slice will reveal if the tissue is more or less filamentous or more or less 'cellular' If there is loose tissue of a universal veil adhering to the cap surface, this too may be mounted and examined similarly. The inner flesh of the various parts of the fruit body is called the trama and tiny blocks or slices, cut from within the trama of the cap and gills especially, may also need to be examined for their predominant cellular make-up in some groups.

Microscopical chemical tests
The microscopical use of some of the chemical reagents employed for macro-chemical tests has already been mentioned; and for critical analysis of some genera and some structures, many more specific staining reactions have been used at various times. Few are necessary routinely, but the following, in addition to Melzer's reagent (p. 36), are valuable for aiding the interpretation of microscopic observations.

METHYLENE BLUE OR TRYPAN BLUE
Buy a ready prepared mixture which keeps well. These are valuable general stains for cytoplasm, and increase the contrast of fungal tissue generally.

Spore stained with cotton blue

COTTON BLUE
Buy ready prepared. Use similarly to Methylene or Trypan Blue, although, in some groups, a characteristic staining of the spore wall by Cotton Blue also occurs and such spores are called cyanophilous.

ADDITIONAL OR DIFFERENT CRITERIA EMPLOYED IN THE IDENTIFICATION OF OTHER GROUPS
Other basidiomycete macro-fungi
BOLETES
Most agaric identification features, apart from the gills, are applicable to boletes. The attachment to the stem of the tubes can be described, moreover, in a manner comparable with that used for gills, although an additional and characteristic form of attachment called *depressed* is found in some species. The pore surface itself has a

characteristic colour, and this may change when it is handled and bruised. Changes in the colour of the cap and stem flesh on exposure to the air are also very important in some genera. The length and colour of the tubes should be noted (these are visible when a fruit body is cut through vertically). The size and shape of the pore openings should also be recorded, although it is normally adequate to note simply if the pores are large enough to be recognisable to the naked eye or are so small as to be visible clearly only with a hand lens, whether they are rounded or angular in outline and if they are arranged in rows. The surface texture of the stem is of special importance with boletes and many have greater or lesser development of a net-like or reticulated pattern, unique to the group.

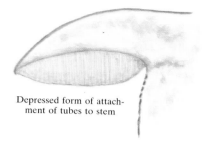

Depressed form of attachment of tubes to stem

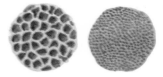

Variations in pore size
large and angular   small and round

PORE-BEARING MEMBERS OF THE ORDER APHYLLOPHORALES (POLYPORES)

Fruit body form should be noted carefully for most pore-bearing basidiomycetes (apart from the boletes) are not stalked; their state is called *sessile*. Most are bracket-shaped (individual fruit bodies sometimes overlapping one another, tile fashion, in a condition called *imbricate*). The dimension usually used for these fruit bodies is the width across the widest part parallel with the substrate. Some species adopt a fruit body form called *resupinate* where they are flattened against the surface on which they grow, and spread widely and irregularly in a manner called *effused*. Diameter or other measurements are not usually recorded for such species. Sometimes the margin of a resupinate fruit body is curled upwards and outwards; this is described as *effuso-reflexed*. Some polypores do not readily form a spore print and dissection of the fruit body will be needed to obtain spores for examination, although this must be performed in the knowledge that some immature spores of small size may thus be obtained. As with the boletes, the way that the tubes open to the exterior at the pores should be checked, although there is a much

FRUIT BODY TYPES
among Polypores

bracket-shaped (solitary)

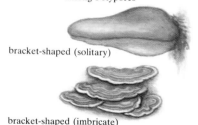

bracket-shaped (imbricate)

effuso-reflexed   effused resupinate

Measuring the width of a bracket-shaped fruit body

39

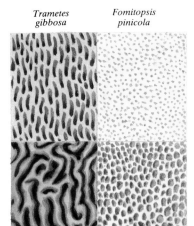

Trametes gibbosa   *Fomitopsis pinicola*

Daedalea quercina   *Polyporus brumalis*

Variations in pore shape

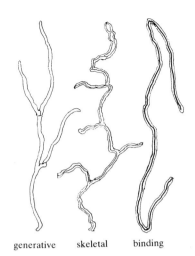

generative   skeletal   binding

Types of hypha

greater range in their shape and size, the pores sometimes adopting an elongated form that can give the pore-bearing surface a maze-like appearance. Commonly, pore size is most easily expressed as number of pores per linear millimetre.

Microscopic examination of these fungi must not be limited to the spores. Small portions of the fruit body flesh should be teased apart and examined too, and the type of hyphae present (the so-called hyphal system) recorded. There are three possible hyphal types, termed *generative, skeletal* and *binding,* the first occurring in all polypores and the other two only in some. The hyphal system in those species with generative hyphae alone is called *monomitic,* in those with skeletal hyphae also *dimitic,* and in those with all three types *trimitic.* The microscopic appearance of each type of hypha is illustrated.

NON-PORE BEARING MEMBERS OF THE ORDER APHYLLOPHORALES AND RELATED MINOR GROUPS
Apart from the occurrence of the spores on exposed surfaces, rather than within tubes, the non-pore bearing members of the Order are identified using the features employed

with the pore formers. Many of the fungi belonging to the family Corticeaceae and its numerous relatives are superficially similar to the bracket-like, resupinate and effuso-reflexed pore-bearing groups; but the flattened spore-bearing surface, although normally smooth, may sometimes be spiny or otherwise ornamented. As with resupinate polypores, size is a very variable criterion of little value in identification, but note should be made if the fruit body is an entire and irregular structure or formed of barely connected patches (discontinuous). Note if the margin of the fruit body is sharp or indefinite and how tightly the whole adheres to the substrate.

In the Clavariaceae and allied families, and to some degree in the Thelephoraceae, a horn- or antler-like fruit body is formed, and the degree of branching that it displays should be recorded. Overall fruit body height rather than diameter is usually recorded in these groups and this is the dimension used in the Directory. Microscopically, the occurrence and appearance of cystidia is often important in the identification of the Aphyllophorales whilst in the Orders of jelly fungi, basidium shape assumes particular significance.

The spiny spore-bearing surface of a species in the Corticeaceae

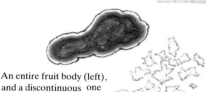

An entire fruit body (left), and a discontinuous one

Measuring the height of an antler-like fruit body

Examples of Gasteromycetes

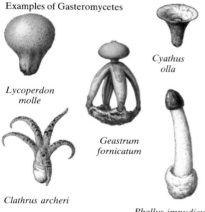

Cyathus olla

Lycoperdon molle

Geastrum fornicatum

Clathrus archeri

Phallus impudicus

A puff-ball bursting open

GASTEROMYCETES

The overall fruit body form in many of the Gasteromycetes is unique; in some orders, including the stinkhorns and the bird's nest fungi, the British species are sufficiently distinct to be identified by this character alone. Among the earth balls, puff-balls and their allies, too, fruit body form is a valuable character, especially when the manner in which it bursts to liberate the spores is also considered, for the spores themselves are remarkably similar in size and shape among many species.

Microscopic basidiomycetes

All of the microscopic basidiomycetes described in the book are plant pathogens and are most easily identified by amateur collectors by a combination of the identity of the host plant on which they occur and the size, shape and/or type of spores produced.

ASCOMYCETES

There are fundamental differences between the procedures to be used for the identification of ascomycetes and basidiomycetes. Some of the characters used for ascomycete identification, even at an amateur level, tend to be more those actually employed in the classification of the group than is the case with basidiomycetes. Although they may seem a daunting group to the mycologist versed only in agarics, the ascomycetes are perhaps easier to identify once familiarity has been gained with them: fewer essential characters are used, only one chemical test is of importance and most of the significant microscopic features are fairly straightforward to examine with a good microscope.

In addition to habitat and substrate details, such gross features as overall colour, size, shape and relative hairiness of the fruit body should of course always be recorded; among a few large types this may be adequate for specific identification. Ascomycete fruit bodies in general, however, tend to be smaller than those of most basidiomycetes, and only when

41

experience has been gained will it be possible to discern the gross differences between many of the smallest species with the aid only of a hand lens. Nonetheless, a basic separation of the group into the old (but taxonomically now redundant) divisions of those with more or less cup- or bowl-shaped fruit bodies or *apothecia* (the 'Discomycetes') and those with more or less spherical or flask-shaped *cleistothecia* or *perithecia* (the 'Plectomycetes' and 'Pyrenomycetes') is readily recognisable. Cutting across this division, however, is a character of fundamental importance: the structure of the *ascus,* the microscopic tubular body within which the spores are borne. The importance of this structure for spore discharge is described later (p. 241); but it is essential in identification to decide if the ascus is *unitunicate* (single walled) or *bitunicate* (double walled), and if it is *operculate* (opening by a hinged apical lid) or *inoperculate* (opening by a pore). Although a generalisation can be made in that almost all apothecia have unitunicate asci, this is about as far as macroscopic deductions can go, and more detailed study is required.

It is perhaps at this stage that most amateur mycologists are frightened away from intimacy with ascomycetes, for, in addition to needing low-power lenses, a microscope with an oil-immersion objective magnifying up to 1,000 times is essential. Small fragments of the spore-bearing surface (and, in some groups, of the exterior of the fruit body too) should be mounted in Melzer's reagent and very carefully teased apart. A squash mount, in which gentle pencil pres-

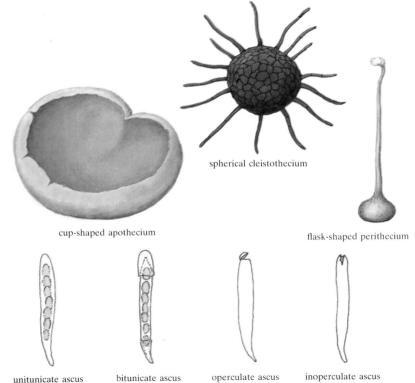

spherical cleistothecium

cup-shaped apothecium

flask-shaped perithecium

unitunicate ascus   bitunicate ascus   operculate ascus   inoperculate ascus

sure is used on the cover glass, will be found useful in forcing apart the spore-bearing asci from other structures; especially the sterile, hair-like bodies called *paraphyses* referred to below. Careful observation must then be made of the structure and staining reaction of the ascus. All of the features to be described will be seen much more clearly in fresh than in dried specimens.

It is generally easiest to look for combinations of characters in deciding if asci are unitunicate or bitunicate. If two small, stained dot-like bodies, a narrow tube or similar structure can be seen at the apex of the ascus, if paraphyses are present with the asci, if the ascus tapers gradually at the base, often into a stalk, if the ascospores are non-septate (and especially if they are also not coloured), if the ascus tip is not broadly rounded with a thickened wall at the tip and if there are not four minute cyanophilous rods in the apical wall, an ascus is almost certainly unitunicate.

Similarly, a combination of features should indicate if an ascus is operculate or inoperculate. A cylindrical ascus with a rather markedly flattened top, lacking an apical pore, having non-septate ascospores that are usually symmetrical about the long and the short axis and have an ornamented spore wall is likely to be operculate.

When determining the size of ascomycete spores, care must be taken to measure only mature spores, preferably those that have burst from the ascus under the pressure of mounting on the slide. Measuring spores while they are still inside an ascus can give misleading results, for they may be immature and thus unduly small; and the ascus wall may further distort the impression of size. The range of size and shape among ascospores is greater than that of basidiospores (see also endpapers), but similar procedures are used in recording them (p. 37). The commonest shapes to be found among ascospores are illustrated. And as with other spore types, surface ornamentation of ascospores is an important criterion in some groups also.

Just as the sterile cystidia are important in the identification of some basidiomycetes, so the size and form of sterile hair-like structures found among the asci are important in some groups of ascomycetes. These bodies are called paraphyses and the commonest types are illustrated. They are usually measured in respect of diameter and length, although care must be taken in recording the latter for it is often difficult to make out where the base of an individual paraphysis lies among the mass of surrounding asci and other tissue. In a few groups, especially some 'Discomycetes', the hairs occurring on the outside of the fruit should be examined similarly.

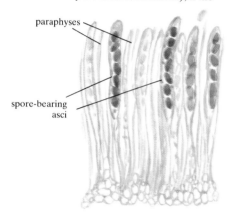

paraphyses

spore-bearing asci

A stained slide showing spore-bearing asci as well as paraphyses in an ascomycete fruit body

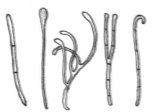

The commonest types of paraphyses

Conidia being discharged from an enclosed pycnidium of a Coelomycete fungus

Conidia being discharged from a more or less exposed acervulus of a Coelomycete fungus

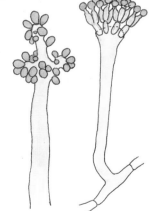

Conidia of two species of Hyphomycete fungi borne on exposed hyphal branches

Other microfungi

The deuteromycetes, which are given only token coverage in the book, are divided into two major groups: the 'Coelomycetes', which have their conidia in enclosed structures called *pycnidia,* or on hyphal aggregates called *acervuli;* and the 'Hyphomycetes', which lack such bodies and bear their conidia on exposed hyphal branches. Sometimes these broad differences are readily discernable with the naked eye, but microscopic examination is always needed for detailed identification.

Other groups of microfungi like Plasmodiophoromycetes, Oomycetes and Zygomycetes are also included in the book, but only to add to the overall impression of the scope of fungal structure and biology: the species coverage is extremely scant. No attempt is made, moreover, to describe the often specialised techniques needed to identify them, for it is anticipated that anyone interested in studying these groups in detail will gain access to specialised technical literature. All of the examples are so common and/or produce such distinctive symptoms that the appearance of gross characters will normally be sufficient to draw attention to them.

FIELD KEY TO FAMILIES

This simple key is intended to aid the identification (in most instances to family level) without using any microscopic characters. It relies entirely on gross, field characters plus the colour of the spore prints obtained from mushroom and toadstool caps.

The key does not include the pathogenic microscopic fungi listed in the Directory but the fungal causes of disease symptoms on higher plants, especially when these are accompanied by mould or other evident fungal growth, may be sought

on the pages where species of the main pathogenic groups are described:

Exobasidiaceae	p. 189
Ustilaginales	p. 199
Uredinales	p. 201
Erysiphaceae	p. 205
Clavicipitaceae	p. 205
Rhytismataceae	p. 208
Loculoascomycetes	p. 222
Deuteromycotina	p. 223
Mycelia sterilia	p. 224
Zygomycotina	p. 224
Mastigomycotina	p. 225

1. FRUIT BODY SHAPE

Skin-like, sometimes with curled-up edges, or crusty, scab-like, flattened onto wood or soil → **Coniophoracea** p. 165. **Corticiaceae** p. 165, **Hymenochaetaceae** p. 174, **Polyporaceae** p. 177, **Stereaceae** p. 185.

Fan-shaped, usually on soil → **Thelephoraceae** p. 187.

Cage or 'octopus' - like → **Clathraceae** p. 198.

Bracket, hoof or shelf-like; growing on wood, sometimes partly contoured to substrate → see **2**.

Finger, horn, club or antler-shaped → see **3**.

Cauliflower, honeycomb or brain-like, sometimes on a stem → see **4**.

More or less spherical or minutely top-shaped, rarely on a tall stem → see **5**.

Cup or bowl-shaped, sometimes with a short stem; often tiny on dead or living plants or soil → see **6**.

More or less umbrella-shaped, tiny, usually on plant material with no obvious spore-bearing surface beneath cap → **Sclerotiniaceae** p. 212, **Heliotiaceae** p. 213.

More or less umbrella or trumpet shaped, sometimes with stem eccentric or almost lateral, with pores, spines, folds or gills beneath cap (includes all typical mushrooms and toadstools) → see **7**. (NB If fruit body is trumpet-shaped but solid within → **Gomphaceae** (*Gomphus* p. 172) and **Thelephoraceae** (*Hydnellum* p. 188))

2. UNDERSIDE

Bearing pores on underside → **Hymenochaetaceae** p. 174, **Fistulinaceae** p. 176, **Ganodermataceae** p. 177, **Polyporacea** p. 177 (Also see → **Corticiaceae** (*Gloeoporus* p. 166))

Bearing gills or folds on underside → **Schizophyllaceae** p. 184, **Pleurotaceae** p. 111, **Cortinariaceae** (*Crepidotus* p. 138), **Corticiaceae** (*Plicaturopsis* p. 169, *Serpula* p. 170, *Merulius* p. 170), **Tricholomataceae** (*Hohenbuehelia* p. 77, *Resupinatus* p. 77, *Panellus* p. 77, *Pleurotellus* p. 87)

Bearing long spines on underside → **Hydnaceae** (*Hericium* p. 174)

3. FRUIT BODY SHAPE

Finger or antler-like, rubbery, on wood → **Dacrymycetaceae** p. 189

Finger or antler-like, not rubbery, on wood → **Xylariaceae** (*Xylaria* p. 207)

Finger-like or with complex, coral-like branching, usually on earth, brittle → **Gomphaceae** p. 172, **Thelephoraceae** p. 187, **Clavariaceae** p. 162

Finger or cigar-like, foul-smelling → **Phallaceae** p. 198

Small, club-headed, on earth → **Geoglossaceae** p. 209

Small, club-headed, on earth from buried bodies of insects; or subterranean fungi → **Clavicipitaceae** (*Cordyceps* p. 205)

4. SIZE

Large or very large, stemless, rooted to stumps → **Sparassidaceae** p. 185

Medium-sized, with stem, on ground → **Morchellaceae** p. 215

Small to medium stemless, often black, gelatinous, on wood → **Tremellaceae** p. 190

5. SUBSTRATE

Usually on ground, whitish to fawn, soft, sometimes with starfish-like base → **Lycoperdales** p. 193

Usually on ground, whitish to fawn, firm → **Sclerodermatales** p. 192

On wood, tiny, yellowish → **Sphaerobolaceae** p. 193, **Nidulariaceae** p. 197

On wood, tiny gelatinous, yellowish → **Dacrymycetaceae** (*Dacrymyces* p. 189).

On wood, fairly large, gelatinous → **Tremellaceae** p. 190

On wood, tiny to large, hard, variously coloured, often black, and often barely emerging through bark → **Hypocreales** p. 206, **Ophiostomatales** p. 206, **Diatrypales** p. 206, **Diaporthales** p. 206, **Sordariaceae** p. 208, **Sphaeriales** p. 207

Subterranean → **Melanogastrales** p. 193, **Elaphomycetaceae** p. 204, **Tuberaceae** p. 219, **Terfeziaceae** p. 219, **Hysterangiaceae** p. 198

On tall stem, on soil → **Tulostomatales** p. 190

6. SIZE AND SHAPE

Irregularly ear-shaped, rubbery, on wood →
  Tremellaceae p. 190, **Auriculariaceae** p. 191
Tiny to medium, bowl-shaped (but often distorted),
  usually on wood or other plant material →
  Cyphellacea p. 184, **Orbiliaceae** p. 209,
  Dermataceae p. 209, **Hyaloscyphaceae** p. 210.
  Helotiaceae p. 213
Tiny to medium, bowl-shaped, usually on dung or
  damp soil, often brightly coloured → **Ascobolaceae**
  p. 219, **Sarcosomataceae** p. 220, **Humariaceae** p.
  220
More or less bowl-shaped, usually fairly large, usually
  on ground → **Helvellaceae** p. 216, **Pezizaceae** p. 217
Tiny, bird's-nest-like, containing 'eggs' →
  Nidulariaceae p. 197

7. Type of SPORE-BEARING SURFACE beneath
  the cap Pores **Boletaceae** p. 47. But also →
  Ganodermataceae (*Ganoderma* p. 177)
  Hymenochaetaceae (*Coltricia* p. 175),
  Polyporaceae (*Polyporus* p. 181, *Albatrellus* p.
  182), **Thelephoraceae** p. 187.
Spines → **Hydnaceae** p. 173, **Auriscalpiaceae** p. 160
Folds → **Cantharellaceae** p. 161, **Auriscalpiaceae** p.
  160, **Tricholomataceae** (*Leptoglossum* p. 71)
Gills → see **8**

8. SPORE PRINT COLOUR [read p. 35]
Black → **Coprinaceae** p. 151
Black-purple to dark brown → see **9**
Pinkish → see **10**
Pale to mid or reddish brown → see **11**
White-cream → see **13**

9. GILLS [read p. 32]
Gills decurrent → **Gomphidiaceae** p. 53
Gills free, stem usually with a ring → **Agaricaceae** p.
  145
Gills adnexed or decurrent → **Strophariaceae** p. 149

10. GILLS [read p. 32]
Gills free, growing on wood or rich soil → **Pluteaceae** p.
  112
Gills more or less decurrent - **Tricholomataceae**
  (*Lepista* p. 65, *Rhodotus* p.78, *Clitopilus* p. 88,
  Rhodocyhe p. 88), **Pleurotaceae** p. 111
Gills adnexed to free → **Tricholomataceae**
  (*Macrocystidia* p. 80)
Gills adnate or decurrent → **Entolomataceae** p. 115

11. GILLS [read p. 32]
Gills decurrent, separating easily form the flesh; fruit
  body very stout → **Paxillaceae** p. 145
Gills not decurrent → see **12**

12. VEIL [read p. 34]
Sometimes a cobweb-like veil present between the cap
  edge and stem, especially on young fruit body →
  Cortinariaceae p. 120
No cobweb-like veil; mainly fragile toadstools on dung
  or rich soil → **Bolbitiaceae** p. 142

13.
Tiny toadstools growing on other decaying toadstools
  → **Tricholomataceae** (*Asterophora* p. 73)
Fruit bodies not as above → see **14**

14. VOLVA [read p. 34]
A volva or pronounced bulb at the stem base →
  Amanitaceae p. 54
No volva at stem base → see **15**

15. RING [read p. 34]
A *pronounced* ring present on the stem → see **16**
No ring present on the stem → see **17**

16.
Fruit bodies growing from wood or from buried roots
  → **Tricholomataceae** (*Armillaria* p. 71,
  Oudemansiella p. 77), **Pleurotaceae** p. 111
Fruit bodies not growing on wood → **Lepiotaceae** p. 57,
  Tricholomataceae (*Catathelasma* p. 71)

17. GILLS
Gills waxy, fruit bodies often brightly coloured →
  Hygrophoraceae p. 88
Gills not waxy → see **18**

18.
Gills very widely spaced; medium-sized toadstools
  growing in rings, or tiny toadstools with hair-like
  stems → **Tricholomataceae** (*Marasmius* p.80)
Gills widely spaced, small toadstools on rotting conifer
  wood → **Tricholomataceae** (*Xeromphalina* p. 87)
Fruit bodies not as above → see **19**

19. GILLS [read p. 32]
Gills more or less decurrent; fruit bodies not growing in
  tufts → **Tricholomataceae** (*Clitocyhe* p. 63,
  Laccaria p. 62, *Omphalina* p. 61, *Leucopaxillus* p.
  73, *Hygrophoropsis* p. 87)
Gills adnate, adnexed, emarginate or free →
  Tricholomataceae (*Tricholoma* p. 67,
  Tricholomopsis p. 66, *Melanoleuca* p. 74, or, if
  from buried cones, *Pseudohiatula* p. 78 or
  Balospora p. 87)
Gills usually adnate; very small, fragile toadstools →
  Tricholomataceae (*Mycena* p. 80, or, if gills
  adnexed to sinuate, *Crinipellis* p. 86)
Fruit bodies not as above → see **20**

20. GILLS [read p. 32]
Gills adnexed; fruit bodies on wood →
  Tricholomataceae (*Flammulina* p. 88)
Gills adnexed; stem deeply-rooting in soil or from
  buried wood → **Tricholomataceae** (*Oudemansiella*
  p. 77)
Gills adnate or slightly decurrent; fruit bodies usually
  growing in tufts → **Tricholomataceae** (*Lyophyllum*
  p. 72, *Collyhia* p. 74, *Cantharellula* p. 73)
Gills usually adnate; fruit bodies not growing in tufts →
  see **21**

21. STEMS
Stems tough → **Tricholomataceae** (*Collyhia* p. 74)
Stems not tough, on soil, bogs or fire sites →
  Tricholomataceae (*Tephrocybe* p. 72, *Myxonphalia*
  p. 86)
Stems not tough, on twigs or needles →
  Tricholomataceae (*Micromphale* p. 76)
Stems brittle → **Russulaceae**
  Fruit bodies exude milky juice when broken →
    (*Lactarius* p. 95)
  Fruit bodies with no milky juice →
    (*Russula* p. 101)

BASIDIOMYCOTINA
Mycelial, either with macroscopic well-defined fruit body or lacking a fruit body and with its function replaced by microscopic hyphal and spore-like structures. Cell walls lack cellulose and contain chitin. Reproduce sexually by formation of basidiospores borne externally on a modified single- or several-celled hyphal structure called a basidium and discharged from it either forcibly or passively. Some also form one or more types of asexual spores. Mostly terrestrial but many also on plant tissues. Saprotrophic or biotrophic, some causing serious crop diseases. Divided on the basis of presence or absence and form of true fruit body, basidium structure and other features into three Classes, Hymenomycetes, Gasteromycetes (p. 000) and Teliomycetes (p. 000).

HYMENOMYCETES
Spores usually produced on ±well-defined fruit body of variable form; toadstool, bracket, cup, disc, club or coral-like, with or without stem, or resupinate, stemless, and±effused; fleshy, leathery, woody, corky, or gelatinous; rarely in some parasitic groups±absent as a recognisable structure. Spore-bearing surface exposed at maturity, one-or two-sided, smooth, folded, gill-like, toothed or tubular. Spores forcibly discharged, variously shaped, smooth or ornamented, variously coloured, usually one-celled, amyloid, dextrinoid, cyanophilous or not. Basidia septate or noneptate, 1 – several spored. Hyphal system mono-, di-or trimitic, colourless or coloured. Saprotrophic or biotrophic. Some edible, some poisonous. Divided into nine Orders (of which the six most important are included here: Agaricales, Aphyllophorales (p. 160), Exobasidiales (p. 189), Dacrymycetales (p. 189) Tremellales (p. 190) and Auriculariales (p. 191) mainly on the basis of formation, septation and overall structure of the basidium although gross fruit body structure correlates fairly well with these features.

AGARICALES
Spore-bearing surface usually two-sided and gill-like, more rarely tubular or one-sided and smooth. Fruit body usually±fleshy, more rarely leathery, typically toadstool-shaped, less commonly bracket-like, resupinate or otherwise. Spores variously shaped but usually±ellipsoid-spherical and variously coloured, but usually white, brownish or black, usually smooth but sometimes characteristically ornamented, amyloid, dextrinoid or neither, one-celled at maturity. Basidia non-septate, usually 4-spored, more rarely 2-spored or exceptionally 8-spored. Hyphal system monomitic, colourless or coloured. Mostly saprotrophic, some biotrophic. Mostly terrestrial but often on plant debris, some on wood. Many mycorrhizal. Some edible and very good, some deadly poisonous. Divided on the basis of many microscopic, structural and biochemical features, (most of which correlate fairly well with macroscopic characters), into sixteen-eighteen families, all represented in Europe although some are predominantly tropical. This order includes all the familiar mushrooms and toadstools.

BOLETACEAE
Toadstool-shaped, bearing pores of varying shape and size, with tubes, pores and flesh of varying colour and displaying characteristic colour changes when cut or bruised, tubes free-depressed to±decurrent, spores ellipsoid – sub-spindle-shaped and smooth, (but±spherical and ornamented in *Strobilomyces*), spore print yellow-brown-black, stem variously ornamented and coloured, cap surface sometimes sticky. Terrestrial (except one). Saprotrophic typically with trees, most mycorrhizal, many edible, few poisonous. *Strobilomyces* [1], *Porphyrellus* [1], *Tylopilus* [1], *Leccinum* [14], *Aureoboletus* [1], *Suillus* [10], *Boletus* [36], *Gyroporus* [2], *Uloporus* [10], (*Boletinus* [1]).

Strobilomyces floccopus
Old Man of The Woods.
Cap, spore print. CAP 5–10, woolly often with overhanging margin. STEM 8–12, shaggy-scaly, rough sheathing ring, ±grooved above. TUBES and PORES white then grey – olive-green, bruising pink or reddish. Tubes adnate-uncinate. Pores large, angular. SPORE PRINT black. SMELL indistinct. FLESH firm, thick, white then pale wine-red, then brown. Usually in small groups. On soil in woods. Autumn. Widespread. Uncommon. Edible. SPORES subspherical – ellipsoid, dark reticulate ornamentation, 10–12×8.5–11.

Porphyrellus pseudoscaber.
Colour, spore print, blue-green in flesh. CAP 5–17, velvety then smooth. STEM 7–17, at first velvety, then smooth,±ribbed. TUBES and PORES pale buff, then olive-green, bruising bluish green. Tubes adnate-uncinate. Pores large, angular. SPORE PRINT purple -brown. SMELL sour, strong. FLESH firm, off-white – olive-green, bluish green in stem apex and above tubes. Usually in small groups. On soil in woods, especially with beech and oak, rarely with conifers. Late summer – autumn. Widespread, especially in North. Uncommon. Edible. SPORES subspindle-shaped, smooth, 12–16×5–6.5.

Tylopilus felleus **Bitter Bolete.** Spore print, pores, stem. CAP 6–12, downy becoming smooth. STEM 7–10, with brown surface network. TUBES and PORES white, then salmon- or coral-pink, sometimes bruising brownish. Tubes adnate-uncinate. Pores large, angular. SPORE PRINT pinkish buff – pale wine-red. SMELL pleasant. FLESH soft, white-cream, becoming buff-pink or buff, especially beneath cap surface. Usually in small groups. On soil in woods, especially with beech and oak; in some areas with conifers. Late summer – autumn. Widespread. Uncommon. Inedible. SPORES sub-spindle-shaped smooth, 11–15×4–5.

Leccinum aurantiacum.
Habitat, cap and stem scale colour and colour changes. CAP 5–15, smooth or slightly downy, margin often slightly overhanging. STEM 8–14, swollen towards base, covered in small white scales that turn rusty then dark brown. TUBES and PORES white, pale wine-red when bruised. Tubes depressed. Pores very small. SPORE PRINT ochre-brown. SMELL pleasant. FLESH firm, cream-white then pale wine-red in cap, stem apex and stem base, otherwise brown. Usually in small groups. On soil with aspen. Late summer – autumn. Widespread. Uncommon. Edible. SPORES subspindle-shaped smooth 15–19×5–6.

BOLETACEAE

Leccinum duriusculum.
Similar to *L. scabrum* but flesh differs; similar to *L. carpini* but cuticle filamentous. CAP 6–12, slightly downy, then smooth, margin often slightly overhanging. STEM 8–14, swollen toward base, covered in dark scales. TUBES depressed, whitish, then off-white. PORES very small, whitish, bruising coffee colour. SPORE PRINT ochre-brown. SMELL indistinct. FLESH very firm, whitish, then salmon-peach, increasingly grey or blackish with bluish green towards stem base. Usually in small groups. On soil, usually with aspen but possibly with birch also. Summer – autumn. Widespread. Rare. Edible. SPORES subspindle-shaped, smooth, 14.5–16×4.5–6.

Leccinum versipelle
Orange Birch Bolete.
Habitat, stem scale colour and cap colour. CAP 8–20, very slightly downy when young, then smooth and dry or faintly sticky, margin overhanging quite distinctly. STEM 8–20, swollen towards base and covered with woolly brown-black scales. TUBES depressed, white then buff, becoming pale wine-red when cut. PORES small grey becoming ochreous, then wine-red grey. SPORE PRINT ochre – brown. SMELL pleasant. FLESH firm, white then pale wine-red, slightly blue-green in stem base, then almost black. Singly or in small groups. On soil with birch. Late summer – autumn. Widespread. Very common. Edible and good. SPORES subspindle-shaped, smooth 12.5–16×4–5.

Leccinum holopus. Similar to *L. scabrum* but cap paler and flesh colour change differs. CAP 4–7, smooth, sticky when fresh. STEM 8–11, covered with white woolly scales that later turn red-brown. TUBES depressed, white-buff. PORES small, white-buff, bruising red-brown. SPORE PRINT ochre – brown. SMELL indistinct. FLESH very soft, white with intense blue-green in stem base. Usually in small groups. Among *Sphagnum* or occasionally other mosses, with birch. Autumn. Widespread. Uncommon. Edible but poor. SPORES subspindle-shaped, 18–19×6–6.5

Leccinum carpini. Habitat and structure of cap cuticle. CAP 3–7, smooth but often cracked and minutely crazed, margin often drawn away from tubes on aging. STEM 8–9, slender and often swollen around midway and toward base. TUBES depressed, white or faintly cream, turning very quickly pink then darkening when cut. PORES small, white, becoming yellowish and quickly turning black on handling. SPORE PRINT ochre – brown. SMELL indistinct. FLESH fairly firm, white or straw-coloured, rapidly darkening when cut, through rose or reddish grey to black, the colours varying throughout stem and cap but always first showing pronounced blue spotting in stem base. Usually in small groups. On soil with hornbeam, hazel or rarely with oak. Summer – autumn. Widespread. Uncommon. Edible but poor. SPORES subspindle-shaped, 15–19×5–6. Cap-surface comprising chains of barrel-like or spherical cells.

Leccinum quercinum. Cap colour and stem scale colours. CAP 6–15, surface minutely scaly to coarse or velvety in patches to smooth. STEM 11–18, often slightly swollen towards base with woolly scales, whitish buff towards base, darker towards apex, darkening on handling. TUBES and PORES dirty white-buff, darkening to pale wine-red then brown. Tubes depressed. Pores small. SPORE PRINT ochre-brown. SMELL pleasant. FLESH firm, white-cream, quickly darkening with wine-red in cap, especially, pink colours; sometimes slightly leaf-green at stem base. Usually in small groups. On soil with oak, possibly lime and beech also. Late summer – autumn. Widespread. Rare. Edible. SPORES subspindle-shaped, smooth 12–15×3.5–5.

Leccinum variicolor. Cap colours, flesh colours, habitat. CAP 5–9, at first felty-downy, dry, then smooth and slightly sticky, margin paler, slightly inrolled. STEM 12–18, swollen towards base, covered in dark scales except at apex,± net-patterned towards base, quickly bruising green-yellow. TUBES and PORES white-cream, bruising slightly pinkish, then ochre. Tubes depressed. Pores small. SPORE PRINT ochre-buff. SMELL pleasant. FLESH white, at first pink in cap, then reddish in cap and stem, blue-green at stem base. Usually in small groups. On soil and amongst moss with birch, especially in wet woods. Summer – autumn. Widespread. Rare. Edible. SPORES subspindle-shaped, smooth, 12.5–16×4.5–6.

Leccinum scabrum **Brown Birch Bolete.** Commoner than most similar species; white flesh that does not change colour and cap margin that does not overhang. CAP 4–15, markedly soft, dry but becoming slightly sticky when wetted by rain. STEM 7–20, with masses of tiny dark scales which are noticeably arranged in lines, especially towards the apex. TUBES depressed, white but changing to pale ochre. PORES small, white, bruising ochre or pale red-brown. SPORE PRINT ochre – brown. SMELL pleasant. FLESH very soft, almost watery, white and scarcely changing when bruised or cut. Solitary or in groups. On soil with birch. Summer – autumn. Widespread. Very common. Edible. SPORES subspindle-shaped, smooth, 14–20×5–6.

Leccinum crocipodium. Yellow tubes, pores and scales. CAP 4–10, faintly downy but soon smooth, margin overhanging tubes. STEM 6–12, swollen towards base, with±irregular lines of yellowish scales that darken when handled. TUBES and PORES lemon- or chrome-yellow, darkening when handled. Tubes depressed. Pores minute. SPORE PRINT ochre – brown. SMELL indistinct. Flesh fairly firm, pale lemon-yellow or straw-coloured in cap, greyish in stem, very quickly darkening but usually with pale wine-red or brick and purple or chestnut tints; some-

times bluish green at extreme base of stem. Usually in small groups. On soil with oaks. Late summer – autumn. Widespread. Rare. SPORES ellipsoid – subspindle-shaped, smooth, 12–17.5×4.5–6.

Aureoboletus (= *Pulveroboletus*) *cramesinus*. Colours and sticky cap. CAP 2–5, sticky then streaked and wrinkled on drying. STEM 5–8, sometimes swollen towards centre, tapering towards base, ±rooting, sticky and sometimes with watery droplets. TUBES and PORES lemon-yellow becoming golden yellow, unchanging when bruised. Tubes uncinate-decurrent. Pores large, angular. SPORE PRINT ochre – buff. SMELL pleasant. FLESH soft, white with slight pink. Usually in small groups. On soil (sometimes on old fire sites) in broad-leaved woods. Late summer – autumn. Widespread. Rare. Edible. SPORES subspindle-shaped, smooth, 11–15×4.5–5.5.

Suillus flavidus. Colour, slender form and gelatinous ring. CAP 2–6, sticky, usually umbonate, often ±streaked. STEM 5–7.5, slender, ring superior, gelatinous, collapsing onto the stem. TUBES and PORES dark straw-coloured. Tubes decurrent. Pores large, compound, angular. SPORE PRINT ochre – brown. SMELL indistinct. FLESH fairly firm, pale lemon yellow, becoming pale wine-red in air. Usually in small groups. On wet soil or among *Sphagnum*, usually with Scots pine in Britain. Late summer. Northern and highland, ± confined to Scotland in Britain. Uncommon. Edible. SPORES ± spindle-shaped – ellipsoid, smooth, 8–10×3.5–4.5.

Suillus luteus **Slippery Jack**. Large membranous ring and cap colour. CAP 5–10, glutinous or mucilaginous, on drying becoming shiny then wrinkled. STEM 5–10, sometimes slightly swollen towards base, darkening rapidly, ring large, membranous, white-cream but darkening to sepia at edge and pale wine-red beneath. TUBES and PORES lemon-yellow to dirty straw-coloured, flushed orange. Tubes adnate. Pores medium, round. SPORE PRINT ochre – buff. SMELL indistinct. FLESH soft, white, yellowish in cap, wine-red at stem base. Usually in small groups. On soil with conifers, especially pines. Autumn. Widespread. Very common. SPORES subspindle-shaped – elongate-ellipsoid, smooth, 7–10×3–3.5.

Suillus granulatus. No ring, droplets exuding from stem apex and pores. CAP 2–8, sticky, becoming shiny when dry and later slightly wrinkled. STEM 3.7–8, slightly swollen at base, granular towards apex, the granules exuding pale watery liquid. TUBES and PORES pale lemon yellow or buff. Tubes adnate–±decurrent. Pores small, exuding pale drops of liquid that darken and harden on drying. SPORE PRINT ochre – orange. SMELL pleasant. FLESH soft, lemon-yellow or straw-coloured, usually paler in the cap and more chrome yellow in the stem. Usually in troops. On soil with conifers. Autumn. Widespread, especially in South. Common. Edible. SPORES subspindle-shaped – ellipsoid, smooth, 8–10×2.5–3.5.

Suillus variegatus. No ring, cap scaly and barely sticky. CAP 6–13, slightly downy, slightly sticky when wet but barely sticky compared with related species, bearing small, flattened dark scales, most noticeably around margin. STEM 6–10, often somewhat club-shaped and with a flattened mycelial plate at the base. TUBES adnate or slightly decurrent, dark buff or ochre. PORES ±angular, unequal, compound, dark straw-colour – ochre, becoming cinnamon and often bruising bluish green. SPORE PRINT brown. SMELL strong, earthy, somewhat like *Scleroderma* species. FLESH fairly soft, lemon-yellow – ochre in cap, pale ochre at stem apex and darker in stem base, sometimes tinged with blue. Usually in small groups. On soil with conifers. Summer – autumn. Widespread. Common. Edible. SPORES subspindle-shaped – elongate-ellipsoid, smooth, 9–11×3–4.

Suillus bovinus. No ring, overall colour, pale cap margin. CAP 3–10, smooth and sticky, with pronounced pale margin. STEM 4–6, generally smooth except at apex when young, often tapering at base. TUBES ±decurrent, greyish wine-red. PORES large, angular, unequal, compound, pale olive-green then buff with pale wine-red tints, scarcely darkening when bruised. SPORE PRINT pale olive-green – brown. SMELL pleasant, sweet or fruity. FLESH soft, whitish becoming pinkish, often with some blue above tubes and in stem base. Often trooping in large groups. On soil with pines or other conifers. Late summer – autumn. Widespread. Common. Edible but poor. SPORES ellipsoid – subspindle-shaped, smooth, 8–10×3–4.

Suillus aeruginascens. Overall colour, sticky ring and habitat. CAP 3–10, sticky, often with fibrils streaked over the surface. STEM 5–9, often slightly swollen below with greyish network towards apex, ring membranous, sticky. TUBES and PORES off white with tinge of yellow or pinkish buff. Tubes adnate–±decurrent. Pores large, angular, unequal. SPORE PRINT brown. SMELL indistinct. FLESH soft, watery, whitish or cream-colour, turning faintly blue-green especially in stem. In small groups. On soil with larch. Summer – autumn. Widespread. Rare. Edible but poor. SPORES ellipsoid-subspindle-shaped, smooth, 10–12×4–5.5.

Suillus grevillei **Larch Bolete**. Overall colour, form of ring and habitat. CAP 3–10, very sticky, markedly shiny and sometimes wrinkled when dry. STEM 5–7, slender, with ± woolly, granular or sometimes reticulate apex, ring upward pointing. TUBES ± decurrent, pale yellow – ochre. PORES small, angular, lemon yellow, becoming rust-coloured on bruising. SPORE PRINT ochre – red-brown. SMELL faint but pleasant. FLESH fairly soft, lemon-yellow or straw-coloured, darkest in the stem, often appearing blue in stem base when first cut. Singly or in small groups. On soil with larch. Summer – autumn. Widespread. Extremely common. Edible. SPORES subspindle-shaped – ellipsoid, smooth, 8–11×3–4.

49

Suillus tridentinus. Uniform colour. CAP 5–12, sticky, slightly wrinkled with dark fibrillose scales. STEM 4–7.5, sometimes slightly swollen below, rust-coloured veining or network above, ring often indefinite, yellowish. TUBES and PORES apricot or orange. Tubes ± decurrent, short. Pores broad, compound, angular. SPORE PRINT dark straw colour. SMELL faint, pleasant. FLESH fairly firm, lemon-yellow, ± apricot when cut. In small groups. On soil with larch or yew. Summer – autumn. Widespread, predominantly southern. Uncommon. Edible. SPORES subspindle-shaped – elongate, smooth, 10–13×4–5.

Boletus albidus (=*radicans*). Reticulations, no red on stem. CAP 8.5–12, downy at first then smooth and sometimes cracking. STEM 5–8, stout, swollen below and sometimes with ± rooting base, usually a yellow net pattern towards apex. TUBES and PORES lemon-yellow, blue on bruising. Tubes adnate. Pores small, round. SPORE PRINT olive-green – brown. SMELL spicy. FLESH fairly firm, white – lemon-yellow in cap, off-white in stem, blue before fading when cut. Solitary or in small groups. On soil with oak and beech. Summer – autumn. Widespread but predominantly southern. Uncommon. Inedible. SPORES subspindle-shaped, smooth, 12–16×4.5–6.

Boletus fechtneri. Similar to *B. albidus* but cap and flesh colours and colour changes differ. CAP 5–15, finely downy, then ± silky and fine cracking at centre. STEM 5–15, cylindrical to club-shaped, reticulate towards apex. TUBES and PORES lemon-yellow, bluish green on bruising. Tubes adnate. Pores small. SPORE PRINT olive-green – brown. SMELL indistinct. FLESH fairly firm, pale lemon-yellow, bluish beneath cap cuticle, reddish in stem and irregularly blue-spotted around tubes. Usually in small groups. On soil in broad-leaved woods, especially with oak and beech. Autumn. Widespread, but predominantly southern. Rare. Edible? SPORES subspindle-shaped – elongate-ellipsoid, smooth, 11–13×4.5–5.

Boletus luridus. Stem reticulations, colour change of pores, red at tube bases. CAP 8.5–12, faintly downy, then smooth. STEM 8–14, marked orange-red reticulations. TUBES free, yellow-green, turning blue when cut. PORES small, round, orange-red turning blue when handled. SPORE PRINT olive-green – brown. SMELL faint but pleasant. FLESH firm, lemon-yellow with some red in stem, quickly turning blue when cut but red line at bases of tubes. Usually in small groups. On soil in broad-leaved woods, especially with beech or oak on chalky soils. Widespread. Common. Inedible. SPORES subspindle-shaped – ellipsoid, smooth, 11–15×4.5–6.5.

Boletus calopus. Stem. CAP 6–12, slightly downy then smooth, sometimes cracked or crazed when old. STEM 7–9, stout, often swollen, usually ± covered with white or straw-coloured network. TUBES and PORES dirty sulphur-yellow, bluish in tubes or greenish on pores when bruised. Tubes depressed. Pores medium, round. SPORE PRINT bronze-brown. SMELL strong, unpleasant. FLESH firm, cream or yellow, quickly turning blue when cut, sometimes red at stem base. Solitary or in small groups. On soil in mixed woods, especially with beech and oak on acid sites. Late summer – autumn. Widespread. Common. Inedible. SPORES subspindle-shaped, smooth, 12–16×4.5–5.5.

Boletus appendiculatus. Cap colour and flesh. CAP 8–14, downy at first, later smoother with cracking towards centre. STEM 11–13, slightly swollen towards centre or base, finely reticulated with yellow. TUBES and PORES lemon-yellow, slightly greenish blue when cut or bruised. Tubes adnate. Pores small. SPORE PRINT olive-green – brown. SMELL pleasant, earthy. FLESH fairly firm, pale sulphur-yellow, bluish in stem apex, red spotting in stem, red-purple under cap cuticle. Solitary or in small groups. On soil with oaks. Late summer – autumn. Widespread but predominantly southern. Uncommon. Edible. SPORES subspindle-shaped, smooth, 12–15×3.5–4.

Boletus queletii. Variable but rich colours and flesh in stem turning blue-purple. CAP 5.5–18, finely downy, especially towards margin, then smooth. STEM 7–10, tapering below with fine orange dots, becoming red below. TUBES depressed, ochre, blue when cut. PORES small, round, peach, then orange becoming blue when handled. SPORE PRINT olive-green – brown. SMELL indistinct. FLESH fairly firm, lemon-yellow in cap, and red in stem, especially in upper part, blue when cut. Usually in small groups. On soil with broad-leaved trees, especially beech, oak and lime. Autumn. Widespread, predominantly southern. Uncommon. Edible. SPORES ± spindle-shaped, smooth, 12–14×5.5–6.5.

Boletus erythropus. Colour change, skin features. CAP 5–16, faintly downy then smooth, sometimes slightly sticky when wet. STEM 4.5–14.5, stout, covered in orange-red dots. TUBES free, lemon yellow, quickly turning blue on cutting. PORES small, round, ± orange, quickly turning blue on bruising. SPORE PRINT olive green-brown. SMELL indistinct. FLESH fairly firm, lemon-yellow ± throughout and quickly turning dark blue on cutting. Usually in small groups. On soil in all types of woodland. Late summer – autumn. Widespread. Common. Edible. SPORES subspindle-shaped, smooth, 12–15×4–6.

Boletus pseudosulphureus (= ? *junquilleus*). Overall colour and colour change when cut. CAP 8.5–15, faintly downy, then smooth. STEM 6.5–18, ±spindle-shaped, covered with yellow, downy spotting. TUBES and PORES chrome-yellow, quickly turning dark blue when cut or handled. Tubes depressed. Pores small, round. SPORE PRINT olive-green – brown. SMELL indistinct. FLESH fairly firm, chrome yellow, quickly becoming dark blue when cut. Usually in small groups. On soil with broad-leaved trees, especially oak, beech or lime. Autumn. Widespread. Rare. Edible? SPORES subspindle-shaped, smooth, 11.5–16.5.

Boletus aereus. Similar to *B. edulis* but darker colours. CAP 6.5–15, finely cracked or crazed causing surface to feel rough. STEM 6–8, stout, swollen at centre or club-shaped, dark buff network in upper part. TUBES and PORES white or cream, becoming slightly olive-green when handled. Tubes depressed. Pores small, round. SPORE PRINT olive-green – brown. SMELL pleasant, strong, earthy. FLESH fairly firm, white. Usually in small groups. On soil with broad-leaved trees. Summer – autumn. Widespread but predominantly southern. Rare. Edible and good. SPORES subspindle-shaped, smooth, 13.5–15.5×4–5.5.

Boletus aestivalis. Very similar to *B. edulis* but often earlier and with more reticulation on stem. CAP 6–20, ±smooth but cracking slightly at centre to form small scales. STEM 5–15, stout, sometimes bulbous and markedly swollen below, often reticulate to below halfway. TUBES and PORES white to dirty yellowish. Tubes depressed. Pores small, round. SPORE PRINT olive-green – brown. SMELL pleasant. FLESH firm, white. Usually in small groups. On soil with beech or oak. Early summer – early autumn. Widespread. Uncommon. Edible and good. SPORES subspindle-shaped, smooth, 12–16×4.5–6.

Boletus satanoides (= *B. splendidus* in part). cap colour and flesh colour change. CAP 5–18, ±smooth. STEM 8–16, often slightly swollen below, bluish on handling, faint orange net towards apex. TUBES and PORES chrome-yellow, pores becoming reddish. Tubes free? Pores small, round. SPORE PRINT olive-green – brown. SMELL unpleasant or spicy. FLESH firm, white to pale yellow, then blue. Solitary or in small groups. On soil with oak. Summer – early autumn. Widespread. Very rare. Poisonous. SPORES subspindle-shaped, smooth, 10.5–12.5×4.5–5.

Boletus edulis **Cep, Penny Bun.** Variable in size and shape but combination of stem and cap colours. CAP 8–20, ±smooth but slightly sticky when wet. STEM 3–23, stout, sometimes bulbous and markedly swollen below, reticulate above. TUBES and PORES white to dirty yellowish. Tubes depressed. Pores small, round. SPORE PRINT olive-green – brown. SMELL pleasant. FLESH fairly firm, white. Solitary or in small groups. On soil in or close to fairly dry woodland of all types. Summer – autumn. Widespread. Very common. Edible and good. SPORES subspindle-shaped, smooth, 14–17×4.5–5.5.

Boletus pinicola Similar to *B. edulis* but for habitat, cap more purple-red, and flesh colour. CAP 9–13, at first smooth and greasy, then dry and finely downy, especially at margin. STEM 8–10, stout, often swollen below, covered in white and red-brown reticulations which bruise red. TUBES and PORES whitish, becoming dirty greenish yellow. Tubes adnate. Pores small, round. SPORE PRINT olive-green – brown. SMELL pleasant. FLESH fairly firm, ±white but becoming pale wine-red in parts of cap and stem, esp. below cap cuticle. Usually in small groups. On soil with conifers. Early summer – late autumn. Widespread. Uncommon. Edible. SPORES subspindle-shaped, smooth, 13–17×4–5.

Boletus satanas **Devil's Bolete.** Cap and stem colours and flesh colour change. CAP 11–27, very finely downy then smooth. STEM 6–9, very stout, swollen in centre and sometimes almost spherical, covered at least to half way with red reticulations. TUBES free, yellow-green, becoming blue at first when cut. PORES small, round, red, orange towards margin, bruising green. SPORE PRINT olive-green – brown. SMELL unpleasant, foetid. FLESH firm, pale straw or white, turning pale blue with rust patches when cut. Solitary or in small groups. On chalky soil with beech. Summer – early autumn. Widespread but predominantly southern. Very rare. Poisonous. SPORES subspindle-shaped, smooth, 11–14×4.5–6.

Boletus impolitus. Smell, size, ± unchanging flesh colour. CAP 5–12, downy, then smooth. STEM 6–10, stout, usually swollen at centre, reddish streaks and dots at apex. TUBES and PORES lemon-yellow, darkening slightly. Tubes depressed. Pores small, round. SPORE PRINT olive-green – brown. SMELL iodine when stem base cut. FLESH fairly firm, white – lemon-yellow, changing slightly to bluish or pink. Usually in small groups. On soil in broad-leaved woods, typically at path edges and especially with oak on clay soils. Summer – autumn. Widespread in southern areas. Uncommon. Edible. SPORES subspindle-shaped – ellipsoid, smooth, 10–14×4.5–5.5.

51

Boletus (*=Chalciporus*) *piperatus* **Peppery Bolete.** Pore colours, flesh colour at stem base. CAP 3–7, usually dry and shiny but sticky at first. STEM 4–7.5, slender, subspindle-shaped with marked downward taper, silky. TUBES ±decurrent, cinnamon then rust-colour. PORES large, angular, rust-colour. SPORE PRINT brown. SMELL indistinct. FLESH fairly soft, overall buff but reddish below cuticle and above tubes, yellow at stem base. Usually trooping in groups. On soil with broad-leaved or mixed trees, often among dry birch scrub. Summer – autumn. Widespread. Common. Edible. SPORES subspindle-shaped, smooth, 8–11×3–4.

Boletus (*=Xerocomus*) *lanatus*. Similar to *B. subtomentosus* but pore colour change and ammonia reaction differs. CAP 4–9, velvety. STEM 4–8, slender with irregular, coarse pattern of dark red reticulations. TUBES and PORES chrome-yellow, turning blue when handled. Tubes depressed. Pores large, angular. SPORE PRINT olive-green – brown. SMELL indistinct. Ammonia on cap, yellow – green-blue-green. FLESH fairly soft, white in cap with dark line below cuticle, more yellow and buff in stem. Usually in small groups. On soil in broad-leaved and mixed woods, especially with birch. Autumn. Widespread. Rare. Edible? SPORES subspindle-shaped, smooth, 13–16×4.5.

Boletus (*=Xerocomus*) *subtomentosus*. Like *B. lanatus* and *B. spadiceus* but flesh colour and/or ammonia reaction differ, like *B. porosporus* but no pore in spore. CAP 5–12, downy, then smooth, some cracking. STEM 3–8, slender, spindle-shaped, sometimes faint ribbing or dots. TUBES and PORES chrome-yellow, then olive-green. Tubes adnate. Pores large, angular. SPORE PRINT olive-green – brown. SMELL indistinct. Ammonia on cap, date-brown – purple. FLESH soft, pale lemon-yellow with purplish line beneath cap cuticle, browner in stem. Usually in small groups. On soil in broad-leaved and mixed woods. Autumn. Widespread. Common. Edible. SPORES subspindle-shaped, smooth, 10–13×3.5–5.

Boletus (*=Xerocomus*) *parasiticus*. Unique substrate. CAP 2–4, finely downy, dry, cracking. STEM 1–4, tapering downwards, usually curved. TUBES and PORES lemon-yellow becoming ochre or rust. Tubes adnate – ±decurrent. Pores compound, ±round. SPORE PRINT olive green – brown. SMELL indistinct. FLESH firm, pale lemon-yellow, slight rust colour at stem base. With *Scleroderma citrinum*. Autumn. Widespread but predominantly southern. Uncommon. Edible. SPORES elongate-subspindle-shaped, smooth, 11–21×3.5–5.

Boletus (*=Xerocomus*) *chrysenteron* **Red Cracked Bolete.** Cap colour and cracking to reveal red flesh. CAP 4–12, faintly downy then smooth, cracking to reveal reddish flesh beneath. STEM 4–8, slender, sometimes tapering upwards, usually with reddish granules. TUBES and PORES sulphur-yellow, usually bruising or turning greenish. Tubes depressed. Pores large, angular. SPORE PRINT olive-green – brown. SMELL indistinct. FLESH soft, white with coral-red line beneath cap cuticle, clay-buff in stem base. Usually in small groups. On soil with broad-leaved trees. Autumn. Widespread. Very common. Edible but poor. SPORES subspindle-shaped, smooth, 12–15×3.5–5.

Boletus (*=Xerocomus*) *spadiceus*. Similar to *B. subtomentosus* but pure white flesh. CAP 4–9, downy becoming smooth. STEM 4–9, slender with irregular, coarse pattern of dark red reticulations. TUBES and PORES lemon-yellow – chrome-yellow, turning blue when handled. Tubes adnate. Pores large, ±angular. SPORE PRINT olive-green – brown. SMELL indistinct. Ammonia on cap, deep purple. FLESH fairly soft, white in cap, cream above tubes, red-brown – buff below cap cuticle, sometimes buff-pink in stem apex. Usually in small groups. On soil in broad-leaved and mixed woods. Autumn. Widespread. Rare. Edible? SPORES subspindle-shaped, smooth, 11–13×3.5–4.5.

Boletus porosporus Pore in spore. CAP 3.5–7.5, downy, then smooth and some cracking to reveal flesh, esp. at centre. STEM 4–6, slender, sometimes tapering upwards, and with faint streaks. TUBES and PORES lemon-yellow, olive-green flush, bluish when bruised. Tubes adnate with tooth. Pores large, angular, compound. SPORE PRINT olive-green – brown. SMELL indistinct. FLESH soft, pale lemon-yellow, faint brown line beneath cap cuticle, chrome-yellow in stem apex, red-brown at base, later bluish, esp. above tubes. Usually small groups. On soil in broad-leaved and mixed woods, esp. with oak. Autumn. Widespread. Uncommon. Inedible. SPORES subspindle-shaped, smooth, with distinct pore, 13–15×4.5–5.5.

Boletus (*=Xerocomus*) *badius* **Bay Bolete.** Viscid cap, pore colour and colour change. CAP 5–13, finely downy then smooth and shiny, sticky when wet. STEM 4.5–12.5, sometimes tapering either upwards or downwards, bearing very fine fibrils. TUBES and PORES cream – lemon-yellow, turning blue-green when handled. Tubes adnate – depressed. Pores large, angular. SPORE PRINT olive-green – brown. SMELL earthy or mushroomy. FLESH fairly soft, white or lemon-yellow, turning blue around pores and in stem apex. Usually in small groups. On soil with conifers. Late summer – autumn. Widespread. Very common. Edible and good. SPORES subspindle-shaped, smooth, 13–15×4.5–5.5.

Boletus pruinatus. Cap colour, no cracking, flesh colour and colour change. CAP 8–10, with fine grape-like 'bloom'. STEM 8–10, subspindle-shaped, with fine reddish dots around the centre. TUBES and PORES lemon-yellow, becoming chrome-yellow then slowly bluish. Tubes adnate. Pores small, angular. SPORE PRINT olive-green – brown. SMELL indistinct. FLESH fairly firm, lemon-chrome, browner in stem base, slowly turning blue-green when cut. Usually in small groups. On soil in broad-leaved woods. Summer – autumn. Widespread. Uncommon. Edible. SPORES subspindle-shaped, smooth, 11.5 –14×4.5–5.5.

Boletus versicolor (=*Xerocomus rubellus*). Overall colour and slender form. CAP 3–6, margin sometimes slightly waved. STEM 3–7.5, slender, relatively and conspicuously long, with faint red spotting throughout. TUBES and PORES lemon yellow, becoming blue when handled. Tubes adnate. Pores large, angular. SPORE PRINT olive green – brown. SMELL indistinct. FLESH soft, dirty straw-coloured in cap, lemon-yellow at stem apex, otherwise ±pale wine red but brown at stem base and slowly turning blue. Usually in small groups. On soil in grass with broad-leaved trees, especially oaks. Autumn. Widespread. Uncommon. Edible and good. SPORES subspindle-shaped, smooth, 11–14×4.5–5.5.

Gyroporus castaneus. Spore print, flesh and pore colours. CAP 3–10. finely downy-velvety then smooth. STEM 3.5–9.5, equal or sometimes tapering upwards or swollen towards centre, finely velvety, at first stuffed, then hollow. TUBES and PORES white, then lemon-yellow. Tubes free. Pores very small, ±round, unequal. SPORE PRINT lemon-yellow. SMELL faint, sweet, pleasant. FLESH firm, white, occasionally flushed pinkish. Solitary or in small groups. On soil, especially among moss, with broad-leaved trees, especially oak. Summer – autumn. Widespread. Rare. Edible and good. SPORES ellipsoid, smooth, 8–11×4.5–6.

Uloporus (=*Gyrodon*) *lividus*. Habitat, overall shape, pores. CAP 4–10, sticky at first, then dry. STEM 5–7.5, equal or slightly swollen towards base, often eccentric and fused. TUBES and PORES dark sulphur-yellow, bruising grey-green. Tubes deeply decurrent, very short. Pores large, irregularly angular. SPORE PRINT olive-green – brown. SMELL indistinct. FLESH pale lemon-yellow in cap, rust-colour towards stem base, becoming blue especially above tubes and in stem apex. In small groups, sometimes±tufted. On soil among grass, with alder, especially in alder carr. Autumn. Widespread. Rare. Edible. SPORES ellipsoid – broadly ellipsoid, smooth, 4.5–6×3–4.

Boletus pulverulentus. Overall colour combinations, and intense colour change when bruised. CAP 5–8, finely downy, then smooth. STEM 5–6.5, usually tapering downwards, with red streaks. TUBES depressed, vivid sulphur-yellow, bruising blue and then darkening. PORES small, round, dirty sulphur-yellow, bruising blue and then darkening. SPORE PRINT olive-green – brown. SMELL pleasant. FLESH fairly firm, lemon-yellow or chrome-yellow, quickly turning blue when cut and then darkening. Usually in small groups, with broad-leaved trees, especially oaks, in open areas in woodland or close to trees in parks and on lawns. Autumn. Widespread, especially in southern and western areas. Very rare. Edible and good. SPORES subspindle-shaped, smooth, 10–14×3.5–6.5.

Boletus (=*Chalciporus*) *rubinus*. Spore shape, tube colour, stature. CAP 2.5–8, cracking irregularly to reveal flesh and ultimately having the appearance of being minutely scaly. STEM 2–4, sometimes slightly swollen or tapering towards base, with red dots at least to half way. TUBES subdecurrent, pale coral-pink or buff, red towards pores. PORES fairly large, round, red. SPORE PRINT COLOUR pale reddish yellow – pale red-brown. SMELL mild. FLESH fairly firm, white in cap with some pale red flushing, chrome-yellow at stem base and sometimes under cap cuticle. Usually in small groups. On soil among grass with oak. Summer – autumn. Widespread. Rare. Edible? SPORES ellipsoid – broadly ellipsoid, smooth, 5.5–7×3.5–4.5.

Gyroporus cyanescens. Spore print, flesh colour change. CAP 4–12, finely-coarsely velvety, especially towards margin. STEM 5–10, sometimes tapering upwards or swollen towards centre, fairly coarsely streaked, often cracking to give ring-like pattern, stuffed then hollow. TUBES and PORES white then pale lemon-yellow, turning blue when touched. Tubes free. Pores very small, round. SPORE PRINT lemon-yellow. SMELL indistinct. FLESH firm, white to buff, becoming very quickly green-blue when cut. Usually in small groups. On acid soil on heathland, with scrub, especially birch. Summer – late autumn. Widespread. Rare. Edible and good. SPORES ellipsoid, smooth, 9–11×4.5–6.

GOMPHIDIACEAE
Toadstool-shaped, with gills relatively thick and waxy, often changing colour on maturing, flesh of varying colour, amyloid (*Chroogomphus*) or not (*Gomphidius*), gills decurrent, often deeply so, spores cylindrical – subspindle-shaped, smooth, spore print±black – brown, cap surface often markedly sticky. Terrestrial. Typically with conifers, mycorrhizal, all edible. *Chroogomphus* [2], *Gomphidius* [4].

53

GOMPHIDIAECEAE

Chroogomphus rutilus **Pine Spike Cap.** Overall shape, habitat, gill form. CAP 3–15, markedly sticky, shiny when dry; usually strongly umbonate. STEM 6–12, sometimes tapering at base, finely scaly, slightly sticky, faint ring patterns. GILLS dull olive-green then black, waxy, fairly distant, deeply decurrent. SPORE PRINT black. SMELL mild. FLESH fairly firm, pale wine-red – salmon in cap, more yellow in stem, especially at base, amyloid. Usually in small groups. On soil with conifers, especially pines. Late summer – late autumn. Widespread. Common. Edible but poor. SPORES subspindle-shaped, smooth 15–22×5.5–7.

Gomphidius roseus **Rosy Spike Cap.** Cap colour. CAP 2–5, very sticky glutinous, slightly wavy, slightly umbonate. STEM 2.5–4.5, equal, glutinous towards base but soon drying, white glutinous indefinite ring zone. GILLS off-white, darkening to grey, broad, thick, distant, forked, deeply decurrent. SPORE PRINT black. SMELL indistinct. FLESH fairly firm, off-white often with coral tint, non-amyloid. Solitary or in small groups. On soil with conifers, especially pines. Autumn. Widespread. Uncommon. Edible but poor. SPORES subspindle-shaped, smooth, 15.5–17.5×5–5.5.

Gomphidius glutinosus **Slimy Spike Cap.** Glutinous cap and stem, stem base colour. CAP 5–12.5, sticky glutinous, slightly wavy, streaked about margin. STEM 3.5–10, glutinous, tapering upwards, glutinous veil forming a blackish, gelatinous ring. GILLS off-white, darkening to almost black, broad, thick, distant, forked, deeply decurrent. SPORE PRINT dark red-brown. SMELL indistinct. FLESH firm, white with wine-red flush but chrome-yellow at stem base, non-amyloid. Solitary or in small groups. On soil with exotic conifers. Autumn. Widespread. Rare. Edible but poor. SPORES subspindle-shaped, smooth, 17–20×5.5–6.

Gomphidius maculatus. Glutinous cap, dry stem, habitat. CAP 3–6, glutinous, umbonate then depressed, grooved at margin. STEM 4.5–7.5, dry especially at apex. GILLS off-white, darkening to almost black, broad, thick, distant, forked, deeply decurrent. SPORE PRINT black. SMELL indistinct. FLESH fairly firm, white in cap and stem but lemon-yellow at stem apex and turning red, brownish or even black, especially towards base, non-amyloid. Usually in small groups. On soil with larch. Autumn. Widespread. Uncommon. Inedible. SPORES subspindle-shaped, smooth, 17-23×6–8.

AMANITACEAE

AMANITACEAE

Toadstool-shaped, with gills crowded, free or almost free, white or greenish-yellow, flesh usually predominantly white but some display characteristic colour changes when cut, spores usually smooth, amyloid or not, spore print white or slightly greenish yellow, cap surface markedly slimy (*Limacella*) or not and often with loose, ±woolly patches (*Amanita*). Stem often with ring and/or volva of characteristic form and often with bulbous base. Terrestrial. Saprotrophic, typically with trees, most mycorrhizal, few edible, many poisonous, some deadly. *Amanita* [20], *Limacella* [5].

Amanita inaurata. Size, cap colour and surface, bands on stem. CAP 7–14, grooved at margin, large, shaggy remnants of veil. STEM 8–14, tapering upwards, bulbous, with bands of woolly veil tissue and very loose volva which falls off leaving ridges on bulb, no ring. GILLS white, crowded, adnate. SPORE PRINT white. SMELL faint but pleasant. FLESH white. Usually in small groups. On soil, especially chalky, in or close to mixed woodland. Autumn. Widespread. Uncommon. Inedible. SPORES spherical, smooth, 10–13, non-amyloid.

Amanita crocea. Overall colour, smooth cap. CAP 4–12, smooth, broadly umbonate, grooved at margin, often upturned at edge when mature. STEM 8–13, tapering upwards, non-bulbous, finely woolly scales throughout, persistent bag-like volva, no ring. GILLS cream, crowded, adnexed-free. SPORE PRINT white. SMELL sweet? FLESH white with orange flush especially below cap cuticle. Usually in small groups. On soil, in broad-leaved or mixed woods, especially when birch present. Summer – autumn. Widespread. Common. Edible. SPORES subspherical, smooth, 11–12.5×9 –10, non-amyloid.

Amanita fulva. Cap colour and margin. CAP 4–9, smooth, broadly umbonate, very distinctly grooved at margin. STEM 8–13, tapering upwards, non-bulbous, persistent bag-like volva, no ring. GILLS white, crowded, free. SPORE PRINT white. SMELL faint but pleasant. FLESH white. Trooping in small or large groups. On soil in broad-leaved or mixed woods, especially when birch present. Summer – autumn. Widespread. Extremely common. Edible. SPORES spherical, smooth, 9–12, non-amyloid.

Amanita vaginata. Very similar to *A. fulva* but colour differs. CAP 4-9, smooth, broadly umbonate, very distinctly grooved at margin. STEM 10–18, tapering upwards, non-bulbous, finely woolly, persistent bag-like volva, no ring. GILLS white, crowded, adnexed-free. SPORE PRINT white. SMELL faint but pleasant. FLESH white. In small or large groups. Trooping in small or large groups. On soil in broad-leaved or mixed woods, especially when birch present. Summer – autumn. Widespread. Very common. Edible. SPORES spherical, smooth, 9–12, non-amyloid.

Amanita caesarea **Caesar's Mushroom.** Overall colour and size. CAP 6–20, smooth, slightly sticky, with large shaggy remnants of veil, faintly lined at margin. STEM 5–12, tapering slightly upwards, very finely woolly, bulbous with large, fairly persistent bag-like volva, large pendulous, somewhat lined superior ring. GILLS chrome-yellow, crowded, free. SPORE PRINT white or slightly yellow. SMELL faint but pleasant. FLESH white with slight chrome-yellow flush, especially below cap cuticle. Solitary or in small groups. On soil especially in broad-leaved but also mixed woods. Summer – autumn. Southern, not Britain. Edible and good. SPORES ellipsoid, smooth, 10–14×6–11, non- amyloid.

Amanita pantherina **Panther Cap.** Overall colour, similar to *A. excelsa* but spores and sulphuric acid reaction differ and fragments on cap differ in colour. CAP 6–10, smooth, with fairly persistent masses of small white woolly spot-like remnants of veil, faintly lined at margin. STEM 8–12, often tapering upwards, very finely woolly, bulbous with one or two woolly ring-like bands above and with a tightly enveloping volva forming a pronounced rim at the top, fragmented, membranous, superior ring. GILLS white, crowded, free. SPORE PRINT white. SMELL faint but unpleasant. FLESH white, buff with sulphuric acid. Solitary or in small groups. On soil in broad-leaved or mixed woods, especially where beech is present. Summer – autumn. Widespread. Uncommon. Poisonous. SPORES broadly ellipsoid, smooth, 8–12×6.5–7.5, non-amyloid.

Amanita phalloides **Death Cap.** Overall colour and form. Cap colour fairly distinctive, although variable and can be pure white (var.*alba*). CAP 4–12, smooth but with fine radial fibres,±shiny when wet, margin barely lined. STEM 5–14, tapering upwards, finely woolly, bulbous with a large bag-like persistent volva, often breaking above the bulb, thin, pendulous, superior±entire lined ring. GILLS white, crowded, free. SPORE PRINT white. SMELL unpleasant, sweet. FLESH white with slight yellowish flush especially beneath cap cuticle. Solitary or in small groups. On soil in broad- leaved woods, especially with oak. Summer – autumn. Widespread. Common in South, rarer northwards. (var.*alba* rare). Deadly poisonous. SPORES ellipsoid – subspherical, smooth, 8–11×7–9, amyloid.

Amanita umbrinolutea =*submembranacea*). Similar to *A. vaginata* but generally larger cap with pronounced pale margin and spores differ. CAP 6–12, smooth, broadly umbonate, very distinctly grooved at margin. STEM 10–18, tapering upwards, non-bulbous, finely woolly, persistent bag-like volva, no ring. GILLS white, crowded, free. SPORE PRINT white. SMELL faint but pleasant? FLESH white. In small or large groups. On soil in coniferous woods, especially montane. Summer – autumn. Widespread especially in mountainous regions. Common. Edible. SPORES subspherical, smooth, 11–16×9.5–13, non-amyloid.

Amanita muscaria **Fly Agaric.** Cap colour. CAP 8–20, smooth, at first with masses of small woolly spot-like remnants of veil, faintly lined at margin. STEM 8–19,±equal, often markedly woolly, bulbous with shaggy remnants of volva, fragmented, membranous superior ring. GILLS white, crowded, free. SPORE PRINT white. SMELL faint but pleasant. FLESH white with slight reddish or yellow flush, especially below cap cuticle. Solitary or in small groups. On soil with birch. Summer – autumn. Widespread. Very common (var. *regalis* rare). Poisonous. SPORES ellipsoid, smooth, 9.5–10.5×7–8, non-amyloid.

Amanita gemmata. Overall colour, size, habitat. CAP 5–7, smooth, at first with flat whitе patches of veil remnants, faintly lined at margin. STEM 7–10,±equal, very finely woolly, bulbous with a short, fairly thin persistent volva, fragmented membranous±inferior ring. GILLS white, crowded, adnexed-free. SPORE PRINT white. SMELL faint and indefinite. FLESH white with slight yellowish flush especially in stem and beneath cap cuticle. Solitary or in small groups. On soil in coniferous or occasionally broad-leaved or mixed woods. Autumn. Widespread. Rare. Poisonous. SPORES spherical – subellipsoid, smooth, 8.5–9×7–7.5, non- amyloid.

Amanita verna **Spring Amanita.** Season. *A. virosa* has scaly stem and different KOH reaction. CAP 7–10, slightly sticky when wet. STEM 5–15, tapering upwards, finely powdery-woolly, bulbous with a large bag-like persistent volva, thin pendulous superior±entire lined ring. GILLS white, crowded, free. SPORE PRINT white. SMELL rather earthy. FLESH white, quickly yellow with KOH. Solitary or in small groups. On soil in coniferous or mixed woods. Summer – autumn. Widespread. Rare. Deadly poisonous. SPORES broadly ellipsoid, smooth, 8–11×7–9, amyloid.

AMANITACEAE

Amanita virosa Destroying Angel. Season. *A. verna* has more powdery stem and different KOH reaction. CAP 5–12, slightly sticky when wet. STEM 9–12, tapering slightly upwards, ±shaggy, bulbous with a slender bulb and a large bag-like persistent volva, thin pendulous very fragile superior ring. GILLS white, crowded, free. SPORE PRINT white. SMELL heavy, sweet, unpleasant. FLESH white, KOH – . Solitary or in small groups. On soil in broad-leaved or mixed woods. Summer – autumn. Widespread. Uncommon in south, common in Scotland. Deadly poisonous. SPORES subspherical, smooth, 8–12, amyloid.

Amanita citrina. Overall colour and smell. CAP 4–10, smooth and dry but with persisting and gradually discolouring veil fragments. STEM 6–8, slender, tapering upwards, large bulb with closely adhering volva forming a gutter around the top, pendulous or slightly flaring lined superior ring, with stem lined above. GILLS white, often with yellowish edge, crowded, adnexed. SPORE PRINT white. SMELL strong, earthy or of raw potatoes. FLESH white or slightly yellowish beneath cap cuticle. Solitary or in small groups. On soil in broad-leaved or mixed woods, especially when beech is present. Summer – autumn. Widespread. Common (var. *alba* uncommon). Edible but too easily confused with deadly poisonous species. SPORES subspherical, smooth, 8–10×7–9, amyloid.

Amanita excelsa (=*spissa*). Similar to *A. pantherina* but spores, sulphuric acid reaction, and cap fragments differ, very variable. CAP 6–10, smooth, covered at first with greyish woolly spot-like remnants of veil, faintly lined at margin. STEM 6–12, often tapering below, markedly finely scaled below, bulbous with bulb deeply buried (almost rooting) and with an indefinite fragile tightly enveloping volva, persistent membranous superior lined ring with stem lines above. GILLS white, crowded, adnexed-free. SPORE PRINT white. SMELL faint but unpleasant, ?radish-like. FLESH white, purple with sulphuric acid. Solitary or in small groups. On soil in broad-leaved or coniferous woods. Summer – autumn. Widespread. Very common. Inedible. SPORES broadly ellipsoid, smooth, 9–10×8–9, amyloid.

Amanita echinocephala. Warts on cap. CAP 6–20, at first covered with pointed, wart-like fragments of the veil, becoming gradually smoother. STEM 6–14, tapering upwards, swollen base deeply rooting and covered with scale-like remains of volva, with thin lined persistent superior ring. GILLS white tinged with green-yellow, markedly broad, crowded, free or with decurrent tooth. SPORE PRINT white, sometimes with slight green-yellow tinge. SMELL unpleasant. FLESH white, sometimes with greenish tinge, bruising yellow especially in stem. Often solitary, sometimes in small groups. On dry chalky soils with grass and trees. Summer – autumn. Southern. Rare. Poisonous. SPORES ellipsoid, smooth, 9.5–11.5×6.5–8, amyloid.

Amanita ovoidea. Overall size, colour, ring features and distribution. CAP 10–30, at first finely floury, then discolouring to straw-yellow and smooth, margin fringed with veil fragments. STEM 10–15, stout, tapering slightly upwards, scaly,± shaggy,± rooting and scarcely bulbous with a white or pale ochre, bag-like pendulous volva, thin ochre pendulous very fragile superior ring with markedly floury-woolly underside. GILLS white, crowded, free. SPORE PRINT white. SMELL indistinct. FLESH white. Solitary or in small groups. On soil in broad-leaved or mixed woods. Summer – autumn. Southern, not Britain. Edible but too easily confused with deadly poisonous species. SPORES ellipsoid, smooth, 10–12×6.5–7.5, amyloid.

Amanita porphyria. Overall colour. CAP 5–9, smooth, ±silky, very broadly umbonate. STEM 6–9, slender, tapering upwards, bulbous with short, fairly persistent volva, pendulous, very fragile superior ring which soon collapses against the stem. GILLS white, crowded, adnexed-free. SPORE PRINT white. SMELL slight but unpleasant. FLESH white becoming brownish. Solitary or in small groups. On soil in coniferous or mixed woods, especially with pines. Summer – autumn. Widespread. Uncommon in south, commoner northwards. Inedible. SPORES spherical, smooth, 7.5–9.5, amyloid.

Amanita rubescens The Blusher. Colour, flesh colour change. CAP 5–15, smooth, covered with white-pinkish woolly remnants of veil. STEM 6–14, equal, slightly bulbous with very indefinite volva usually only as patches, scarcely-persisting membranous superior lined ring (persistent and sulphur-yellow in var. *annulosulphurea*). GILLS white, often red-spotted, crowded, free. SPORE PRINT white. SMELL faint. FLESH white, red when cut or bruised esp. where bored by insect larvae. Usually in small groups. On soil in broad-l. or conif. woods. Early summer – autumn. Widespread. Extremely common (var. *annulosulphurea* uncommon). Inedible. SPORES ellipsoid, smooth, 8–10×5–5.5, amyloid.

Amanita strobiliformis (=*solitaria*). Colour and shaggy appearance. CAP 6–18, densely covered with thick shaggy scales which hang down to give a curtain-like margin. STEM 6–10, tapering upwards with gradually swollen rooting bulbous base covered with fragments of volva, shaggy, with scales becoming finer below, ring pendulous, thin, mealy, superior. GILLS white, crowded, free. SPORE PRINT white. SMELL slight, mild, pleasant. FLESH white, slightly cream in stem. Solitary or in small groups. On chalky soils with broad-leaved trees. Summer – autumn. Southern. Rare. Edible but too easily confused with deadly poisonous species. SPORES broadly ellipsoid, smooth, 10–12.5×8–10, amyloid.

Limacella glioderma. Gluti-
ous cap, stem features.
AP 2.5–6, glutinous-sticky.
TEM 4–8, equal, markedly
woolly scaly below the
flaring, silky, often fragmented superior ring, no
volva. GILLS white or
cream-colour crowded,
almost free. SPORE PRINT
white. SMELL ? FLESH soft,
white becoming slightly
pink especially in stem.
Usually in small groups. On
soil in coniferous or rarely
broad-leaved woods.
Summer – early autumn.
Widespread. Rare. Edible?
PORES subspherical,
smooth, 4–5, non-amyloid.

Limacella guttata. Gluti-
ous cap, stem features,
liquid droplets. CAP 5–11,
glutinous-sticky, slightly
paler at margin, often
somewhat dimpled in the
centre. STEM 7–11, equal,
but with slightly bulbous
base, often deeply buried
and almost rooting, finely
fibrous-woolly, especially
above the flaring, fairly
persistent ring which may
exude watery droplets
especially in wet weather,
no volva. GILLS white,
crowded, free, exuding
droplets as ring. SPORE
PRINT white. SMELL floury.
FLESH fairly soft, white
becoming slightly pink
especially in stem base.
Usually in small groups. On
soil in coniferous or mixed
woods. Summer – early
autumn. Widespread.
Rare. Edible? SPORES sub-
spherical, smooth, 4.5–
5×5, non-amyloid.

LEPIOTACEAE
Toadstool-shaped, with
gills relatively crowded,
usually white but some-
times changing colour at
maturity and rarely green
or reddish, flesh usually
white but also sometimes
changing slightly, gills free,
spores varying from
subspherical – ellipsoid –
spindle-shaped – bullet-
shaped, dextrinoid, amy-
loid or neither, usually
smooth, spore print usually
white but sometimes
cream-colour or rarely
greenish (Melanophyllum),
cap surface usually smooth,
sometimes silky, often with
characteristic warts or
scales, occasionally sticky.
Often with a ring that may
disappear quickly and leave
a zone on the stem. No
volva. Usually terrestrial
and typically close to trees.
Saprotrophic. Few edible,
some poisonous. Mela-
nophyllum [2], Drosella [1],
Cystoderma [6], Lepiota
[59], Leucocoprinus [2].

Melanophyllum echinatum.
Gill colour, spore print. CAP
1–3, finely granular with
remnants of veil forming a
pronounced marginal cur-
tain. STEM 2–4, slender,
granular-mealy, flexuous,
rapidly-vanishing (often
absent) granular inferior
ring. GILLS blood-red,
darkening to wine-red,
crowded, free. SPORE PRINT
reddish grey, somewhat
like cucumber. SMELL strong,
FLESH thin, white in cap,
pale wine-red in stem, darker at base. Solitary or in
small groups. On rich soil
in woods, gardens, under
hedges, also on fire sites,
chalky sites and amongst
herbaceous vegetation and
moss. Spring – autumn.
Widespread. Apparently
rare but probably over-
looked. Inedible. SPORES
ellipsoid – ±kidney-
shaped, smooth? 5–6×2.5–
3.5.

Melanophyllum eyrei. Gill
colour and form, spore
print. CAP 1–3, finely granular with remnants of veil
sometimes forming a mar-
ginal curtain, broadly
umbonate. STEM 1.5–2.5,
slender, granular especially
at apex, flexuous. GILLS
bluish green, broad, dis-
tant, forked, free. SPORE
PRINT pale green. SMELL
cucumber. FLESH fairly
thin, white in cap, brownish
yellow in stem. Solitary or
in small groups. On soil in
broad-leaved woods, espe-
cially on chalky sites and
among herbaceous vegeta-
tion and moss. Summer –
autumn. Widespread.
Rare. Poisonous? SPORES
ellipsoid, smooth, 3.5–
4×2–2.5.

Drosella fracida (= Lepiota
irrorata = Chamaemyces
fracidus). Watery droplets
on cap and stem. CAP 2.5–9,
smooth and slightly glutinous with watery droplets
which dry to discoloured
patches. STEM 4–5, usually
curved and silky, finely granular surface below weak,
quickly-vanishing superior
ring, watery droplets. GILLS
white, later cream, crowded, free. SPORE PRINT white.
SMELL unpleasant, mush-
roomy or radishy. FLESH
fairly firm, white. Usually
in small groups. On soil in
pastures or open grassy
areas in woods. Spring –
autumn. Widespread. Un-
common. Inedible. SPORES
ellipsoid, smooth, 4.5–5×4,
non-amyloid. Abundant
club-shaped or spindle-
shaped cystidia on gill face.

Cystoderma amianthinum.
Colour, stem features, flesh
colour, KOH reaction. CAP
3–5, mealy and wrinkled,
usually umbonate, often
slightly fringed margin.
STEM 3–5, equal, smooth at
apex, coarsely granular-
mealy below rapidly-vanishing upward-pointing superior ring. GILLS white, later
cream-yellow, crowded, adnate. SPORE PRINT white.
SMELL mouldy, unpleasant.
10% KOH on cap, brown.
FLESH thin, dirty yellow. ±
tufted in small groups. On
soil in coniferous woods,
lawns, heaths. Late
summer – autumn. Wide-
spread. Common. Edible.
SPORES ellipsoid, smooth,
4–6×3–4, amyloid.

Cystoderma carcharias.
Colour, stem features, ring,
KOH reaction. CAP 2–6,
mealy and wrinkled, ±
wavy, usually umbonate,
sometimes with slightly
fringed margin. STEM 4–7,
equal, smooth at apex but
coarsely granular- mealy below fairly persistent upward
-pointing superior ring.
GILLS white, crowded,
adnate. SPORE PRINT white.
SMELL mouldy, unpleasant.
10% KOH on cap – . FLESH
thin, white – dirty yellow.
In small groups±tufted. On
soil among grass in coniferous woods or on heaths.
Late summer – autumn.
Widespread. Rare. Inedi-
ble. SPORES subspherical,
smooth, 4–5.5×3–4, amy-
loid.

57

LEPIOTACEAE

Cystoderma granulosum, Cap colour, stem features, KOH reaction, spore reaction. CAP 3–6, surface markedly mealy and wrinkled, not usually umbonate, sometimes with very slightly fringed margin. STEM 4–6, equal, smooth at apex but coarsely granular-mealy below fairly persistent upward-pointing superior ring. GILLS cream, crowded, ±adnexed. SPORE PRINT white. SMELL indistinct. 10% KOH on cap, red-brown. FLESH thin, white – dirty yellow or slightly red-tinged. In small groups±tufted. On soil among grass in coniferous woods or on heathland. Late summer – autumn. Widespread. Uncommon. Inedible. SPORES ellipsoid, smooth, 3–5×2–3, non-amyloid.

Lepiota (=*Cystolepiota*) **sistrata.** Similar to *L. bucknallii* but paler and differs. CAP 0.5–1.5, mealy, markedly umbonate. STEM 1.5–2.5, slender, tapering slightly upwards, finely mealy floury or almost silky, bruising slightly pink-violet, especially towards base, ring mealy, rapidly-vanishing and often absent, superior. GILLS white, free. SPORE PRINT white. SMELL indefinite. FLESH white, pinker or faintly purplish in stem. Usually±tufted in small groups. On soil and among grass close to trees or in open grassy areas in woods. Autumn. Widespread. Uncommon. Inedible, poisonous? SPORES ellipsoid, smooth, 3–4×2–2.5, non-dextrinoid.

Lepiota (=*Cystolepiota*) **hetieri.** Colour change. CAP 2–3, mealy, broadly umbonate, with overhanging± toothed margin. STEM 2–3, slender, tapering slightly upwards, finely woolly-scaly, bruising pink – reddish brown, especially towards base, ring mealy, fairly persistent, superior. GILLS white, then pink or red, free. SPORE PRINT white. SMELL unpleasant, radishy. FLESH white, quickly pink or reddish. Usually±tufted in small groups. On soil and among grass close to trees. Late summer – autumn. Widespread. Rare. Inedible, poisonous? SPORES ellipsoid, smooth, 4–6×2–3, non-dextrinoid.

Lepiota friesii (=*aspera*=*acutisquamosa* var. *furcata*). Cap features structure of scales on cap and gill form. CAP 6–10, at first almost spherical, then flattened, not umbonate, conspicuously covered with dark brown-black pointed scales, especially towards margin. STEM 3–5, equal, slightly bulbous,±smooth or slightly dark scaly below ring fairly broad, spreading, persistent, slightly woolly and often remaining attached to cap edge, superior. GILLS white, crowded, forked, free – remote. SPORE PRINT white. SMELL strong, unpleasant. FLESH thin, white, turning slightly yellow. Usually in small groups. On soil in gardens and in broad-leaved woods. Autumn. Widespread. Uncommon. Inedible? SPORES ellipsoid – narrow spindle-shaped, smooth, 6 8×3–4, dextrinoid. Cystidia on gill edge thin- walled, subspherical. Extreme tips of cap scales of brown spherical cells.

Lepiota (=*Cystolepiota*) **bucknallii.** Overall colour, especially when young or bruised, smell. CAP 2–4, finely mealy floury, umbonate, becoming paler at maturity. STEM 2–4.5, slender, tapering slightly upwards, mealy, bruising violet, especially towards base, ring mealy, rapidly-vanishing and often absent, superior. GILLS cream-yellow, free. SPORE PRINT white. SMELL strong, of coal tar (like *Tricholoma sulphureum*). FLESH white, deep lilac towards stem base. Usually±tufted in small groups. On soil and among grass in damp broad-leaved woods. Autumn. Widespread. Uncommon. Poisonous? SPORES elongate-ellipsoid, smooth, 7.5–9×3–3.5, dextrinoid.

Lepiota rosea (=*Cystolepiota moelleri*). Cap surface features. CAP 2–3, markedly granular-mealy, markedly broadly umbonate, with very pronounced overhanging, toothed margin. STEM 5–6, equal or tapering slightly upwards, slender, finely woolly scaly, especially towards base below very narrow, rapidly- vanishing superior ring. GILLS white, becoming cream, free. SPORE PRINT white. SMELL indistinct or faint, pleasant, fruity. FLESH white, pinker or faintly purplish in stem. Usually±tufted in small groups. On soil and among grass in damp broad-leaved woods. Autumn. Widespread. Rare. Inedible, poisonous? SPORES ellipsoid, smooth, 4.5–6×2.5–3.5, non-dextrinoid.

Lepiota hystrix. Overall size and structure of scales on cap. CAP 4–6, at first almost spherical, then flattened, broadly umbonate, conspicuously covered with dark brown- black pointed scales, margin markedly overhanging and exuding dark reddish liquid droplets. STEM 5–6, equal, pale at apex and exuding dark reddish liquid droplets, as cap margin, scaly below as cap, ring narrow, spreading, persistent, dark scaly below, superior. GILLS white with black edges (use hand-lens), crowded, not forked, free-remote. SPORE PRINT white – very pale ochreous. SMELL strong, radishy. FLESH thin, white. Usually in small groups. On soil in broad-leaved woods. Late summer – early autumn. Widespread. Uncommon. Inedible. SPORES subcylindrical – ellipsoid, smooth, 6–7×2.5–3, dextrinoid. Cystidia on gill edge thin-walled, club-shaped. Extreme tips of cap scales of brown spherical cells.

Lepiota cristata Stinking Parasol. Size, cap features and smell. CAP 2–4.5, markedly umbonate, very silky and covered with small scales. STEM 2–3.5, equal, firm,±silky, ring narrow, barely persistent, superior. GILLS white, darkening slightly at maturity, crowded, free. SPORE PRINT white. SMELL unpleasant, boiled sweets or radishy. FLESH thin, white becoming slightly brownish. Usually±tufted On soil among plant debris in woods, gardens, hedgerows. Summer – autumn. Widespread. Very common. Poisonous? SPORES bullet-shaped, smooth, 6–7.5×3–3.5, dextrinoid.

58

...iota fulvella. Size, cap ...ures and microscopic ..., CAP 2–5, ±umbonate, ...y and smooth, then ...llar, not scaly. CAP 3– ...qual or slightly swollen ...ards base, firm, ±woolly ...w narrow, barely per-...ent, superior ring. GILLS ...te – slightly yellowish ...cially at edge, free. ...RE PRINT white. SMELL ...leasant, mushroomy? ...SH thin, white becoming ...ntly brownish especially ...em. Usually ±tufted ...in small groups. On ...p soil among plant ...ris in woods especially ...broad-leaved trees. ...e. Poisonous? SPORES ...et-shaped, smooth, 8– ....5–4.5, dextrinoid. ...rs from cap surface con-... brown granules quickly ...olving in ammonia.

Lepiota alba. Overall col-our and stem features, simi-lar to *L. clypeolaria* but spores differ. CAP 3–7, apparently almost smooth at first but becoming silky-fibrous (use hand-lens) especially at margin, umbonate. STEM 4–6, equal or tapering downwards, finely woolly below woolly, narrow, quickly-vanishing superior ring. GILLS white, then yellowish, crowded, free. SPORE PRINT white. SMELL? FLESH thin, white becoming yellowish, espe-cially in stem. Usually in small groups. On soil, among grass, often close to woods. Autumn. Wide-spread. Uncommon. Edi-ble? SPORES ellipsoid – subspindle shaped, smooth, 12–14×5.5–6.5, dextrinoid.

Lepiota ventriosospora. Similar to several related species, but spore size and shape distinct. CAP 4–8, covered with flattened scales, irregular margin and pronounced darker umbo. STEM 3–4, equal or tapering slightly upwards, markedly woolly, increasingly so towards base, very quickly vanishing narrow±median ring. GILLS white, crowded, free. SPORE PRINT white. SMELL faint but pleasant. FLESH thin, white, becom-ing red-brown, especially in stem. Usually in small groups. On soil in broad-leaved woods. Autumn. Widespread. Rare. Edible. SPORES spindle-shaped, with pronounced central depression, smooth, 14.5–17.5×4–5, dextrinoid.

Lepiota felina. Similar to several other small species but habitat and spore shape and size are fairly reliable. CAP 2–3, almost black when young then surface breaks up into massed very small pointed scales, ±umbonate with markedly darker cen-tre. STEM 3–5, finely fibrillar-silky with few scales, especially towards base, ring barely persistent, darker below, with few scales, superior. GILLS white or slightly yellowish, fairly crowded, free. SPORE PRINT white. SMELL strong, unpleasant, mushroomy. FLESH thin, white, becom-ing slightly yellow-brown. Solitary or in small±tufted groups. On soil with coni-fers. Autumn. Widespread. Uncommon. Inedible. SPORES ellipsoid, smooth, 6.5–7.5×3.5–4, dextrinoid.

...iota castanea. Size and ...features, similar to *L.* ...ella but microscopic test ...ative and spores larger. ...2–4.5, umbonate, silky ...l covered with small ... each composed of ...sses of hairs (use hand-...s). STEM 2.5–3.5, slen-..., equal or slightly swol-...towards base, firm, ±...olly below narrow, ...ckly-vanishing, superior ...g. GILLS white turning ...htly yellow-brown at ...turity, free. SPORE PRINT ...te. SMELL unpleasant, ...shroomy. FLESH thin, ...te becoming slightly ...m. Usually ±tufted but ...o trooping in small ...ups. On damp soil ...ong plant debris in ...ods. Autumn. Wide-...ead. Uncommon. Poiso-...us? SPORES bullet-...ped, smooth, 9–...×3.5–5, dextrinoid.

Lepiota subgracilis. Similar to several related species, but ring position, spore size and habitat fairly reliable. CAP 2–3, smooth at first but quickly breaking into small red-brown scales, overall± woolly, wavy, margin often irregular, broadly umbo-nate. STEM 3–4, equal or tapering slightly upwards with base±bulbous, finely granular below finely scaly-silky narrow fairly quickly vanishing median ring which may split into upper and lower parts, giving a bracelet effect. GILLS white, crowded, free. SPORE PRINT white. SMELL? FLESH thin, slightly woolly, white. Usually in small groups. On soil, in broad-leaved woods, especially with beech. Autumn. Wide-spread. Uncommon. Edi-ble. SPORES ellipsoid, smooth, 9–11×5–6, dextri-noid.

Lepiota clypeolaria. Similar to several related species, especially *L. alba* but spores differ. CAP 4–8, covered with flattened woolly scales, irregular margin, broadly umbonate and only slightly darker in centre. STEM 5–10, equal or tapering slightly upwards, markedly woolly, increasingly so towards base, very quickly vanishing narrow woolly superior ring. GILLS white, sometimes turning slightly yellowish, crowded, free. SPORE PRINT white. SMELL faint but pleasant. FLESH white, ±woolly. Usually in small groups. On soil, in broad-leaved and conifer-ous woods. Autumn. Wide-spread. Uncommon. Edi-ble. SPORES spindle-shaped, smooth, 13–15×6, dextri-noid.

Lepiota (=*Pseudobaeospora*) *serena.* Cap colour and stem base. CAP 2–4, smooth, but becoming yel-lowish and silky on aging, fragile, margin slightly lined. STEM 4–7, equal or tapering upwards from markedly bulbous or club-shaped base, very quickly vanishing narrow woolly superior ring. GILLS white, crowded, free. SPORE PRINT white. SMELL? FLESH white, ±woolly. Usually in small groups. On soil, in broad-leaved and conifer-ous woods. Autumn. Wide-spread. Inedible. SPORES ellipsoid, smooth, 7–9×4–4.5, dextri-noid.

LEPIOTACEAE

1
Lepiota (=*Macrolepiota*)
procera **Parasol mushroom.**
Overall form and size. CAP
10–25, flattened or±depressed at maturity, umbonate with large dark,±flattened scales. STEM 15–30,
tapering slightly upwards
from bulbous base, woolly-felty, gradually breaking
up into irregular markings
like snake-skin, large,±
spreading, double, movable, superior ring. GILLS
white, crowded, free – remote. SPORE PRINT white.
SMELL indefinite, slightly
sweet. FLESH soft, white,
thin. Often solitary or in
small trooping groups. On
soil among grass at woodland edges, roadsides,
woodland glades. Summer
– autumn. Widespread.
Uncommon. Edible and
good. SPORES elliptical with
pronounced pore, smooth,
15–20×10–13, dextrinoid.

2
Lepiota (=*Macrolepiota*)
rhacodes **Shaggy Parasol.**
Flesh colour change, similar to *L. procera* but smaller, more shaggy and spores
differ. CAP 5–15, flattened
at maturity, broadly umbonate with large fairly dark,
±flattened and±woolly
scales (var. *hortensis* has
larger, smooth, angular
scales). STEM 10–15, fairly
stout, tapering slightly upwards from slightly eccentric bulbous base,±woolly-felty, large,±spreading,
double movable superior
ring. GILLS white bruising
reddish, crowded, free.
SPORE PRINT white. SMELL
fairly strong, pleasant.
FLESH soft, white becoming
reddish when cut, thin.
Usually in small trooping
groups. On soil among
grass at woodland edges,
roadsides, woodland
glades, especially when

conifers are present.
Summer – autumn. Widespread. Uncommon (var.
hortensis in gardens, greenhouses, rare). Edible and
good but some people react
adversely. SPORES ellipsoid
with pronounced pore,
smooth, 10–12×6–7,
dextrinoid.

3
Lepiota (=*Macrolepiota*)
excoriata. Similar to *L.
leucothites* but cap surface
and spores differ. CAP 6–10,
very finely scaly on smooth
surface, usually drawing
away from the edge
(excoriating), fairly uniform colour,±umbonate.
STEM 4–6, smooth, slender,
equal but with slightly swollen base,±woolly, narrow,
persistent±spreading,
movable, superior, ring.
GILLS white or slightly
cream, crowded, free-remote. SPORE PRINT white-cream. SMELL faint but
pleasant. FLESH soft, white.
Usually in small trooping
groups. On soil among
grass in pastures and other
grassy places. Summer –
autumn. Widespread.
Rare. Edible. SPORES ellipsoid with pore, smooth, 12–
15×8–9, dextrinoid.

4
Lepiota (=*Macrolepiota*)
mastoidea. Similar to *L.
leucothites* and *L. excoriata*
but with very pronounced
umbo. CAP 8–12, very finely
scaly on smooth surface,
often±depressed when
mature, very distinctly umbonate with darker centre.
STEM 8–10, slender,±equal
but with very slightly swollen base, fairly smooth, narrow, persistent±spreading,
movable superior ring.
GILLS white or slightly
cream, crowded, remote.
SPORE PRINT white. SMELL
faint but pleasant. FLESH

soft, white. Usually in small
trooping groups. On soil
among grass in woodland
glades, at woodland edges
and other open grassy
places. Autumn. Widespread. Uncommon. Edible. SPORES ellipsoid with
pore, smooth, 12–15×8–9,
dextrinoid.

5
Lepiota leucothites
(=*naucina*). Similar to *L.
excoriata* but cap surface
and spores differ. CAP 5–8,
smooth-silky, sometimes
peeling slightly but lacking
any surface scales, not
umbonate. STEM 5–8,
slender,±equal but with
very slightly swollen base,
smooth, narrow, barely
persistent, superior, ring.
GILLS white or slightly pink-cream, crowded, free.
SPORE PRINT white. SMELL
faint but pleasant. FLESH
soft, white, becoming
brown in the stem. Solitary
or in small trooping groups.
On soil among grass in
woodland glades, at woodland edges and other open
grassy places, especially in
gardens. Summer –
autumn. Widespread.
Rare. Inedible. SPORES
broadly ellipsoid with pore,
smooth, 7–9×4.5–5, dextrinoid.

6
Leucocoprinus brebissonii.
Similar to several small
Lepiota species but spores
and cap edge differ. CAP
2–3, edge distinctly lined,
later sometimes split, with
markedly dark small umbo,
and covered with small,±
flat dark scales. STEM 4.5–6,
smooth,±equal or tapering
slightly upwards from
slightly swollen base. GILLS
white, thin, collapsing,
crowded, free – remote.
SPORE PRINT white. SMELL
indefinite but mild. FLESH

white, thin. Solitary or in
small groups. On soil and
among plant debris with
broad-leaved or conifer
trees. Autumn. Widespread. Uncommon. Poisonous? SPORES broadly
ellipsoid – almond shape
with pore, smooth, 9–
12.5×5.5–7.

7
Leucocoprinus birnbaumi
(=*Lepiota lutea*). Overall
colour and habitat. CAP 3-
almost smooth but with
small slightly paler scales
concentrated towards centre, edge distinctly lined,
later sometimes split, with
marked umbo. STEM 6–10,
smooth,±equal or tapering
slightly upwards from
slightly swollen base. GILLS
pale yellow, thin, collapsing crowded, free. SPORE
PRINT creamy yellow. SMELL
faint but slightly bitter.
FLESH yellow-cream, thin.
Solitary or in small groups.
On soil in greenhouses. All
year. Widespread. Locally
common in appropriate
habitat. Poisonous? SPORES
broadly ellipsoid with pore
smooth, 8–11×5–6, non-amyloid.

TRICHOLOMATACEAE

Very diverse. Toadstool-shaped, or sometimes with
stem lateral, rarely otherwise, gills typical to ridge-like, flesh often white, gills
usually adnate-decurrent,
spores variable, often
subspherical – ellipsoid,
usually smooth but sometimes ornamented, amyloid
or non-amyloid, spore print
usually±white but also
pinkish, slightly lilac or
rarely pink-buff. Saprotrophic or biotrophic. Some
mycorrhizal. Most terrestrial, some on wood.
Omphalina [29], *Laccaria*
[6], *Clitocybe* [58], *Lepista*

60

, *Tricholomopsis* [3],
choloma [53], *Armillaria*
, *Leptoglossum* [3],
ophyllum [9],
ohrocybe [14], *Aster-
hora* [2], *Cantharellula*
, *Leucopaxillus* [3],
lanoleuca [9], *Collybia*
], *Micromphale* [5],
henbuehelia [7], *Resupi-
tus* [5], *Panellus* [4],
demansiella [4], *Pseudo-
tula* [3], *Rhodotus* [1],
rasmius [30], *Macrocy-
dia* [1], *Mycena* [102],
inipellis [1], *Myxompha-
[1], *Xeromphalina* [3],
eospora [1], *Hygrophor-
sis* [4], *Pleurotellus* [8],
odocybe [9], *Flammu-
a* [1], *Clitopilus* [4],
quamanita [1]), (*Clitocy-
la* [1]), (*Dermoloma* [3]),
ayodia [1]).

nphalina ericetorum.
olour and habitat. CAP
5–2, ±flat, then
pressed – almost funnel-
aped, marked darker
es especially at edge,
ky when dry. STEM 1–2.5,
ual, often curved, dark
e at base of gills, base
ten darker and downy.
LS white-yellow, later
eam, very broad, very
stant, decurrent. SPORE
INT white. SMELL indis-
ct. FLESH thin, white –
rty yellow-ochre. In
all groups, trooping
±tufted. On peaty soil on
aths, moorland. Spring –
inter. Widespread. Very
mmon. Inedible. SPORES
ipsoid, smooth, 8–
×4.5–5.5, non-amyloid.

mphalina luteolilacina.
ze and habitat, similar to
. *ericetorum* but colour
ffers. CAP 1–1.5, at first
nvex, then depressed or
nnel-shaped, very finely

downy, later smooth, mar-
gin slightly toothed, then
lined and paler. STEM 1–1.5,
tapering slightly down-
wards, finely downy. GILLS
pale cream, thick, distant,
adnate-decurrent. SPORE
PRINT white. SMELL? FLESH
thin, white or slightly
cream. Usually in small
groups, ±trooping. On acid
soil and peat, often with
algae on mountains.
Summer – autumn. Wide-
spread, montane. Locally
common. Inedible. SPORES
ellipsoid, smooth, 7–8×4–
4.5, non-amyloid.

Omphalina luteovitellina.
Colour and habitat. CAP
0.5–1.5, ±flat, very
markedly wavy with irregular wavy margin. STEM 1–2,
stout, equal or tapering
slightly downwards, usually
slightly curved. GILLS yellowish, thick, fleshy,
sparse, very distant,
strongly decurrent. SPORE
PRINT white. SMELL? FLESH
thin, yellowish. Trooping in
small groups or±tufted. On
wet, peaty soil on moun-
tains. Late summer –
autumn. Widespread,
montane. Locally common.
Inedible. SPORES ellipsoid,
smooth, 6.5–9×3.5–4, non-
amyloid.

Omphalina wynniae
(=*abiegna* =*grossula*).
Habitat. CAP 2–5, at first
domed, then convex,
usually slightly umbilicate –
±depressed, margin at margin when wet. STEM 1.5–2.5,
slender, equal or tapering
slightly downwards. GILLS
white, narrow, thin, fairly
distant, decurrent. SPORE
PRINT white. SMELL strong,
unpleasant. FLESH thin,
white. Usually±tufted. On
coniferous needles, litter
and stumps. Autumn.

Widespread. Uncommon.
Inedible. SPORES ellipsoid,
smooth, 7–8×5–6, non-
amyloid.

Omphalina velutina. Overall form and habitat, basidia. CAP 0.5–1, at first
domed, then convex,
usually slightly umbilicate,
distantly lined when wet.
STEM 2–3, very slender,
equal with very slightly
swollen base, faintly
downy, more obviously so
at base. GILLS white, very
broad, distant, sometimes
branched, decurrent. SPORE
PRINT white. SMELL? FLESH
thin, greyish. Usually
trooping. On damp, espe-
cially poor, acid soil, with
algae. Widespread. Uncommon.
Inedible. SPORES ellipsoid,
smooth, 7–9×3.5–5, non-
amyloid, basidia usually 2-
spored.

Omphalina pyxidata. Colour, habitat and spore
form. CAP 0.5–2, flat –
convex, umbilicate-
depressed or funnel-
shaped, distantly lined,
often tough. STEM 2–3,
fairly stout and tough –
cartilaginous, equal and
usually wavy. GILLS greyish,
fairly narrow, distant,
decurrent. SPORE PRINT
white. SMELL? FLESH thin,
pinkish. Solitary or in small
groups, usually trooping
when on soil. On walls, on
sandy soils on roadsides or
grassy banks. All year.
Widespread. Uncommon.
Inedible. SPORES ellipsoid –
pip-shaped, smooth, 9–
10×4.5–5, non- amyloid.

Omphalina rustica. Similar
to several other small species, especially *O. griseopallida* but more taller and
basidia 4-spored. CAP 0.5–
1.5, flat – convex, then
umbilicate – depressed or
funnel-shaped, distantly
lined. STEM 1–1.5, slender,
often wavy. GILLS greyish,
darkening on aging, dis-
tant, arc-like at edge,
decurrent. SPORE PRINT
white. SMELL? FLESH thick,
white. Usually in small
groups, trooping. On soil,
usually on fairly acid sites
with trees and poor grass.
Summer – autumn. Wide-
spread. Rare. Inedible.
SPORES ellipsoid, smooth,
8–10×4–5, non-amyloid.
Basidia 4-spored.

Omphalina obscurata. Size
and habitat. CAP 0.25–0.75,
flat-convex, then±funnel-
shaped, faintly lined at
margin, paler when dry.
STEM 0.5–1, equal, fairly
slender, often±woolly at
base and arising from a
flattened mycelial plate.
GILLS dark, grey-brown,
very broad, distant, decurrent. SPORE PRINT white.
SMELL? FLESH fairly thick,
dirty white – pale brown.
Usually in small groups,
trooping. On soil, with
mosses, sometimes
(always?) on fire sites.
Summer – autumn. Wide-
spread, usually northern.
Rare. Inedible. SPORES very
variable, subcylindrical –
subspindle-shaped,
smooth, 7.5–11.5×4–5.5,
non-amyloid.

TRICHOLOMATACEAE

Omphalina oniscus. Cap features, gill colour and habitat. CAP 2–3, convex, becoming umbilicate or funnel-shaped, often markedly irregular and wavy with finely lined margin. STEM 2.5–3, fairly tough – cartilaginous, often wavy and sometimes compressed. GILLS grey – almost black, almost distant, shortly decurrent. SPORE PRINT white. SMELL? FLESH thin, greyish. Usually in small groups, trooping. On wet soil and among mosses in wet woods and at the edge of bogs. Autumn – winter. Widespread. Uncommon. Inedible. SPORES ellipsoid, smooth, 7–8×4–5, non-amyloid.

Omphalina griseopallida. Overall size, habitat and basidia. CAP 0.5–1.5, flat – convex then umbilicate-depressed, usually paler when dry. STEM 0.5–1.5, often attached eccentrically, rather stout, often finely downy, especially towards base, often wavy. GILLS grey-brown, becoming darker, thick, broad, distant, decurrent. SPORE PRINT white. SMELL? FLESH grey-brown, thin. Usually in small groups, trooping. On soil in dry and sandy places with mosses and grasses, also on dry walls. Autumn – winter. Widespread. Rare. Inedible. SPORES ellipsoid – pip-shaped, smooth, 9–16×4–5, non-amyloid. Basidia usually 2-spored.

Omphalina (= Gerronema) postii. Colour and habitat, similar to some small *Mycena* species but habitat generally differs. CAP 2–6.5, convex but soon becoming umbilicate-depressed, very finely lined at margin. STEM 2–8.5, equal, slender, often slightly curved at base, GILLS yellowish, broad, fairly distant, decurrent. SPORE PRINT white – yellowish. SMELL indistinct. FLESH thin, yellowish. Usually trooping. On damp soil with mosses or on ashes, charcoal and clinker, fire sites? Spring – autumn. Widespread. Rare. Inedible. SPORES ellipsoid, smooth, 6–9×4.5–5, non-amyloid.

Laccaria bicolor. Cap our and form, spores. 2–5, at first convex, la very slightly depresse with incurved margin, finely scaly, drying pa STEM 5–15, slender, li with fibrils, often sligh twisted, becoming increasingly fine-wool with lilac tinge below. lilac, becoming buff th greyish, fairly thick, b distant, adnate with d rent tooth. SPORE PRIN white. SMELL indistinc FLESH thin, whitish or pink-lilac. Usually in groups, trooping or tu On soil in mixed wooc especially when pine a birch are present. Summer – autumn. W spread. Uncommon. I ble. SPORES broadly ellipsoid – spherical, s 7–9.5×6–7.5, non-am

Omphalina sphagnicola. Size and habitat. CAP 2–4, flat – convex then umbilicate-depressed – funnel-shaped, sometimes faintly scaly towards centre, very faintly lined. STEM 2.5–5, generally fragile, finely scaly at first, especially at apex, fairly slender, often wavy. GILLS dirty ochreous, thick, narrow, ±distant, edge±flat, markedly decurrent. SPORE PRINT white. SMELL? FLESH thick, white. Usually in small groups, trooping. Among *Sphagnum* in wet woods and bogs. Summer – autumn. Widespread. Rare. Inedible. SPORES elongate-ellipsoid – pip-shaped, smooth, 8–12×3.5–5, non-amyloid.

Omphalina chrysophylla (= Gerronema chrysophyllum). Colour, habitat, spore size. CAP 2–4, markedly paler when dry, deeply umbilicate, finely woolly-scaly. STEM 2.5–5, equal, base often coarsely woolly and rooting, tough. GILLS golden-yellow, broad, very distant, strongly decurrent. SPORE PRINT white – yellowish. SMELL? FLESH fairly thin, yellow-green in cap, yellow in stem. Usually tufted or in small groups. On rotting conifer stumps or other rotting conifer wood, or sawdust. Late summer – autumn. Widespread. Rare. Inedible. SPORES ellipsoid, smooth, 11–12×4.5–5.5, non-amyloid.

Laccaria amethystea **Amethyst Deceiver.** Overall form and colour. CAP 1.5–6, at first convex and±umbonate, later umbilicate-depressed, drying paler. STEM 4 –10, often twisted, markedly mealy at apex, becoming increasingly fine-woolly below. GILLS lilac, with floury covering, thick, broad, distant, adnate with decurrent tooth. SPORE PRINT very pale lilac. SMELL indistinct. FLESH thin, whitish or pale lilac. Usually in small groups, trooping or tufted. On soil in broad-leaved or coniferous woods. Summer – winter. Widespread. Extremely common. Edible. SPORES spherical, spiny, 9–11, non-amyloid.

Laccaria laccata **Decei** Overall form and colo although extremely va able ('deceiving'), spc CAP 1–5, at first conve very slightly umbonat later depressed, lined margin, drying paler a becoming slightly flou often markedly wavy. 5–10, slender, tough, flattened and±twisted GILLS orange- pink wi floury covering, fairly thick, broad, fairly dis adnate. SPORE PRINT w SMELL indistinct. FLES thin, pale red-brown. Usually in small grou trooping or tufted. O in broad-leaved or co ous woods, on moorla heaths, among short g Summer – winter. Wi

62

spread. Extremely common. Edible. SPORES spherical, spiny, 7–10, non-amyloid.

Laccaria proxima. Overall form and colour, habitat, similar to *L. laccata* but spores differ. CAP 2–7, convex but sometimes very slightly depressed, drying paler and slightly scaly. STEM 3–12, stout, tapering slightly upwards, with fine fibrils, ±woolly-downy towards the base. GILLS very pale pink, fairly thick, broad, fairly distant, adnate. SPORE PRINT white. SMELL indistinct. FLESH thin, whitish or pale pink-buff. Usually trooping in small groups. On acid soils in poor woodland, on heaths, moors and close to bogs. Autumn. Widespread. Common. Edible. SPORES broadly ellipsoid – subspherical, spiny, 7–10×6–8, non-amyloid.

Laccaria tortilis. Size, overall form and habitat. CAP 0.5–1.5, at first ±convex but soon markedly depressed and wavy with irregular margin, drying paler and slightly scaly. STEM 0.25–1, fairly slender, usually curved, markedly woolly-downy towards the base. GILLS pale pink, fairly thick, broad, often with connecting veins, distant, adnate, usually with small decurrent tooth. SPORE PRINT white. SMELL indistinct. FLESH very thin, whitish or pale pink-buff. Usually trooping in small groups. On wet soil especially on stream and pond-sides. Autumn. Widespread. Uncommon. Edible. SPORES spherical, spiny, 11–14, non-amyloid. Basidia 2-spored.

Clitocybe phyllophila. Similar to related species in the same habitat but cap shape usually reliable. CAP 3–10, at first convex, then funnel-shaped and wavy with overall bloom or floury covering. STEM 4–8, tapering upwards from swollen woolly base to which leaves remain attached. GILLS white or pale pinkish, crowded, decurrent. SPORE PRINT dirty straw-coloured. SMELL sweet. FLESH thin, white or pink-buff. Usually trooping in small groups. On leaf litter in broad-leaved woods, especially with beech. Autumn. Widespread. Rare. Poisonous? SPORES ellipsoid, smooth, 4–4.5×2.5–3.5, non-amyloid.

Clitocybe clavipes **Club Foot.** Overall form, especially ratio of cap to stem size and cap margin. CAP 4–8, at first convex and± umbonate, then very slightly depressed, usually paler towards margin. STEM 4–8, finely silky, pronounced club-shape, tapering markedly upwards from very swollen woolly base. GILLS pale creamy-yellow, narrow, thin, deeply decurrent. SPORE PRINT white. SMELL sweet. FLESH thick, watery, white tending to yellow in stem base. Solitary or trooping in small groups. On leaf litter in broad-leaved woods, especially with beech. Summer – autumn. Widespread. Common. Inedible. SPORES ellipsoid – subspherical, smooth, 4.5–5×3.5–4, non-amyloid.

Clitocybe odora **Aniseed Toadstool.** Colour and smell. CAP 3–10, at first convex and broadly umbonate, then flatter and with±wavy margin. STEM 3–6, finely silky, often distorted or twisted upwards from very slightly swollen white woolly base. GILLS white, tinged blue-green, fairly broad,±distant, adnate-decurrent. SPORE PRINT white. SMELL very strongly of aniseed. FLESH tough, white-green. In small groups, trooping. On leaf litter in broad-leaved woods, especially with beech. Summer-autumn. Widespread. Common. Edible. SPORES ellipsoid, smooth, 6–8×3–4, non-amyloid.

Clitocybe inornata. Stout appearance, smell, habitat. CAP 5–9, at first convex then flatter and markedly depressed with margin inrolled, finely downy and±lined. STEM 4–6, very stout,±equal, finely woolly with a more coarsely woolly white base to which leaves and litter remain attached. GILLS brown-grey, broad, crowded, adnate-decurrent. SPORE PRINT white. SMELL strong, rancid or radish-like. FLESH firm, thick, grey-brown. In small groups, often±tufted. On soil or among grass at field edges, woodland clearings. Autumn. Widespread. Rare. Inedible. SPORES spindle-shaped, smooth, 8–9×3–4, non-amyloid.

Clitocybe geotropa. Overall size, habit, smell, habitat. CAP 4–20, at first convex and broadly umbonate, then flatter and markedly depressed with margin inrolled. STEM 5–15,±equal with markedly bulbous slightly downy base. GILLS whitish buff, broad, crowded, deeply decurrent. SPORE PRINT white. SMELL faint but pleasant, sugary. FLESH firm, thick, white. Solitary or in small or large groups, sometimes in rings. On soil or among grass in fields or woodland clearings. Autumn. Widespread. Uncommon. Edible. SPORES subspherical, smooth, 6.5–7×5–6, non-amyloid.

Clitocybe infundibuliformis **Common Funnel Cap.** Cap form, habitat, smell, spore shape. CAP 3–8, silky, very markedly funnel-shaped, usually with a wavy margin. STEM 3–8, fairly slender,± equal or with slightly swollen base. GILLS white tinged pale pinkish buff, narrow, crowded, deeply decurrent. SPORE PRINT white. SMELL faint but pleasant, sweet or almond-like. FLESH soft, thick, white. Usually in small groups. On soil or among grass in fields, heaths and moors or woodland clearings. Spring – autumn. Widespread. Very common. Edible. SPORES ellipsoid – teardrop-shaped, smooth, 6–7×3.5–4, non-amyloid.

63

TRICHOLOMATACEAE

Clitocybe sinopica. Cap form, colour, habitat, smell. CAP 2–5, usually slightly depressed, surface broken up into tiny scales, margin wavy and silky. STEM 3–5, stout and often curved,±equal or tapering slightly downwards, covered with fine fibrils. GILLS white, becoming cream or yellowish, fairly broad, crowded, deeply decurrent. SPORE PRINT white. SMELL strong, mealy. FLESH thick, white but reddish beneath cap cuticle. Usually in small groups. On acid soil on heaths, in woodland and on fire sites with mosses. Spring – autumn. Widespread. Rare. Inedible. SPORES subspherical, smooth, 8–9×6–7, non-amyloid.

Clitocybe cerussata. Cap form, colour, habitat, smell. CAP 3–8, at first convex, then umbilicate-depressed or funnel-shaped with inrolled margin, smooth, appearing silky or with bloom which discolours when wet or handled. STEM 4–8, equal, tough, shiny, sometimes somewhat flattened and finely downy, with curved, hairy±rooting base. GILLS white, narrow, crowded, adnate-decurrent. SPORE PRINT white. SMELL strong, pleasant, floury. FLESH thin, white. Usually in small groups, sometimes tufted. On soil and among litter in broad-leaved and coniferous woodland. Autumn. Widespread. Uncommon. Poisonous. SPORES ellipsoid, smooth, 6–7×4, non-amyloid.

Clitocybe dealbata. Colour, habit, habitat, like *C. rivulosa* but cap spotted not wrinkled. CAP 2–4, first convex, then slightly depressed with slightly inrolled margin, smooth, appearing finely floury or silky (handlens),±spotted. STEM 2–3.5, equal, stout, tough, smooth, silky, slightly floury at apex, rather commonly fused. GILLS white or pale pinkish buff, narrow, crowded, adnate-decurrent. SPORE PRINT white. SMELL strong, pleasant, faintly mealy. FLESH thin, white. In small groups, usually tufted, often in rings and with *Marasmius oreades*. On soil in short grass on lawns, parks, pastures. Summer – late autumn. Widespread. Common in south, rarer northwards. Deadly poisonous. SPORES ellipsoid, smooth, 4–5.5×2–3, non-amyloid.

Clitocybe suaveolens. Ver similar to *C. fragrans* but cap darker, more depressed. CAP 2–5, first convex then markedly depressed paler when dry but darke centre, margin finely line STEM 3–6, equal, slender, smooth, silky or floury at apex, slightly woolly at curved base. GILLS white buff, crowded, adnate-decurrent. SPORE PRINT white with slight pink tin SMELL strong, aniseed. FLESH thin, white or buff. Usually in small groups, ten±tufted. On leaf litter or soil with grasses and moss with broad-leaved trees. Summer – late autumn. Widespread. Uncommon. Inedible. SPORES ell ipsoid, smooth, 6–8×3.5–4, non-amyloid.

Clitocybe candicans. Cap form, colour. CAP 1.5–5, at first domed or convex, then umbilicate-depressed with inrolled margin, smooth, appearing silky and shiny when wet. STEM 2–5, equal, tough, cartilaginous, shiny, usually twisted with curved, hairy base to which leaves adhere. GILLS white, narrow, crowded, adnate-decurrent. SPORE PRINT white. SMELL faint and mild. FLESH thick, white. Usually in small groups. On soil and among litter in broad-leaved woodland, especially with beech, also with alder, occasionally conifers. Summer – autumn. Widespread. Rare. Inedible. SPORES ellipsoid, smooth, 4–5×3–3.5, non-amyloid.

Clitocybe rivulosa. Colour, habit, habitat, like *C. dealbata* but cap wrinkled not spotted. CAP 2–5, first convex, then slightly depressed, slightly wavy, with slightly inrolled margin, smooth, appearing finely floury or silky (hand-lens) with faint ±concentric wrinkled lines, streaks. STEM 2–4, equal, slender, tough, smooth, slightly silky or floury, woolly at base. GILLS white or pale pinkish buff, narrow, crowded, adnate-decurrent. SPORE PRINT white. SMELL faint, pleasant, slightly sweet. FLESH thin, white. In small groups, usually tufted, often in rings and with *Marasmius oreades*. On soil in short grass on lawns, parks, maritime pastures. Summer – late autumn. Widespread. Uncommon. Deadly poisonous. SPORES ellipsoid, smooth, 4–5.5.× 2–5, non-amyloid.

Clitocybe fragrans. Form, smell, like *C. suaveolens* but cap paler, less depressed. CAP 1.5–4, first convex, then slightly depressed, paler when dry but darker centre, margin barely lined. STEM 3–6, equal, fairly slender, smooth, slightly silky or floury at apex, slightly woolly at curved base. GILLS white or buff, crowded, adnate-decurrent. SPORE PRINT white. SMELL strong, of aniseed. FLESH thin, white or buff. Usually in small groups, often±tufted. On leaf litter or soil with grasses and moss in woods. Summer – late autumn. Widespread. Uncommon. Inedible. SPORES ellipsoid, smooth, 6–8×3.5–4, non-amyloid.

Clitocybe dicolor. Similar to several other species, b no smell. CAP 3–5, at first convex, then markedly depressed, paler (almost white) when dry but darke centre, margin finely line STEM 3–6, equal, becoming hollow, fairly slender, smooth, silky, woolly at curved and swollen base. GILLS white-grey, crowde decurrent. SPORE PRINT white. SMELL indistinct. FLESH thin, white or grey-buff. Usually in small groups, often±tufted. On leaf litter or on soil with grasses and moss with broad-leaved trees. Autumn. Widespread. Rare. Inedible. SPORES ellipsoid, smooth, 5–7×3–4, non-amyloid.

tocybe ditopus. Similar
several other species, but
ell, spores and habitat
fer. CAP 2–4, at first con-
and depressed, then
nel shaped, paler over-
when dry but darker
tre, margin slightly
urved. STEM 2.5–4,
ial, becoming hollow,
rly slender, smooth,
ved base. GILLS grey,
wded, adnate–
lecurrent. SPORE PRINT
ite. SMELL markedly
aly. FLESH thin, brow-
h. Usually in small
ups, often±tufted. On
dle litter or on soil with
sses and moss in conifer-
s woods. Autumn. Wide-
ead. Rare. Inedible.
RES subspherical,
ooth, 3–3.5×2.5–3, non-
yloid.

Clitocybe langei. Similar to
C. ditopus but gills paler.
CAP 2–5, at first convex then
depressed, much paler
overall when dry, finely
lined. STEM 2.5–4, equal,
becoming hollow, fairly
slender and fragile, smooth
at apex, sometimes finely
silky towards curved base.
GILLS grey, crowded, decurrent. SPORE PRINT white.
SMELL faint of meal or
cucumber. FLESH thin, pale
brownish. Usually in small
groups, often±tufted. On
leaf litter or on soil with
grasses and moss in coniferous or mixed woods.
Autumn. Widespread.
Common. Inedible. SPORES
ellipsoid, smooth, 5–
6.5×3–3.5, non-amyloid.

Clitocybe flaccida **Tawny
Funnel Cap**. Similar to
several related species but
spores distinctive (also see
Lepista inversa). CAP 2–5, at
first convex then deeply
funnel-shaped, margin
slightly wavy. STEM 2–5,
equal, fairly stout, becoming hollow, smooth at apex,
usually finely woolly
towards curved base. GILLS
white or buff, crowded,
deeply decurrent. SPORE
PRINT white. SMELL indis-
tinct. FLESH thin, white–
buff. Usually in small
groups, often±tufted. On
leaf litter in coniferous or
broad-leaved woods.
Autumn. Widespread.
Uncommon. Inedible?
SPORES ellipsoid, minutely
spiny, 4–5×3–4, non-
amyloid.

Clitocybe nebularis **Cloud-
ed Agaric**. Size. CAP 5–20,
first convex then flat and
slightly depressed with
slightly inrolled pale margin, often with whitish
bloom. STEM 5–10, tapering
upwards, stout, fibrous,
brittle, becoming hollow.
GILLS white or buff, crowded, decurrent. SPORE PRINT
white – cream. SMELL
strong, sugary or fruity.
FLESH thick, white or white-
buff. Usually trooping in
small groups or rings. On
leaf litter in coniferous or
broad-leaved woods. Late
summer – autumn. Wide-
spread. Uncommon. Ined-
ible? SPORES ellipsoid,
smooth, 5.5–8×3.5–5, non-
amyloid.

itocybe vibecina. Similar
several related species
t paler than *C. ditopus*
d spores differ. CAP 1.5–
at first convex then
pressed, much paler
erall when dry, finely
ed at margin, darker
ien wet. STEM 3–5, equal,
coming hollow, fairly
ender, smooth at apex,
metimes finely silky
wards curved base, espe-
ally when young. GILLS
aff–grey, fairly crowded,
:current. SPORE PRINT
white mealy. FLESH
in, pale brownish.
sually in small groups,
ten±tufted. On leaf litter
on soil with grasses
acken and moss in con-
erous or mixed woods.
utumn. Widespread.
ncommon. Inedible?
ORES ellipsoid, smooth,
5–7×3.5–4, non-amyloid.

Clitocybe hydrogramma.
Similar to several related
species but cap surface cells
distinctive. CAP 2–5, at first
convex then depressed or
funnel-shaped, much paler
overall when dry, finely
lined at margin. STEM 5–8,
equal, becoming hollow,
fairly slender, smooth at
apex, sometimes finely
silky towards curved base.
GILLS white or off-white,
not very crowded, deeply
decurrent. SPORE PRINT
white. SMELL strong, ran-
cid, unpleasant. FLESH
white. Usually in small
groups, often±tufted. On
leaf litter in broad-leaved
woods. Autumn. Wide-
spread. Rare. Inedible?
SPORES ellipsoid, smooth,
5–6.5×3–3.5, non-amy-
loid. Cap surface cells with
spherical or spindle-shaped
swellings, 15–20.

Clitocybe gilva. Similar to
several other species especially *C. flaccida*, but smell
and spores distinctive. CAP
4–10, at first convex then
slightly depressed with
slightly inrolled margin,
often±irregularly spotted.
STEM 3–6, equal or tapering
slightly upwards, fairly
stout, becoming hollow,
smooth at apex, usually
finely woolly at curved
base. GILLS white or buff,
crowded, deeply decurrent.
SPORE PRINT white–cream.
SMELL slightly acrid. FLESH
white–buff. Usually in
small groups, often±tuf-
ted. On leaf litter in coniferous or broad-leaved
woods. Late summer –
autumn. Widespread.
Rare. Inedible? SPORES
spherical, minutely spiny,
3.5–5, non-amyloid.

Lepista nuda **Wood Blewit**.
Size, spore print and young
gill colour. CAP 6–12, at
first±convex and umbon-
ate, then depressed with
irregularly wavy margin,
drying paler. STEM 5–9,
equal or slightly swollen at
base, fairly stout, finely
fibrous or woolly. GILLS rich
lilac, fading to buff,
crowded, sinuate. SPORE
PRINT pale pink. SMELL
sweet, perfume-like. FLESH
thick, lilac-blue. Usually in
small groups, trooping or
often in rings. On soil and
among litter in mixed
woods, hedgerows,
gardens. Autumn – winter.
Widespread. Uncommon.
Edible, but some people
allergic. SPORES ellipsoid,
minutely spiny or warty, 6–
8×4–5, non-amyloid.

TRICHOLOMATACEAE

Lepista sordida. Spore print, gill colour and habitat. CAP 3–9, at first ± convex than flattened or depressed and slightly umbonate with slightly wavy margin, drying paler. STEM 4–6, equal or slightly swollen at base, fairly stout, finely fibrous or woolly. GILLS pale grey-lilac, fading to buff, crowded, sinuate. SPORE PRINT pale pink. SMELL sweet, perfume-like. FLESH fairly thick, grey-lilac. Often in large groups. On soil and among plant debris, in hedgerows and around compost in gardens. Summer – autumn. Widespread. Uncommon. Edible. SPORES ellipsoid, minutely spiny or warty, 6–7×3.5–4, non-amyloid.

Lepista irina. Spore print, overall colour, smell. CAP 6–12, at first convex or domed, then more flattened with slightly wavy margin. STEM 5–9, usually tapering upwards with slightly swollen base, fairly stout, fibrous. GILLS yellowish white, becoming brownish, crowded, adnate-sinuate. SPORE PRINT pale pink. SMELL strong, sweet, perfume-like, *Iris*-like? FLESH fairly thick, white. Often in large groups. On soil in open grassy areas in woodland or in grass close to trees. Autumn. Widespread. Rare. Edible, good. SPORES ellipsoid, minutely spiny or warty, 6–9×3–5, non-amyloid.

Lepista rickenii. Size, habitat, distribution. CAP 5–15, at first convex or domed, then more flattened and ± umbonate, leathery with darker spots or marbling especially towards centre. STEM 4–10, usually tapering slightly upwards, stout, fibrous, darker below with slightly curved base. GILLS white- buff, crowded, ± decurrent. SPORE PRINT pale pink. SMELL slight, mealy. FLESH thick, white-buff. Often ± tufted in large groups. On soil in pastures, on lawns and parkland and other open grassy places, copses. Autumn. Widespread, not Britain. Edible but some people react adversely. SPORES ellipsoid, 6–7×3.5–4, non-amyloid.

Tricholomopsis decora. Colour and habitat. CAP 4–10, at first convex, then depressed with wavy margin, covered with small, dark flat scales, especially in centre. STEM 4–8, equal, slender, often twisted, finely scaly. GILLS golden yellow, very broad, crowded, sinuate. SPORE PRINT white. SMELL indistinct. FLESH thin, golden yellow. Usually in small groups, often ± tufted. On conifer stumps or other rotten conifer wood. Late summer – autumn. Widespread, highland. Uncommon. Indible. SPORES ellipsoid – subspherical smooth, 5–7×4–5, non-amyloid.

Lepista saeva (=*personata*). **Blewit.** Spore print, overall colour, size and habitat. CAP 6–12, at first ± convex then flattened or depressed with slightly wavy margin, often drying paler. STEM 5–10, equal or slightly swollen at base, fairly stout, fibrous. GILLS white-grey, thin, crowded, sinuate. SPORE PRINT pale pink. SMELL strong, sweet, perfume-like. FLESH fairly thick, white – pinkish buff. Often in large groups or rings. On soil on chalky pastures and other grassland. Autumn – late winter. Widespread. Rare. Edible, good. SPORES ellipsoid, minutely spiny or warty, 7–9×4–5, non-amyloid.

Lepista luscina. Spore print, smell, habitat. CAP 4–9, at first convex or domed, then more flattened or depressed with slightly wavy margin, often slightly spotted and floury especially towards margin. STEM 3–5, usually tapering downwards and ± rooting, fairly stout, fibrous. GILLS white, becoming grey, crowded, decurrent. SPORE PRINT pale pink. SMELL strong, sweet, mealy. FLESH fairly thick, white. Often ± tufted in large groups or rings. On soil in pastures, on downs and parkland and other open grassy places. Autumn. Widespread. Rare. Edible, good. SPORES ellipsoid, minutely spiny or warty, 5–7×3.5–4.5, non-amyloid.

Lepista inversa. Similar to several *Clitocybe* species but spores distinctive, in Britain, this species is considered synonymous with *Clitocybe flaccida q.v.* CAP 4–8, at first convex then funnel-shaped, often somewhat spotted, margin slightly wavy and inrolled. STEM 3–5, equal, fairly stout, becoming hollow, smooth at apex, usually finely woolly towards curved base. GILLS pale orange or reddish buff, crowded, deeply decurrent. SPORE PRINT white. SMELL strong, unpleasant, bitter. FLESH thick, reddish brown. Usually in small groups, often ± tufted. On leaf litter in coniferous and broad-leaved woods. Late summer – autumn. Widespread. Uncommon. Inedible? SPORES spherical, minutely spiny, 3–4, non-amyloid.

Tricholomopsis (=*Collybia*=*Oudemansiella*) *platyphylla.* Stem base. CAP 8–15, at first convex, then depressed with wavy margin, streaked when covered with small, dark flat scales especially towards margin. STEM 4–8, tough, equal or tapering downwards into rooting base with long mycelial strands, stout, fibrillar. GILLS cream-white, very broad, almost distant adnexed. SPORE PRINT white. SMELL indistinct. FLESH thin, white. Usually solitary. Attached to rotten wood of broad-leaved trees. Late summer – autumn. Widespread. Very common. Inedible. SPORES ellipsoid – subspherical, smooth, 6–8×6–7, non-amyloid.

Tricholomopsis rutilans **Plums and Custard**. Overall colour. CAP 4–13, at first convex, then broadly umbonate, with dense covering of ±fibrous scales. STEM 4–9, tough, ±equal and often slightly twisted with curved base, covered scales as cap. GILLS golden yellow, very broad, crowded, adnexed. SPORE PRINT white. SMELL musty. FLESH thin, yellow-cream. Usually in small tufts. On or close to rotten conifer wood. Late summer – autumn. Widespread. Extremely common. Inedible. SPORES ellipsoid smooth, 7–8×5–6, non-amyloid.

Tricholoma colossum. Overall size, spore size. CAP 10–25, at first domed then convex – flattened with inrolled margin, rather shiny, greasy or sticky, ±smooth, but±fibrous at margin. STEM 6–10, stout, ±equal or tapering downwards with white apex, becoming brownish on handling, often with superior fibrous ring-zone. GILLS greyish buff, often spotted reddish, fairly crowded, adnexed-free. SPORE PRINT white. SMELL faint, mild. FLESH fairly thick, white, turning reddish when cut. Solitary or in small±tufted groups. On soil in coniferous woods. Autumn. Widespread. Rare. Inedible. SPORES white, subspherical – ellipsoid, smooth, 8–10× 5–6, non-amyloid.

Tricholoma ustaloides. Cap and stem colours and pattern, smell, habitat. CAP 5–10, at first convex, then flattened, markedly sticky, smooth, margin usually persistently inrolled and lined-grooved. STEM 6–10, fairly stout, ±equal, iregularly concentric scaly bands, indefinite irregular scaly-woolly superior ring zone. GILLS white, often slightly reddish spotted, crowded, emarginate. SPORE PRINT white. SMELL strong, floury-mealy. FLESH firm, white. Solitary or in small groups. On soil with broad-leaved trees. Autumn. Widespread. Rare. Inedible. SPORES broadly ellipsoid, smooth, 6–7×4–5, non-amyloid.

Tricholoma fulvum (=*flavobrunneum*). Overall form, smell, habitat. CAP 7–12, at first convex then more flattened and±umbonate, slightly sticky, finely fibrous. STEM 3–7, fairly slender, equal or subspindleshaped, at first slightly sticky. GILLS yellowish, becoming spotted redbrown, crowded, emarginate. SPORE PRINT white. SMELL mealy. FLESH fairly thick, white in cap, markedly yellow in stem. Solitary or in small groups. On soil in mixed or broadleaved woods with birch. Autumn. Widespread. Common. Edible but poor. SPORES white, ellipsoid, smooth, 5–7×3–4.5, non-amyloid.

Tricholoma focale. Stem features, ring, spore size. CAP 4–9, markedly scaly or fibrous, margin paler and often with remnants of veil at first. STEM 6–8, stout, tapering downwards with± banded appearance from rather rough woolly scales lower part below rather shaggy, ±spreading superior ring. GILLS white, becoming slightly reddish later, adnexed-free. SPORE PRINT white. SMELL faint slightly of cucumber. FLESH fairly thick, white. Solitary or in small±tufted groups. On soil in coniferous woods. Autumn. Widespread. Rare. Inedible. SPORES white, subspherical – ellipsoid, smooth, 3–4.5 ×4.5–5.5, non-amyloid.

Tricholoma aurantium. Cap and stem colours and pattern, smell, habitat. CAP 5–10, at first convex, then flattened, ±flecked-scaly, markedly sticky at first, then less so. STEM 5–9, fairly stout, ±equal, concentrically patterned with scaly bands, irregular scaly-woolly superior ring zone. GILLS white-slightly orange, edges often reddish-orange, crowded, emarginate. SPORE PRINT white. SMELL floury-mealy. FLESH firm, white with slight orange flush beneath cap surface. Solitary or in small groups. On soil with coniferous trees, especially (always?) pine in Britain. Summer – autumn. Widespread, northern, highland in Britain. Rare. Inedible. Poisonous? SPORES broadly ellipsoid, smooth 4–5×3– 3.5, non-amyloid.

Tricholoma acerbum. Colour, cap features. CAP 7–12, at first domed then convex with markedly inrolled margin, often with pronounced marginal ridges, colouring slightly reddish, smooth, slightly greasy. STEM 3–8, stout, tapering downwards and almost bulbous with sub-rooting base, finely granular scaly at apex. GILLS whiteyellowish, becoming spotted red-brown, crowded, emarginate-adnate. SPORE PRINT white. SMELL faint, sweet or fruity, unpleasant. FLESH fairly thick, white. Solitary or in small groups. On soil in mixed woods especially with oak. Autumn. Widespread. Rare. Poisonous. SPORES white, subspherical – ellipsoid, smooth, 4–6×3– 4, non-amyloid.

Tricholoma populinum. Habitat, smell. CAP 8–10, at first convex, then flattened and±umbonate, sticky, smooth. STEM 4–10, fairly stout, ±equal or tapering towards base, smooth or very slightly scaly. GILLS at first white, then slightly reddish, crowded, emarginate. SPORE PRINT white. SMELL strong, mealy. FLESH firm, white. Solitary or in small groups. On soil with poplars. Autumn. Widespread. Rare. Edible. SPORES broadly ellipsoid, smooth, 5.5–6×3–3.5, nonamyloid.

TRICHOLOMATACEAE

Tricholoma pessundatum.
Smell, habitat, spore size.
CAP 5–12, at first domed,
then convex – flattened,
smooth, slightly sticky,
often±spotted and paler at
margin. STEM 4–10, fairly
slender, equal, finely
fibrous and slightly woolly
at base. GILLS white,
becoming red-brown,
crowded, adnexed. SPORE
PRINT white. SMELL strong,
mealy. FLESH fairly thick,
white. Solitary or in small
groups. On soil in coniferous woods, especially with
pines. Autumn. Wide-
spread, Rare. Inedible,
poisonous. SPORES ellip-
soid, smooth, 4–6×2.5–3,
non-amyloid.

Tricholoma albobrunneum.
Cap surface, flesh, habitat,
smell. CAP 5–8, at first
domed, then convex –
flattened and±umbonate,
covered with fine radiating
fibrils, sticky, often inrolled
at margin. STEM 5–8, fairly
slender, equal, fairly scaly
at apex with rather inde-
finite fibrous superior ring
zone. GILLS white, becom-
ing red-brown, fairly
crowded, very broad,
emarginate-adnate. SPORE
PRINT white. SMELL faint,
mealy. FLESH fairly thick,
white, reddish brown below
cap cuticle and in stem
base. Solitary or in small
groups. On soil in coniferous woods. Autumn. Wide-
spread, northern in Britain.
Rare. Inedible. SPORES
subspherical – ellipsoid,
smooth, 5×3–4.5, non-
amyloid.

Tricholoma imbricatum.
Cap surface, habitat. CAP
4–9, at first domed –
conical, then convex
and±umbonate, smooth
then covered with small,
dark, sometimes overlap-
ping scales, with margin
often irregularly scaly. STEM
3.5–4.5, stout, tapering
upwards, base±rooting,
finely fibrous or scaly,
fibrous at apex. GILLS
white, becoming pale pink-
buff, fairly crowded,
adnate, often with decur-
rent tooth. SPORE PRINT
white. SMELL mealy. FLESH
fairly thick, white, then
reddish brown. Solitary or
in small groups. On soil in
coniferous woods.
Autumn. Widespread.
Uncommon. Inedible.
SPORES subspherical –
ellipsoid, smooth, 5–
6.5×4–4.5, non-amyloid.

Tricholoma flavovirens.
Overall colour, size, habitat, often less stout than *T.
auratum*. CAP 5–8, at first
convex then flattened,
broadly umbonate, slightly
wavy, smooth or with few
scales towards centre,
slightly sticky. STEM 5–10,
stout, tapering slightly
upwards, smooth or slightl
scaly. GILLS sulphur-yellow
broad, fairly crowded,
adnexed – emarginate.
SPORE PRINT white. SMELL
faint, indistinct. FLESH
fairly thin, white, often yel
lowish below cap cuticle.
Usually trooping in small
groups. On soil in coniferous or rarely broad-leaved
woods. Autumn. Wide-
spread, generally northern
in Britain. Rare. Edible.
SPORES ellipsoid, smooth,
6–8×3–5, non-amyloid.

Tricholoma ustale. Overall
form, habitat, lack of smell.
CAP 5–12, at first domed,
then convex – flattened
and often rather wavy,
smooth, sticky, usually
paler at margin and often
turning almost black later.
STEM 3–7, fairly stout,
fibrous, tapering upwards
and±bulbous at base. GILLS
white, becoming red-brown
or blackish, crowded, sinuate. SPORE PRINT white.
SMELL indistinct. FLESH
fairly thick, white, often
turning reddish. Solitary or
in small groups. On soil in
broad-leaved woods, espe-
cially with beech. Autumn.
Widespread. Common.
Poisonous. SPORES ellip-
soid, smooth 5.5–7×4–5,
non-amyloid.

Tricholoma vaccinum. Cap
surface, habitat. CAP 5–8, at
first convex then±flattened
and umbonate, covered
with small, woolly scales,
with margin often irregular
and woolly. STEM 3–5, slender, equal, finely fibrous or
scaly. GILLS white, becoming pale pink-buff,±dis-
tant,±adnate. SPORE PRINT
white. SMELL slightly acrid.
FLESH fairly thick, white,
then reddish brown. Solitary or in small groups. On
soil in coniferous woods.
Autumn. Widespread.
Rare. Inedible. SPORES subspherical – ellipsoid,
smooth, 5–7×4.5–5, non-
amyloid.

Tricholoma portentosum.
Overall colour, cap surface,
habitat. CAP 5–10, at first
convex then flattened,
broadly umbonate, slightly
wavy, covered with fine
dark radiating streaks,
sticky. STEM 5–10, stout,
tapering upwards, often±
curved, slightly yellowish
below, base slightly bul-
bous±rooting, smooth.
GILLS white, becoming yellowish, broad, fairly distant, sinuate. SPORE PRINT
white. SMELL mealy. FLESH
fairly thin, white, then
often yellowish. Usually
trooping in large groups.
On soil in coniferous
woods. Autumn. Wide-
spread. Uncommon. Edi-
ble and good. SPORES
subspherical – ellipsoid,
smooth, 5–6×3.5–5, non-
amyloid.

Tricholoma auratum. Ove
all colour, habitat, stouter
and more greenish than *T.
flavovirens*. CAP 7–12, at
first convex then flattened
broadly umbonate, slightl
wavy, smooth or with scale
scales towards centre,
slightly sticky. STEM 4–6,
stout, tapering slightly
upwards, often yellowish
scaly. GILLS sulphur- or
greenish yellow, broad,
fairly crowded, adnexed –
emarginate. SPORE PRINT
white. SMELL faint, indistinct. FLESH fairly thin,
white, often yellowish
below cap cuticle. Usually
trooping in small groups.
On acid, sandy soil in coniferous woods. Autumn.
Widespread, confused wit
T. flavovirens in Britain.
Rare. Edible. SPORES ellip
soid, smooth, 6–7×3–4,
non-amyloid.

richoloma sejunctum.
verall colour, habitat,
nell. CAP 4–10, at first con-
x then flattened, broadly
nbonate, very slightly
id radial fibrillar streaks,
ghtly sticky. STEM 5–8,
irly slender, equal or
pering slightly upwards,
irvy, with paler margin
nooth or spotted towards
pex. GILLS whitish or
intly ochre, very broad,
irly crowded, sinuate.
ORE PRINT white. SMELL
ealy. FLESH fairly thin,
hite, often yellowish
clow cap cuticle. Solitary
more usually trooping in
nall groups. On soil in
iixed and coniferous
pods especially with birch.
utumn. Widespread.
ncommon. Inedible.
ORES ellipsoid, smooth,
–8×4–6, non-amyloid.

Tricholoma inamoenum.
Habitat, smell, overall colour. CAP 3–7, at first convex, then flattened and
usually ± umbonate, slightly
silky-fibrous or matt, dry.
STEM 5–8, fairly slender, ±
equal or tapering slightly
upwards, often rather cur-
ed, fibrous lined. GILLS
white-ochreous, fairly
broad, distant, emarginate.
SPORE PRINT white. SMELL
strong, gas. FLESH fairly
thin, white. Solitary or in
small groups. On soil with
coniferous trees. Summer –
autumn. Predominantly
northern, highland in Britain. Rare. Inedible. SPORES
ellipsoid, smooth, 8–10×4–
5.5, non-amyloid.

Tricholoma lascivum.
Overall colour, smell.
CAP 4–7, at first convex then
flattened – slightly depressed, at first finely silky, then
smooth, dry. STEM 7.5–11,
fairly slender, ± equal, becoming brownish on aging,
fibrous, floury at apex,
downy-hairy at base. GILLS
at first white, then cream,
fairly broad, crowded, ±
decurrent. SPORE PRINT
white. SMELL pleasant,
sweet. FLESH fairly thick,
white. Usually in small ±
trooping groups. On soil in
broad-leaved woods. Aut-
umn. Widespread. Rare.
Inedible, poisonous?
SPORES ellipsoid, smooth,
3.5–4×6–7, non-amyloid.

Tricholoma resplendens.
Cap features. CAP 5–10, at
first convex then flattened,
often faintly water-spotted
when mature and yellowish
at centre, slightly sticky,
shiny when dry. STEM 5–8,
fairly slender, ± equal,
often slightly bulbous,
finely scurfy-scaly at apex.
GILLS white, crowded,
emarginate. SPORE PRINT
white. SMELL faint, inde-
finite, pleasant or indistinct. FLESH fairly thick,
white. Usually in small ±
trooping groups. On soil in
broad-leaved woods, cop-
ses, hedges. Autumn. Widespread. Rare. Inedible.
SPORES ellipsoid – sub-
spherical, smooth, 4–5×
4–6, non-amyloid.

richoloma sulphureum.
verall colour, smell. CAP
–8, at first convex then
ore flattened – slightly
epressed, barely umbon-
e, at first ± silky, then
nooth. STEM 5–10, fairly
ender, equal, often rather
irved, fibrous lined. GILLS
ilphur – yellow, fairly
road, fairly distant,
nuate – emarginate.
ORE PRINT white. SMELL
rong, tar, coal-gas. FLESH
irly thin, sulphur-yellow.
roups. On soil in broad-
aved or more rarely con-
erous woods. Autumn.
/idespread. Common.
iedible. SPORES ellipsoid,
nooth, 5–6×9–12, non-
myloid.

Tricholoma album. Overall
lack of colour, smell. CAP
5–10, at first convex then
flattened, usually slightly
umbonate, often slightly
wavy at margin, smooth,
dry. STEM 6–9, fairly
slender, tapering upwards,
base ± bulbous, smooth –
fibrous lined, floury at
apex. GILLS white, fairly
broad, fairly crowded,
emarginate. SPORE PRINT
white. SMELL mealy, often
rather rancid. FLESH thick,
white. Usually in small ±
trooping groups. On soil in
broad-leaved or mixed
woods. Autumn. Wide-
spread. Rare. Poisonous.
SPORES ellipsoid, smooth,
3–4.5×7–8, non-amyloid.

Tricholoma columbetta.
Overall colour, stem fea-
tures. CAP 5–10, at first convex then flattened, often
pinkish blue spotted when
mature, at first smooth,
then finely silky – almost
scaly, often rather wavy,
rather downy at margin.
STEM 5–10, fairly slender,
equal or tapering slightly
downwards – almost root-
ing, smooth-fibrous lined,
often ± greenish blue at
base. GILLS white, crowded,
emarginate – free. SPORE
PRINT white. SMELL faint,
indefinite. FLESH fairly
thick. Usually in
small ± trooping groups. On
soil in broad-leaved or coniferous woods. Summer –
autumn. Widespread.
Uncommon. Edible but
easily confused with poisonous species. SPORES ellipsoid, smooth, 3.5–5×5.5–7,
non-amyloid.

Tricholoma saponaceum
Soap-scented Tricholoma.
Variable colour but reddish
spotting and smell unique
CAP 5–10, at first convex
then flattened, broadly
umbonate, commonly split
at margin and with surface
cracks. STEM 5–10, fairly
stout, swollen towards middle and tapering markedly
into rooting base. GILLS
whitish or faintly greenish
ochre, often becoming reddish spotted, fairly distant,
sinuate. SPORE PRINT white.
SMELL soapy, of institu-
tional washrooms. FLESH
fairly firm, white, becoming
slightly pinkish. Solitary,
trooping or in small ± tufted
groups. On soil in mixed
and coniferous woods. Late
summer – autumn. Wide-
spread. Common. Inedible.
SPORES ellipsoid, smooth,
5–6×3–4, non-amyloid.

69

TRICHOLOMATACEAE

Tricholoma sciodes. Cap features. CAP 5–10, at first convex or conic, then flattened, broadly umbonate, often almost lumpy, covered with dark radiating fibrils, margin inrolled and ± woolly. STEM 5–8, fairly slender, tapering upwards from ± bulbous base, covered with dark fibrils. GILLS grey-white or faintly pinkish, very broad, fairly distant, sinuate. SPORE PRINT white. SMELL strong, unpleasant. FLESH thick, white turning greyish. Solitary, trooping or in small ± tufted groups. On soil in mixed woods, especially with beech. Autumn. Widespread. Uncommon. Inedible. SPORES ellipsoid, smooth, 6.5–8.5×5–6.5, non-amyloid.

Tricholoma orirubens. Overall colour and smell, flesh features. CAP 4–8, at first convex or conic, then flattened, markedly umbonate, paler towards margin, covered with dark fibrous scales especially towards centre. STEM 4–8, fairly slender, equal, often flecked red and with green-yellow fibres at base. GILLS grey-white, sometimes slightly darker edge, later pink-flushed, distant, emarginate – adnate. SPORE PRINT white. SMELL strong, mealy. FLESH thick, white turning greyish or pink. Solitary, trooping or in small ± tufted groups. On soil in broad-leaved or occasionally coniferous woods. Autumn. Widespread. Rare. Edible. SPORES ellipsoid, smooth, 4–6.5×3–4.5, non-amyloid.

Tricholoma cingulatum. Stem features, ring, smell, habitat. CAP 3–6, at first broadly convex then more flattened, umbonate, often with slightly inrolled and rather woolly margin, covered in dark, felt-like scales. STEM 5–8, fairly slender, equal or tapering slightly upwards, small, ± woolly, superior ring. GILLS white, fairly crowded, adnexed – emarginate. SPORE PRINT white. SMELL strong, mealy. FLESH thin, white. Solitary, or in small ± tufted groups. On soil, usually (always?) with willows. Late summer – autumn. Widespread. Rare. Edible. SPORES ellipsoid, smooth, 4–5.5×2.5–3.5, non-amyloid.

Tricholoma pardinum. Cap features, similar to *T. atrosquamosum* but distribution differs and stem usually paler and more bulbous. CAP 4–12, at first broadly convex then more flattened, slightly umbonate, often with slightly inrolled margin, covered in dark, felt-like overlapping scales. STEM 3–9, variable, slender – stout, usually tapering upwards from swollen reddish brown-flecked base, finely woolly at apex. GILLS white – off-white, fairly crowded, sometimes with darker edge, adnexed – emarginate. SPORE PRINT white. SMELL strong, mealy. FLESH thin, whitish. Usually in small ± tufted groups. On soil in coniferous or mixed woods. Late summer – autumn. Widespread, usually montane, not Britain. Poisonous. SPORES ellipsoid, smooth, 8–10×5.5–6, non-amyloid.

Tricholoma virgatum. Cap features. CAP 3–7, at first convex, then flattened, broadly umbonate, coarsely dark-streaked or radially scaly, markedly dry. STEM 5–9, fairly slender, ± equal, fibrous lined – ± scaly. GILLS at first white, then greyish pink, broad, crowded, emarginate. SPORE PRINT white. SMELL unpleasant, mouldy. FLESH thin, greyish white. Solitary, trooping or in small ± tufted groups. On soil in broad-leaved or coniferous woods. Autumn. Widespread. Uncommon. Inedible. SPORES ellipsoid, smooth, 6.5–8.5×5–6, non-amyloid.

Tricholoma argyraceum (= *scalpturatum*). Gill colours. CAP 4–8, at first convex then flattened, umbonate, often irregularly wavy with slightly inrolled margin, covered in dark, felt-like scales when older. STEM 4–8, fairly slender, equal or tapering slightly upwards, often flecked with small dark scales. GILLS white or slightly yellowish, fairly crowded, sinuate. SPORE PRINT white. SMELL strong, mealy. FLESH thick, white in cap, more greyish in stem. Solitary, trooping or in small ± tufted groups. On soil in broad-leaved or mixed woods, especially with pine, oak or beech. Late summer-autumn. Widespread. Common. Edible. SPORES ellipsoid, smooth, 5–6×3–4, non-amyloid.

Tricholoma atrosquamosum. Overall colour, cap surface, smell, habitat. CAP 4–12, at first broadly convex then more flattened, slightly umbonate, often with slightly inrolled margin, covered in dark, felt-like scales. STEM 3–9, variable slender – stout, equal or tapering slightly upwards, covered with dark fibrous scales. GILLS white-greyish, fairly distant, sometimes with darker edge, emarginate. SPORE PRINT white. SMELL strong, slightly acrid or peppery. FLESH thin, greyish. Usually in small ± tufted groups. On soil in coniferous or broad-leaved woods. Autumn. Widespread. Rare. Edible. SPORES ellipsoid, smooth, 5–8×3.5–5, non-amyloid.

Tricholoma terreum. Similar to several related species but smell not mealy. CAP 4–7, at first convex, then more flattened, broadly umbonate, finely downy or fibrous. STEM 5–8, fairly stout, finely fibrous, more finely downy at apex. GILLS white – off-white, sometimes becoming slightly yellowish, adnexed – emarginate. SPORE PRINT white. SMELL indistinct. FLESH thin, soft, greyish. Usually in small groups. On soil in coniferous or mixed woods. Summer – autumn. Widespread. Uncommon. Edible. SPORES ellipsoid, smooth, 6–7.5×3.5–4.5, non-amyloid.

70

Tricholoma inocybeoides.
Overall features, very like an *Inocybe*. CAP 2–4, at first convex or almost dome-shaped, then flattened, markedly umbonate, often with split margin, smooth or sometimes later covered in fine brownish fibres. STEM 2–6, slender, usually equal, smooth or with brownish streaks. GILLS white – off- white, sometimes becoming slightly yellowish, fairly crowded, adnexed – emarginate. SPORE PRINT white. SMELL unpleasant, earthy-mealy. FLESH thin, whitish. Usually in small trooping groups. On soil in broad-leaved woods or close to broad-leaved trees, often with birch. Spring – autumn. Widespread. Rare. Poisonous. SPORES ellipsoid, smooth, 4.5–6×2.5–3, non-amyloid.

Tricholoma gambosum
(=*Calocybe gambosa*) **St George's Mushroom**. Season, colour, size, habitat. CAP 5–12, at first convex or domed, then more flattened, smooth or slightly cracked, often slightly wavy and with slightly inrolled margin. STEM 3–8, stout, equal or tapering slightly upwards, smooth. GILLS white, narrow, very crowded, sinuate. SPORE PRINT white. SMELL strongly mealy. FLESH white, thick, soft. Often in rings but also trooping. On soil in pastures, sand-dunes, roadsides or other grassland, but often close to trees, especially (?) birch. Spring. Widespread. Common. Edible. SPORES ellipsoid, smooth, 5–6×3–4, non-amyloid.

Catathelasma imperiale.
Habitat, smell, overall form, distribution. CAP 10–18, at first domed, then convex, then flattened-slightly depressed, smooth-finely fibrous, margin markedly inrolled. STEM 7–13, very stout, tapering slightly downwards to±rooting base,±scaly, double, superior, upward pointing ring. GILLS white-ochreous, often with slightly darker edges, fairly crowded, decurrent. SPORE PRINT white. SMELL mealy-floury. FLESH firm, thick, white. Solitary or in small groups. On soil with coniferous trees. Summer – autumn. Predominantly northern and montane, not Britain. Edible. SPORES spindle-shaped, smooth, 11–14×5–6, amyloid.

Armillaria tabescens. Very similar to *A. mellea* but no ring. CAP 4–10, at first convex, then flattened and± depressed, with dark fibrous scales, especially towards centre. STEM 5–10, equal or tapering slightly either upwards or downwards, finely woolly, especially below. GILLS white, turning pink-brown, crowded, adnate – decurrent. SPORE PRINT creamy. SMELL slightly acrid. FLESH white, fairly firm. Tufted. On wood, on or close to stumps of broad-leaved trees, especially oak. Summer – late autumn. Widespread. Rare. Edible when cooked but some people react adversely. SPORES ellipsoid, smooth, 8–10×5–7, non-amyloid.

Tricholoma carneum
(=*Calocybe carnea*). Colour, size, habitat. CAP 1.5–4, at first convex, then more flattened, smooth, often with persistently inrolled margin, sometimes umbonate. STEM 2–4, slender, equal, smooth, sometimes pale at apex. GILLS white, very crowded, adnate with decurrent tooth. SPORE PRINT white. SMELL indistinct. FLESH white, thin, soft. Often solitary but also trooping in small groups or tufted. On soil in pastures or other grassland. Summer – autumn. Widespread. Common. Edible. SPORES ellipsoid, smooth, 4.5–5.5×2.5–3, non-amyloid.

Tricholoma (=*Calocybe*) *ionides*. Size and colour, flesh colour. CAP 3–6, at first convex, then more flattened, often slightly umbonate, smooth, slightly inrolled margin. STEM 3–8, slender, equal or tapering slightly upwards, smooth, covered with fine fibres, slightly woolly at base. GILLS white, becoming slightly yellowish, narrow, crowded, emarginate. SPORE PRINT white. SMELL pleasant, slightly mealy. FLESH white with violet tinge at stem base and under cap cuticle. Usually in small trooping groups. On soil in broad-leaved and mixed woods. Late summer – autumn. Widespread. Rare. Edible. SPORES ellipsoid, smooth, 5–6×3–4, non-amyloid.

Armillaria mellea **Honey Fungus**. Size, ring, habitat, formerly confused with several related species. CAP 4–15, at first convex, then flattened and ±depressed, with dark fibrous scales, especially towards centre. STEM 5–16, equal or tapering slightly either upwards or downwards, finely woolly, especially below, white or yellowish± woolly, superior, moderately persistent ring. GILLS white, turning yellowish brown, crowded, decurrent. SPORE PRINT cream. SMELL slightly acrid. FLESH white, fairly firm. Tufted. On wood, on or close to stumps of broad-leaved or coniferous trees causing serious decay. Summer – late autumn. Widespread. Extremely common. Edible when cooked but some people react adversely. SPORES ellipsoid, smooth, 8–10×5–7, non-amyloid.

Leptoglossum lobatum.
Overall form, habitat, similar to *L. muscigenum* but lacks stem. CAP 1–5, bowl-like, irregularly lobed, smooth. STEM absent. GILLS absent, underside of cap veined, net-like at margin. SPORE PRINT white. SMELL indistinct. FLESH greyish, very thin. As loosely grouped individuals. On mosses. Winter – spring. Widespread. Rare. Inedible. SPORES broadly ellipsoid, smooth, 9–11×6–7, non-amyloid.

71

TRICHOLOMATACEAE

Leptoglossum muscigenum. Overall form, habitat, similar to *L. lobatum* but with stem. CAP 1–2, ±mussel-shaped, often with concentric furrowing. STEM 0.1–0.5, lateral, very finely downy-velvety. GILLS± absent, underside of cap usually folded, almost gill-like. SPORE PRINT white. SMELL indistinct. FLESH greyish, very thin. As loosely grouped individuals. On mosses. Winter – spring. Widespread. Rare. Inedible. SPORES broadly ellipsoid, smooth, 6–9×3.5–5, non-amyloid.

Lyophyllum decastes. Very variable (may be several separate species), colour, habit, habitat. CAP 4–11, at first convex – domed, later more flattened, umbonate and often with wavy margin,±covered with silky streaks. STEM 4–8, variable, often eccentric, often± equal, but may be either swollen or tapered at base, smooth, tough, rather fibrous, often fused. GILLS white – yellowish cream, narrow, fairly crowded, adnate. SPORE PRINT white. SMELL usually indistinct. FLESH white, firm, tough. Tufted, often densely. On soil, possibly from buried roots or on stumps. Summer – autumn. Widespread. Common. Edible but poor. SPORES subspherical, smooth, 5–7×5–6, non-amyloid.

Lyophyllum fumosum. Similar to *L. decastes* but stem base differs. CAP 5–8, at first convex – domed, later more flattened, umbonate and often with wavy margin, smooth. STEM 7–8, variable, sometimes eccentric, usually tapering upwards from swollen, often tough and fused base. GILLS white – greyish, crowded, adnate. SPORE PRINT white. SMELL faint, unpleasant, FLESH white, firm, rather tough. Densely tufted and often fused into a solid root-like base. On soil possibly from buried roots or on stumps. Summer – autumn. Widespread. Common. Inedible. SPORES subspherical, smooth, 5–7×4–6, non-amyloid.

Lyophyllum loricatum. Cap surface, habit. CAP 5–12, at first convex, later more flattened and slightly umbonate, shiny, often with wavy margin, cuticle thick and tough. STEM 5–10, stout, tough, finely downy above, equal or tapering slightly downwards to± rooting base. GILLS white – dirty buff, fairly crowded, broad, tough, adnate – ± decurrent. SPORE PRINT white. SMELL indistinct. FLESH white, sometimes becoming grey, firm, rather tough. Solitary or in small± tufted groups. On soil in broad-leaved and mixed woods. Summer – autumn. Widespread. Uncommon. Edible. SPORES spherical, smooth, 6–7, non-amyloid.

Lyophyllum fumatofoetens. Colour, habitat, spores. CAP 3–7, at first convex – domed, later more flattened, often with slightly wavy margin, blackening when handled,±covered with rather indistinct silky streaks. STEM 3–7, equal or±spindle-shaped, usually shortly rooting and streaked, blackening when handled. GILLS dirty yellowish-grey, blackening when bruised, crowded, adnexed – free. SPORE PRINT white. SMELL unpleasant, foetid. FLESH brownish grey, blackening when cut. Usually in small, often tufted groups. On soil in coniferous woods, with pines. Late summer – autumn. Widespread. Rare. Inedible. SPORES narrowly ellipsoid, minutely spiny, 6–9×2.5–4, non-amyloid.

Lyophyllum connatum. Colour, habit, habitat, chemical test. CAP 3–7, at first convex – domed, later more flattened and often with wavy margin, smooth, becoming blotched. STEM 3–8, variable, often±equal, but may be either swollen or tapered at base, smooth. GILLS white – cream, narrow, fairly crowded, adnate – decurrent. SPORE PRINT white. SMELL pleasant, indefinitely mealy-chalky. FLESH white, firm. Iron salts on flesh and gills, purple. Tufted, often densely. On soil among grass, usually in open areas in woods, gardens or track-sides close to trees. Autumn. Widespread. Common. Inedible. SPORES ellipsoid, smooth, 5–6×2–4, non-amyloid.

Lyophyllum infumatum. Overall form, gill and flesh colour, spores. CAP 5–8, at first convex, later more flattened, and often with wavy margin, finely fibrous (use hand lens) or almost veined. STEM 4–5, stout, tough, finely downy above, equal or tapering slightly downwards to±rooting base. GILLS white – greyish, sometimes turning black at margin, fairly crowded, broad, adnate. SPORE PRINT white. SMELL slightly rancid. FLESH white becoming grey, firm, rather tough. Densely tufted and often fused into a solid root-like base. On soil in broad-leaved and coniferous woods. Summer – autumn. Widespread. Rare. Edible. SPORES ellipsoid but± triangular from some angles, smooth, 8–9×4.5–5.5, non-amyloid.

Tephrocybe atrata. Habitat, overall colour, very similar to *T. anthracophila* but spores differ. CAP 2–4, at first convex, then flattened or±depressed with lined margin, smooth. STEM 2–4, slender, often twisted or wavy above. GILLS white turning grey, fairly distant, adnate. SPORE PRINT white. SMELL mealy. FLESH thin,±off-white – grey. Usually in small trooping groups. On soil of fire sites. Late summer – late autumn. Widespread. Rare. Inedible. SPORES ellipsoid, smooth, 5–7×3–5, non-amyloid.

Tephrocybe anthracophila.
Habitat, overall colour, very similar to *T. atrata* but spores differ. CAP 1–3, at first convex, then flattened or ± depressed with lined margin, smooth. STEM 2–3, slender, often twisted or wavy, paler above. GILLS white turning grey, fairly distant, adnate. SPORE PRINT white. SMELL mealy. FLESH thin, off-white – grey. Usually in small trooping groups. On soil of fire sites. Late summer – late autumn. Widespread. Rare. Inedible. SPORES subspherical, warty, 4–6×3–6, non-amyloid.

Tephrocybe rancida. Habitat, stem base, overall colour, smell. CAP 1–4, at first domed, then more flattened, markedly umbonate, often with wavy margin, covered when young with whitish bloom. STEM 4–8, relatively stout, densely white-woolly at base, long rooting. GILLS grey, crowded, free. SPORE PRINT white. SMELL of rancid meal. FLESH thin, off-white – buff or grey. Usually (always?) solitary. On soil in broad-leaved woods. Autumn – winter. Widespread. Rare. Inedible. SPORES ellipsoid, 7–8.5×3–4.5, non-amyloid.

Asterophora lycoperdoides.
Habitat, size, very similar to *A. parasitica* but spore shape differs. CAP 0.5–1.5, domed or subspherical, often barely opening, with coarse floury covering (chlamydospores). STEM 0.5–1, slender, often twisted. GILLS greyish when young, usually absent later. SMELL indistinct. FLESH thin, grey-brown. Usually ± tufted. On rotting agaric caps, especially of *Russula nigricans*. Summer – winter. Widespread. Common. Inedible. SPORES, basidiospores usually absent except when very young, ellipsoid, smooth, 5–5.5×3–4, non-amyloid, chlamydospores subspherical, star-shaped, 12-16.

Cantharellula (= *Pseudoclitocybe*) *cyathiformis* **The Goblet.** Form and colour. CAP 2–6, funnel-shaped with firm, inrolled margin. STEM 4–8, slender, tapering upwards, silky fibrous, downy at base. GILLS grey, later brown, narrow, fairly crowded, adnate – decurrent. SPORE PRINT white. SMELL earthy, mushroomy. FLESH thin, watery, greyish. Trooping or in small tufted groups. On soil, in leaf litter or other plant debris, or in grass. Late autumn – winter. Widespread. Rare. Edible. SPORES ellipsoid, smooth, 7–10×5–6, amyloid.

Tephrocybe palustris. Habitat, overall size and colour. CAP 1–2, at first convex – domed, then more flattened or slightly depressed, lined with ± transparent lines from centre almost to the edge of the paler margin. STEM 2–3, slender, usually markedly straight and relatively long. GILLS pale buff – greyish, fairly distant, adnexed. SPORE PRINT white. SMELL mealy. FLESH thin, off-white – buff or grey. Usually in small trooping groups. Among *Sphagnum* in bogs and other wet places. Spring – autumn. Widespread. Common. Inedible. SPORES ellipsoid, 4–8.5×3–5, non-amyloid.

Asterophora parasitica.
Habitat, size, very similar to *A. lycoperdoides* but spore shape differs. CAP 0.5–1.5, domed or subspherical, then more flattened, with coarse floury covering (chlamydospores). STEM 0.5–1, slender, often twisted. GILLS greyish brown when young, later indistinct and with coarse floury covering (chlamydospores). SMELL indistinct. FLESH thin, grey-brown. Usually ± tufted. On rotting caps of several species of *Russula* and *Lactarius*. Summer – winter. Widespread. Common. Inedible. SPORES, basidiospores usually absent except when very young, ellipsoid, smooth, 5–5.5×3–4, non-amyloid, chlamydospores ellipsoid, smooth, 14–15×9–11.

Cantharellula umbonata.
Overall form and colour. CAP 2–4, at first convex, umbonate, then flattened – depressed, smooth or with fine silky- woolly covering, margin paler and inrolled. STEM 5–8, fairly slender, ± equal, silky fibrous, downy at base. GILLS white, becoming pink-spotted, crowded, narrow, branching, decurrent. SPORE PRINT white. SMELL ? FLESH white, thin, often pinkish when cut. Trooping or in small tufted groups. On acid lawns and peaty soils, especially among heathers. Late autumn – winter. Widespread. Uncommon. Edible. SPORES spindle-shaped, smooth, 8–11×3–4, amyloid.

Leucopaxillus giganteus
Giant Funnel Cap. Size, form, habit. CAP 10–30, at first flat or slightly convex, then deeply funnel-shaped, apparently smooth but finely velvety (hand-lens), later slightly scaly or cracked towards centre, margin inrolled. STEM 4–25, stout, equal or tapering slightly into ± bulbous base, smooth or finely downy. GILLS white, then buff, variable, often branched, very crowded, decurrent. SPORE PRINT white. SMELL faint, mild, pleasant. FLESH firm, white, often tough. In large groups, often rings. On soil in grass in pastures, parkland, roadsides, not usually with trees. Late summer – autumn. Widespread. Uncommon. Edible when young but some people react adversely. SPORES ellipsoid, smooth, 6–8×3–4, amyloid.

73

TRICHOLOMATACEAE

Melanoleuca strictipes.
Flesh colour, spores, smell. CAP 4–10, at first domed, then flattened, persistently umbonate, smooth but sometimes cracking and flaking when older, especially at centre. STEM 5–10, equal or tapering slightly upwards from ± bulbous white-woolly base, slender, apex slightly floury, relatively long, fibrous, often twisted. GILLS white-creamy, crowded, sinuate. SPORE PRINT white. SMELL mealy. FLESH soft, rather fibrous in stem, white, sometimes red-tinged when cut. Usually in small groups. On soil, among grass in pastures, meadows and other grassy places. Spring – autumn. Widespread. Rare. Edible. SPORES ellipsoid, warty, 7–9×4–5, amyloid. Gill edge cystidia spindle-shaped.

Melanoleuca exscissa.
Habitat, stem, spores. CAP 3–7, at first convex, then flattened or depressed, umbonate, smooth. STEM 2 –5, stout, relatively very short, equal or tapering slightly upwards, smooth. GILLS whitish, narrow, crowded, emarginate. SPORE PRINT white. SMELL ? FLESH thin, whitish or dirty straw-coloured. Solitary or in small groups. On soil among grass in pastures, gardens, parkland, Spring – autumn. Widespread. Rare. Edible? SPORES ellipsoid, warty, 9–10×6–7, amyloid. Gill edge cystidia absent or spindle-shaped.

Melanoleuca melaleuca.
Very variable but stem, spores and lack of smell fairly reliable. CAP 3–8, at first convex, then flattened or depressed-umbilicate, umbonate, smooth, dark when moist but much paler when dry. STEM 5–8, stout tapering slightly upwards from bulbous base, covered with brownish fibres. GILLS white at first, then creamy, rather broad, crowded, sinuate. SPORE PRINT white. SMELL indistinct. FLESH rather thick, soft, whitish, browner in stem. Usually trooping in small groups. On soil in pastures and other grassy places, and in broad-leaved woods. Summer – autumn. Widespread. Common. Edible. SPORES ellipsoid, warty, 7–9×4.5–5.5, amyloid. Gill edge cystidia spindle-shaped.

Collybia cirrhata. Size, habitat. CAP 0.5–1, at first convex, then flattened, umbilicate – depressed, very finely silky, later ± lined. STEM 1.5–4, slender, relatively tall, often twisted, deeply rooting. GILLS white, very narrow, crowded, adnate. SPORE PRINT white. SMELL? FLESH very thin, white. Usually in small ± tufted groups. On decaying fruit bodies of other agarics, sometimes apparently from soil, especially in broad-leaved woods. Summer – autumn. Widespread. Common. In edible. SPORES ellipsoid, smooth, 4–6×2–3, non-amyloid.

Melanoleuca grammopo-dia. Habitat, size, stem, smell, spores. CAP 8–15, at first convex, then flattened or depressed – umbilicate, umbonate, smooth, moist. STEM 5–10, stout, tapering slightly upwards from bulbous base, covered with woolly fibres. GILLS white at first, then creamy, narrow, crowded, often branched, sinuate. SPORE PRINT white. SMELL unpleasant, mouldy. FLESH thick, spongy, whitish, becoming brownish when older but drying paler. Solitary, trooping or in rings. On soil among grass in pastures, sand dunes, gardens, parkland and in broad-leaved woods. Autumn. Widespread. Uncommon. Edible? SPORES ellipsoid, warty, 8.5–9.5×5–6, amyloid. Gill edge cystidia long-necked flask-shaped.

Melanoleuca brevipes. Habitat, stem, spores. CAP 5–7, at first convex, then flattened or depressed, umbonate, smooth or finely fibrous, often rather wet, margin usually inrolled at first. STEM 2–4, stout, relatively very short, ± club-shaped, finely woolly-fibrous. GILLS white, crowded, sinuate. SPORE PRINT white. SMELL faint, mild. FLESH brownish, drying paler, firm especially when young. Solitary or in small groups. On soil in woods, by paths, especially of cinders. Spring – autumn. Widespread. Rare. Edible. SPORES ellipsoid, warty, 7–9×4–6, amyloid. Gill edge cystidia long-necked flask-shaped.

Melanoleuca cognata. Colour, spores, habitat. CAP 4–10, at first convex, then flattened, very broadly umbonate, very smooth. STEM 6–12, slender, relatively tall, tapering slightly upwards from bulbous base, covered with brownish fibres. GILLS creamy, rather broad, fairly crowded, emarginate. SPORE PRINT white. SMELL faint but unpleasant, floury. FLESH fairly thick, soft, cream. Usually in small groups. On soil and among plant debris in coniferous woods. Spring and autumn. Widespread. Rare. Edible. SPORES ellipsoid, warty, 9–10×5.5–6, amyloid. Gill edge cystidia spindle-shaped.

Collybia tuberosa. Size, stem base, habitat. CAP 0.5–1, at first convex, then flattened, umbilicate – depressed, very finely silky, often slightly wavy especially at margin. STEM 1.5–3, slender, relatively tall, often twisted, arising from elongate reddish brown sclerotium. GILLS white, very narrow, crowded, adnate. SPORE PRINT white. SMELL ? FLESH very thin, white. Usually in large groups. On decaying fruit bodies of other agarics, especially of *Russula nigricans* and *Lactarius deliciosus.* Autumn. Widespread. Uncommon. Inedible. SPORES ellipsoid, smooth, 3–5×2–3, non-amyloid.

Collybia cookei. Size, stem base, habitat. CAP 0.1–1.3, at first convex, then flattened, umbilicate – depressed, very finely silky, often slightly wavy. STEM 1.5–3, slender, relatively very tall, usually twisted, very deeply rooting, arising from ±spherical, ochre sclerotium. GILLS white, very narrow, crowded, adnate. SPORE PRINT white. SMELL ? FLESH very thin, white. Usually in large groups. On decaying fruitbodies of other agarics, often apparently (actually?) from soil. Autumn. Widespread. Uncommon. Inedible. PORES ellipsoid, smooth, 5–6×2–3, non-amyloid.

Collybia confluens **Clustered Tough Shank.** Habit, stem features, habitat. CAP 2–5, at first convex, then sometimes slightly flattened, markedly thin at margin, becoming wrinkled and leathery when old, very pale when dry. STEM 3–8, equal or tapering slightly downwards, hollow, often flattened, tough, covered with dense white down. GILLS cream or buff, narrow, crowded, adnexed. SPORE PRINT white. SMELL distinct, of unopened houses. FLESH white, very thin. In dense tufts, often in rings. On leaf-litter in broad-leaved woods. Summer – autumn. Widespread. Very common. Inedible. SPORES ellipsoid, smooth, 7–9×3–4, non-amyloid.

Collybia acervata. Habit, habitat, very similar to *C. erythropus* but gills especially differ. CAP 3–6, at first convex, then flattened, barely umbonate, often wavy, especially at margin. STEM 5–10, equal or tapering slightly upwards, smooth and rather shiny, covered at base with fine down. GILLS pinkish buff, becoming paler, narrow, very crowded, adnexed – free. SPORE PRINT white. SMELL greyish in cap, more reddish in stem. Usually in tufts. On conifer stumps. Summer – autumn. Widespread. Uncommon. Inedible? SPORES ellipsoid, smooth, 6–7×2.5–3, non-amyloid.

Collybia dryophila **Russet Shank.** Habit, habitat. CAP 2–5, at first convex, becoming flattened and slightly depressed, smooth, often ± wavy, especially at margin. STEM 3–6, slender, hollow, equal but slightly bulbous at base, usually ± rooting. GILLS white, becoming buff, narrow, crowded, adnexed – free. SPORE PRINT white. SMELL indistinct. FLESH whitish, thin. Usually ±tufted. On soil and leaf-litter in broad-leaved woods, especially with oak. Spring – autumn. Widespread. Extremely common. Inedible. SPORES ellipsoid, smooth, 4–7×3–4, non-amyloid.

Collybia peronata **Wood Woolly Foot.** Stem base, habitat. CAP 3–6, at first convex, then flattened and usually broadly umbonate, often becoming markedly wrinkled and leathery when old. STEM 3–6, equal, slender, densely covered at base with long woolly hairs to which leaves remain attached. GILLS cream or buff, crowded, adnexed – free. SPORE PRINT white. SMELL indistinct. FLESH white, becoming yellowish. Usually in small tufted groups. On leaf-litter in broad-leaved woods. Autumn. Widespread. Extremely common. Inedible. SPORES ellipsoid, smooth, 7–9×3–4, non-amyloid.

Collybia succinea. Habit, stem features, habitat. CAP 2–5, at first convex, then slightly flattened and ± umbonate, sometimes becoming leathery when old. STEM 2.5–6, equal or tapering slightly downwards, usually hollow, tough, shiny above, covered at base with fine down. GILLS greyish cream, then buff, broad, thick, fairly distant, adnexed – adnate. SPORE PRINT white. SMELL ? FLESH reddish brown, very thin. Solitary or more usually in small groups, often ± tufted. On soil and on wood, especially when buried, in broad-leaved (and coniferous?) woods. Spring – autumn. Widespread. Rare. Inedible? SPORES ellipsoid, smooth, 7–8×3–4, non-amyloid.

Collybia erythropus (= *marasmioides*). Habit, habitat, very similar to *C. acervata* but gills especially differ. CAP 3–7, at first convex, then flattened, barely umbonate, often wavy, especially at margin. STEM 5–10, equal or tapering slightly upwards, smooth and rather shiny, covered at base with fine down. GILLS pinkish buff, becoming paler, narrow, fairly crowded, adnexed – free. SPORE PRINT white. SMELL mushroomy. FLESH greyish in cap, more reddish in stem. Usually in tufts but sometimes in ± trooping groups. On conifer and broad-leaved stumps. Summer – autumn. Widespread. Uncommon. Inedible? SPORES ellipsoid, smooth, 6–7×3–4.5, non-amyloid.

Collybia butyracea **Greasy Tough Shank, Butter Cap.** Feel of cap. CAP 3–7, at first convex, becoming flattened and umbonate, smooth, greasy to touch. STEM 2.5–5, slender, especially when old, tapering upwards, bulbous at base, smooth above but bulb covered with white woolly hairs. GILLS white, broad, crowded, adnexed – free. SPORE PRINT white. SMELL mushroomy or slightly rancid. FLESH whitish, thin, rather watery. Usually ± tufted, often in rings. In soil and among leaf-litter in broad-leaved and coniferous woods. Autumn – winter. Widespread. Common. Inedible. SPORES ellipsoid, smooth, 6.5–8×3–3.5, non-amyloid.

75

TRICHOLOMATACEAE

Collybia asema (=*C. butyracea* var. *asema*). Feel of cap, like *C. butyracea* but cap colour differs. CAP 3–7, first convex, then flattened and umbonate, smooth, greasy to touch. STEM 2.5–5, slender, hollow, especially when old, tapering upwards, bulbous at base, smooth above but bulb covered with white woolly hairs. GILLS white, broad, crowded, adnexed-free. SPORE PRINT white. SMELL mushroomy. FLESH whitish, thin, watery. Usually ± tufted. On soil and in leaf litter in broad-leaved and coniferous woods. Autumn – winter. Widespread. Common. Inedible. SPORES ellipsoid, smooth, 6.5–8×3–3.5, non-amyloid.

Collybia maculata **Spotted Tough Shank.** Overall colour and spotting. CAP 4–10, at first convex and umbonate, becoming flattened, margin wavy and at first inrolled, smooth, becoming markedly spotted at maturity. STEM 4–9, equal or tapering slightly upwards, usually grooved, rather firm, often rooting. GILLS white, then spotted reddish brown, broad, fairly crowded, sinuate. SPORE PRINT white. SMELL mild. FLESH whitish, thick, firm. Usually in tufted groups. On soil on heaths and in coniferous and occasionally broad-leaved woods. Spring – winter. Widespread. Extremely common. SPORES ellipsoid – subspherical, smooth, 5–6×4–5, non-amyloid.

Collybia tesquorum (now considered a species of *Tephrocybe*). Size, habitat, spores. CAP 1–1.5, convex, umbonate, variably lined and grooved. STEM 2–4, slender, relatively long, equal, smooth, powdery at apex. GILLS off-white – buff, very broad, free. SPORE PRINT white. SMELL floury. FLESH greyish, very thin. Usually solitary. On soil in open areas in coniferous (and broad-leaved?) woods. Autumn. Widespread. Uncommon. Inedible. SPORES ellipsoid – subspherical, minutely spiny, 6–7×5.5–6, non-amyloid.

Micromphale perforans. Size, cap features, habitat. CAP 0.5–1, at first convex, then more flattened or depressed, deeply grooved from margin to centre. STEM 2–3, very slender, almost hair-like, velvety (use hand-lens). GILLS white, narrow, distant, adnate. SPORE PRINT white. SMELL unpleasant, rather strong, garlic. FLESH very thin, greyish buff in cap, ±black in stem. In large trooping groups. On fallen spruce needles, one fruit body from each needle. Summer – autumn. Widespread. Uncommon. Inedible. SPORES ellipsoid, smooth, 7–9×3–4, non-amyloid.

Collybia fusipes **Spindle Shank.** Stem, habit, habitat. CAP 3–7, at first convex and umbonate, becoming flattened, margin wavy and inrolled, slightly sticky when wet, smooth when dry. STEM 4–9, rather stout, spindle-shaped, twisted and often deeply grooved, tapering into rooting base, usually fused. GILLS white, then spotted reddish brown, broad, rather irregular, fairly distant, free. SPORE PRINT white. SMELL mild, faint. FLESH whitish with slight reddish tinge, firm. Tufted from common rooting base. On wood at base of stumps of broad-leaved trees, especially of beech and oak. Spring – winter. Widespread. Common. Inedible. SPORES ellipsoid, smooth, 4–6×2–4, non-amyloid.

Collybia distorta. Colour, gills habitat. CAP 3–7, at first convex, becoming flattened and umbonate, somewhat wavy and margin at first inrolled, smooth. STEM 4–6, equal or tapering slightly upwards, usually grooved and twisted. GILLS white, then irregularly spotted reddish brown, edge often irregular, fairly crowded, adnate. SPORE PRINT white. SMELL indistinct. FLESH reddish buff, fairly thick, firm. Usually in tufted groups. On soil in coniferous woods. Autumn. Widespread. Rare. Inedible. SPORES spherical, smooth, 3–4.5, non-amyloid.

Micromphale foetidum. Size, cap features, habitat. CAP 1–3, at first convex, then more flattened or depressed, rubbery, rather deeply grooved from margin to centre. STEM 1–2.5, rather stout, tapering downwards, relatively short, tough, velvety. GILLS buff pink, rather distant, ± decurrent. SPORE PRINT white. SMELL unpleasant, foetid. FLESH reddish buff, very thin. In trooping groups. On fallen twigs of broad-leaved trees, especially hazel. Summer – winter. Widespread. Uncommon in South, rare in North. SPORES ellipsoid, smooth, 8–10×3–4, non-amyloid.

Micromphale brassicolens. Overall colour, smell, habitat. CAP 1–2, at first convex, then flattened or depressed, somewhat lined at margin when moist, smooth when dry. STEM 1.5–2.5, slender, equal or often tapering slightly downwards. GILLS white then greyish brown, broad, rather distant, irregular, ±adnate. SPORE PRINT white. SMELL very unpleasant, of rotten cabbage, garlic and foul water. FLESH thin, white – brownish. In large trooping groups. On fallen beech leaves and occasionally twigs also. Autumn. Widespread. Rare. Inedible. SPORES ellipsoid, smooth, 5–7×3–3.5, non-amyloid.

Hohenbuehelia atrocaerulea. Overall form, habitat. CAP 2.5–5, at first resupinate, then reflexed,±circular or kidney-shaped, finely velvety, often wrinkled when dry. STEM absent. GILLS white then dirty yellow, broad, usually reaching to base. SPORE PRINT white. SMELL faint, pleasant. FLESH thin, rather gelatinous under cap cuticle. In large groups. On living or dead wood of broad-leaved trees, especially beech. Autumn. Widespread. Rare. Inedible. SPORES subellipsoid, smooth, 7–8×3–3.5, non-amyloid. Gill face cystidia lance-shaped, thick-walled, encrusted.

Resupinatus applicatus. Overall form and habitat. CAP 0.5–1, cup-, kidney-or shell-shaped, finely lined, finely downy or smooth. STEM absent. GILLS greyish, thin, narrow, rather distant, radiating from point of attachment to substrate. SPORE PRINT white. SMELL ? FLESH thin, greyish. In small or large groups,± overlapping. On woody debris, sawdust. Summer – autumn. Widespread. Uncommon. Inedible. SPORES ±spherical, smooth, 5–7, non-amyloid.

Panellus stipticus. Overall form, habitat, spores. CAP 1–3, kidney shaped, tough, finely lined. STEM 0.25–0.5, stout, tapering downwards, flattened. GILLS yellowish or pinkish buff, narrow, very crowded, inter-connected, adnate – decurrent. SPORE PRINT white. SMELL indistinct? FLESH white – strawcoloured, very tough. Often in large overlapping groups. On fallen logs and stumps, especially of oak. All year. Uncommon. Inedible, poisonous? SPORES ellipsoid, smooth, 3–6×2–3, amyloid.

Hohenbuehelia petaloides. Very variable but overall form and habitat reliable. CAP 2–8, at first±resupinate, ear-like – funnel-shaped, with inrolled margin,±gelatinous. STEM absent or very short, eccentric – lateral, continuous with cap. GILLS white – creamy, thin, narrow, very crowded, deeply decurrent. SPORE PRINT white. SMELL faint, mealy. FLESH thin, rather leathery. In small or large,±overlapping tufts. On woody debris, sawdust, or on soil among woody debris. Autumn. Widespread. Rare. Inedible. SPORES ellipsoid, smooth, 7–10×4–5, non-amyloid. Gill face cystidia lance-shaped, thick-walled, encrusted.

Panellus serotinus. Overall form, spores, cystidia. CAP 3–8, kidney shaped, soft, at first slightly downy then smooth, sticky when wet. STEM 1–1.5, stout, lateral, covered with tiny rough scales. GILLS yellow, narrow, crowded, adnate. SPORE PRINT white. SMELL ? FLESH white, gelatinous beneath cap cuticle. In small or large groups, often ±overlapping. On fallen logs, especially of beech. Autumn-winter. Widespread. Rare. Inedible. SPORES cylindrical, curved, smooth, 4–7×1–2, amyloid. Cystidia on gill face and edge, spindle-club shaped with yellow contents.

Panellus mitis. Overall form, habitat, spore features, spores. CAP 1–2, kidney-shaped, rather rubbery, with peelable, elastic skin,±smooth. STEM 0.5–1, stout,±equal, lateral, with mealy granules. GILLS white, narrow, crowded, adnate. SPORE PRINT white. SMELL indistinct? FLESH whitish, thin, rather rubbery. In small-large groups, often± overlapping. On twigs of coniferous trees. Autumn – winter. Widespread. Rare. Inedible. SPORES ellipsoid, smooth, 3.5–5×1–1.5, amyloid.

Oudemansiella mucida **Slimy Beech Cap, Porcelain Fungus, Poached Egg Fungus.** Colour, texture, habitat, spores. CAP 3–10, at first convex then flattened, umbonate, wrinkled, slimy. STEM 5–8, slender, equal or tapering slightly downwards, lined above,±scaly below, with membranous, often lined or grooved, superior ring. GILLS white, then yellowish, broad, distant, adnate – subdecurrent. SPORE PRINT white. SMELL indistinct. FLESH white, thin, soft, slimy. In tufts. On trunks and branches of beech. Summer – autumn. Widespread. Very common. Edible. SPORES spherical, smooth, 13–19, non-amyloid.

Oudemansiella longipes. Overall form, stem base. CAP 3–6, at first convex then flattened, broadly umbonate,±downy with whitish bloom. STEM 7–10, slender, tapering upwards, grooved, finely velvety towards base, rooting. GILLS dirty white then yellowish, thick, distant, interconnected, adnate. SPORE PRINT white. SMELL indistinct. FLESH white, thin, fairly soft. Usually solitary. On soil in broad-leaved woods. Autumn. Widespread. Rare. Inedible? SPORES ellipsoid, smooth, 8–9×6–6.5, non-amyloid.

TRICHOLOMATACEAE

Oudemansiella radicata. Overall form, stem base. CAP 3–10, at first convex then flattened, broadly umbonate, wrinkled, rubbery, slimy. STEM 8–20, slender, tapering upwards, relatively very tall, firm, deeply rooting. GILLS white, thick, broad, distant, adnexed. SPORE PRINT white. SMELL ? FLESH white, thin, fairly soft, rather rubbery. Often solitary on soil with broad-leaved trees, attached to roots or buried wood, especially beech. Summer – autumn. Widespread. Extremely common. Edible but poor. SPORES ellipsoid, smooth, 12–16×10–12, non-amyloid.

Pseudohiatula (=*Strobilurus*) *stephanocystis*. Overall form, stem base, substrate, very similar to *P. esculenta* but cystidia differ. CAP 1–2, at first convex then flattened, smooth. STEM 2–7, slender, tapering upwards, relatively very tall, very finely velvety (use hand-lens), often with a long 'rooting' base. GILLS white or creamy, crowded, adnexed. SPORE PRINT white. SMELL indistinct. FLESH white, thin. Often solitary or in small groups. On soil emerging from buried pine cones. Autumn - spring. Widespread, mainly northern. Uncommon. Edible? SPORES ellipsoid, smooth, 6–8×3–4, non-amyloid. Gill cystidia broadly club-shaped with large grains at apex.

Rhodotus palmatus. Overall colour, habit, habitat. CAP 5–10, at first convex or with depressed areas, then flattened, floury, finely wrinkled, margin inrolled, often fused with neighbouring caps. STEM fairly stout, ±equal, usually curved, floury, fibrous-lined. GILLS pale pink-orange, broad, crowded, interconnected, sinuate. SPORE PRINT pinkish. SMELL pleasant. FLESH whitish flushed pink-orange. Tufted. On elm wood, especially on fallen trunks of trees killed by elm disease. Widespread. Uncommon, locally common. Inedible. SPORES subspherical, warty, 5–7.

Marasmius graminum. Overall appearance, gill attachment, substrate. CAP 0.5–1, parachute-like but umbonate, deeply grooved. STEM 2–4, equal, very slender, relatively very long, rather wiry, shiny. GILLS cream, broad, very distant, adnate to distinct stem collar. SPORE PRINT white. SMELL indistinct. FLESH extremely thin, white in cap, ±brownish in stem. In large±trooping groups. On dead grass leaves and stems. Late summer – autumn. Widespread. Uncommon. Inedible. SPORES ellipsoid, smooth, 8–12×4–6, non-amyloid.

Pseudohiatula (=*Strobilurus*) *esculenta*. Overall form, stem base, substrate, cystidia. CAP 1–2, at first convex then flattened, smooth. STEM 2–7, slender, tapering upwards, relatively tall, very finely velvety (use hand-lens), often with a long 'rooting' base. GILLS white or slightly greyish, crowded, adnexed. SPORE PRINT white. SMELL indistinct. Often solitary or in small groups. On soil emerging from buried spruce cones. Autumn – spring. Widespread, mainly northern. Locally common. Edible but poor. SPORES ellipsoid, smooth, 5–7×2–4, non-amyloid. Gill cystidia±bluntly spindle-shaped, usually with crystals at apex.

Pseudohiatula (=*Strobilurus*) *tenacella*. Overall form, stem base, substrate, cystidia. CAP 1–2.5, at first convex then flattened, smooth, often slightly lined when damp. STEM 2–7, slender, tapering upwards, relatively very tall, very finely velvety (use hand-lens), often with a long 'rooting' base. GILLS white or creamy, crowded, adnexed. SPORE PRINT white. SMELL ? FLESH white, thin. Often solitary or in small groups. On soil emerging from buried pine cones. Autumn – spring. Widespread. Edible? SPORES ellipsoid, smooth, 6–7.5×2.5–3.5, non-amyloid. Gill cystidia pointed, usually without crystals or grains.

Marasmius rotula Little Wheel Toadstool. Overall appearance, gill attachment, substrate. CAP 0.5–1.5, parachute-like, umbilicate, deeply grooved. STEM 2–7, equal, very slender, relatively very long, wiry, shiny. GILLS white, broad, very distant, adnate to distinct stem collar. SPORE PRINT white. SMELL indistinct. FLESH extremely thin, white in cap, ±brownish in stem. In large±trooping groups. On dead twigs, roots and other woody material. Late summer – autumn. Widespread. Very common. Inedible. SPORES ellipsoid, smooth, 7–10×3–5, non-amyloid.

Marasmius androsaceus Horse Hair Toadstool. Overall appearance, stem features, substrate. CAP 0.5–1, crudely parachute-like, umbilicate, rather wavy, deeply grooved. STEM 2–6, equal, very slender, relatively extremely long, wiry, shiny. GILLS buff, broad, distant, adnate – decurrent. SPORE PRINT white. SMELL indistinct. FLESH extremely thin, white in cap, ±brownish in stem. In large groups, often with stems intertwined. On dead heather (*Calluna*), also pine needles and other conifer litter. Spring – late autumn. Widespread. Very common. Inedible. SPORES ellipsoid, smooth, 7–9×3–4, non-amyloid.

Marasmius splachnoides. Overall appearance like *M. androsaceus*, stem colour, substrate. CAP 0.5–1, convex at first, then flattened, slightly umbilicate, grooved. STEM 2–4, equal, very slender, relatively very long, wiry, at first, hairy at base, shiny. GILLS white, narrow, crowded, ±decurrent. SPORE PRINT white. SMELL indistinct. FLESH extremely thin, white in cap, ±brownish in stem. Usually in large groups. On dead leaves in broad-leaved, coniferous and mixed woods. Autumn. Widespread. Rare. Inedible. SPORES ellipsoid, smooth, 8–9×4, non-amyloid.

Marasmius scorodonius. Overall appearance, cap features, habitat. CAP 1–3, convex at first, then flattened or slightly depresssed, markedly wrinkled towards margin. STEM 3–6, equal, very slender, relatively very long, smooth, shiny. GILLS white or with pinkish flush, narrow, distant, adnexed–free. SPORE PRINT white. SMELL indistinct. FLESH thin, whitish in cap, brownish in stem. Usually in small groups. On dead leaves and coniferous needles. Autumn. Widespread. Rare. Inedible. SPORES elongated ellipsoid, smooth, 8–9×4–5, non-amyloid.

Marasmius cohaerens. Stem features, habitat. CAP 1–3, convex – dome-shaped at first, then slightly flattened, umbonate, finely velvety, lined or grooved at margin. STEM 5–10, equal, slender, stiff, smooth, shiny, woolly at base. GILLS yellow-cream, usually with brown edge, broad, distant, adnexed – free. SPORE PRINT white. SMELL ? FLESH thin, white-buff in cap, ± brownish in stem. Usually in small trooping groups. On dead leaves, especially (always?) of beech. Autumn – winter. Widespread. Uncommon. Inedible. SPORES ellipsoid, smooth, 8–10×2–5, non-amyloid. Cap surface cystidia thick-walled, brown.

Marasmius wynnei. Gills, habit. CAP 2–6, convex at first, then slightly flattened, smooth, finely wrinkled and lined at margin when moist. STEM 2–8, equal or tapering slightly downwards, slender, finely velvety. GILLS white turning creamy or slightly lilac, narrow, distant, adnexed. SPORE PRINT white. SMELL mushroomy, creamy, woody. FLESH rather thin, whitish in cap, ±brown in stem. Tufted in small groups. Among leaf litter in beech woods. Summer – autumn. Widespread. Uncommon. Inedible. SPORES ellipsoid, smooth, 6–7×3–4, non-amyloid.

Marasmius epiphyllus. Overall appearance, gills, substrate. CAP 0.25–1, slightly convex at first, then often depressed, wrinkled. STEM 1.5–3, equal, very slender, relatively very long, wiry, shiny. GILLS white, narrow, extremely distant, branched, ± decurrent. SPORE PRINT white. SMELL indistinct. FLESH extremely thin, white in cap, ±brownish in stem. Usually in large groups. On dead leaves and leaf stalks, twigs. Autumn. Widespread. Uncommon. Inedible. SPORES elongate – ellipsoid, smooth, 10–11×3–4, non-amyloid.

Marasmius alliaceus. Smell, stem features. CAP 1–4, convex at first, then slightly flattened, very broadly umbonate, lined or grooved at margin. STEM 4–20, tapering slightly upwards, very slender, relatively very long, finely velvety, rooting. GILLS white or greyish, narrow, distant, adnexed – free. SPORE PRINT white. SMELL very strong, garlic. FLESH thin, white in cap, ±brownish in stem. Usually in small groups. On dead leaves, other litter, buried plant debris. Late summer – autumn. Widespread. Uncommon. Inedible. SPORES ellipsoid, smooth, 7–10×6–8, non-amyloid.

Marasmius oreades Fairy Ring Mushroom. Colour, gills, habit. CAP 2–5, convex at first, then flattened – depressed, broadly umbonate, smooth, lined or grooved at margin. STEM 2–9, equal, slender, stiff, smooth. GILLS whitish then creamy buff, rather broad, distant, adnexed – free. SPORE PRINT white. SMELL mushroomy, creamy, woody. FLESH rather thin, tough, white-buff. In rings. On soil on lawns pastures and other grassy places. Spring – autumn. Widespread. Very common. Edible, good. SPORES ellipsoid, smooth, 7–10×4–6, non-amyloid.

Marasmius lupuletorum. Gills, habitat, spores. CAP 1–3.5, convex at first, then slightly flattened, umbonate, smooth, finely lined especially at margin, especially when moist. STEM 3–8, equal or tapering slightly downwards, slender, finely velvety (use hand-lens), rather woolly at base. GILLS creamy white, sometimes turning slightly reddish, broad, distant, adnexed – free. SPORE PRINT white. SMELL mushroomy, creamy, woody. FLESH thin, whitish in cap, reddish brown in stem. Usually in small groups. In leaf litter in beech woods. Summer-autumn. Widespread. Rare. Inedible. SPORES ellipsoid, smooth, 7.5–10×3.5–4.5, non-amyloid.

79

TRICHOLOMATACEAE

Marasmius calopus (=*Marasmiellus languidus*). Overall cap and stem features, stem colour, habitat. CAP 0.5–1.5, slightly convex at first, then flattened or very slightly depressed, finely wrinkled and lined, especially at margin. STEM 1–3, tapering downwards, slender,± smooth. GILLS white, broad, distant,±decurrent. SPORE PRINT white. SMELL indistinct. FLESH thin, whitish in cap, reddish brown in stem. Usually in small groups. On leaf litter, grass leaves and stems, other plant debris. Autumn. Widespread. Uncommon. Inedible. SPORES elongate-ellipsoid, smooth, 7–8.5× 3–4.5, non-amyloid.

Macrocystidia cucumis. Smell, spore print. CAP 1–6, convex, finely downy, edge usually paler, usually lined, esp. when wet. STEM 0.25–2, tapering downwards, slender, often slightly curved, velvety, especially at apex. GILLS whitish then often slightly pink, variable, narrow – broad, adnexed – free. SPORE PRINT creamy pink. SMELL unpleasant, cucumber or fishy. FLESH thin, whitish, dark in stem. Usually in trooping groups. On soil among grass and leaves, usually close to trees. Autumn. Widespread. Uncommon. Inedible. SPORES ellipsoid, smooth, 7–10 4–5, non-amyloid.

Mycena epipterygia. Similar to *M. viscosa* but stem features and overall colours differ. CAP 1–3, at first convex – dome-shaped, then slightly flattened, covered with peelable, sticky skin, lined especially towards margin. STEM 5–8, equal, rather slender, sticky. GILLS off-white or slightly pinkish, with peelable sticky edge, narrow, fairly distant,±decurrent. SPORE PRINT white – cream. SMELL faint, mild or slightly rancid. FLESH thin, white. In small,±trooping groups. On soil, among moss, on leaf litter, in woods, fields, at path edges. Autumn. Widespread. Common. Inedible. SPORES ellipsoid, smooth, 8–10×4.5, amyloid. Gill edge cystidia club-shaped with finger-like protrusions.

Mycena rorida. Cap surface, stem features. CAP 0.5–1.5, first convex – dome-shaped, then flattened, often with small umbo, lined at margin, becoming grooved when wet,±scurfy when dry, margin becoming finely toothed. STEM 1–2, equal, tough, with sticky sheath. GILLS white, narrow, fairly distant, adnate – ±decurrent. SPORE PRINT white – cream. SMELL indistinct. FLESH thin, white. In small ±trooping groups. On plant debris in woods. Late summer – autumn. Widespread. Uncommon. Inedible. SPORES ellipsoid, smooth, 9–12×3.5–5, amyloid. Gill edge cystidia cylindrical.

Marasmius (=*Marasmiellus*) *ramealis*. Habit, habitat, size. CAP 0.25–1.5, at first convex, then flattened – depressed, finely wrinkled and lined, especially at margin. STEM 0.25–2, equal or tapering very slightly downwards, slender, curved, finely roughened, especially at base. GILLS whitish – pale pinkish buff, rather narrow, distant,± adnate. SPORE PRINT white. SMELL indistinct. FLESH thin, whitish. In large groups. On dead twigs, herbaceous stems, especially bramble. Summer – autumn. Widespread. Very common. SPORES elongate-ellipsoid, smooth, 8.5–10×3–4.5, non-amyloid.

Mycena viscosa. Similar to *M. epipterygia* (q.v.). CAP 1–3, at first convex – dome-shaped, then slightly flattened, covered with peelable, sticky skin, reddish patches towards centre, lined esp. towards margin. STEM 5–8, equal, rather stout, sticky. GILLS pinkish or off-white, with peelable sticky edge, narrow, fairly distant, ±decurrent. SPORE PRINT white – cream. SMELL unpleasant, rancid. FLESH thin, white turning reddish. In small,±trooping groups. On conifer stumps or on needle litter in coniferous woods. Autumn. Widespread. Uncommon. Inedible. SPORES ellipsoid, smooth, 8–10×4.5, amyloid. Gill edge cystidia club-shaped with finger-like protrusions.

Mycena vulgaris. Cap features. CAP 0.5–1.5, convex, umbilicate, covered with peelable sticky skin, lined especially towards paler margin. STEM 3–4, equal, tough, sticky, rooting. GILL white then greyish, with peelable sticky edge, fairly narrow, fairly distant, adnate. SPORE PRINT white. SMELL faint, slightly rancid. FLESH thin, white. In small, ±trooping groups. On soil or among needle litter, in coniferous woods. Late summer – autumn. Widespread. Rare. Inedible. SPORES ellipsoid, smooth 7–10×4–4.5, amyloid. Gill edge cystidia branched with finger-like protrusions.

Mycena crocata. Juice colour and habitat. CAP 1–3, at first convex, then slightly flattened, umbonate, often stained reddish, lined at margin, smooth or silky. STEM 0.5–1, equal, slender, smooth, woolly below, orange juice when broken. GILLS white, stained orange, fairly distant, adnate – adnexed. SPORE PRINT white – pale buff. SMELL indistinct. FLESH thin, orange. In small,± trooping groups. On leaf litter and from buried twigs in broad-leaved woods esp. beech. Autumn. Mainly southern. Locally common. Inedible. SPORES ellipsoid smooth, 7–10×5–6, amyloid. Gill edge cystidia club – pear-shaped, warty

Mycena sanguinolenta. Juice, gill edge, cystidia. CAP 0.5–2, at first ± bell-shaped, then slightly flattened, umbonate, lined, smooth. STEM 0.5–1, equal, slender, smooth, woolly below, blood-red juice when broken. GILLS white – pinkish, dark red-brown edge, fairly distant, adnate. SPORE PRINT white. SMELL indistinct. FLESH thin, reddish. Usually in small, ± trooping groups. On soil, in grass, among litter in woods, lawns, pastures. Summer – autumn. Widespread. Very common. Inedible. SPORES ellipsoid, smooth, 8–10×4–5.5 amyloid. Gill edge cystidia spindle-shaped with sharp point.

Mycena galopus. Overall colour, juice colour, cystidia. CAP 1–2, at first ± bell-shaped, then flattened – ± depressed, lined, smooth. STEM 5–10, equal, slender, smooth, woolly below – ± rooting, white juice when broken. GILLS white – grey, finely downy (use hand-lens) fairly distant, adnate. SPORE PRINT white. SMELL indistinct. FLESH thin, white. Trooping. On soil and among leaf litter, in woods, on lawns, pastures, path edges. Summer – autumn. Widespread. Extremely common. Inedible. SPORES ellipsoid, smooth, 10–13×5–6, amyloid. Gill edge cystidia ± spindle-shaped.

Mycena leucogala (=*galopus* var. *nigra*). Overall colour, juice colour, habitat, cystidia. CAP 1–2, at first ± bell-shaped, then flattened and umbonate, markedly lined, smooth. STEM 5–10, equal, slender, smooth, woolly below, ± rooting, white juice when broken. GILLS grey, finely downy (use hand-lens) fairly distant, adnate. SPORE PRINT cream. SMELL indistinct. FLESH thin, white. Trooping. On soil and among leaf litter, in woods, heaths, path edges, often on fire sites. Autumn. Widespread. Uncommon. Inedible. SPORES ellipsoid, smooth, 10–13×5–6, amyloid. Gill edge cystidia ± spindle-shaped.

Mycena stylobates. Size, colour, habitat. CAP 0.5–1, at first convex, then ± flattened, lined, covered with tiny hairs (hand lens). STEM 2–2.5, equal, very slender, smooth above, more downy below, finely downy disc at base. GILLS white, crowded, narrow, free. SPORE PRINT white. FLESH very thin, white. Usually solitary. On leaves, twigs, dead grass stalks. Summer – autumn. Widespread. Common. Inedible. SPORES ellipsoid, smooth, 7–10×3.5–4, amyloid. Gill edge cystidia hair-shaped.

Mycena haematopus. Juice colour, gill edge, habit, cystidia. CAP 2–4, at first ± bell-shaped, then slightly flattened, sub-umbonate, lined, smooth. STEM 5–10, equal, slender, at first velvety then smooth, woolly below, blood-red juice when broken. GILLS white – grey or purplish, with dark red-brown edge, fairly distant, adnate. SPORE PRINT white. SMELL indistinct. FLESH thin, red. Tufted. On stumps of broad-leaved trees. Autumn. Widespread. Common. Inedible. SPORES ellipsoid, smooth, 7–10×5–6, amyloid. Gill edge cystidia flask-shaped with long neck.

Mycena galopus var. *candida.* Overall colour, juice colour, cystidia. CAP 1–2, at first ± bell-shaped, then flattened – ± depressed, lined, smooth. STEM 5–10, equal, slender, smooth, woolly below, ± rooting, white juice when broken. GILLS white, finely downy (use hand-lens) fairly distant, adnate. SPORE PRINT white. SMELL indistinct. FLESH thin, white. Trooping. On soil and among leaf litter, in woods, on lawns, pastures, path edges. Summer – autumn. Widespread. Extremely common. Inedible. SPORES ellipsoid, smooth, 10–13×5–6, amyloid. Gill edge cystidia ± spindle-shaped.

Mycena tenerrima. Size, colour. CAP 0.25–0.75, at first convex, then ± flattened, lined, covered with shining grains. STEM 1–2.5, equal, very slender, smooth above, more downy below, finely downy disc at base. GILLS white, crowded, adnexed – free. SPORE PRINT white. SMELL indistinct. FLESH very thin, white. In small or large groups. On bark of living or dead trees and woody debris. Late summer – autumn. Widespread. Uncommon. Inedible. SPORES subspherical – ellipsoid, smooth, 8–10×5–7, amyloid. Gill edge cystidia variable, club or flask-shaped with spike, warty. Basidia 2-spored.

Mycena longiseta. Size, colour, fragility. CAP 0.1–0.5, at first conic, then ± flattened, often with upturned margin, lined or ± grooved, covered with long hairs (hand-lens). STEM 1–3, equal, v. slender, fragile, smooth or finely downy, minutely bulbous. GILLS greyish, fairly distant, narrow, adnexed – free. SPORE PRINT white. SMELL indistinct. FLESH v. thin, white. Solitary or in small groups. On leaves, twigs, debris in broad-leaved (?) and coniferous woods. Summer – autumn. Widespread. Rare. Inedible. SPORES ellipsoid, smooth, 6–8×3–4, non-amyloid. Gill edge cystidia club-shaped – cylindrical with needle-like projection(s).

81

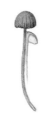

Mycena bulbosa. Size, cap form, habitat. CAP 0.25–0.75, convex, covered with peelable gelatinous skin, lined. STEM 0.5–1, equal, very slender, often curved, fragile, smooth or finely downy, with downy convex basal disc. GILLS white–greyish, crowded, adnexed – free. SPORE PRINT white. SMELL indistinct. FLESH very thin, white. Usually tufted. At and in base of rushes. Summer – autumn. Widespread. Uncommon. Inedible. SPORES ellipsoid, smooth, 8–10×3.5–4.5, non-amyloid. Gill edge cystidia club-shaped, often branched.

Mycena corticola. Size, habitat, spores. CAP 0.25–0.5, convex – almost spherical, later slightly flattened above, finely downy (use hand-lens), coarsely lined, very variable in colour. STEM 0.5–2, equal, very slender, often curved, finely downy (use hand-lens), later more smooth. GILLS greyish, distant, very broad, adnate – subdecurrent. SPORE PRINT white. SMELL indistinct. FLESH thin, variable (as cap colour). Usually in large groups. On bark of living or dead broad-leaved trees. Autumn. Widespread. Uncommon. Inedible. SPORES subspherical, smooth, 7–10×7.5–8, amyloid. Gill edge cystidia club-shaped, warty or with hair-like protrusions.

Mycena hiemalis. Size, habitat, spores. CAP 0.5–1.5, at first convex later ± flattened, often with small umbo, lined, margin ± wavy. STEM 1–3, equal, very slender, often curved, densely downy-velvety (use hand-lens), later smooth, often ± rooting. GILLS white, fairly distant, variable, narrow – broad, adnate. SPORE PRINT white. SMELL indistinct. FLESH thin, white, brown when moist. Usually in large groups. On moss-covered bark of living or dead broad-leaved trees. Autumn. Widespread. Uncommon. Inedible. SPORES ellipsoid, smooth, 8–9×5.5–6, non-amyloid. Gill edge cystidia cylindrical.

Mycena acicula. Size, overall form, colour. CAP 0.25–1, first convex, later ± flattened and with small umbo, lined, at first v. finely downy (hand-lens), then smooth. STEM 2–5, equal, v. slender, smooth above, downy at base, rooting. GILLS yellow, whitish edge, fairly broad, fairly distant, adnate – adnexed. SPORE PRINT white. SMELL indistinct. FLESH thin, white, red in cap. Usually solitary or in small groups. On wood, twigs, other woody debris. Summer – autumn. Common. Inedible. SPORES ± spindle-shaped, smooth, 9–12×3–4, non-amyloid. Gill edge cystidia small, cylindrical – spindle-shaped.

Mycena amicta. Form, cap and stem features. CAP 1–2, at first convex then slightly flattened and umbonate, lined, at first finely downy, then smooth, covered with peelable gelatinous skin. STEM 6–8, equal, very slender, finely downy, later more smooth, often ± rooting. GILLS grey, crowded, narrow, edge finely toothed. SPORE PRINT white – creamy. SMELL faint, indefinite. FLESH thin, brownish. Usually in groups, ± trooping. On soil in coniferous woods. Autumn. Widespread. Uncommon. Inedible. SPORES ellipsoid, smooth, 6–7×3.5–4, amyloid. Gill edge cystidia cylindrical or with taper to blunt tip.

Mycena speirea. Size, overall form, habitat, spores. CAP 0.25–1.5, at first convex later ± flattened, especially in centre, often with small umbo, lined, at first very finely downy (use hand-lens). STEM 2–2.5, equal, very slender, smooth above, densely downy at base. GILLS white, fairly crowded, variable, narrow – broad, adnexed – decurrent. SPORE PRINT white. SMELL indistinct. FLESH thin, off-white. Usually in large groups. On wood, twigs, woody plant debris. Autumn. Widespread. Uncommon. Inedible. SPORES subspherical – ellipsoid, smooth, 8–10×5–5.5, non-amyloid. Gill edge cystidia cylindrical. Basidia mostly 2-spored.

Mycena flavo-alba. Colour, habitat. CAP 1–2, at first convex – bell-shaped, later ± flattened and umbonate, lined, smooth. STEM 2–3, equal, slender, rather rigid, smooth above, downy at base. GILLS white, variable, narrow – broad, fairly distant, adnexed. SPORE PRINT pale yellow. SMELL indistinct, faintly radish-like. FLESH thin, white. Usually in small trooping groups. On soil among short grass on lawns. Summer – autumn. Widespread. Uncommon. Inedible. SPORES elongate-ellipsoid, smooth, 6–8×3.5–4, non-amyloid. Gill edge cystidia small, ± spindle-shaped.

Mycena pelianthina. Gill colour, habitat. CAP 2–4, at first more flattened and broadly umbonate, lined, especially when wet. STEM 5–6, equal, rather stout and fibrous. GILLS grey-violet with dark violet-brown edge, broad, distant, adnate – adnexed. SPORE PRINT white, faint, radish-like. FLESH thin, at first slightly violet then white. Usually in small trooping groups. On soil among leaf litter in broad-leaved woods, esp. (always ?) with beech. Summer – autumn. Mainly southern. Uncommon. Inedible. SPORES ellipsoid, smooth, 5–7×2.5–3, amyloid. Gill edge cystidia cylindrical or ± spindle-shaped.

82

Mycena pura. Like *M. pelianthina* and *Laccaria amethystina* but gills differ and colour v. variable. CAP 2–4, first convex, later more flattened or depressed, broadly umbonate, lined, colour often faded. STEM 5–10, equal, rather stout and rigid, smooth above, downy below. GILLS pale lilac, broad, distant, adnate. SPORE PRINT white. SMELL faint, radish-like. FLESH rather thick, white. Often in large trooping groups. On soil among leaf litter in broad-leaved woods, especially (always ?) with beech. Summer – late autumn. Widespread. Very common. Inedible. SPORES ellipsoid, smooth, 6–8×3.5–4, amyloid. Gill edge cystidia ±flask shaped.

Mycena capillaris. Colour, size and habitat. CAP 0.1–0.25, at first bell-shaped then convex, later more flattened, lined or grooved. STEM 2–4, equal, very slender, almost hair-like, finely velvety at apex, then smooth, downy at base. GILLS whitish, variable, broad – narrow, distant – sparse, ±free. SPORE PRINT white. SMELL indistinct. FLESH extremely thin, white. Solitary or trooping in small or large groups. On fallen beech leaves. Autumn. Widespread. Uncommon. Inedible. SPORES elongate-ellipsoid, smooth, 7.5–9×3–4, amyloid. Gill edge cystidia pear-shaped, warty.

Mycena aurantiomarginata. Gill colours, habitat, cystidia. CAP 1–2.5, at first convex, then more flattened, umbonate, grooved at margin. STEM 4–6.5, equal, slender, smooth, orange and hairy-bristly at base. GILLS greyish brown with reddish orange edges, narrow, crowded, adnexed. SPORE PRINT white. SMELL faint, indefinite. FLESH thin, greyish yellow. Usually trooping in small groups. On soil and needle litter with coniferous trees, especially spruce. Late summer – autumn. Widespread. Rare. Inedible. SPORES ellipsoid, smooth, 7–9×4–4.5, amyloid. Gill edge cystidia pear-shaped, very warty.

Mycena citrinomarginata. Colour, gill colour. CAP 1–2.5, at first conical then more flattened and ±umbonate, lined or grooved. STEM 5–6, equal, slender, smooth, hairy at base. GILLS white or yellowish, often with more yellow edge, fairly narrow, crowded, adnate. SPORE PRINT white. SMELL faint, radish-like. FLESH thin, white. Usually trooping in small groups. On soil, especially with conifers. Late summer – autumn. Widespread. Rare. Inedible. SPORES ellipsoid, smooth, 8–10×4.5–5, amyloid. Gill edge cystidia variable, club-shaped – spindle-shaped.

Mycena pearsoniana. Colour and habitat. CAP 1–2.5, at first convex, later flattened, at first lined at margin. STEM 3–6, equal or tapering slightly upwards, finely velvety at apex, then smooth, downy and with rooting fibrils at base. GILLS white with violet tinge, fairly broad, rather crowded, adnate with decurrent tooth. SPORE PRINT white. SMELL faint, radish-like. FLESH very thin, white or slightly lilac. Usually in small ±trooping groups. On needle litter with spruce (*Picea* spp.) Summer – autumn. Widespread. Rare. Inedible. SPORES broadly ellipsoid, smooth, 5–7×3.5–4.5, non-amyloid. Gill edge cystidia club-shaped or cylindrical.

Mycena rosella. Colour, size and habitat. CAP 0.5–1.5, at first conical, then convex, later more flattened, often with small umbo, lined. STEM 2–4, equal, very slender, ±smooth, downy at base. GILLS pale pink with darker pink edge, fairly distant, adnate – ±decurrent. SPORE PRINT white. SMELL faint, mild. FLESH thin, pink. Usually trooping in small or large groups. On fallen conifer needles. Autumn. Widespread. Rare. Inedible. SPORES ellipsoid, smooth, 8–10×4–5, amyloid. Gill edge cystidia elongate-ellipsoid – spindle-shaped, warty.

Mycena chlorantha. Colour, habitat. CAP 1–2.5, at first conical then more flattened and ±umbonate, lined or grooved. STEM 4–10, equal, slender, smooth and rather shiny, hairy at base. GILLS white or slightly greenish with darker edge, narrow, crowded, adnate. SPORE PRINT white. SMELL faint, iodine. FLESH thin, white. Usually trooping in small groups. On sandy soils, especially with conifers, dunes. Late summer – autumn. Widespread. Rare. Inedible. SPORES ellipsoid, smooth, 8–9×5–6, amyloid. Gill edge cystidia ±club-shaped, warty.

Mycena seynii. Habitat, spores. CAP 2–4, at first almost ellipsoid, then conical, later finely silky. STEM 5–9, equal, slender, smooth, hairy at base. GILLS white or faintly lilac, with darker and rather ragged edge, fairly narrow, distant, adnate. SPORE PRINT white. SMELL faint, pleasant, rather radish-like. FLESH thin, white. Solitary or in small groups. On pine cones. Autumn. Mainly southern. Rare. Inedible. SPORES elongate-ellipsoid, smooth, 12–13×6–8, amyloid. Gill edge cystidia club-shaped.

Mycena rubromarginata.
Habitat, spores, cystidia.
CAP 1–2, at first almost
ellipsoid then convex and
more flattened, lined, often
much paler when dry. STEM
2–4, equal, very slender,
smooth except sometimes
at extreme base. GILLS
whitish with red-brown
edge, fairly broad, rather
distant, adnate. SPORE PRINT
white. SMELL indistinct.
FLESH thin, white. Usually
in small groups. On conifer
twigs, especially among litter. Autumn. Widespread.
Uncommon. Inedible.
SPORES ellipsoid, smooth,
10–12×5–7, amyloid. Gill
edge cystidia narrowly
spindle-shaped – needle-
like.

Mycena pudica
(=*quisquiliaris*). Overall
form and size, habitat. CAP
0.1–1, convex or umbili-
cate, becoming grooved
with irregular margin, very
finely downy (use hand-
lens). STEM 0.5–3, equal,
extremely slender, fragile,
very finely downy (use
hand-lens), often minutely
bulbous. GILLS white, narrow, distant – sparse, edge
toothed (use hand-lens),
adnate. SPORE PRINT white.
SMELL ? FLESH extremely
thin, white. Usually in large
trooping groups. On dead
marsh plants, especially
Molinia caerulea. Autumn
– winter. Widespread. Un-
common. Inedible. SPORES
ellipsoid – subspindle-
shaped, smooth, 11–13×4–
6, amyloid. Gill edge cystidia variable, broadly
spindle-shaped, often
sharply pointed.

Mycena metata (=*phyllo-
gena*). Smell, habitat, cystidia. CAP 1–2, first conical or
bell-shaped, then more flattened, umbonate, lined.
STEM 5–8, equal, slender,
fragile, smooth but downy
at extreme base. GILLS
white or pinkish, narrow,
fairly distant, adnate. SPORE
PRINT white. SMELL strong,
iodine. FLESH white. Solitary or trooping. On soil and
among litter, woods or pastures near trees. Late
summer – autumn. Wide-
spread. Uncommon. Inedi-
ble. SPORES ellipsoid,
smooth, 7.5–10×4–5, amy-
loid. Gill edge cystidia
broadly spindle-shaped,
bristly-warty.

Mycena uracea. Smell,
stem base, habitat. CAP 1–3,
at first conical then more
flattened and usually umbonate, lined or grooved,
margin later upturned. STEM
2–3, equal, slender, smooth,
shiny, hairy at base, often
rooting. GILLS white or
greyish, then pinkish, narrow, distant, emarginate.
SPORE PRINT white. SMELL indistinct. FLESH white or
greyish, rather thick. Solitary or trooping. On fire
sites, soil, peat, on roots,
esp. heather. Late summer
– autumn. Widespread.
Rare, commoner in north.
Inedible. SPORES spherical –
broadly ellipsoid, smooth,
9–13×6–7, amyloid. Gill
edge cystidia broadly
spindle-shaped, warty.
Some 2-spored basidia with
larger spores.

Mycena oortiana. Smell,
habitat. CAP 1–5, first conical then more flattened and
±umbonate, lined or groo-
ved, margin later irregular.
STEM 2–4, equal, slender,
smooth, shiny, hairy at
base. GILLS white then
pinkish, rather narrow,
crowded, adnexed. SPORE
PRINT white. SMELL strong,
iodine. FLESH whitish, thin.
Usually in small groups. On
stumps and wood of broad-
leaved trees. Autumn.
Widespread. Uncommon.
Inedible. SPORES broadly
ellipsoid, smooth, 7–8×4.5
–5, amyloid. Gill edge cystidia broadly spindle-
shaped, warty.

Mycena galericulata. Size,
form, habitat, season. CAP
2–8, first conical then more
flattened, broadly umbon-
ate, smooth and lined when
wet, grooved when dry.
STEM 5–12, equal, often
flattened, slender, smooth
and shiny, coarsely hairy at
base, rooting. GILLS white
then pinkish, broad, fairly
distant, adnate, decurrent
tooth. SPORE PRINT creamy.
SMELL strong, rancid. FLESH
greyish, thin. Tufted. On
stumps and wood of broad-
leaved trees, esp. oak. All
year. Widespread. Very
common. Inedible. SPORES
ellipsoid, smooth, 9–12×6
–8, amyloid. Gill edge cystidia club-shaped with long
projections. Basidia usually
2-spored.

Mycena filopes
(=*amygdalina*). Size, ov
all form, habitat. CAP 1.5–
2.5, at first conical then
more flattened and broad
umbonate, smooth, lined
STEM 4–7.5, equal, very
slender, smooth, shiny,
hairy at base, ±rooting.
GILLS whitish grey, narro
crowded, adnate. SPORE
PRINT white. SMELL iodine
FLESH whitish, thin. Solit
ary or trooping. On soil
from buried twigs in mix
woods. Autumn. Wide-
spread. Uncommon. Ine
ble. SPORES ellipsoid,
smooth, 8–10×4.5–5.5,
amyloid. Gill edge cystic
subspherical with elonga
warts. Basidia usually 2-
spored.

Mycena maculata. Stem
form, gill colour, habitat
CAP 1–3, at first conical th
more flattened and
markedly umbonate,
smooth, lined, margin
upturned. STEM 2–7, equa
slender, smooth, shiny,
hairy-downy at base, fuse
below. GILLS grey with re
dish spotting, rather broa
fairly crowded, adnate w
decurrent tooth. SPORE
PRINT white. SMELL earth
FLESH whitish with reddis
spotting, thin. Tufted. O
stumps or other wood of
beech. Autumn. Wide-
spread. Rare. Inedible.
SPORES ellipsoid, smooth
7–11×4–5, amyloid. Gill
edge cystidia subspherica
with elongated finger-lik
projections.

ycena inclinata. Habit, bitat, 'skirt' on cap margin, smell. CAP 2–4, at first nical or subspherical, en convex, ±umbonate, nooth, lined when wet, ooved when dry, margin en irregular. STEM 6–10, ual, slender, finely silky, nsely downy at base, ± oting. GILLS white, then nkish, fairly broad and stant, adnate. SPORE PRINT nite. SMELL rancid. FLESH nitish, thin. Tufted. On umps or wood of broad-aved trees, esp. oak. ate summer – autumn. idespread. Common. Inedible. SPORES broadly ellsoid, smooth, 8–10×6–7, nyloid. Gill edge cystidia ub-shaped with thin, regular projections.

Mycena leptocephala (=*chlorinella*). Habitat, smell, cystidia. CAP 1.5–2, at first conical then convex or bell-shaped, smooth, atomate-matt, lined when wet, grooved when dry. STEM 2.5–5, equal, slender, smooth, shiny, downy-woolly at base, rooting. GILLS smoke grey, with pale edge when mature, fairly narrow, fairly distant, adnate. SPORE PRINT white. SMELL strong, ammonia. FLESH white – greyish, fairly thin. Usually trooping in small groups. On soil among grass or in woods. Autumn. Widespread. Very common. Inedible. SPORES ellipsoid, smooth, 6–10×4–7, amyloid. Gill edge cystidia flask-shaped, often with forked apex.

Mycena zephirus. Overall features, habitat. CAP 2–5, first conical then convex, umbonate, smooth, lined or grooved. STEM 3–8, equal, slender, smooth, minutely fibrous, downy at base. GILLS white, later stained reddish brown, broad, fairly crowded, adnate. SPORE PRINT white. SMELL indistinct. FLESH reddish brown, thin. Usually trooping in small groups. In conifer needle litter. Autumn. Widespread. Rare. Inedible. SPORES elongate-ellipsoid, smooth, 10–12×4–5, amyloid. Gill edge cystidia spindle- to club-shaped.

Mycena aetites. Smell, habitat. CAP 1–2, first conical or bell-shaped then more flattened, very broadly umbonate, smooth, markedly lined when wet, grooved when dry. STEM 3–5, equal, slender, downy at base. GILLS greyish, paler edge, fairly narrow, fairly distant, adnate with decurrent tooth. SPORE PRINT white. SMELL faint, ammonia. FLESH white – greyish, thin. Usually trooping in small groups. On soil in grass and plant debris. Autumn. Widespread. Uncommon. Inedible. SPORES ellipsoid, smooth, 9–10×5–6, amyloid. Gill edge cystidia spindle-shaped.

ycena vitilis. Habit, habit. CAP 0.5–1.5, at first nical then convex and nbonate, smooth, lined. EM 6–15, equal, very slener, smooth, shiny, arkedly straight, tough, ooting. GILLS whitish or ey, often with pale edge hen mature, fairly narw, fairly distant, adnate. ORE PRINT white. SMELL distinct. FLESH whitish, in. Usually trooping in nall groups. Among leaf tter, from buried twigs in road-leaved woods. utumn – spring. Widespread. Uncommon. Inedile. SPORES broadly ellip-oid, smooth, 9–12×5–7, myloid. Gill edge cystidia regularly club-shaped ith irregular projections.

Mycena fagetorum. Stem base, habitat. CAP 1–3, at first conical then convex and±umbonate, smooth, lined. STEM 3–8, equal, slender, smooth, shiny, hairy at base, rooting and usually markedly bent. GILLS white or brownish. fairly narrow, fairly distant, adnate with decurrent tooth, often rather detached from stem on a collar. SPORE PRINT white. SMELL faint, mealy. FLESH white – greyish, thin. Usually trooping in small groups. On beech leaves, usually one fruit body on each leaf. Autumn. Southern. Rare. Inedible. SPORES elongate-ellipsoid, smooth, 9–10×3–4.5, amyloid. Gill edge cystidia±club-shaped with sparse finger-like projections.

Mycena polygramma. Size, stem, habitat. CAP 2–5, first conical then more flattened, broadly umbonate, first with white bloom then smooth, lined or grooved. STEM 6–10, equal, slender, finely grooved often spirally, rigid, hairy at base, rooting. GILLS white, greyish or pinkish, fairly narrow and distant, adnexed. SPORE PRINT white. SMELL indefinite, pleasant. FLESH greyish, thin. Solitary or in small troops. On soil by stumps of broad-leaved trees. Late summer – autumn. Widespread. Uncommon. Inedible. SPORES ellipsoid, smooth, 9–10×6–7, amyloid. Gill edge cystidia irregular with many slender, often branched projections.

Mycena alcalina. Smell, habitat. CAP 2–3, first conical or bell-shaped then convex, umbonate, smooth, markedly lined when wet, grooved when dry. STEM 5–8, equal, slender, rigid, smooth, downy at base, ± rooting. GILLS grey-brown, paler edge, fairly broad, fairly distant, adnate. SPORE PRINT white. SMELL strong, ammonia. FLESH white, fairly thin. In small±tufted groups. On stumps, esp. of conifers. FLESH white, fairly thin. Widespread. Very common. Inedible. SPORES elongate-ellipsoid, smooth, 8–11×4.5–6, amyloid. Gill edge cystidia spindle-shaped.

85

TRICHOLOMATACEAE

Mycena (*=Hydropus*) *floccipes*. Colour, microscopic features. CAP 1–2, at first conical or bell-shaped then more flattened, convex and umbonate, smooth, lined, sometimes slightly grooved at margin. STEM 2–4, equal, slender, rather rigid, finely scaly, rooting. GILLS white, rather variable, fairly broad, fairly distant, adnexed – free. SPORE PRINT white. SMELL indistinct. FLESH white – greyish, fairly thin. In small,±tufted groups. On soil or woody debris, close to stumps of broad-leaved trees, especially of beech. Summer – autumn. Mainly southern. Uncommon. Inedible. SPORES broadly ellipsoid – subspherical, smooth, 5–6×4–5, non-amyloid. Gill edge cystidia±cylindrical.

Mycena lactea. Size, habitat, microscopic features. CAP 0.5–1.5, at first conical – bell-shaped then more flattened, smooth, lined when wet. STEM 3–7, equal, very slender, smooth but hairy at base. GILLS white, narrow, very crowded, adnate. SPORE PRINT white. SMELL indistinct. FLESH white, thin. Trooping. On plant debris, especially conifer twigs and needles. Summer – autumn. Widespread. Uncommon. Inedible. SPORES lanceolate, smooth, 9–11×3–4, non-amyloid. Gill edge cystidia small, irregularly hair-like. Basidia usually 2-spored.

Mycena (*=Rickenella =Omphalina =Omphalia =Gerronema*) *fibula*. Colour, habitat. CAP 0.5–2, at first convex or bell-shaped, then more flattened, umbilicate or ±funnel-shaped, finely downy (use hand-lens), lined when wet. STEM 3–4, equal, slender, finely downy (use hand-lens). GILLS white or yellowish, broad, distant, deeply decurrent. SPORE PRINT white. SMELL earthy. FLESH orange, thin. Trooping. On soil among short grass and moss, on lawns. Summer – autumn. Widespread. Very common. Inedible. SPORES elongate-ellipsoid, smooth, 4–5×2–2.5, non-amyloid. Gill edge cystidia flask-shaped with long neck.

Mycena (*=Delicatula*) *integrella*. Size, colour, gills. CAP 0.5–1.25, at first convex, then more flattened, often with upturned margin, smooth, lined. STEM 1–2, equal, fairly stout, finely downy (use hand-lens), hairy at base, slightly curved, bulbous. GILLS white, very narrow row, distant – sparse, reduced to irregular branched ridges,±adnate. SPORE PRINT white. SMELL indistinct. FLESH whitish, very thin. Trooping. On plant debris, especially rotting wood. Summer – autumn. Widespread. Rare. Inedible. SPORES broadly ellipsoid, smooth, 7.5–8×4–5, amyloid. Gill edge cystidia absent. Basidia 2-spored?

Mycena tortuosa. Size, habitat, microscopic features. CAP 0.1–0.75, at first convex or slightly conical, then more flattened, very finely downy (use hand-lens) and holding water droplets, lined when wet. STEM 0.1–2.5, equal or tapering slightly upwards or downwards, variable, slender or fairly stout, sometimes±eccentric, very finely downy (use hand-lens) and holding water droplets. GILLS white, narrow, crowded, variable, adnate with tooth – free. SPORE PRINT white. SMELL indistinct. FLESH white, very thin. Trooping. On plant debris, especially of alder, in damp places. Spring – autumn. Widespread. Uncommon. Inedible. SPORES spindle-shaped – lanceolate, smooth, 7–11×2.5–3.5, non-amyloid. Gill edge cystidia±spindle-shaped, curled, with sharp point. Some basidia 2-spored.

Mycena (*=Hemimycena*) *delectabilis*. Size, habitat, smell. CAP 0.5–1, convex – bell-shaped with very tiny papilla, smooth, lined or grooved. STEM 1–2, equal or tapering slightly downwards, slender, usually slightly curved, smooth but finely downy at base. GILLS white, fairly broad, fairly distant, decurrent. SPORE PRINT white. SMELL strong, unpleasant, acrid. FLESH white, extremely thin. Trooping. On plant debris, especially conifer twigs. Summer – autumn. Widespread. Rare. Inedible. SPORES broadly ellipsoid, smooth, 6–7×3–4, non-amyloid. Gill edge cystidia variable,±spindle-shaped – almost hair-like.

Mycena swartzii (*=Mycena* (*Rickenella*) *setipes*). Very similar to *M. fibula* but colour differs. CAP 0.5–2, at first convex or bell-shaped, then more flattened, usually markedly umbilicate or±funnel-shaped, lined when wet. STEM 3–6, equal, slender, finely downy (use hand-lens). GILLS whitish, broad, distant, deeply decurrent. SPORE PRINT white. SMELL indistinct. FLESH creamy, thin. Trooping. On soil among short grass and moss, on lawns. Summer – autumn. Widespread. Common. Inedible. SPORES elongate- ellipsoid, smooth, 4–5×2–2.5, non-amyloid. Gill edge cystidia club – skittle-shaped.

Crinipellis stipitarius. Size, cap and stem features. CAP 0.5–1.25, at first convex, but soon markedly flattened with small papilla, concentrically scaly or finely fibrous, usually grooved at margin. STEM 2–5, equal, slender, grooved, covered with dark, shaggy hairs. GILLS white, fairly broad, fairly distant, adnexed – sinuate. SPORE PRINT white. SMELL? FLESH brownish. Trooping. On plant debris, especially rotting wood, on soil among grass. Summer – autumn. Widespread. Rare. Inedible. SPORES broadly ellipsoid, smooth, 6–9×4–8, non-amyloid.

Myxomphalia maura. Colour, cap features, habitat. CAP 1–3, at first convex, but soon more flattened and umbilicate – depressed, smooth and rather shiny with removable 'skin', markedly paler when dry. STEM 2–4, equal, fairly stout, smooth, tough. GILLS white – greyish, fairly crowded, adnate – decurrent. SPORE PRINT white. SMELL faint, rather sweet. FLESH white – greyish. Usually in very large groups, trooping. On soil of fire sites, usually in coniferous woods. Autumn. Widespread. Uncommon. Inedible. SPORES broadly ellipsoid, smooth, 4.5–6×3.5–4, amyloid.

Baeospora myosura. Habitat, spore size, similar to *Pseudohiatula* spp. but spores differ. CAP 1–2, at first convex, then more flattened, smooth. STEM 2–6, equal, slender, often slightly wavy, fairly tough, finely velvety with hairy rooting base. GILLS white, very narrow, very crowded, adnate – adnexed. SPORE PRINT white. SMELL earthy. FLESH yellow-brownish. Usually in small groups. Among coniferous debris from buried cones. Autumn – winter. Widespread. Rare. Inedible. SPORES ellipsoid, smooth, 3–3.5×1.5–2, amyloid.

Hygrophoropsis pallida **Pale False Chanterelle.** Very similar to *H. auran-tiaca* but paler, usually considered a var. in Britain. CAP 2–7, at first slightly convex, then umbilicate-depressed – funnel-shaped, very finely downy, margin usually incurved. STEM 2–5, equal, fairly stout, usually curved. GILLS cream-white, narrow, crowded, slightly forked, deeply decurrent. SPORE PRINT white. SMELL earthy. FLESH creamy. Usually in small trooping groups. On soil, usually with conifers in woods and on heaths. Summer – winter. Widespread. Rare. Inedible. SPORES broadly ellipsoid, smooth, 5–7×3.5–5, non-amyloid.

Pleurotellus (=*Pleurocybella*) *por-rigens.* Lack of colour, habitat. CAP 2–10, ±tongue-shaped, becoming increasingly lobed, finely fibrous and shiny but smooth at margin. STEM absent. GILLS white, narrow, very crowded, decurrent into base. SPORE PRINT white. SMELL? FLESH white, thin. Usually in tightly overlapping groups or tufted. On conifer wood, usually rotten. Autumn. Predominantly northern. Common. Inedible. SPORES subspherical, smooth, 6–7×5–6, non-amyloid.

Xeromphalina campanella. Cap features, habitat. CAP 0.5–2, at first convex, but then more flattened and±umbilicate, lined or grooved. STEM 2–5, equal with slightly swollen base, smooth, often hairy at base. GILLS yellowish, inter-connecting, fairly distant, adnate – decurrent. SPORE PRINT white. SMELL? FLESH yellowish. Usually in small groups,±trooping. On rot-ting coniferous wood. Autumn. Widespread. Uncommon. Inedible. SPORES ellipsoid, smooth, 6–7.5×3–4, amyloid.

Hygrophoropsis aurantiaca **False Chanterelle.** Colour, cap, gills, sometimes con-fused with *Cantharellus cibarius* but gills very diffe-rent. CAP 2–7, at first slightly convex, then umbilicate-depressed – funnel-shaped, very finely downy, margin usually incurved. CAP 2–5, equal, fairly stout, usually curved. GILLS orange, narrow, crowded, slightly forked, deeply decurrent. SPORE PRINT white. SMELL earthy. FLESH yellow. Usually in small trooping groups. On soil, usually with conifers in woods and on heaths. Summer – winter. Wide-spread. Very common. Inedible. SPORES broadly ellipsoid, smooth, 5–7×3.5–5, non-amyloid.

Pleurotellus acerosus. Habit, size. CAP 1–3,± kidney-shaped, lobed and downy at margin, finely fibrous. STEM 0.5–1, equal, stout, lateral, covered with fine scales. GILLS greyish, narrow, fairly distant, adnate – decurrent. SPORE PRINT white. SMELL? FLESH greyish, fairly thin. Usually in small±overlapping groups. On soil among rot-ting plant debris or on rot-ting wood. Summer – winter. Widespread. Uncommon. Inedible. SPORES broadly ellipsoid – pip-shaped, smooth, 7–8×3–4, non-amyloid.

Rhodocybe popinalis. Spore print, habitat. CAP 2–5, at first convex, then flattened and broadly umbonate, smooth at first, then often with concentric cracks, margin usually incurved. STEM 1.5–3, equal, often curved, fairly stout, finely downy. GILLS grey, fairly crowded, decur-rent. SPORE PRINT pink. SMELL mealy. FLESH greyish. Solitary or in small groups. On bare soil or sand, fields, dunes. Late summer – autumn. Wide-spread. Uncommon. Inedi-ble. SPORES subspherical – ellipsoid, finely warty, 4.5–5.5×4–4.5, non-amyloid.

TRICHOLOMATACEAE

Rhodocybe truncata. Spore print, habitat, spores. CAP 4–8, convex, becoming slightly flattened, smooth and very finely scaly, margin usually incurved. STEM 3–5, equal or tapering slightly downwards, stout, finely fibrous below, mealy towards apex. GILLS grey-brownish, narrow, crowded, emarginate – decurrent. SPORE PRINT pinkish buff. SMELL indefinite, slightly sweet. FLESH white. Usually in small groups, trooping. On soil, especially among grass, in coniferous woods. Autumn. Widespread. Rare. Inedible. SPORES subspherical – ellipsoid, irregularly angular, 5.5–6×4–4.5, non-amyloid.

Clitopilus hobsonii. Habitat, gill and spore print colour, spores. CAP 0.5–2, at first convex, then more flattened, rounded or slightly kidney-shaped, finely silky, becoming smoother on aging, margin usually incurved. STEM usually absent, rarely 0.5–1.5, lateral, stout, densely downy. GILLS whitish, very slowly turning dirty cream or pinkish, fairly broad, crowded, meeting at an eccentric point. SPORE PRINT pink. SMELL mealy. FLESH white, thin. In small, ± overlapping groups. On stumps, twigs and other woody and herbaceous plant debris. Autumn – late winter. Widespread, predominantly southern. Uncommon. Inedible. SPORES ellipsoid, longitudinally ribbed, 6–10×4–5.5, non-amyloid.

Flammulina velutipes **Velvet Shank.** Cap and stem features, season. CAP 2–8, at first convex, then more flattened, smooth, shiny, slimy. STEM 4–10, equal, usually curved, very tough, finely velvety below, smoother above. GILLS whitish, turning dirty yellow, fairly broad, crowded, adnexed. SPORE PRINT white. SMELL indefinite, pleasant. FLESH yellowish, thin. Tufted. On dead and dying wood of broad-leaved trees. Autumn – spring. Widespread. Common. Edible. SPORES ellipsoid, smooth, 7.5–10×3.5–4, non-amyloid.

Clitopilus prunulus **The Miller.** Cap features, spore print, spores. CAP 3–10, at first convex, then depressed and markedly wavy, dry, rather shiny, with texture of chamois leather. STEM 2–4, equal or tapering slightly upwards, often rather eccentric, fairly slender, finely downy, more downy at base. GILLS whitish, slowly turning pinkish, fairly broad, crowded, decurrent. SPORE PRINT pink. SMELL mealy. FLESH white. Usually in small trooping groups. On soil among grass, often close to trees. Summer – autumn. Widespread. Very common. Edible, good. SPORES ellipsoid, longitudinally ribbed, 8–13×5–7, non-amyloid.

HYGROPHORACEAE

HYGROPHORACEAE

Toadstool-shaped, caps often sharply conical, often brightly coloured (yellow, orange, red, green), with gills distant, usually thick and waxy, free to decurrent, variously coloured, spores ellipsoid, smooth, usually non-amyloid, spore print white, cap surface slimy, sticky or dry. Typically among grass (*Camarophyllus*, *Hygrocybe*) but some (*Hygrophorus*) with trees and probably mycorrhizal. Saprotrophic. Many edible, few good, none poisonous. *Hygrophorus* [26], *Camarophyllus* [14], *Hygrocybe* [49].

Hygrophorus chrysodon. Cap features. CAP 4–8, at first convex, then flattened, sticky, margin usually incurved with small, ± woolly scales. STEM 5–7, equal or tapering slightly upwards, with small rather woolly scales, especially towards apex. GILLS white – yellowish, fairly broad, fairly distant, adnate – decurrent. SPORE PRINT white. SMELL earthy. FLESH white often with reddish tinge. Usually in small groups, ± trooping. On soil in broad-leaved woods, especially with oak and beech. Autumn. Widespread. Rare. Edible. SPORES ellipsoid, smooth, 6.5–9×4–5, non-amyloid.

Hygrophorus karstenii. G colours, habitat. CAP 2–6.5 at first convex, then flattened, barely sticky. STEM 3–5, equal or more usually tapering slightly downwards, smooth, darkening with age. GILLS ochreorange, fairly broad, fairly distant, decurrent. SPORE PRINT white. SMELL indistinct. FLESH white. Usually in small groups, ± trooping On soil in coniferous or beech woods. Late summer – autumn. Widespread, predominantly northern and/or montane. Rare. Inedible. SPORES ellipsoid smooth, 8–10×5–7, non-amyloid.

Hygrophorus eburneus **Ivory Wax Cap.** Colour, cap features. CAP 4–9, at first convex, then flattened very slimy. STEM 4–8, equal or more usually tapering slightly downwards, especially towards base, slimy with small mealy granules towards apex. GILLS white fairly broad, fairly distant decurrent. SPORE PRINT white. SMELL faint, pleasant. FLESH white. Usually in small groups, ± trooping or in rings. On soil in broad-leaved woods, especially with oak and beech. Late summer – autumn. Widespread. Uncommon Inedible. SPORES ellipsoid, smooth, 6–9×4–5, non-amyloid.

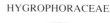

Hygrophorus cossus **Goat Moth Wax Cap.** Colour, smell, cap features. CAP 4–8, at first convex, then flattened, very slimy. STEM 4–8, equal or more usually tapering slightly downwards, especially towards base, slimy with small mealy granules towards apex. GILLS white, fairly broad, fairly distant, decurrent. SPORE PRINT white. SMELL unpleasant, goat-like. FLESH white. Usually in small groups,±trooping or in rings. On soil in broad-leaved woods, especially with beech on chalky sites. Autumn. Widespread. Rare. Inedible. SPORES ellipsoid, smooth, 9–9×4–5, non-amyloid.

Hygrophorus erubescens **Blushing Wax Cap.** Colour and colour change, habitat. CAP 5–10, at first convex, then flattened or slightly depressed, covered with very small pinkish scales or fibres, sticky when wet. STEM 6–10, tapering slightly downwards, with small mealy granules towards apex, turning yellowish when bruised. GILLS white, then usually increasingly pinkish, fairly broad, fairly distant, decurrent. SPORE PRINT white. SMELL unpleasant? FLESH white, turning yellowish. Usually in small groups,±trooping or in rings. On soil in coniferous woods. Late summer – autumn. Widespread, predominantly northern. Rare. Inedible. SPORES ellipsoid, smooth, 6–10×5–6, non-amyloid.

Hygrophorus leucophaeus. Cap features. CAP 2–5, at first convex, then flattened and umbonate or slightly depressed, finely silky towards margin, slightly sticky. STEM 3–7, tapering slightly downwards, fairly slender,±fibrous. GILLS white – yellow brown, fairly narrow, fairly distant, decurrent. SPORE PRINT white. SMELL indistinct. FLESH whitish, thick. Usually in small groups,± trooping. On soil in broad-leaved woods, especially with beech. Autumn. Widespread. Rare. Edible. SPORES ellipsoid, smooth, 6–8×4–5, non-amyloid.

Hygrophorus discoideus. Stem features, habitat. CAP 3–6, at first convex, then slightly flattened, sticky. STEM 3.5–5, tapering downwards – club-shaped, sticky, with marked superior sticky ring-like zone. GILLS at first white, then yellowish, fairly broad, distant, decurrent. SPORE PRINT white. SMELL indistinct. FLESH white. Usually in small groups,±trooping. On soil in coniferous and broad-leaved woods. Autumn. Widespread. Rare. Edible. SPORES ellipsoid, smooth, 6–9×3–5, non-amyloid.

Hygrophorus chrysaspis. Colour and colour change, smell. CAP 3–7, at first convex, then flattened, very slimy, soon turning yellowing brown. STEM 4–7, tapering downwards, especially towards base, slimy with small mealy granules towards apex, soon turning yellowish brown. GILLS white, becoming brownish when±black when dry, fairly broad, fairly distant, decurrent. SPORE PRINT white. SMELL strong, unpleasant, rather acrid. FLESH white, turning yellow or brownish. Usually in small groups,±trooping or in rings. On soil in broad-leaved woods, especially with beech on chalky sites. Autumn. Widespread. Common. Inedible. SPORES ellipsoid, smooth, 6–9×4–5, non-amyloid.

Hygrophorus russula. Colour and colour change, habitat. CAP 8–15, at first convex, then flattened or slightly depressed,±covered with very small pinkish scales or fibres, darker towards centre, sticky. STEM 5–9, tapering slightly downwards, stout, with small mealy granules towards apex, turning reddish when bruised. GILLS white, then usually increasingly spotted pinkish, fairly broad, fairly crowded, sinuate – emarginate. SPORE PRINT white. SMELL? FLESH white, turning reddish, very thick. Solitary or more usually in small groups,±trooping. On soil in broad-leaved woods. Late summer – autumn. Widespread. Rare. Edible. SPORES ellipsoid, smooth, 6–8×4–6, non-amyloid.

Hygrophorus arbustivus. Colour, cap features. CAP 3–8, at first convex, then flattened – umbonate, finely silky, woolly-hairy at margin, slightly sticky. STEM 5–8, tapering slightly downwards, sticky, with small mealy granules towards apex. GILLS white – creamy, fairly narrow, fairly distant,±decurrent. SPORE PRINT white. SMELL faint, pleasant. FLESH whitish, thick. Usually in small groups,±trooping. On soil in broad-leaved woods, especially with oaks. Autumn. Widespread. Rare. Inedible. SPORES ellipsoid, smooth, 6–9×5–6, non-amyloid.

Hygrophorus hypothejus **Winter Wax Cap, Herald of the Winter.** Stem features, season, habitat. CAP 3–7, at first convex, then flattened – depressed, very finely fibrous, slimy-sticky. STEM 4–8, tapering slightly downwards, slimy-sticky below superior ring-like swelling. GILLS yellow, darkening with age, fairly broad, fairly distant, decurrent. SPORE PRINT white. SMELL indistinct. FLESH whitish – yellowish, bruising yellow-orange. Usually in small groups,±trooping. On soil in coniferous woods. Late autumn, usually after first frost. Widespread. Common. Edible. SPORES ellipsoid, smooth, 7–10×4–5, non-amyloid.

HYGROPHORACEAE

Hygrophorus dichrous.
Chemical test, stem features, habitat. CAP 4–8, at first convex, then flattened, umbonate, sticky. STEM 8–11, equal, slender, sticky, irregularly concentric ring patterning. GILLS white, often faint green-blue flush, fairly broad, distant, decurrent. SPORE PRINT white. SMELL indistinct. FLESH white. Green with ammonia. Usually in small groups, ±trooping. On soil in broad-leaved woods. Autumn. Widespread. Rare. Inedible. SPORES ellipsoid, smooth, 9–13×5–7.5, non-amyloid.

Hygrophorus mesotephrus.
Cap and stem features. CAP 2–5, at first convex then more flattened, sometimes ±umbonate, very slimy-sticky, often lined at margin when mature. STEM 5–11, equal or tapering very slightly downwards, sticky, with small mealy granules towards apex. GILLS white, fairly broad, fairly distant, adnate – decurrent. SPORE PRINT white. SMELL? FLESH white, fairly thick. Usually in small groups, trooping. On soil in broad-leaved woods. Autumn. Widespread. Rare. Inedible. SPORES ellipsoid, smooth, 9–11×6–8, non-amyloid.

Hygrophorus pustulatus.
Stem features, size, habitat. CAP 2–6, at first convex, then flattened-slightly depressed, dry. STEM 2.5–5, equal, fairly slender, with small, irregular brown-black tufts. GILLS white, broad, distant, decurrent. SPORE PRINT white. SMELL indistinct. FLESH white. Usually in small groups, ± trooping. On soil in coniferous woods. Autumn. Predominantly northern. Rare. Edible. SPORES ellipsoid, smooth, 7–10×4.5–5.5, non-amyloid.

Hygrophorus camarophyllus. Overall colour, cap features, habitat. CAP 4–12, at first convex – conic then more flattened or umbonate – depressed, margin often incurved an wavy, smooth, dry, markedly fibrous. STEM 3–12, stout, equal or tapering downwards, finely lined. GILLS white, turning blue-grey, broad, fairly distant decurrent. SPORE PRINT white. SMELL pleasant. FLESH white. Usually in small groups, trooping. On soil, among litter and mos in coniferous woods. Autumn. Predominantly northern and montane. Rare. Edible. SPORES ellipsoid, smooth, 8–9×4–5, non-amyloid.

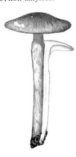

Hygrophorus olivaceo-albus. Stem features, habitat, spores. CAP 2–6, at first convex – conic, then flattened, umbonate – umbilicate, very slimy-sticky, often lined at margin when mature. STEM 5–10, equal or tapering very slightly downwards, ± woolly-scaly in irregular bands and slimy below superior ring-like swelling. GILLS white, fairly broad, distant, decurrent. SPORE PRINT white. SMELL faint, pleasant. FLESH white, fairly thick. Usually in small groups, ±trooping. On soil in coniferous woods. Late summer – autumn. Widespread, predominantly northern. Rare. Edible. SPORES ellipsoid, smooth, 12.5–15.5×7–8.5, non-amyloid.

Hygrophorus agathosmus.
Smell, habitat. CAP 4–8, at first convex – conic then more flattened, sometimes ±broadly umbonate, sticky, often with whitish granules, especially towards centre. STEM 5–10, rather stout, equal, finely lined, with small mealy granules towards apex. GILLS white, fairly broad, fairly distant, decurrent. SPORE PRINT white. SMELL sweet, bitter almonds. FLESH white, soft and watery. Usually in small groups, trooping. On soil in coniferous woods. Autumn. Widespread. Rare. Inedible. SPORES ellipsoid, smooth, 8–11×5–6, non-amyloid.

Hygrophorus marzuolus.
Season, habitat. CAP 4–10, at first convex – conic then more flattened, often rather wavy at margin, darkening on maturing, smooth, dry, finely fibrous. STEM 5–8, stout, tapering upwards, ±bulbous, finely lined. GILLS white, turning grey, broad, fairly distant, ±decurrent. SPORE PRINT white. SMELL pleasant, sweet. FLESH white, firm, thick. Usually in small groups, trooping. On soil, among litter or moss, in coniferous and broad-leaved woods. Winter – early spring. Predominantly southern and montane, not Britain. Edible, good. SPORES ellipsoid, smooth, 7–9×4–5, non-amyloid.

Camarophyllus russocoriaceus. Overall colour and form, smell. CAP 0.75–2, a first convex then slightly flattened, very slightly sticky, smooth, lined. STE 2–3.5, slender, equal or tapering slightly downwards, often rather wavy smooth. GILLS white, broad, distant, decurrent. SPORE PRINT white. SMELL pleasant, cedar wood. FLESH white or yellowish, rather thick. Usually in groups, ±trooping. On so often acidic, among short grass. Autumn. Uncommon. Inec ble. SPORES ellipsoid, smooth, 7.5–9×4–5, non-amyloid.

90

amarophyllus niveus
1owy Wax Cap. Overall
>lour and form, spores.
\P 1–3, at first convex then
attened and±depressed,
nooth, lined, especially
ery slightly greasy,
nooth, lined, especially
hen moist. STEM 2.5–4,
ender, tapering slightly
>wnwards, sometimes
ightly wavy, smooth.
LLS white, broad, distant,
:current. SPORE PRINT
hite. SMELL faint, inde-
nite. FLESH white, fairly
ick. Usually in groups,±
>oping. On soil, often aci-
c, in grass, meadows,
>en areas in woods. Aut-
nn. Widespread. Com-
on. Edible. SPORES ellips-
d, smooth, 7–9×4–5.5
orms with 4-spored basid-
) or10–12×5–6 (forms
ith 2-spored basidia),
>n-amyloid.

amarophyllus lacmus.
ill colour, stem base col-
1r. CAP 2–4, at first convex
en flattened and±broadly
nbonate – depressed,
th upturned margin,
1ooth but lined when
0ist. STEM 3–4, equal or
ghtly spindle-shaped,
1ooth. GILLS lilac-grey,
1rly narrow, distant, with
terconnecting veins,
:current. SPORE PRINT
nite. SMELL? FLESH
nite – greyish, yellow
1ged at stem base.
sually in groups,±troop-
3. On soil, among short
1ass, meadows, heaths,
1stures. Autumn. Wide-
read. Uncommon. Edi-
e. SPORES subspherical,
1ooth, 6–6.5×5–5.5, non-
1yloid.

Camarophyllus pratensis.
Overall colour and form.
CAP 3–7, at first convex then
flattened and broadly
umbonate, smooth but very
finely cracked or crazed
when dry. STEM 2–5, often
fairly stout, tapering downwards, smooth. GILLS
yellowish – straw-
coloured, broad, distant,
deeply decurrent. SPORE
PRINT white. SMELL earthy.
FLESH ochre, fairly thick.
Usually in groups,±troop-
ing. On soil, among grass,
meadows, pastures. Aut-
umn. Widespread. Com-
mon. Edible. SPORES ellipsoid – subspherical,
smooth, 5–6×4–5.5, non-
amyloid.

Camarophyllus virgineus.
Overall colour and form,
very similar to *C. niveus*
but spores and cap spotting
differ. CAP 2–6, at first convex then flattened and
often±broadly umbonate,
smooth, lined, especially
when moist, often with reddish spotting caused by
Fusarium sporotrichoides.
STEM 3–7, slender, equal or
tapering slightly down-
wards, smooth. GILLS
white, broad, distant,
decurrent. SPORE PRINT
white. SMELL indistinct.
FLESH white, fairly thick.
Usually in groups,±troop-
ing. On soil, often acidic,
among grass, meadows,
open areas in woods. Aut-
umn. Widespread. Uncom-
mon. Edible. SPORES ellipsoid, smooth, 9–12×5–6,
non-amyloid.

Camarophyllus cinereus.
Overall colour. CAP 2–5, at
first dome-shaped then convex and broadly umbonate,
smooth but usually lined at
margin on aging. STEM 4–6,
fairly stout, tapering
slightly downwards, often
rather wavy, smooth. GILLS
grey, fairly narrow, distant,
deeply decurrent. SPORE
PRINT white. SMELL? FLESH
greyish. Usually in groups,
trooping. On soil, among
short grass, meadows,
heaths, pastures. Autumn.
Widespread. Rare. Edible?
SPORES subspherical,
smooth, 7–9×4.5–6, non-
amyloid.

Hygrocybe ovina. Colour
change, smell. CAP 2–8, at
first convex then more
flattened or slightly
depressed, finely silky-
scaly, bruising red. STEM
5–8, fairly slender, equal or
tapering slightly upwards,
often rather wavy and compressed, bruising red. GILLS
brownish, bruising red,
broad, distant, emarginate.
SPORE PRINT white. SMELL
strong, ammonia but some-
times apparently absent.
FLESH brownish grey, red-
dening. Sometimes solitary
but usually in small groups,
trooping. On soil among
grass, meadows, heaths,
pastures. Late summer –
autumn. Rare. Inedible.
SPORES elongaated ellip-
soid, smooth, 7–12×4.5–6,
non-amyloid.

Hygrocybe nitrata. Smell.
CAP 2–4, first convex then
more flattened, often wavy
at margin, generally irregular, first slightly sticky and
shiny, soon becoming finely
silky-scaly, fragile. STEM
2–10, fairly stout, equal but
usually tapering sharply at
base, often twisted to
compressed. GILLS whitish,
staining reddish brown,
broad, distant, with interconnecting veins,
emarginate – free. SPORE
PRINT white. SMELL strong,
unpleasant, bleaching powder. FLESH whitish. Usually
in groups, trooping. On soil
in grass, meadows, heaths,
pastures. Late summer –
autumn. Widespread.
Rare. Inedible. SPORES ellipsoid, smooth, 7–10×4.5–
5.5, non-amyloid.

Hygrocybe metapodia. Colour change, spores. CAP 4.5
–12, first convex then more
flattened, sticky and shiny,
soon finely silky-scaly,
slowly turning reddish
when handled. STEM 6–9,
stout, equal or tapering
slightly downwards, finely
lined, slowly turning reddish. GILLS white – grey,
darkening on aging, some-
times slightly reddish,
broad, fairly distant,
adnate – emarginate, often
with decurrent tooth. SPORE
PRINT white. SMELL mealy.
FLESH greyish, slowly turning reddish, then black. Usually in groups, trooping.
On soil, often acidic, in
short grass, heath, pasture.
Autumn. Widespread.
Rare. Inedible. SPORES
elongate-ellipsoid, smooth,
6–8×3–3.5, amyloid.

HYGROPHORACEAE

Hygrocybe psittacina **Parrot Toadstool.** Cap colour and persistent green at stem apex. CAP 1.5–4, at first ±bell-shaped then more flattened and broadly umbonate, covered when young with greenish jelly-like glue causing marked and irregular changes in colouration. STEM 2–4, fairly slender, equal, slimy, smooth. GILLS yellowish green, broad, fairly distant, adnate. SPORE PRINT white. SMELL earthy. FLESH white with green and yellow patches. Usually in small groups, trooping. On soil among grass, meadows, heaths, pastures. Late summer – autumn. Common. Inedible. SPORES ellipsoid, smooth, 7–10×4–6, non-amyloid.

Hygrocybe unguinosa. Overall colour, persistent stickiness. CAP 2–3, at first convex – bell-shaped then flattened and very broadly umbonate, very sticky and shiny, lined towards margin. STEM 4–6, often fairly stout, equal or tapering slightly downwards, rather wavy and often±flattened, slimy, smooth. GILLS whitish grey, broad, distant with interconnecting veins, adnate, usually with decurrent tooth. SPORE PRINT white. SMELL indistinct. FLESH greyish. Usually in small groups, trooping. On soil among grass, meadows, heaths, pastures. Autumn. Widespread. Uncommon. Inedible. SPORES broadly ellipsoid, smooth, 6–8.5×4–5.5, non-amyloid.

Hygrocybe ceracea. Overall colour, cap and stem features. CAP 1–3, convex, flattening slightly, dry or slightly greasy, lined towards margin. STEM 2.5–5, slender, equal or tapering towards base, often slightly wavy, dry, smooth, sometimes finely downy at base. GILLS pale yellow, darkening to egg-yellow, broad, fairly distant with interconnecting veins, adnate – decurrent. SPORE PRINT white. SMELL? FLESH yellow, thin. Usually in small groups, trooping. On soil among short grass, pastures, lawns. Autumn. Widespread. Rare. Edible. SPORES ellipsoid, smooth, 5–7×3–4, non-amyloid.

Hygrocybe vitellina. Size, overall colour, gill features habitat. CAP 1–2, convex – dome-shaped, flattening slightly, lined or slightly grooved, especially toward margin. STEM 1–3.5, rather slender, tapering slightly downwards, smooth. GILLS persistently egg-yellow, broad, distant, decurrent. SPORE PRINT white. SMELL? FLESH yellow, thin. Usually in small groups, trooping. On soil among mosses or short grass. Autumn. Widespread. Rare. Inedible. SPORES ellipsoid, smooth, 6–8×4.5–5, non-amyloid.

Hygrocybe chlorophana. Gill colour, often confused with *H. flavescens* which seems commoner. CAP 2–4, at first convex then more flattened and broadly umbonate, very sticky, lined. STEM 4–7, fairly slender, equal, slimy, smooth. GILLS often whitish at first but then persistently lemon-yellow, broad, fairly distant, adnate. SPORE PRINT white. SMELL indistinct? FLESH yellow, slightly darker below cap cuticle. Usually in small groups, trooping. On soil among grass, meadows, heaths, pastures. Late summer – autumn. Common. Edible. SPORES ellipsoid, smooth, 6.5–9×4.5–6, non-amyloid.

Hygrocybe laeta. Overall colour, gill features, green-grey at stem apex, persistent stickiness. CAP 1–3, convex, flattening slightly, very slimy-sticky and shiny, lined towards margin. STEM 3–7, slender, equal, often slightly wavy, very slimy-sticky, smooth. GILLS pinkish grey, slowly becoming more pink, broad, distant with interconnecting veins, decurrent. SPORE PRINT white. SMELL unpleasant, rubbery or absent. FLESH straw-coloured, thin. Usually in small groups, trooping. On acid soil among grass, mosses, bracken, often with conifers. Autumn. Widespread. Common. Edible. SPORES broadly ellipsoid, smooth, 5.5–8×4–5, non-amyloid.

Hygrocybe glutinipes. Overall colour, cap and stem features. CAP 0.5–2.5, convex, flattening slightly, persistently slimy-sticky, lined, especially towards margin. STEM 2.5–4, slender, ±equal, often slightly wavy, very slimy-sticky, smooth. GILLS pale yellow, fairly broad, fairly distant, adnate with decurrent tooth. SPORE PRINT white. SMELL? FLESH pale yellow, fairly thin. Usually in small groups, trooping. On soil among short grass, pastures, lawns. Autumn. Widespread. Uncommon. Inedible? SPORES ellipsoid, smooth, 6–8×3–4, non-amyloid.

Hygrocybe reai. Overall colour. CAP 0.5–2.5, at first ±bell-shaped, then convex – flattened, smooth, sticky, lined towards margin. STEM 2–4, slender, equal or tapering slightly downwards, rather wavy, smooth. GILLS pale egg-yellow, gradually darkening and often flushed with orange towards base, broad, fairly distant, adnate with decurrent tooth. SPORE PRINT white. SMELL indistinct. FLESH yellow with orange flush, especially below cap cuticle, fairly thick. Usually in small groups, trooping. On soil among grass, woods, lawns, pastures. Autumn. Widespread. Rare. Inedible. SPORES ellipsoid, smooth, 6.5–9×4–5, non-amyloid.

...ygrocybe nigrescens
...ackening Wax Cap. Col-
...r and rapid change. CAP
...5–6, first ±bell-shaped,
...on conical, then convex –
...ttened, finely fibrous,
...ackening markedly on
...ng. STEM 3–7.5, stout,
...ual, finely lined, fibrous,
...ch paler at base, black-
...ing rapidly. GILLS pale
...llow, blackening rapidly,
...rly broad and distant,
...nexed – free. SPORE
...NT white. SMELL indis-
...ct. FLESH white stem, yel-
...w cap, very quickly black-
...ing. Usually in small
...oups, trooping. On soil
...nong grass, pastures,
...eadows, woods. Autumn.
...idespread. Common.
...edible. SPORES ellipsoid,
...ooth, 8–12×5–6, non-
...nyloid.

Hygrocybe conica. Cap
form, colour, colour
change, spores. CAP 2–5,
acutely conical, flattening
slightly, margin often
irregular, blackening slowly
on aging. STEM 2–6, fairly
slender, equal, finely lined,
fibrous, blackening. GILLS
greyish yellow, fairly
broad, fairly crowded,
adnexed – free. SPORE
PRINT white. SMELL indis-
tinct. FLESH yellow, blackening when bruised.
Usually in small groups,
trooping. On soil among
grass, lawns, pastures,
meadows. Late summer –
autumn. Widespread. Very
common. Inedible. SPORES
ellipsoid, smooth, 7–9×4–5
(4-spored basida) or 9–
12×6–8 (2-spored basidia),
non-amyloid.

Hygrocybe calyptraeformis.
Overall colour, fragile. CAP
3–6, first conical then more
flattened and acutely
umbonate, margin often
irregular and split, finely
fibrous. STEM 6–12, slender,
spindle-shaped, lined, fragile, often split lengthwise
GILLS pink, becoming whitish on aging, fairly broad,
fairly distant, free. SPORE
PRINT white. SMELL indis-
tinct. FLESH white in stem,
pink in cap. Usually in
small groups, trooping. On
soil among grass, pastures.
Autumn. Widespread. Un-
common. Inedible. SPORES
ellipsoid, smooth, 7–8×4.5
–6, non-amyloid.

Hygrocybe splendidissima.
Colour, like *H. coccineus*,
stouter, gills and spores
differ. CAP 3–10, first convex then more flattened
and slightly umbonate –
depressed, margin often
irregular and wavy, slightly
greasy when moist, silky
when dry, sometimes lined
at margin when wet. STEM
3–9, fairly stout, ±spindle-
shaped, often twisted, flattened, grooved,±smooth,
GILLS egg-yellow turning
reddish from base on aging,
fairly broad and crowded,
adnate – adnexed – free.
SPORE PRINT white. SMELL
indistinct. FLESH deep yellow, reddish tinge esp.
above gills and below cap
cuticle. Usually in small
groups, trooping. On soil
among grass, pastures. Autumn. Widespread. Rare. Inedible. SPORES ellipsoid
smooth, 7.5–10×4.5–5.5,
non-amyloid.

...ygrocybe conicoides. Col-
...r, colour change, habi-
.. CAP 1.25–4, at
...st±bell-shaped, but soon
...nical, then convex –
...ttened, with papilla,
...ely silky when dry,
...ackening very slowly and
...ghtly on aging. STEM 2.5–
...fairly slender,equal,
...ely lined, fibrous, often
...ler at base, blackening
...pidly. GILLS egg-yellow,
...rning orange or reddish
...om base, edge blackening
...pidly, fairly broad, fairly
...owded, adnate – adnexed
...free. SPORE PRINT white.
...ELL indistinct. FLESH yel-
...w-orange stem, red cap,
...ickly blackening when
...uised. Usually in small
...oups. On sand dunes.
...utumn. Coastal. Uncom-
...on. Inedible. SPORES elon-
...ted ellipsoid, smooth,
...–13×4–5, non-amyloid.

Hygrocybe obrussea. Cap
form, colour, stem fea-
tures. CAP 2.5–7, bell-
shaped – convex, then
more flattened, margin
often irregular, finely
fibrous. STEM 5–8, stout,
tapering towards base,
smooth, often rather
flattened. GILLS whitish yellow, often darker yellow at
base, fairly broad, fairly
distant, free. SPORE PRINT
white. SMELL indistinct.
FLESH yellow, thin. Usually
in small groups, trooping.
On soil among grass, especially in woods. Autumn.
Widespread. Uncommon.
Inedible. SPORES ellipsoid,
smooth, 7–9×4.5–6, non-
amyloid.

Hygrocybe punicea. Overall colour, similar to *H.
coccineus* but stouter and
stem base colour differs.
CAP 4–7, at first bell-shaped
then more flattened and
broadly umbonate, margin
often irregular and wavy,
greasy. STEM 5–10, stout,
equal or tapering down-
wards, fibrous-lined, consistently pale at base. GILLS
yellowish, turning reddish
on aging, broad, distant,
adnexed – free. SPORE
PRINT white. SMELL indis-
tinct. FLESH white in stem,
yellowish in cap, fairly
thick. Usually in small
groups, trooping. On soil
among grass, pastures.
Autumn. Widespread. Un-
common. Inedible. SPORES
ellipsoid, smooth, 8.5–11×
5–6, non-amyloid.

Hygrocybe langei
(=*acutoconica*). Overall
colour, not blackening,
spores. CAP 3–10, acutely
conical, then flattening
slightly and broadly
umbonate, slightly slimy-
sticky, lined at margin.
STEM 3–5, fairly stout, equal
or tapering slightly downwards, finely lined, dry.
GILLS pale yellow, fairly
narrow, fairly crowded,
adnexed – free. SPORE
PRINT white. SMELL indis-
tinct. FLESH yellow. Usually
in small groups, trooping.
On soil in grass, pastures,
open areas in woods.
Summer – autumn. Wide-
spread. Uncommon. Ined-
ible. SPORES elongated ellipsoid, smooth, 11–14×5.5
–7.5, non-amyloid. Basidia
2-spored.

HYGROPHORACEAE

Hygrocybe quieta. Smell, spores, no stickiness. CAP 2–6, first bell-shaped, then flattened or±depressed, broadly umbonate, greasy. STEM 2–6, fairly slender, equal or tapering slightly downwards, often rather flattened, moist-greasy, not sticky. GILLS yellow with orange or olivaceous tinge towards base, broad, distant, adnate – emarginate. SPORE PRINT white. SMELL strong, oily. FLESH yellowish. Usually in small groups, trooping. On soil in grass, pastures. Autumn. Widespread. Uncommon. Inedible. SPORES elongated ellipsoid with central constriction, smooth, 7.5–10×4–5, non-amyloid.

Hygrocybe marchii. Cap surface features, overall colour. CAP 2–4.5, at first convex then more flattened – depressed, smooth with silky sheen. STEM 3–6, fairly slender, equal or tapering slightly downwards, smooth or finely silky. GILLS golden-yellow, fairly broad, fairly distant, decurrent. SPORE PRINT white. SMELL faint, unpleasant. FLESH yellowish. Usually in small groups, trooping. On soil among grass, pastures, meadows, open areas in woods. Autumn. Widespread. Common. Inedible. SPORES broadly ellipsoid, smooth, 6.5–8.5×4–5, non-amyloid.

Hygrocybe turunda. Overall colour, cap features, spores. CAP 1–3, at first convex then more flattened – umbilicate,±covered with dark pointed scales, margin irregularly toothed. STEM 1.5–4, fairly slender, equal, often slightly wavy, rather downy at base. GILLS white, turning yellowish, broad, fairly distant, decurrent. SPORE PRINT white. SMELL indistinct. FLESH yellow, fading to whitish. Solitary or in small groups, trooping. On damp soil or in moss. Late summer – autumn, probably northern. Rare. Inedible. SPORES elongated ellipsoid, smooth, 8.5–11×4.5–5.5, non-amyloid.

Hygrocybe cantharellus. Overall colour, cap surface gills, habitat. CAP 0.5–4, at first convex then more flattened and depressed – funnel-shaped, ±covered with very fine scurfy scales margin often wavy. STEM 3–7, fairly slender,±equal often slightly wavy, smooth. GILLS pale yellow, slowly deepening and often with orange-red flush, fairly broad, fairly distant, deeply decurrent. SPORE PRINT white. SMELL? FLESH reddish orange. Usually in small groups,±trooping. Among *Sphagnum* or on soil among grass, in wet woods, marshes, pastures, heaths. Autumn. Widespread. Uncommon. Inedible. SPORES ellipsoid, smooth, 8–10×5–6, non-amyloid.

Hygrocybe coccinea **Scarlet Hood.** Cap shape, overall colour. CAP 1.5–5, at first bell-shaped, then convex or flattened, slightly greasy at first, then dry and smooth. STEM 2–5, fairly stout, tapering slightly downwards, often rather flattened, smooth or finely silky lined. GILLS yellow but turning red except at edge, fairly broad, distant, adnate – emarginate with decurrent tooth. SPORE PRINT white. SMELL indistinct. FLESH reddish yellow. Usually in small groups, trooping. On soil in grass, pastures. Late summer – autumn. Widespread. Uncommon. Edible. SPORES broadly ellipsoid, smooth, 7–9×4–5, non-amyloid.

Hygrocybe strangulata. Overall colour, habitat, spores. CAP 0.5–3.5, at first convex then more flattened – depressed with wavy margin, slightly sticky or greasy and lined at margin when moist, then finely scaly, especially in centre. STEM 1.5–5, fairly slender, equal or tapering slightly downwards, often slightly wavy, sometimes flattened, shiny and greasy when wet, silky smooth when dry. GILLS pale yellow, turning darker and with reddish or orange flush, fairly broad, fairly distant, adnate – ± decurrent. SPORE PRINT white. SMELL indistinct. FLESH orange, fading to yellowish. Usually in small groups, trooping or±tufted. On sandy soil among grass, pastures, meadows, heaths, dunes. Autumn. Widespread. Uncommon. Inedible. SPORES elongated-ellipsoid, smooth 7–9×4–5, sometimes appearing constricted, non-amyloid.

Hygrocybe miniata. Overall colour, cap surface. CAP 0.5–1.5, at first convex then more flattened,±covered with fine scurfy scales. STEM 2–5, rather stout,±equal, often slightly wavy, smooth and very shiny. GILLS orange-red with yellow edge, fading to yellow, fairly broad, fairly distant, adnate. SPORE PRINT white. SMELL indistinct. FLESH reddish orange. Usually in small groups, trooping. On soil among grass, pastures, heaths, open areas in woods. Late summer – autumn. Widespread. Uncommon. Inedible. SPORES ellipsoid, smooth, 7.5–10×5–6, non-amyloid.

RUSSULACEAE
Toadstool-shaped,±brittle cap±flattened and at least slightly depressed, often (*Russula*) brightly and variably coloured, gills crowded or distant, adnate – decurrent, white or pale, flesh usually white, many exuding white or coloured milk (*Lactarius*), spores ellipsoid – ±spherical, with amyloid ornamentation (see endpapers), spore print colour critical from white ochre (see endpapers), cap surface smooth and ± sticky (most *Russula*) – woolly (some *Lactarius*). Taste and smell often distinctive. Typically with trees, probably all mycorrhizal. Saprotrophic. Some edible few good, few poisonous. *Lactarius* [56], *Russula* [1]

94

actarius vellereus **Fleecy ilk Cap.** Size, colour, lid flesh. CAP 10–28, at st convex then more attened and depressed – nnel-shaped, margin arkedly inrolled at first, nely velvety. STEM 5–8, rry stout,±equal, finely ılvety. GILLS white then rning pale ochre, narrow, stant, decurrent. SPORE INT white (A). TASTE rid. SMELL indistinct. LK white, acrid. FLESH hite, very thick and hard. sually in small groups,± ooping. On soil in broad-aved woods. Summer – utumn. Widespread. Very mmon. Inedible. SPORES lipsoid – subspherical, namentation (L1), 8–10 7–9.

Lactarius scrobiculatus. Cap and stem features, habitat. CAP 10–20, at first convex then more flattened and depressed – funnel-shaped, densely downy, slimy especially when wet, often patchily coloured, margin markedly inrolled with shaggy hairs. STEM 6–12, stout,±equal, fairly sticky-slimy, with darker coloured pitting, base downy. GILLS white – yellowish, fairly narrow, crowded, decurrent. SPORE PRINT cream (D). TASTE very acrid, hot. SMELL indistinct. MILK white, quickly turning sulphur-yellow, very acrid. FLESH white, turning yellowish, thick. Usually in small groups, in coniferous woods. Summer – autumn. Predominantly northern. Rare, locally common. Edible. SPORES ellipsoid, ornamentation (L6), 8–9×6.5–7.

Lactarius turpis (=*necator*) **Ugly Milk Cap.** Cap features, overall colour, habitat. CAP 5–25, at first convex then more flattened and depressed – funnel-shaped, finely downy, sticky-slimy, margin markedly inrolled and fairly woolly. STEM 4–8, stout,±equal or tapering slightly downwards, fairly sticky-slimy,±regularly pitted. GILLS cream – straw-coloured, bruising brown, fairly narrow, crowded, decurrent. SPORE PRINT cream (D). TASTE very acrid, hot. SMELL indistinct. MILK white, very acrid. Ammonia on all parts, violet. FLESH white. Solitary or in small groups,±trooping. On soil with birch, especially in damp woods. Summer – autumn. Widespread. Very common. Inedible. SPORES ellipsoid, ornamentation (L9), 7.5–8×6–6.5.

Lactarius aspideus. Colours, colour change, habitat. CAP 4–8, at first convex, then more flattened and depressed – slightly funnel-shaped or umbilicate, at first slightly woolly at margin, then smooth, sometimes slightly zoned, slightly sticky. STEM 2.5–6, fairly slender,±equal, smooth, slightly sticky. GILLS cream, bruising slightly lilac, fairly narrow, crowded, decurrent. SPORE PRINT cream (D). TASTE slightly bitter. SMELL faint, indefinite. MILK white, copious, quickly turning violet, first mild, then hot. FLESH white, quickly turning violet when bruised. Usually in small groups,± trooping. On soil in damp places, especially with willows. Late summer – autumn. Widespread. Rare. Inedible. SPORES ellipsoid, ornamentation (L7 – L13), 7.5–8.5×7.5–9.

actarius piperatus **Peppery ilk Cap.** Size, colour, ste. CAP 8–18, at first con-x then more flattened d depressed – funnel-aped, margin markedly curved at first, smooth. EM 3–7, stout,± ual, very fine bloom at st, then smooth. GILLS ite then turning cream, rrow, crowded, repeat-ly branched, decurrent. ORE PRINT white (A). STE very acrid, hot. SMELL distinct. MILK white, very rid hot. FLESH white, tur-ng slightly yellowish on ing, thick. Usually in all groups,±trooping. n soil in broad leaved oods. Summer-autumn. idespread. Common. In-ible. SPORES ellipsoid, namentation (L1), 6–8 5–6.

Lactarius repraesentaneus. Cap features, overall colour changes. CAP 8–16, at first convex then more flattened and depressed – funnel-shaped or slightly umbonate, scaly downy but smooth in centre, sticky, margin markedly inrolled with long shaggy hairs. STEM 6–12, stout,±equal or tapering slightly downwards, fairly sticky-slimy. GILLS pale cream with violet staining, bruising violet, fairly narrow, crowded, decurrent. SPORE PRINT cream–yellowish (E). TASTE and SMELL rather sweet, thyme or resin-like. MILK white, at first mild, then bitter. FLESH cream, turning violet. Usually in small groups. On acidic soils in coniferous and broad-leaved woods. Summer – autumn. Predominantly northern. Rare, locally common. Edible. SPORES ellipsoid, ornamentation (L7), 9–11×8–9.

Lactarius mairei var. *zonatus.* Cap features, taste, smell, similar to *L. torminosus* but spores, size and habitat differ. CAP 5–6, at first convex then more flattened and depressed – funnel-shaped, with ±concentric darker zoning, covered with±flattened scales, at first sticky-slimy, margin markedly inrolled with shaggy hairs. STEM 4–6, stout, equal, at first finely downy then smooth. GILLS pale orange-buff, narrow, crowded, adnate – ±decurrent. SPORE PRINT cream (D). TASTE acrid. SMELL pleasant, strong. MILK white, very acrid. FLESH very pale buff – straw-coloured. Solitary or in small groups,±trooping. On soil in broad-leaved or mixed woods, especially (?) with oak. Summer – autumn. Predominantly southern, only var. *zonatus* in Europe. Rare. Inedible. SPORES ellipsoid, ornamentation (L9), 7–7.5×6–7.

Lactarius torminosus **Woolly Milk Cap.** Cap features, taste, smell, similar to *L. mairei* var *zonatus* but spores, size and habitat differ. CAP 4–12, at first convex then more flattened and depressed, with±concentric darker zoning, sticky-slimy, esp. when wet, fibrous, margin markedly inrolled with shaggy hairs. STEM 5–9, stout, equal – ±spindle-shaped, at first finely downy then smooth, sometimes rather pitted. GILLS pinkish white, narrow, crowded,±decurrent. SPORE pale cream – cream (C-D). TASTE acrid. SMELL faint, turpentine. MILK white, very acrid. FLESH white with some pink flushes. Solitary or in small groups,±trooping. On acid soil, usually with birch, heaths, woods. Summer – autumn. Widespread. Common. Poisonous. SPORES ellipsoid, ornamentation (L5), 8–10×6–7.5.

1

Lactarius pubescens. Cap features, taste, smell, similar to *L. torminosus* but paler and smaller. CAP 4–8, at first convex then more flattened and depressed, with some darker, irregular patches, dry, fibrous, margin markedly inrolled with shaggy hairs. STEM 2–5, stout, equal or tapering slightly downwards, at first finely downy then smooth. GILLS whitish pink, narrow, crowded,±decurrent. SPORE PRINT pale cream – cream (C-D), sometimes faintly pinkish. TASTE acrid. SMELL faint, pelargonium-like. MILK white, often rather sparse, very acrid. FLESH white – pinkish. Solitary or in small groups, ±trooping. On acid soil, usually with birch, heaths, woods. Summer – autumn. Widespread. Uncommon. Poisonous. SPORES ellipsoid, ornamentation (L5-L6), 6.5–8.5×5.5–6.5.

2

Lactarius lignyotus. Cap features, overall colour, stem apex. CAP 4–8, at first convex then flattened and slightly depressed – umbilicate, finely velvety, becoming markedly wrinkled on aging. STEM 6–12, fairly slender, equal,±smooth, but markedly wrinkled towards apex. GILLS white, turning pinkish brown, becoming reddish-stained, fairly broad, fairly distant, decurrent. SPORE PRINT yellowish cream (E). TASTE mild. SMELL faint, indefinite. MILK white, slowly turning reddish brown, mild. FLESH white, then turning pinkish red. Solitary or in small groups, ±trooping. On soil with conifers, especially spruce. Summer – autumn. Predominantly highland. Rare. Edible. SPORES subspherical, ornamentation (L8-L9), 8–10×9–11.

3

Lactarius picinus. Cap features, overall colour, very similar to *L. lignyotus* but

lacks wrinkling. CAP 4–8, at first convex then flattened and slightly depressed, finely velvety. STEM 3–6, fairly stout, equal,±smooth but often downy-hairy at base. GILLS straw-coloured, then±ochre, fairly broad, fairly crowded, adnate – decurrent. SPORE PRINT yellowish cream (E) TASTE at first mild, then acrid. SMELL faint, indefinite. MILK white, slowly turning yellowish, at first mild, then acrid, hot. FLESH white, then turning reddish. Solitary or in small groups± trooping. On soil with conifers. Summer – autumn. Predominantly highland. Rare. Edible? SPORES subspherical, ornamentation (L8-L9), 8–10×9–11.

4

Lactarius fuliginosus. Cap features, overall colour, similar to *L. lignyotus* but lacks wrinkling and habitat differs. CAP 5–9, at first convex then flattened and slightly depressed – umbonate, very finely velvety with inrolled margin. STEM 4–10, rather slender, equal – ±spindle-shaped, very finely velvety. GILLS at first white, then buff with slight pink flush, staining reddish pink, fairly narrow, fairly crowded, decurrent. SPORE PRINT yellowish cream (E). TASTE mild. SMELL? MILK white, slowly turning pinkish in contact with flesh but not in air, at first mild, then acrid. FLESH whitish, usually± spotted salmon-pink. Usually in small groups,± trooping. On soil in broad leaved and mixed woods. Summer – autumn. Widespread. Uncommon. Inedible. SPORES subspherical, ornamentation (L9), 7.5–8.5×9.5–10.5.

5

Lactarius acris. Colour changes in flesh and milk, spores, habitat. CAP 4.5–8, at first convex then flattened and slightly depressed,±smooth, rather shiny, becoming finely wrinkled radially at matur-

ity. STEM 3–8, fairly stout, equal or tapering slightly downwards, especially towards base. GILLS at first cream, then ochreous, fairly narrow, fairly crowded, adnate – ±decurrent. SPORE PRINT yellowish cream (E). FLESH white, turning reddish, then fading to brown. TASTE very acrid. SMELL? MILK white, quickly turning reddish, very acrid. FLESH white, quickly turning reddish, then fading to brown. Solitary or in small groups,± trooping. On soil in broad-leaved woods especially (always?) with beech on chalky sites. Summer – autumn. Widespread. Uncommon. Inedible. SPORES subspherical, ornamentation (L8, but very pronounced), 7.5–8×7–7.5.

6

Lactarius pterosporus. Very similar to several related species but spores distinct. CAP 5–8, at first convex then flattened and depressed – funnel-shaped, often±umbonate-umbilicate, finely velvety, sometimes becoming finely wrinkled at maturity. STEM 3–8, fairly stout, equal, tapering slightly downwards or±spindle-shaped. GILLS at first cream, then ochreous, fairly narrow, very crowded, adnate – ±decurrent. SPORE PRINT yellowish cream (E). TASTE very acrid. SMELL faint, pleasant. MILK white, very slowly turning red on drying, very acrid. FLESH white, then quickly turning pinkish. Solitary or in small groups,±trooping. On soil in broad-leaved woods with oaks, beech or hornbeam. Summer – autumn. Distribution unknown as confused with other species, certainly occurs in Britain. Rare. Inedible. SPORES subspherical, ornamentation (L14), 7.5–8×7–7.5.

7

Lactarius azonites. Similar to *L. fuliginosus* but much paler and spores differ. CAP 4–8, at first convex then

flattened and slightly depressed – umbonate, very finely velvety with inrolled margin. STEM 4–8 rather slender, equal – ±spindle-shaped, very finely velvety. GILLS at first white, then creamy yellow fairly narrow, fairly crowded,±decurrent. SPORE PRINT yellowish cream (E). TASTE at first mild, then acrid. SMELL? MILK white, slowly turning pinkish in contact with fle but not in air, at first mild then acrid. FLESH white, fairly quickly turning pink then more orange. Usuall in small groups,±troopin On soil in broad-leaved woods, especially with oaks. Summer – autumn. Widespread. Uncommon Inedible. SPORES subspher ical, ornamentation (L8, but very pronounced), 8– 9×7.5–8.5.

8

Lactarius deliciosus **Saffr Milk Cap**. Often confused in past with other spp. especially *L. deterrimus* b flesh colour change and milk differ. CAP 5–15, at first convex then flattened and depressed – funnel-shaped, slightly sticky, rather brittle, with darker patches in concentric zones, margin inrolled. STEM 3–6, stout, equal, smooth, usually with som greenish patches, often with small, crater-like spots. GILLS pinkish orange – yellowish, slow-turning orange and bruising green, narrow, crowded,±decurrent. SPORE PRINT pale ochre (F TASTE mild or slightly bitt SMELL sweet, fruity. MILK orange, mild or slightly b ter. FLESH pale yellow, stained orange by milk after about 1 hour, then greenish. Usually in small groups,±trooping. On so in coniferous woods, especially with pine or spruce Summer – autumn. Wide spread but predominantly northern. Uncommon. E ble. SPORES ellipsoid, orn mentation (L9), 8–9×6–7

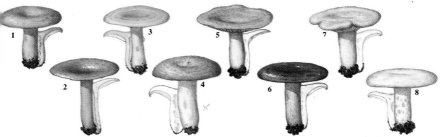

1

Lactarius deterrimus. Often confused in past with other sp. especially *L. deliciosus* but flesh colour change and milk differ. CAP 5–15, at first convex then flattened and depressed – funnel-shaped, slightly sticky, rather brittle, with darker patches in concentric zones, margin inrolled. STEM 3–6, stout, equal, smooth, usually with marked greenish patches, often with small, crater-like spots. GILLS pinkish orange – yellowish, slowly turning orange and bruising green, narrow, crowded,±decurrent. TASTE bitter. SMELL sweet, fruity. MILK orange, bitter. FLESH pale yellow, soon stained pale wine-red by milk, then dark wine-red after about 1 hour, then greenish. Usually in small groups,±trooping. On soil in coniferous woods, especially with spruce. Summer – autumn. Widespread but predominantly northern. Uncommon. Edible. SPORES ellipsoid, ornamentation (L9). 8–9×6–7.

2

Lactarius uvidus. Overall colour combinations and habitat. CAP 4–8, at first convex then flattened and depressed, barely umbonate, smooth, shiny-sticky when moist, finely downy at margin. STEM 3–7, fairly stout, equal or tapering slightly downwards, smooth or finely veined, usually slightly sticky. GILLS whitish pink, bruising lilac, narrow, fairly crowded, decurrent. SPORE PRINT cream-yellowish cream (D-E). SMELL indistinct. MILK white, turning lilac, slightly bitter, acrid. FLESH greyish white, slowly turning lilac. Usually in small groups,±trooping. On wet soil in woods, especially with birch and willow. Summer – autumn. Widespread,

predominantly northern. Uncommon. Inedible. SPORES ellipsoid, ornamentation (L8), 7.5–8.5×9–11.

3

Lactarius chrysorrheus. Milk colour change. CAP 4–8, at first convex then flattened and depressed, smooth. STEM 3–7.5, fairly stout, equal or tapering slightly upwards, often slightly bulbous, smooth. GILLS cream with pink flush, narrow, fairly crowded, decurrent. SPORE PRINT white – pale cream (A–C), sometimes with slight salmon-pink flush. TASTE slowly developing, bitter. SMELL indistinct. MILK white, very quickly turning sulphur-yellow, at first faint, then hot, bitter. FLESH greyish white, quickly stained yellow by milk. Usually in small groups,±trooping. On soil with oaks. Summer – autumn. Widespread. Common. Inedible. SPORES ellipsoid, ornamentation (L7), 7.5–8×6–7.

4

Lactarius bresadolianus (=*zonarioides*). Colours, milk, habitat, distribution. CAP 5 – 12, at first convex, then more flattened and depressed,±zoned, greasy, often very finely downy-velvety at margin. STEM 2.5–6, fairly stout, equal or tapering slightly upwards, sometimes slightly bulbous, smooth or with slight cavities. GILLS ochre-yellow – ochre, often spotted greyish olive from milk, narrow, fairly crowded, decurrent. SPORE PRINT? TASTE acrid. SMELL indistinct? MILK white, usually slowly turning green-grey, acrid. FLESH white, slowly changing reddish then grey-lilac, then grey-olive, especially in stem. Usually in small groups,±trooping. On soil with coniferous trees, especially (always?) spruce. Late summer – autumn. Predominantly

northern and montane, not Britain. Inedible. SPORES ellipsoid, ornamentation (L3–L6), 8–9.5×7–8.5.

5

Lactarius acerrimus. Taste, spore features. CAP 7–12, at first convex or dome-shaped, then flattened and±funnel-shaped, often markedly irregular with wavy margin, inrolled at first, smooth and often slightly sticky when wet. STEM 2–6, often eccentric, very stout,±equal, often irregularly cratered or mottled, smooth. GILLS at first buff but turning darker reddish brown, fairly narrow, fairly crowded, usually markedly wrinkled,±decurrent. SPORE PRINT cream – yellowish cream (D-E). TASTE very acrid, hot. SMELL sweet, fruity, pears. MILK white, very acrid, hot. FLESH whitish, very thick. Usually in small groups,± trooping. On soil with broad-leaved trees, especially oaks. Summer – autumn. Widespread. Rare. Inedible. SPORES subspherical – ellipsoid, ornamentation (L6), 10.5–13.5×8.5 –10. Basidia 2-spored.

6

Lactarius blennius **Slimy Milk Cap**. Size, taste, habitat. CAP 4–10, at first convex then flattened and depressed, often with darker concentric pattern of blotches, margin inrolled, very slimy. STEM 4–5, very stout,±equal, smooth, slimy. GILLS at first whitebuff, bruising darker brown, narrow, crowded, decurrent. SPORE PRINT pale cream (C), often with slight buff-pink flush. TASTE very acrid, hot. SMELL indistinct. MILK white, turning grey on drying, very acrid, hot. FLESH whitish. Usually in small groups,±trooping. On soil with broad-leaved trees, especially beech. Summer – autumn. Widespread. Extremely common. Inedible. SPORES ellip-

soid, ornamentation (L7-L13), 7.5–8×6–7.

7

Lactarius controversus. Size, habitat. CAP 6–25, at first convex then flattened and depressed, often with irregular darker pattern, margin inrolled and± woolly, slimy when wet. STEM 2–7, sometimes eccentric, very stout, equal or tapering slightly downwards, smooth, slimy. GILLS pinkish buff, narrow, very crowded, decurrent. SPORE PRINT pale cream (C). TASTE acrid. SMELL faint, pleasant. MILK white, acrid. FLESH white. Usually in small groups,±trooping. On soil with poplars, on dune slacks with *Salix repens*. Summer – autumn. Widespread. Uncommon. Inedible. SPORES ellipsoid, ornamentation (L9), 7–8×5–6.

8

Lactarius musteus. Spores, distribution, habitat. CAP 4–10, at first convex then flattened and depressed, often with irregular blotches, margin inrolled, slightly slimy-sticky when wet, very finely downy-velvety. STEM 4–8, fairly stout, equal, smooth, slimy-sticky when wet, finely veined, often spotted with small cavities. GILLS white – cream, often with pinkish flush, very slowly bruising dirty grey-green, narrow, crowded,±decurrent. SPORE PRINT pale cream (C). TASTE mild. SMELL? MILK white, at first mild, then±acrid. FLESH white – very pale buff. Solitary or in small groups,± trooping. On soil with *Sphagnum* or other mosses, in pine woods. Summer – autumn. Northern, highland. Rare. Inedible. SPORES ellipsoid, ornamentation (L3-L9), 8–10×7–8.5.

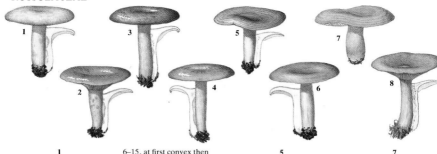

1

Lactarius pallidus. Overall colour, lack of colour change, habitat. CAP 5–10, at first convex then flattened and depressed, margin inrolled, smooth, sticky. STEM 3–10, fairly stout, equal or tapering slightly downwards, smooth, slimy-sticky. GILLS white – cream, often with pinkish flush, narrow, crowded,±decurrent. SPORE PRINT yellowish cream (E-F). TASTE mild, then slightly acrid. SMELL faint, pleasant, sweet-fruity. MILK white, at first mild, then± acrid. FLESH white – very pale pinkish buff. Usually in small groups,±trooping. On soil in beech woods. Summer – autumn. Widespread. Common. Inedible. SPORES ellipsoid, ornamentation (L7-L13), 8–10 ×6.5–7.

2

Lactarius hysginus. Cap form, colour, lack of colour change, habitat. CAP 5–8, at first convex then flattened and depressed – funnel-shaped, margin inrolled, often rather wrinkled, sticky and shiny. STEM 3–6, rather slender, equal, tapering slightly downwards or±spindle-shaped, often fairly wrinkled, slimy-sticky, especially when wet. GILLS pale yellow, narrow, crowded,±decurrent. SPORE PRINT yellowish cream (E). TASTE very acrid. SMELL faint, pleasant, peculiar, sweet-fruity? MILK white, very acrid. FLESH white with slight reddish flush. Usually in small groups,±trooping. On soil in coniferous woods and with birch. Summer – autumn. Widespread. Rare. Inedible. SPORES broadly ellipsoid, ornamentation (L11), 6– 7×5.5–6.5.

3

Lactarius trivialis. Cap features, milk, habitat. CAP at 6–15, at first convex then flattened and slightly depressed, often with irregular darker patches, margin inrolled and slightly downy at first, smooth, slimy-sticky and shiny. STEM 5–10, rather slender, ±spindle-shaped, often slightly wrinkled and pitted, slimy-sticky, especially when wet. GILLS pale straw-coloured, staining reddish brown, narrow, crowded, decurrent. SPORE PRINT yellowish cream (E). TASTE acrid? SMELL faint, pleasant, sweet-fruity. MILK white, very slowly turning greenish-grey, mild then slowly very acrid. FLESH white. Usually in small groups,±trooping. On wet soil with mosses, in coniferous woods and with birch. Summer – autumn. Widespread. Uncommon. Edible when cooked. SPORES broadly ellipsoid, ornamentation (L7), 8–10×7– 8.5.

4

Lactarius vietus **Grey Milk Cap.** Cap features, milk, habitat. CAP 2–7, at first convex then flattened and depressed – funnel-shaped, sometimes±umbonate, margin inrolled and slightly downy at first, smooth, slimy-sticky and shiny, especially when wet. STEM 4–8, rather slender,±equal, slimy-sticky, especially when wet. GILLS at first whitish, then pale yellow – straw-coloured, staining brownish, narrow, crowded,±decurrent. SPORE PRINT white (A-B). TASTE acrid. SMELL indistinct. MILK white, very slowly turning grey-green on gills, mild then quickly acrid. FLESH white – pale buff. Usually in small groups,±trooping. On wet soil, coniferous woods and with birch. Late summer – autumn. Widespread. Very common. Edible when cooked. SPORES ellipsoid, ornamentation (L8), 8–9×6.5–7.

5

Lactarius circellatus. Cap features, habitat. CAP 4–10, at first convex then flattened and depressed, often rather irregular-wavy, with concentric darker banding, margin inrolled and slightly downy at first, rather rough, slimy-sticky and shiny, especially when wet. STEM 3–5, rather slender,±equal or spindle-shaped, slimy-sticky, especially when wet. GILLS at first yellowish, then pale ochre, staining brownish, narrow, crowded, adnate – ±decurrent. SPORE PRINT cream (D). TASTE acrid? SMELL faint, rather fruity. MILK white, mild then slowly very acrid. FLESH white. Usually in small groups,± trooping. On soil with hornbeam. Late summer – autumn. Widespread. Rare, locally common. Inedible. SPORES ellipsoid – subspherical, ornamentation (L12), 6–7×5–6.5.

6

Lactarius pyrogalus. Cap and stem features, habitat. CAP 5–9, at first convex then flattened and depressed – funnel-shaped, sometimes with very faint concentric darker banding, margin slightly inrolled, slightly slimy-sticky, especially when wet. STEM 4–6, rather slender,±equal or spindle-shaped, very finely downy, slightly slimy-sticky, especially when wet. GILLS at first yellowish, then ochre, narrow, fairly crowded,± decurrent. SPORE PRINT yellowish cream – pale ochre (E-F). TASTE acrid. SMELL faint, rather fruity. MILK white, very acrid. FLESH white. Usually in small groups,±trooping. On soil with hazel (*Corylus*) Summer – autumn. Widespread. Very common. Inedible. SPORES broadly ellipsoid – subspherical, ornamentation (L12), 7– 8×5–6.

7

Lactarius flexuosus. Cap features, stem, gills, habitat. CAP 5–9, at first convex then flattened and depressed – funnel-shaped often with concentric darker banding, margin slightly inrolled, velvety and often irregular, wavy, dry, smooth. STEM 2–5, stout, tapering downwards very finely downy, often± pitted. GILLS at first pale yellowish, then±pinkish, narrow, fairly distant, adnate. SPORE PRINT yellowish cream – pale ochre (E–F) TASTE acrid. SMELL faint, indefinite. MILK white, very acrid. FLESH white. Usually in small groups,±trooping. On soil among grass in or close to broad-leaved and coniferous woods. Summer – autumn. Widespread. Uncommon. Inedible. SPORES subspherical, ornamentation (L9), 7–7.5×6– 6.5.

8

Lactarius helvus. Smell, milk, habitat. CAP 5–15, at first convex then flattened and±depressed, often broadly umbonate,±covered with small, woolly scales, margin slightly inrolled. STEM 5–12, rather slender, equal or±spindle-shaped, often very finely downy. GILLS pale ochre, often with slight pinkish flush, narrow, fairly crowded, adnate – ±decurrent. SPORE PRINT pale cream (C) TASTE mild. SMELL faint when fresh, strong when dry, coumarin. MILK watery, mild or very slightly bitter. FLESH whitish buff. Usually in small groups,±trooping. On wet acid soils, usually with conifers, woods, heaths. Summer – autumn. Widespread. Uncommon. Poisonous when fresh. SPORES broadly ellipsoid, ornamentation (L5), 5–9×5–7.

1

actarius spinulosus. Size,
p surface, habitat. CAP
-6, at first convex then
attened and depressed –
nnel-shaped, ±covered
ith small, dark fleck-like
ales, margin slightly
rolled at first. STEM 2.5–
5, rather slender, equal
· tapering slightly down-
ards, very finely scaly,
ther woolly at base. GILLS
le yellow – buff, narrow,
owded, decurrent. SPORE
INT cream – yellowish
eam (D-E). TASTE mild,
definite. SMELL faint,
definite. MILK white, mild
en slowly acrid. FLESH
hite – pinkish buff. Usu-
ly in small groups, ±troo-
ng. On soil in broad-
aved and mixed woods,
pecially with birch on wet
es. Summer – autumn.
idespread. Uncommon.
edible. SPORES subspher-
al, ornamentation (L9),
-7.5×6–6.5.

2

actarius glyciosmus
oconut-scented Milk Cap.
nell. CAP 2–6, at first con-
ex then flattened and
epressed – umbilicate,
ery finely and obscurely
aly, margin slightly inrol-
d at first. STEM 2–7, fairly
out, equal, tapering
ghtly upwards or±club-
aped, finely silky-scaly.
LLS pale yellow-buff,
ten with pinkish flush,
arrow, crowded, decur-
nt. SPORE PRINT pale
eam – cream (C-D).
STE mild, slowly turning
rid. SMELL faint, to strong
esiccated coconut. MILK
hite, mild then slowly
rid. FLESH creamy-buff.
ften in fairly large groups,
trooping. On soil with
road-leaved trees,
pecially birch. Summer –
itumn. Widespread. Very
ommon. Inedible. SPORES
roadly ellipsoid, orna-
entation (L7–L13), 7–
×5.5–7.

3

Lactarius fuscus (=_mam-
mosus_ in part). Colours,
smell, habitat. CAP 4–8, at
first convex, then more
flattened, often rather
sharply umbonate at first,
then broader, very finely
and obscurely scaly. STEM
3–6, fairly stout, equal or
tapering slightly upwards,
sometimes slightly bulbous,
±smooth. GILLS ochre-
ellow – ochre-orange, narrow, crowded, decurrent.
SPORE PRINT pale cream (C).
TASTE at first mild, then
bitter. SMELL coconut. MILK
white, mild at first, then
acrid. FLESH white-greyish.
Usually in small groups,±
trooping. On soil with coniferous trees, especially
pine, or rarely with birch.
Late summer – autumn.
Predominantly northern
and montane. Rare. Edi-
ble. SPORES ellipsoid, ornamentation (L9), 6–10×5–8.

4

Lactarius volemus. Overall
colour and cap features,
smell. CAP 5–12, at first
convex then flattened –
depressed, very finely
velvety or smooth, margin
usually smooth. STEM 5–10,
fairly stout, equal or
broadly spindle-shaped,
finely velvety-smooth, concentrically cracking. GILLS
pale yellow, bruising dark
brown, narrow, crowded,
±decurrent. SPORE PRINT
white (A-B). TASTE mild.
SMELL fishy. MILK white,
mild. FLESH whitish, bruising brown. Usually in small
groups,±trooping. On soil
in broad-leaved and con-
iferous woods, especially
with beech. Summer –
autumn. Widespread.
Uncommon. Edible.
SPORES subspherical, ornamentation (L10), 8–10×8–
9.5.

5

Lactarius rubrocinctus. Cap
surface, smell. CAP 4–9, at
first convex then flattened –
depressed, covered with
coarse, rough warty scales.
STEM 2–6, stout,±equal,
dark zone at extreme apex,
smooth but hairy at base.
GILLS cream with pinkish
flush, bruising lilac-brown,
narrow, crowded,±decur-
rent. SPORE PRINT white (A-
B)? TASTE? SMELL rancid,
oily. MILK white, mild.
FLESH whitish. Usually in
small groups,±trooping.
On soil in broad-leaved
woods, especially with
beech on chalky sites.
Summer – autumn. Wide-
spread, predominantly
northern. Rare. Inedible.
SPORES subspherical, ornamentation (L4–L5?), 7–7.5
×6–6.5.

6

Lactarius fulvissimus. Cap
surface, habitat, milk,
often confused with other
species. CAP 5–7, at first
convex then flattened and
depressed – funnel-shaped,
smooth, slightly sticky,
margin often paler and±
regularly notched. STEM 2–
5, rather stout,±equal,
smooth. GILLS buff, nar-
row, crowded, decurrent.
SPORE PRINT cream – yel-
lowish cream (D-E). TASTE
faint, mild. SMELL indis-
tinct. MILK white, turning
yellow on white handker-
chief, mild or slightly acrid.
FLESH whitish, with reddish
brown flush. Usually in
small groups,±trooping.
On soil in broad-leaved or
mixed woods, usually with
oak. Summer – autumn.
Widespread. Uncommon.
Inedible. SPORES subspherical, ornamentation (L4-
L5), 7–7.5×6–6.5.

7

Lactarius mitissimus. Size,
cap features, overall colour. CAP 3–7, at first convex
then flattened and depressed, often slightly umbonate
or with small papilla,±
velvety, slightly slimy, margin inrolled at first. STEM 3–
7, rather slender, equal or
tapering slightly down-
wards,±smooth. GILLS buff
– pale ochre, narrow,
crowded, adnate – ±decur-
rent. SPORE PRINT pale
cream (C). TASTE faint,
mild or very slightly bitter.
SMELL slight, unpleasant.
MILK white, mild. FLESH
whitish. Usually in small
groups,±trooping. On
soil in broad-leaved or coniferous woods. Summer –
autumn. Widespread.
Common. Inedible. SPORES
subspherical, ornamentat-
ion (L7), 8–9.5×6–7.5.

8

Lactarius decipiens. Smell,
milk, habitat. CAP 2–7, at
first convex then flattened
and slightly depressed,
often slightly umbonate,
dry and±smooth, not
shiny, margin often slightly
irregular. STEM 2–8, rather
slender, equal or±spindle-
shaped,±smooth, not
hiny. GILLS pinkish buff –
pale ochre, fairly narrow,
crowded, decurrent. SPORE
PRINT pale cream – cream
(C-D). TASTE at first mild
then bitter. SMELL pelargoniums. MILK white, turning
yellow after few minutes on
white handkerchief, mild
then bitter and hot. FLESH
whitish buff, slowly turning
yellow when cut. Usually in
small groups,±trooping.
On soil in broad-leaved or
mixed woods, especially
(always?) with hornbeam.
Summer – autumn. Wide-
spread. Rare. Inedible.
SPORES broadly ellipsoid,
ornamentation (L6-L9),
7.5–9×6.5–7.5.

99

1

Lactarius rufus. Cap colour and features, taste, habitat. CAP 3–10, at first convex then flattened and slightly depressed, with slightly pointed umbo, dry and±smooth, not shiny. STEM 5–8, rather slender, equal,±smooth, not shiny, whitish downy at base. GILLS at first creamy buff then reddish, fairly narrow, crowded,±decurrent. SPORE PRINT white (B), often with slight salmon-pink flush. TASTE hot, acrid. SMELL faint, resinous. MILK white, briefly mild then acrid and hot. FLESH white. In groups, often large, trooping. On soil in coniferous woods especially with pines, or rarely broad-leaved woods on acid soils. Summer – autumn. Widespread. Extremely common. Edible. SPORES ellipsoid, ornamentation (L5), 8–9.5×6–7.5.

2

Lactarius camphoratus **Curry-scented Milk Cap.** Size, smell. CAP 3–6, at first convex then flattened and slightly depressed, often umbonate,±smooth, not shiny, margin usually grooved. STEM 3–5, rather slender, equal or tapering slightly downwards,± smooth, not shiny, often slightly velvety at apex. GILLS pale reddish buff, narrow, crowded, decurrent. SPORE PRINT pale cream – cream (C-D). TASTE mild. SMELL at first faint and unpleasant, then strongly of curry on drying. MILK fairly watery, mild. FLESH reddish brown. In groups, often fairly large, trooping. On soil in coniferous and broad-leaved woods. Summer – autumn. Widespread. Very common. Edible, as seasoning. SPORES subspherical, ornamentation (variable, L4 and L9), 7.5–8.5×6.5–7.5.

3

Lactarius quietus **Oak Milk-Cap.** Overall colour, smell, habitat. CAP 3–8, at first convex then flattened and slightly depressed,± smooth, not shiny, usually with±concentric bands of spotting. STEM 4–9, rather slender, equal, not shiny, often slightly grooved. GILLS pale buff, turning reddish brown on aging, fairly narrow, crowded,± decurrent. SPORE PRINT pale cream – cream (C-D), often with slight salmon-pink flush. TASTE mild. SMELL faint, unpleasant, oily. MILK white, mild. FLESH whitish buff. Usually in groups±trooping. On soil with oaks. Autumn. Widespread. Extremely common. Inedible. SPORES ellipsoid, ornamentation (L6), 7.5–9.5×6.5–8.

4

Lactarius subdulcis. Overall colour, smell, habitat, similar to *L. tabidus* but milk and spores differ. CAP 3–7, at first convex then flattened and slightly depressed, sometimes slightly umbonate,± smooth, not shiny, sometimes slightly wrinkled, margin often furrowed. STEM 3–6, rather slender,± equal – spindle-shaped, not shiny, often slightly grooved. GILLS whitish buff, often with pink or pale wine-red flush, fairly narrow, crowded,±decurrent. SPORE PRINT pale cream – cream (C-D), often with slight salmon-pink flush. TASTE at first mild, then slightly bitter. SMELL faint, indefinite or slightly oily. MILK white, unchanging, mild, then slightly bitter. FLESH whitish buff. Usually in groups,± trooping. On soil in broad-leaved woods, especially with beech. Summer – autumn. Widespread. Extremely common. Edible. SPORES ellipsoid, ornamentation (L7), 7.5–9.5×6.5–8.

5

Lactarius serifluus. Overall colour, smell, milk. CAP 2–6, at first convex then flattened and slightly depressed, sometimes slightly umbonate,±smooth, not shiny, margin often rather wavy. STEM 3–6, rather slender,±equal, not shiny, often±hairy at base. GILLS yellowish ochre, often with pink or reddish flush, rather broad, crowded,± decurrent. SPORE PRINT pale cream – cream (C-D). TASTE mild or none. SMELL faint, slightly oily. MILK watery, mild – tasteless. FLESH reddish buff. Usually in groups,±trooping. On soil in broad-leaved woods, especially on sandy sites. Summer – autumn. Widespread. Uncommon. Edible. SPORES ellipsoid, ornamentation (L9), 7–8×8–9.

6

Lactarius cimicarius. Overall colour, size, cap margin, smell. CAP 3–6, at first convex then flattened and slightly depressed,± smooth, not shiny, margin often±pleated. STEM 3–5, rather stout,±equal or spindle-shaped, not shiny and sometimes slightly roughened. GILLS yellowish ochre, often with pink or reddish flush, fairly broad, fairly crowded, decurrent. SPORE PRINT pale cream – cream (C-D). TASTE mild. SMELL strong, unpleasant, oily. MILK watery, mild. FLESH yellowish, turning pale reddish brown. Usually in groups,±trooping. On soil in broad-leaved and mixed woods. Summer – autumn. Widespread. Uncommon. Inedible. SPORES subspherical, ornamentation (L9), 7.5–8.5×7–7.5.

7

Lactarius hepaticus. Cap colour, milk, taste, habitat. CAP 2–6, at first convex then flattened and slightly depressed, sometimes slightly umbonate,±smooth, appearing greasy, margin often±irregularly notched. STEM 3–6, fairly slender,± equal,±smooth or finely lined or patterned. GILLS yellowish buff, turning more ochreous, fairly narrow, crowded, decurrent. SPORE PRINT white – pale cream (B-C). TASTE mild, slowly turning acrid. SMELL faint, pleasant. MILK white, quickly turning yellow on white handkerchief, at first usually mild, then hot and acrid. FLESH pinkish buff, slowly darkening or turning yellowish. Usually in groups,±trooping. On soil in pine woods. Autumn. Predominantly southern. Uncommon, locally common. Inedible. SPORES broadly ellipsoid, ornamentation (L9), 6–7×7–9.

8

Lactarius tabidus. Similar to *L. subdulcis* but spores and milk differ. CAP 2–5, at first convex then flattened and slightly depressed, often umbilicate, dry,± smooth or slightly wrinkled, margin often lined or grooved. STEM 2–5, fairly slender,±equal or tapering upwards,±smooth or finely grooved. GILLS buff, usually with slight pinkish flush, fairly narrow, crowded,± decurrent. SPORE PRINT white – pale cream (B-C). TASTE faint, mild, slowly turning acrid. SMELL indistinct. MILK white, slowly turning yellow on white handkerchief, at first mild, then hot and acrid. FLESH whitish, turning slightly yellow. Usually in groups, ±trooping. On soil in wet woods, especially with birch. Summer – autumn. Widespread. Very common. Inedible. SPORES ellipsoid, ornamentation (L3), 7–9.5×6–7.

1
Lactarius obscuratus. Size, habitat. CAP 1–2, at first slightly convex then flattened and slightly depressed or shallowly umbilicate, smooth, lined at margin. STEM 1.5–2.5, fairly slender, equal or tapering upwards, very finely velvety. GILLS creamy buff, sometimes with slight pinkish flush, fairly broad, fairly crowded, adnate – ±decurrent. SPORE PRINT white (A-B). TASTE faint, mild – slightly acrid. SMELL indistinct. MILK white, unchanging, mild – slightly acrid. FLESH pinkish buff, often with reddish flush. Usually in groups, ± trooping. On wet soil with alder. Summer – autumn. Common. Inedible. SPORES ellipsoid, ornamentation (L3), 6.5–7.5× 8.5–9.5.

2
Russula delica **Milk-White Russula**. Colour, size, overall form. CAP 5–16, at first, sometimes slightly convex, soon depressed – broadly funnel-shaped, dry, at first often finely velvety then smooth, margin markedly inrolled, cuticle not peeling. STEM 2–6, very stout, ± broadly spindle-shaped, finely velvety. GILLS whitish, spotting reddish-brown, variable broad-narrow, decurrent. SPORE PRINT white (A-B) or very slightly cream. TASTE hot, acrid, bitter. SMELL unpleasant, fishy-oily. FLESH white, unchanging or reddish brown in stem. Iron salts±salmon pink. Usually in groups, ±trooping. On soil with broad-leaved or coniferous trees. Autumn. Widespread. Very common. Edible. SPORES ellipsoid, ornamentation (R3-R6), 8–12×7–9. Cap cystidia worm-like – cylindrical, sulphovanillin almost – .

3
Russula chloroides. Very similar to *R. delica* but gills and stem apex differ. CAP 6–12, at first convex, then depressed – funnel-shaped, dry, at first often finely velvety then smooth, cuticle not peeling. STEM 3–6, very stout, equal or tapering downwards, very finely wrinkled, usually blue-green at apex. GILLS whitish or greenish, narrow, ± decurrent. SPORE PRINT white (A-B) or very slightly cream. TASTE hot, acrid, bitter. SMELL unpleasant, fishy-oily. FLESH white, unchanging. Iron salts±salmon-pink. Usually in groups, ±trooping. On soil with broad-leaved or coniferous trees. Autumn. Widespread. Uncommon. Inedible. SPORES broadly ellipsoid, ornamentation (R3/R6), 7–11×8.5. Cap cystidia worm-like – cylindrical, sulphovanillin almost – .

4
Russula nigricans **Blackening Russula**. Size and colour change, gill spacing. CAP 10–20, at first convex, then depressed, usually dry, smooth, cuticle three-quarters peeling. STEM 3–8, very stout, equal or tapering slightly downwards, smooth. GILLS straw-coloured – tinged olive-green, bruising greyish pink, then black, thick, distant, adnate. SPORE PRINT white (A). TASTE faint then slowly turning hot. SMELL fruity. FLESH white, turning red, greyish pink, then black. Iron salts pink then dirty greenish. Usually in groups, ±trooping. On soil with broad-leaved or coniferous trees. Autumn. Widespread. Extremely common. Edible. SPORES broadly ellipsoid – subspherical, ornamentation (R1/R11), 7–8×6–7. Cap cystidia absent.

5
Russula albonigra. Size and colour change. CAP 7–15, at first convex, then depressed, at first slightly sticky, then dry, ±smooth, cuticle three-quarters peeling, margin inrolled. STEM 3–6, stout, ±equal, finely velvety patterned, bruising black. GILLS±white-buff, rapidly bruising black, narrow, decurrent. SPORE PRINT white (A). TASTE mild or slightly hot, becoming bitter. SMELL indistinct. FLESH white, turning black when cut or bruised. Iron salts± salmon-pink. Usually in groups, ±trooping. On soil with broad-leaved or coniferous trees. Summer – autumn. Widespread. Uncommon. SPORES broadly ellipsoid – subspherical, ornamentation (R1/R11), 7–9×7–8. Cap cystidia absent.

6
Russula densifolia. Size, similar to *R. adusta* but taste and colour change differ. CAP 5–15, at first slightly convex, then depressed – funnel-shaped, sticky, then dry, ±smooth, cuticle moderately peeling, margin inrolled at first. STEM 3–6, stout, ±equal, bruising reddish. GILLS white – pale cream, narrow, crowded±decurrent. SPORE PRINT white (A). TASTE usually very hot, occasionally mild. SMELL indistinct. FLESH white, turning red then grey and almost black when cut or bruised. Iron salts pink then greenish. Usually in groups, ± trooping. On soil with broad-leaved or coniferous trees. Summer – autumn. Widespread. Very common. Edible. SPORES broadly ellipsoid – subspherical, ornamentation (R1/R11), 7–9×6–7. Cap cystidia sparse, narrow, sulphovanillin – .

7
Russula adusta. Similar to *R. densifolia* but colour change and taste differ. CAP 5–17, at first slightly convex, then depressed – funnel-shaped, sticky, then dry, ±smooth, cuticle scarcely peeling, margin inrolled at first. STEM 4–11, very stout, ±equal, bruising reddish. GILLS white – cream, not changing when bruised, ±decurrent. SPORE PRINT white (A). TASTE mild. SMELL unusual, old wine-casks. FLESH white, slowly turning pinkish then grey when cut or bruised. Iron salts pink then greenish. Usually in groups, ± trooping. On soil with pines. Summer – autumn. Widespread. Uncommon. Edible. SPORES broadly ellipsoid – subspherical, ornamentation (R1/R11), 7–9 ×6–8. Cap cystidia sparse, worm-like – cylindrical, headed, sometimes branched, sulphovanillin – .

8
Russula farinipes. Colour, smell, habitat. CAP 3–6, at first convex, then flattened and±depressed, ±smooth, cuticle scarcely peeling, margin markedly grooved and with small irregular lumps. STEM 3–6, fairly slender, ±equal but tapering sharply at base, finely floury at apex. GILLS white – pale straw-coloured, narrow, ±decurrent. SPORE PRINT white (A). TASTE very hot. SMELL fruity. FLESH white, flushed slightly yellow below cap cuticle. Iron salts±salmon-pink. Usually in groups, ±trooping. On soil with broad-leaved trees. Summer – autumn. Widespread. Common. Inedible. SPORES ellipsoid, ornamentation (R2), 5–7×6–8. Cap cystidia spindle-shaped, sulphovanillin purplish.

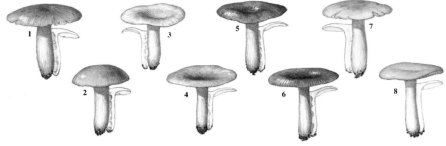

1

Russula foetens **Foetid Russula** Colour, smell, spores. CAP 5–15, at first markedly subspherical, then flattened and often slightly depressed, slimy-sticky especially at first, cuticle quarter – half peeling, margin markedly grooved and with small irregular warts. STEM 5–12, fairly stout, ±equal or sub-spindle-shaped, grooved or wrinkled. GILLS cream often with brown spotting, distant, adnexed. SPORE PRINT white – cream (B-D). TASTE gills very hot, stem more mild. FLESH whitish, turn ng reddish within when cut. Iron salts ± salmon-pink. Usually in groups, ± trooping. On soil with broad-leaved or coniferous trees. Summer – autumn. Widespread. Very common. Inedible. SPORES subspherical, ornamentation (R4), 7–9×8–10. Cap cystidia spindle-shaped, cylindrical or tapered, suphovanillin –

2

Russula laurocerasi. Similar to *R. foetens* but size, cap features, spores and smell differ. CAP 4–8, at first markedly subspherical, then flattened and often slightly depressed, slimy-sticky, especially at first, cuticle quarter – half peeling, margin markedly grooved and with small irregular warts. STEM 4–10, fairly stout, ±equal or subspindle-shaped, grooved or wrinkled. GILLS cream often with brown spotting, distant, adnexed. SPORE PRINT white – cream (B-D). TASTE variable, mild – hot. SMELL bitter almonds. FLESH whitish, turning reddish tawny within when cut. Iron salts ± salmon pink. Usually in groups, ± trooping. On soil with broad-leaved or coniferous trees, especially with oak. Summer –

autumn. Widespread. Common. Inedible. SPORES subspherical, ornamentation (R3/R13), 7–9×8–10. Cap cystidia spindle-shaped, cylindrical or tapered, sulphovanillin – .

3

Russula pectinatoides. Overall colour, cap margin, smell. CAP 4–7, at first convex – dome-shaped, then flattened and slightly depressed, slightly greasy, cuticle one-third – two-thirds peeling, margin markedly grooved and with small irregular warts. STEM 3–4, fairly stout, ±equal. GILLS yellowish buff – greyish, often forked or with interconnections, adnexed. SPORE PRINT white – cream (B-D). TASTE faint, mild. SMELL faint, fruity. FLESH whitish. Iron salts ± salmon-pink. Usually in groups, ± trooping. On soil with broad-leaved trees. Summer – autumn. Widespread. Rare. Inedible. SPORES subspherical, ornamentation (R2/R10), 5–6×6.5–8. Cap cystidia narrowed with terminal appendage, sulphovanillin ± - .

4

Russula pectinata. Similar to *R. pectinatoides* but colour, stickiness and smell differ. CAP 3–6, at first convex – dome-shaped, then flattened and slightly depressed, often with rusty spots, sticky, cuticle one-third – two-thirds peeling, margin markedly grooved and with small irregular warts, appearing like teeth of a comb. STEM 3–5, fairly stout, ±equal, floury at apex, stained rusty-red at base. GILLS white, turning cream, adnexed. SPORE PRINT cream – pale ochreous (D-F). TASTE unpleasant, oily. SMELL oily. FLESH whitish. Iron salts ± salmon pink. Usually in groups, ± trooping. On soil with coniferous or

broad-leaved trees, especially oaks. Summer – autumn. Widespread. Uncommon. Inedible. SPORES ellipsoid, ornamentation (R2-R6), 5.5–6×8–9. Cap cystidia cylindrical-tapered, some with terminal appendage, sulphovanillin slightly purple.

5

Russula amoenolens. Overall colour, smell, habitat, similar to *R. sororia* q.v. CAP 3–6, at first convex, then flattened and slightly depressed, slightly sticky when wet, cuticle half peeling, margin grooved and with small irregular warts. STEM 3–6, fairly stout, ± equal, smooth. GILLS cream – dirty white, later with brownish edge, ± adnexed. SPORE PRINT white – cream (B–D). TASTE unpleasant, oily, turning hot. SMELL rancid. FLESH white. Iron salts ± salmon pink. Usually in groups, ± trooping. On soil with oaks. Summer – autumn. Widespread. Uncommon. Inedible. SPORES broadly ellipsoid, ornamentation (R2-R7). 7–9×5–7. Cap cystidia tapered, sulphovanillin very faintly purple.

6

Russula sororia. Similar to *R. amoenolens* but size, spores, smell and stem colour differ. CAP 5–12, at first convex, then flattened and slightly depressed, slightly sticky when wet, cuticle half peeling, margin grooved and with small irregular warts. STEM 5–9, fairly stout, ± equal, smooth. GILLS cream – dirty white, ± adnexed. SPORE PRINT white – cream (B-D). TASTE unpleasant, rather acrid. SMELL faint, slightly fruity or fishy, not rancid. FLESH white. Iron salts ± salmon pink. Usually in groups, ± trooping. On soil with oaks. Summer – autumn. Widespread. Common. Inedible. SPORES

subspherical, ornamentation (R1/R7), 6–8.5×5.5–7. Cap cystidia tapered, sulphovanillin very faintly purple.

7

Russula fellea **Pelargonium scented Russula.** Colour, smell, habitat. CAP 4–9, at first convex, then flattened and ± broadly umbonate, slightly sticky, especially when wet, cuticle one-third peeling, margin smooth or slightly grooved. STEM 2–6, fairly stout, ± equal or tapering slightly upwards, smooth. GILLS pale straw – ochre, adnexed. SPORE PRINT white – pale cream (A-C). TASTE hot. SMELL pelargoniums. FLESH white. Iron salts buff. Usually in groups, ± trooping. On soil with beech. Summer – autumn. Widespread. Extremely common. Inedible. SPORES ellipsoid, ornamentation (R11), 7.5–9×6–7. Cap cystidia cylindrical – ± club-shaped, sulphovanillin purple.

8

Russula ochroleuca. Overall colour, microscopic features, habitat. CAP 4–12, at first convex, then flattened and slightly depressed, cuticle two-thirds peeling, slightly sticky when wet, margin smooth at first then slightly grooved. STEM 4–7, fairly slender, usually tapering slightly upwards, smooth. GILLS cream, adnexed. SPORE PRINT white – pale cream (A-C). TASTE mild – fairly hot. SMELL indistinct. FLESH white. Iron salts ± salmon-pink. Usually in groups, ± trooping. On soil with coniferous or broad-leaved trees. Summer – autumn. Widespread. Extremely common. Inedible. SPORES ellipsoid, ornamentation (R10), 8–10×7–8. Cap cystidia absent.

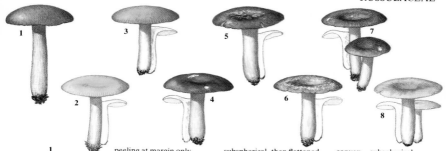

1
Russula consobrina. Overall colour, microscopic features, habitat. CAP 8–12, at first convex then flattened, cuticle? peeling, shiny, minutely and obscurely fibrous. STEM 6–10, fairly stout, tapering slightly upwards – almost club-shaped, smooth. GILLS white, adnexed. SPORE PRINT white-pale cream (B–C). TASTE fairly acrid. SMELL faint, indefinite or very slightly fruity. FLESH white-greyish, often turning slightly reddish. Iron salts? Usually in groups,± trooping. On soil in wet places, especially with spruce. Late summer – autumn. Predominantly northern and montane. Rare. Inedible. SPORES ellipsoid, ornamentation (R3/R12), 6–10×5–8.

2
Russula claroflava **Yellow Swamp Russula.** Overall colour, habitat. CAP 4–10, at first convex, then flattened and slightly depressed, slightly sticky, especially when wet, cuticle half – two-thirds peeling, margin smooth at first then slightly grooved. STEM 4–19, fairly stout, slender, usually tapering slightly upwards, smooth. GILLS pale ochre, adnexed. SPORE PRINT pale ochre (F). TASTE mild – slightly hot. SMELL indistinct. FLESH white. Iron salts reddish, then grey. Usually in groups,± trooping. On wet soil with birch. Spring – autumn. Widespread. Very common. Edible. SPORES ellipsoid, ornamentation (R10), 9–10×7.5–8. Cap cystidia absent.

3
Russula decolorans. Overall colour, cap features, habitat. CAP 4–11, at first convex – dome-shaped, then flattened and slightly depressed, slightly sticky, especially when wet, cuticle

peeling at margin only, margin smooth at first then usually slightly grooved. STEM 4–10, fairly stout, usually tapering slightly upwards, smooth. GILLS pale ochre, blackening when handled, adnexed. SPORE PRINT yellowish cream – pale ochre (E-F). TASTE mild. SMELL indistinct. FLESH whitish but soon turning grey when cut. Iron salts±salmon-pink. Usually in groups,± trooping. On soil with conifers. Summer – autumn. Northern. Rare. Edible. SPORES ellipsoid, ornamentation (R4/R9), 7–12×9–14. Cap cystidia±club-shaped, sometimes with cross-wall, sulphovanillin moderately purple.

4
Russula obscura. Overall colour, colour change, cap features, microscopic features, habitat. CAP 4–11, at first convex then flattened and slightly depressed, cuticle half – two-thirds peeling, margin smooth at first then grooved. STEM 6–12, fairly slender, usually tapering slightly upwards, smooth. GILLS yellowish straw-coloured, with slightly purple edging, turning markedly black when handled, strong interveining between, adnexed. SPORE PRINT yellowish cream – pale ochre (E-F). TASTE mild. SMELL indistinct. FLESH whitish but soon turning slightly pinkish then black when cut. Iron salts slightly reddish, then grey. Usually in groups,± trooping. On soil with conifers. Summer – autumn. Northern, highland. Rare. Edible. SPORES ellipsoid and flattened (R4), 8–11.5×6.5–9. Cap cystidia absent.

5
Russula cutefracta. Very similar to *R. cyanoxantha* but cap surface differs. CAP 5–15, at first convex –

subspherical, then flattened and slightly depressed, eventually cracking into small fragments, very variable colours, greasy when wet, with radiating, branching veins. STEM 5–10, fairly stout, usually tapering slightly upwards, smooth. GILLS white or very pale cream, feeling oily and flexible, partly forked, narrow, adnexed. SPORE PRINT white (A). TASTE mild. SMELL indistinct. FLESH white. Iron salts – . Usually in groups,± trooping. On soil with broad-leaved trees. Summer – autumn. Widespread. Uncommon. Edible. SPORES broadly ellipsoid, ornamentation (R2), 6–7×7–9. Cap cystidia short, very narrow, sulphovanillin strongly purple.

6
Russula virescens. Cap features, microscopic features, habitat. CAP 5–12, at first convex – subspherical then flattened and usually rather wavy, gradually breaking into small granular patches, cuticle half peeling, margin smooth or slightly grooved. STEM 4–9, fairly stout, usually±equal but narrowing below, floury at apex, smooth. GILLS cream, rather interveined at base, adnexed. SPORE PRINT white (A-B). TASTE mild. SMELL indistinct. FLESH white. Iron salts±salmon pink. Usually in groups,± trooping. On soil with broad-leaved trees, especially beech. Summer – autumn. Widespread. Common. Edible. SPORES broadly ellipsoid – subspherical, ornamentation (very variable R1–3/R6–12), 6–7×7–9. Cap cystidia absent.

7
Russula cyanoxantha **The Charcoal Burner.** Cap colours, gill features, iron salts reaction, microscopic features. CAP 5–15, at first

convex – subspherical, then flattened and slightly depressed, very variable colours (completely green in var. *peltereaui*), cuticle half peeling, greasy when wet, with radiating, branching veins. STEM 5–10, fairly stout, usually tapering slightly upwards, smooth. GILLS white or very pale cream, feeling oily and flexible, partly forked, narrow, adnexed. SPORE PRINT white (A). TASTE mild. SMELL indistinct. FLESH white. Iron salts – . Usually in groups,± trooping. On soil with broad-leaved trees. Summer – autumn. Widespread. Extremely common. (var. *peltereaui* Uncommon). Edible. SPORES broadly ellipsoid, ornamentation (R2), 6–7×7–9. Cap cystidia short, very narrow, sulphovanillin strongly purple.

8
Russula heterophylla. Iron salts, spore print colour, spore size. CAP 5–10, at first convex – subspherical, then flattened and slightly depressed, variable colours (yellow in var. *chlora*), cuticle ? peeling, slightly sticky, with radiating, branching veins. STEM 3–6, stout, usually±equal or tapering slightly at base, smooth. GILLS white or very pale cream, interveined and forking, crowded, adnexed. SPORE PRINT white (A). TASTE mild. SMELL indistinct. FLESH white. Iron salts strongly salmon-pink. Usually in groups,± trooping. On soil with broad-leaved trees. Summer – autumn. Widespread. Uncommon. (var. *chlora* Rare). Edible. SPORES broadly ellipsoid – subspherical or pear-shaped, ornamentation (R1/R7), 5–7×4–6. Cap cystidia variable, club-shaped, spindle-shaped, tapered or cylindrical, sulphovanillin slightly purple.

103

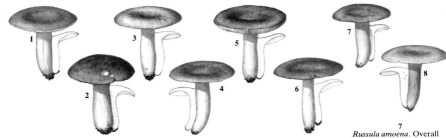

1

Russula vesca **Bared Teeth Russula.** Cap margin, iron salts. CAP 6–10, at first convex – subspherical, then flattened and slightly depressed, variable colours, cuticle half peeling and drawing from margin so gills appear teeth-like, slightly sticky, smooth. STEM 3–10, stout, usually± equal or tapering slightly upwards but narrowed at extreme base, smooth. GILLS white or very pale cream, slightly interveined, narrow, crowded, adnexed. SPORE PRINT white (A). TASTE mild, nutty. SMELL indistinct. FLESH white. Iron salts quickly salmon-pink. Usually in groups,± trooping. On soil with broad-leaved trees. Summer – autumn. Widespread. Very common. Edible. SPORES subspherical, ornamentation (R1/R6), 5–6×6–8. Cap cystidia spindle-shaped or cylindrical, sulphovanillin – .

2

Russula mustelina. Overall features and habitat. CAP 5–10, at first subspherical, then convex – flattened, cuticle half peeling when mature, slightly sticky when wet, smooth – finely granular, margin smooth or slightly grooved. STEM 3–8, fairly stout,± spindle-shaped or equal, but narrowed at extreme base, mealy-floury at apex. GILLS cream – pale straw-coloured, forked close to stem, adnate – sinuate. SPORE PRINT white – cream (B-D). TASTE mild. SMELL indistinct. FLESH white. Iron salts brownish pink. Usually in groups,± trooping. On soil with conifers. Summer – autumn. Northern?, highland. Rare. Inedible. SPORES broadly ellipsoid, ornamentation (variable, R1–R2/R6–R9), 7–10 ×6–8. Cap cystidia sparse, club-shaped or cylindrical, sulphovanillin – .

3

Russula aeruginea. Cap colour, habitat. CAP 4–9, at first convex then flattened-depressed, cuticle half peeling, slightly sticky when wet, smooth or radially veined, margin smooth or slightly grooved. STEM 4–8, with rust-coloured spots, fairly stout,±equal, smooth. GILLS yellowish buff, usually forked, adnexed. SPORE PRINT cream – yellowish cream (D-E). TASTE mild – slightly hot. SMELL indistinct. FLESH white. Iron salts±salmon pink. Usually in groups,±trooping. On soil with birch. Summer – autumn. Widespread. Common. Edible. SPORES ellipsoid, ornamentation (R1/R12), 6–10×5–7. Cap cystidia spindle-shaped – cylindrical, sulphovanillin moderately purple.

4

Russula grisea. Extremely similar to *R. ionochlora*, only microscopic features differ reliably. CAP 5–11, at first convex then flattened – depressed, cuticle quarter – half peeling, slightly sticky when wet, sometimes slightly floury, smooth, margin smooth or slightly grooved. STEM 4–9, fairly stout,±equal, smooth. GILLS ochre – cream, adnexed. SPORE PRINT cream (D). TASTE mild – slightly hot. SMELL indistinct. FLESH white. Iron salts±salmon-pink. Usually in groups,± trooping. On soil, usually with beech. Summer – autumn Widespread. Common. Edible. SPORES ellipsoid, ornamentation (R3/R5), 6.5–8×5.5–6.5. Cap cystidia mostly club-shaped, sulphovanillin strongly purple. Tips of cap surface hyphae long and narrow.

5

Russula parazurea. Overall features. CAP 3–8, at first convex then flattened or slightly depressed, cuticle half – two-thirds peeling, slightly sticky when wet, sometimes slightly floury when dry, smooth, margin smooth. STEM 3–7, fairly stout,±equal or tapering slightly upwards, smooth. GILLS pale buff, often forked, adnexed. SPORE PRINT pale cream – cream (C-D). TASTE mild – slightly hot. SMELL indistinct. Iron salts pale salmon-pink. Usually in groups,±trooping. On soil, usually with broad-leaved trees. Summer – autumn. Widespread. Common. Edible. SPORES ellipsoid, ornamentation (R2/R11–R12), 5.5–8.5×5–6.5. Cap cystidia club-shaped – cylindrical, sometimes with appendages, sulphovanillin±moderately purple.

6

Russula ionochlora. Extremely similar to *R. grisea*, only microscopic features differ reliably. CAP 4.5–7, at first convex then flattened – depressed, cuticle quarter – half peeling, with irregular radial veining, slightly sticky when wet, smooth, margin smooth or slightly grooved. STEM 3–7, fairly stout,± equal, often rather distorted, smooth. GILLS pale cream, sometimed forked, adnexed. SPORE PRINT white – pale cream (B-C). TASTE hot when young, then mild. SMELL indistinct. FLESH white. Iron salts±salmon-pink. Usually in groups,± trooping. On soil with beech. Summer – autumn. Widespread. Common. Edible. SPORES ellipsoid, ornamentation (R1–R2), 6.5–7.5 ×4.5–6. Cap cystidia cylindrical, club-shaped, or± spindle-shaped, sulphovanillin strongly purple. Tips of cap surface hyphae broad and rounded.

7

Russula amoena. Overall colour, gill colour, chemical test. CAP 2–5, at first convex then flattened-depressed, cuticle scarcely peeling, usually dry, very finely velvety, margin smooth. STEM 2–5, fairly slender,±equal but markedly narrowed at base, very finely downy-floury. GILLS pale cream, fairly narrow, fairly crowded, often slightly purple in parts at edge, adnexed. SPORE PRINT pale cream – cream (C-D). TASTE mild. SMELL strong, curious, fishy. Phenol on flesh, carmine purple. FLESH white. Iron salts±salmon pink. Usually in groups,±trooping. On soil with coniferous or broad-leaved trees. Summer – autumn. Widespread. Uncommon. Inedible. SPORES subspherical, ornamentation (R2/R10–R11), 6–7×5.5–6.5. Cap cystidia absent.

8

Russula violeipes. Similar to *R. amoena* q.v. but chemical test differs. CAP 4–8, at first convex – dome-shaped, then flattened – depressed, cuticle scarcely peeling, very finely granular-velvety, margin smooth. STEM 4–7, fairly slender,±equal but markedly narrowed at base, very finely downy-floury, especially towards apex. GILLS pale buff – straw-coloured, fairly narrow, fairly crowded, especially when young, usually forked close to stem, inter-veined, rather greasy to feel,±decurrent. SPORE PRINT pale cream – cream (C-D). TASTE mild. SMELL faint, fishy, shrimps. Phenol on flesh brownish wine red. FLESH white. Iron salts±salmon-pink. Usual in groups,±trooping. On soil with coniferous or broad-leaved trees. Summer – autumn. Widespread. Uncommon. Edible. SPORES subspherical, ornamentation (R3/R11–R12), 6.5–9×6–8. Cap cystidia absent.

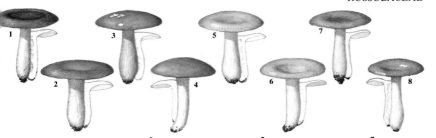

1

ssula turci. Similar to *R. rubea* but smell and ores differ, cap never h prominent central bo, also to *R. cessans*. CAP 3–10, at first conx then flattened – pressed, cuticle one-third en dry. STEM 3–7, fairly nder, usually tapering wards – ±club-shaped, y finely downy-floury. LS yellow, strongly interned, adnexed. SPORE NT ochreous (G). TASTE d. SMELL iodine, espeally at stem base. FLESH ite. Iron salts±salmonk. Usually in groups,± oping. On soil with conifus trees. Summer – aut-.n. Predominantly north-. Rare. Edible. SPORES psoid, ornamentation 11–R12), 6–8×7–9. Cap tidia absent.

2

ssula rubra. Smell, miccopic features. CAP 4–11, irst convex, then tened – depressed, cutiscarcely peeling,±finely vety, often with whitish om. STEM 4–7, fairly nder, equal, often finely nkled. GILLS strawoured, forked, adnexed. RE PRINT yellowish am – ochreous (E-F). STE fairly hot. SMELL ney. FLESH white, redh below cap cuticle. Iron ts±salmon-pink. Usually groups,±trooping. On l with broad-leaved es. Summer – autumn. despread. Uncommon. edible. SPORES subspher-l, ornamentation (R2– /R7–R9), 6–8×7–9. Cap tidia variable, mostly b-shaped, also indrical – spindleaped, sulphovanillin ong.

3

Russula lepida. Taste, smell, microscopic features. CAP 4–10, at first convex then flattened – depressed, cuticle scarcely peeling, dry, often downyfloury. STEM 3–7, fairly stout, tapering upwards – ±club-shaped, very finely downy-floury. GILLS pale cream, fairly crowded, adnexed – free. SPORE PRINT white – pale cream (B-C). TASTE bitter, resinous, cedarwood. SMELL faint, fruity, menthol. FLESH white. Iron salts±salmon-pink. Usually in groups,±trooping. On soil with broad-leaved trees, especially beech. Summer – autumn. Widespread. Common. Inedible. SPORES subspherical, ornamentation (R2/R11–R12), 7–8×8–9. Cap cystidia variable, spindle-shaped,± club-shaped, cylindrical or tapering, sulphovanillin – .

4

Russula pseudointegra. Smell, habitat, microscopic features. CAP 4–10, at first convex – dome-shaped, then flattened – slightly depressed, cuticle onethird – two-thirds peeling, slightly sticky when wet, later dry, often downyfloury. STEM 3–7, fairly slender,±equal or tapering slightly upwards,±smooth. GILLS pale yellow, adnexed. SPORE PRINT pale ochreous – ochreous (F-G). TASTE bitter – not. SMELL rather faint, pelargonium, menthol. FLESH white. Iron salts±salmon pink. Usually in groups,±trooping. On soil with broad-leaved trees, especially oak on clayey sites. Summer – autumn. Widespread. Uncommon. Inedible. SPORES subspherical, ornamentation (R2/R9–R10), 6.5–8×7–9. Cap cystidia absent.

5

Russula rosea. Chemical test. CAP 4–9, at first convex then flattened – slightly depressed, cuticle half peeling, dry, often downyfloury, margin smooth then slightly lined. STEM 4–7, slender, equal or tapering slightly upwards, rather floury, especially towards apex and when young. GILLS pale cream, forked, especially close to stem, adnexed. SPORE PRINT white (B). TASTE mild. SMELL indistinct or slightly fruity. Sulphovanillin on stem when dry, carmine. FLESH white. Iron salts±salmon-pink. Usually in groups,± trooping. On soil with broad-leaved trees. Summer – autumn. Widespread. Common. Edible. SPORES broadly ellipsoid – subspherical, ornamentation (R1/R12), 6–8×5–6.5. Cap cystidia absent.

6

Russula lutea. Size, overall colour, cap surface features, smell features, smell. CAP 2–7, at first convex then flattened – broadly depressed, cuticle threequarters – completely peeling, margin usually smooth or very slightly lined. STEM 2–6, fairly stout,±equal or tapering slightly upwards, rather silky. GILLS deep yellow, strongly interveined, adnexed. SPORE PRINT ochre (H). TASTE mild. SMELL at first indistinct, then fruity (apricots?). FLESH white. Iron salts±salmon-pink. Usually in groups,±trooping. On soil with broadleaved trees. Summer – autumn. Widespread. Very common. Edible. SPORES broadly ellipsoid, ornamentation (R5/R6), 6–8×7.5–9. Cap cystidia absent.

7

Russula odorata. Overall colour, stem colour, habitat, similar to *R. nauseosa* but habitat and spores differ. CAP 2–5, at first convex then flattened – depressed, cuticle almost completely peeling, margin at first smooth then grooved. STEM 2.5–5, fairly stout,±equal, tapering upwards or±clubshaped, very slowly bruising yellowish. GILLS yellow, strongly interveined, adnexed. SPORE PRINT ochreous – ochre (G-H). TASTE mild or slightly hot. SMELL fruity. FLESH white. Iron salts±salmon-pink. Usually in groups,±trooping. On soil in broad-leaved and mixed woods. Summer – autumn. Widespread. Uncommon. Inedible? SPORES ellipsoid, ornamentation (R3/R11), 6.5–8.5× 5.5–7. Cap cystidia cylindrical – ±club-shaped, sulphovanillin purple.

8

Russula nauseosa. Overall colour, stem colour, less distinct odour, habitat, similar to *R. odorata* but habitat and spores differ. CAP 2–7, at first convex then flattened – broadly depressed, cuticle easily and almost completely peeling, margin usually grooved and with small warty bumps. STEM 2–7.5, fairly stout,±equal or tapering upwards, bruising yellow or greyish brown. GILLS yellow, interveined, adnexed. SPORE PRINT ochreous – ochre (G-H). TASTE mild or slightly hot. SMELL indistinct or very slightly fruity. FLESH white. Iron salts±salmon-pink. Usually in groups,±trooping. On soil in coniferous woods. Summer – autumn. Predominantly northern, at least in Britain. Uncommon. Inedible. SPORES ellipsoid, ornmanetation (R3), 7–11×6–9. Cap cystidia cylindrical – narrowed, sometimes swollen at tip, sulphovanillin purple.

105

RUSSULACEAE

1

Russula cessans. Overall colour, habitat, similar to *R. turci* but lack of smell and presence of cap cystidia differ. CAP 3–7, at first convex then flattened – depressed, cuticle half peeling, sticky when wet, margin smooth or very faintly lined. STEM 3–5, fairly stout, ±equal or tapering slightly downwards, very finely veined. GILLS yellow, adnexed. SPORE PRINT ochreous (G). TASTE mild. SMELL indistinct. FLESH white. Iron salts±salmon-pink. Usually in groups, ±trooping. On soil with pines. Summer – autumn. Widespread. Uncommon. Inedible. SPORES subspherical, ornamentation (R2–R3/R8–R11), 8–9.5×7.5–8. Cap cystidia cylindrical – club-shaped, sulphovanillin purple.

2

Russula brunneoviolacea. Overall colour, habitat. CAP 3–7, at first convex then flattened – depressed, cuticle three-quarters peeling, slightly sticky when wet, margin at first smooth then grooved. STEM 3–6, fairly slender, ±equal or tapering slightly upwards. GILLS cream, adnexed. SPORE PRINT pale cream – yellowish cream, (C-E). TASTE mild. SMELL indistinct. FLESH white. Iron salts±salmon-pink. Usually in groups, ±trooping. On soil with broad-leaved trees, especially oaks. Summer – autumn. Widespread. Uncommon. Edible. SPORES broadly ellipsoid – subspherical, ornamentation (R2–R3/R7–R8), 7–9×6–7.5. Cap cystidia mostly club-shaped, some cylindrical, sulphovanillin moderately purple.

3

Russula nitida. Overall colour, gills, habitat, similar to *R. puellaris* but no yellow bruising. CAP 2–6, at first convex then flattened – depressed, cuticle half – two-thirds peeling, slightly sticky when wet, margin usually markedly grooved. STEM 2–6, fairly slender, ± equal or tapering slightly upwards. GILLS straw-coloured, sometimes reddish in parts at margin, interveined, fairly distant, adnexed. SPORE PRINT yellowish cream – ochreous (E-G). TASTE mild or very slightly hot. SMELL indistinct. FLESH white. Iron salts±salmon-pink. Usually in groups, ±trooping. On soil or among *Sphagnum* or other mosses in damp birch woods. Summer – autumn. Widespread. Very common. Edible. SPORES ellipsoid, ornamentation (R2–R3–R6), 6–9×8–11. Cap cystidia cylindrical, spindle-shaped or club-shaped, sulphovanillin purple.

4

Russula puellaris. Overall colour, gills, habitat, colour change on bruising. CAP 2.5–5, at first convex then flattened – depressed, cuticle half – two-thirds peeling, slightly sticky when wet, margin usually markedly powdered and grooved. STEM 2–6.5, fairly slender, ±equal or tapering slightly upwards, bruising yellow. GILLS pale ochreous, adnexed. SPORE PRINT cream – yellowish cream (D-E). TASTE mild. SMELL indistinct. FLESH white. Iron salts±salmon-pink. Usually in groups, ±trooping. On soil with coniferous or broad-leaved trees. Summer – autumn. Common. Edible. SPORES ellipsoid, ornamentation (R3–R6) 6.5–9×5.5 –7. Cap cystidia mostly club-shaped, some cylindrical, sulphovanillin purple.

5

Russula melliolens. Size, smell, microscopic features. CAP 3–8, at first convex – dome-shaped, then flattened – depressed, cuticle half peeling, slightly sticky when wet, margin at first fairly smooth but often slightly grooved on aging. STEM 4–10, fairly slender, ±equal or tapering slightly upwards, bruising and discolouring rather brownish, especially in grooves. GILLS cream, often stained brownish, fairly broad, forked, adnexed. SPORE PRINT cream (D). TASTE mild. SMELL faint, sweet, honey, gingerbread. FLESH white. Iron salts±salmon-pink. Usually in groups, ±trooping. On soil with broad-leaved trees. Summer – autumn. Widespread. Uncommon. Inedible. SPORES subspherical, ornamentation (R1/R12) 8.5–11×8–9.5. Cap cystidia very elongated with up to 12 cross-walls, sulpho-vanillin moderately.

6

Russula erythropus. Size, chemical tests, smell; this is the true *R. xerampelina* and habitat differs from other forms of this species. CAP 6–11, at first convex then flattened – depressed, cuticle peeling at margin only, slightly sticky when wet, margin at first fairly smooth but grooved on aging. STEM 4–13, fairly slender, ±equal or tapering slightly upwards, bruising strongly brownish, especially on veins, slightly floury at apex. GILLS buff, fairly distant, interveined, adnexed. SPORE PRINT yellowish cream – pale ochre (E-F). TASTE mild. SMELL fishy, crabs. FLESH white. Iron salts dull green. Usually in groups, ±trooping. On soil with coniferous trees. Summer – autumn. Widespread but predominantly northern. Uncommon. Edible. SPORES ellipsoid, ornamentation (R3/R6-R7) 7– 8.5×8–10. Cap cystidia sparse, mostly cylindrical or spindle-shaped, sulphovanillin – .

7

Russula xerampelina. Size chemical tests, smell, extremely variable, an aggregate composed of several species. CAP 5–14, first convex then flattene depressed, extremely vari able colour, red – purple green – buff – whitish, cuticle up to one quarter peeling, slightly sticky when wet, margin at first smooth but often groove on aging. STEM 3–11, fairl slender, ±equal or taperi slightly upwards, bruising brownish ochre, especial on veins. GILLS pale ochreous, fairly broad, fairly thick, often inter-veined, adnexed. SPORE PRINT yellowish cream – pale ochre (E-F). TASTE mild. SMELL fishy, crabs. FLESH white. Iron salts du green. Usually in groups, ±trooping. On so with broad-leaved trees, especially beech and oak. Summer – autumn. Wide spread. Very common. Edible. SPORES ellipsoid, ornamentation (R3/R6– R8) 6.5–9×8–11. Cap cys tidia variable, mostly club shaped, cylindrical, taper ing or spindle-shaped, sulphovanillin – .

8

Russula caerulea. Cap fea tures, habitat. CAP 3–8, at first convex – conical, the flattened and acutely – broadly umbonate, cuticle one-quarter – two-thirds peeling, very slightly stick when wet, margin faintly lined especially on aging. STEM 4–9, slender, ±equal or tapering upwards, ofte rather bumpy and wavy. GILLS pale ochre, fairly crowded, adnexed. SPORE PRINT ochreous (G). TASTE mild, cap rather bitter. SMELL indistinct. FLESH white. iron salts±salmon-pink. Usually in groups, ± trooping. On soil with pines. Summer – autumn Widespread. Edible. SPORES ellipsoid, ornamentation (R3–R4/R R9), 7–9×8–10. Cap cyst dia absent.

106

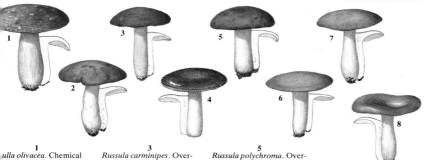

1

ulla olivacea. Chemical
s, habitat, similar to *R.
.acea* but stem colour
spores differ. CAP 6–16,
rst convex – dome-
ped, then flattened –
ressed, cuticle up to
-third peeling, only very
ntly sticky when wet,
concentric cracking on
ag. STEM 5–10, fairly
der,±equal or tapering
vards, often with pinkish
h at apex, brownish at
e. GILLS buff – straw-
oured, forked and inter-
ed, adnexed. SPORE
T ochreous – ochre (G-
TASTE mild, nutty.
LL indistinct. FLESH
te. Iron salts±salmon-
k. Phenol on stem deep
ple. Usually in groups,
ooping. On soil with
ch trees. Summer – aut-
n. Widespread. Com-
n. Edible. SPORES ellips-
ornamentation (R2–
R6–R7), 7–9×8–11.
cystidia absent.

2

sula alutacea. Chemical
s, habitat, similar to *R.
.acea* but stem colour
spores differ. CAP 7–13,
rst convex – dome-
ped, then flattened –
ressed, cuticle up to
-quarter peeling, only
slightly sticky when
, margin smooth, some-
es with concentric
:king on aging. STEM 3–
fairly slender,±equal or
ering upwards, often
pinkish flush at base.
s pale yellowish,
ed and interveined,
exed. SPORE PRINT
reous – ochre (G-H).
TE mild. SMELL indis-
t. FLESH white. Iron
s±salmon-pink. Phenol
tem deep purple.
ally in groups,±troop-
On soil with broad-
ed trees. Summer –
umn. Widespread. Un-
mon. Edible. SPORES
osoid, ornamentation
/R8–R10)6.5–8.5×8–
Cap cystidia absent.

3

Russula carminipes. Overall colour, cap surface features, stem colours, spores.
CAP 4–10, at first convex –
±dome-shaped, then
flattened – depressed, cuticle one-quarter – halp peeling, very slightly sticky,
smooth or minutely
roughened. STEM 3–6, fairly
stout,±equal or tapering
slightly upwards, often with
pinkish flush, bruising yellowish brown, often floury
at apex, often with purple at edge,
adnexed. SPORE PRINT
ochreous (G). TASTE mild.
SMELL indistinct. FLESH
white. Iron salts±salmon-
pink. Usually in groups,±
trooping. On soil with
broad-leaved trees. Sum-
mer – autumn. Wide-
spread. Uncommon. Edi-
ble? SPORES ellipsoid, ornamentation (R1/R10–R11),
6.5–8×8–10. Cap cystidia
sparse, club-shaped –
cylindrical, sulphovanillin
moderately purple.

4

Russula integra. Overall
colour, spores, habitat. CAP
6–10, at first convex then
flattened-depressed, cuticle? peeling, very slightly
sticky, margin at first
smooth then slightly
grooved. STEM 4–6, fairly
stout,±equal or tapering
slightly upwards. GILLS
deep straw-colour,
adnexed. SPORE PRINT
ochreous? (G). TASTE mild.
SMELL indistinct. FLESH
white. Iron salts±salmon-
pink. Usually in groups,±
trooping. On soil with
broad-leaved trees espec-
ially (always?) beeches.
Summer – autumn. Wide-
spread. Rare. Edible?
SPORES broadly ellipsoid –
subspherical, ornamenta-
tion (R1/R6–R7), 8–
8.5×7.5–8.5. Cap cystidia?

5

Russula polychroma. Overall colour, spores, habitat,
sometimes confused with
R. integra but habitat and
spores differ. CAP 5–12m at
first convex then flattened –
depressed, cuticle half peeling, very slightly sticky
when wet, margin grooved
like teeth of a comb. STEM
3–9, fairly stout, equal.
GILLS yellow, adnexed.
SPORE PRINT ochreous –
ochre (G-H). TASTE mild.
SMELL indistinct. FLESH
white. Iron salts±salmon-
pink. Usually in groups,±
trooping. On soil in coniferous woods. Summer – aut-
umn. Northern, predomin-
antly highland, Scotland in
Britain. Uncommon. Edi-
ble. SPORES ellipsoid, ornamentation (R4), 7–9.5×9–
11. Cap cystidia club-
shaped – cylindrical, sulphovanillin moderately
purple.

6

Russula curtipes. Stem features, spores, habita. CAP
5–12, at first convex then
flattened – depressed, cuticle half peeling, barely
sticky when wet, smooth
but small concentric cracks
at margin. STEM 3–7,
stout,±equal. GILLS pale
yellow, adnexed. SPORE
PRINT pale ochreous (F).
TASTE mild. SMELL indis-
tinct. FLESH white. Iron
salts±salmon-pink. Usually
in groups,±trooping. On
soil with beech trees.
Summer – autumn. Wide-
spread. Uncommon. Edi-
ble. SPORES subspherical,
ornamentation (R4/R5), 7–
7.5×6–6.5. Cap cystidia
sparse, cylindrical,
sulphovanillin – .

7

Rusulla romellii. Microscopic features. CAP 6–15, at
first convex then flattened –
depressed, cuticle at least
half peeling, very slightly
sticky when wet, smooth,
margin usually grooved.
STEM 3–9, stout,±equal.
GILLS pale yellow, inter-
veined, adnexed. SPORE
PRINT pale ochreous (F-G).
TASTE mild. SMELL indis-
tinct. FLESH white. Iron
salts±salmon-pink. Usually
in groups,±trooping. On
soil with broad-leaved
trees. Summer – autumn.
Widespread. Uncommon.
Edible? SPORES broadly
ellipsoid – subspherical,
ornamentation (R2–R4/
R9–R10), 7–9×6–7. Cap
cystidia sparse, worm-like
or club-shaped, sulphova-
nillin weakly purple.

8

Russula paludosa. Size,
microscopic features, habitat. CAP 4–16, at first convex
then flattened – depressed,
usually broadly umbonate,
cuticle half – three-
quarters peeling, very
slightly sticky when wet,
smooth, margin grooved on
aging. STEM 4–15, fairly
slender,±equal – spindle-
shaped, sometimes pink-
flushed. GILLS pale yellow,
sometimes with reddish
flush at edge, interveined,
adnexed. SPORE PRINT pale
ochreous (F). TASTE mild.
SMELL indistinct. FLESH
white. Iron salts±salmon-
pink. Usually in groups,±
trooping. On soil, often
among mosses, with coni-
fers. Summer – autumn.
Predominantly northern.
Uncommon. Edible.
SPORES ellipsoid, ornamentation (R2–R3/R7–R9), 7–
8×8–10.5. Cap cystidia
sparse, club-shaped – cylindrical, sulphovanillin
moderately purple.

RUSSULACEAE

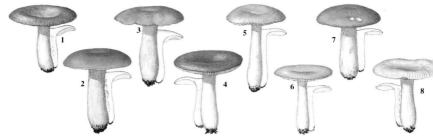

1
Russula velenovskyi. Size, microscopic features, habitat. CAP 2–8, at first convex – ±dome-shaped, then flattened – depressed, often broadly umbonate, cuticle two-thirds peeling, slightly sticky when wet, smooth. STEM 3–6, fairly slender, equal or tapering upwards, often flushed pink near base, floury towards apex. GILLS cream, sometimes with reddish flush at edge, adnexed. SPORE PRINT yellowish cream – pale ochreous (E-F). TASTE mild. SMELL indistinct. FLESH white. Iron salts±salmon-pink. Usually in groups,± trooping. On soil with broad-leaved trees or pines. Summer – autumn. Widespread. Common. Edible. SPORES ellipsoid, ornamentation (R2–R3/R6–R7), 6.5–9×5.5–7.5. Cap cystidia sparse, club-shaped – cylindrical, sulphovanillin moderately purple.

2
Rusula aurata. Overall bright colours, microscopic features. CAP 4–9, at first convex – dome-shaped, then flattened – depressed, cuticle half peeling, sticky when wet, smooth, margin usually grooved on aging. STEM 3–6, fairly slender, equal, white or entirely yellow. GILLS pale yellow, often deeper yellow at edge, adnexed. SPORE PRINT ochre (H). TASTE mild. SMELL indistinct. FLESH white. Iron salts±salmon-pink. Usually in groups,± trooping. On soil with broad-leaved trees. Summer – autumn. Widespread. Uncommon. Edible. SPORES ellipsoid, ornamentation (R2-R3/R8-R9), 7.5–10×6–8. Cap cystidia absent.

3
Russula luteotacta. Size, overall colour and colour change, smell, microscopic features. CAP 3–8, at first convex, then flattened – depressed or slightly funnel-shaped, cuticle scarcely peeling, slightly sticky when wet, smooth, margin usually slightly grooved on aging. STEM 3–7, fairly slender,±club-shaped, usually with pinkish flush, becoming yellow. GILLS pale cream becoming yellow, fairly narrow,±decurrent. SPORE PRINT white (A). TASTE hot. SMELL faint, rather sweet, coconut. FLESH white. Iron salts±salmon-pink. Usually in groups,±trooping. On soil with broad-leaved trees, especially on wet, clayey sites. Summer – autumn. Widespread. Uncommon. Poisonous. SPORES ellipsoid, ornamentation (R2–R3/R6–R7), 7–9×6–7.5. Cap cystidia variable, cylindrical, club-shaped – spindle-shaped, often rather wavy, sulphovanillin moderately purple.

4
Russula emetica **The Sickener**. Cap flesh colour, taste, smell, microscopic features, habitat. CAP 3–8, at first convex – dome-shaped, then flattened – depressed, cuticle one-third – completely peeling, slightly sticky when wet, smooth, markedly shiny, margin usually grooved on aging. STEM 5–8, fairly slender,±equal, sometimes slightly greyish. GILLS cream, turnign pale straw-coloured, adnexed. SPORE PRINT white (A). TASTE very hot. SMELL slightly fruity . FLESH white, red under cap cuticle. Iron salts±salmon-pink. Usually in groups,± trooping. On soil with pines. Summer – autumn. Widespread. Very common. Poisonous. SPORES ellipsoid, ornamentation (R3/R12), 7.5–8.5×9–11. Cap cystidia large, variable, mostly club-shaped, also cylindrical – spindle-shaped, sulphovanillin purple.

5
Russula betularum. Cap flesh colour, taste, smell, microscopic features, habitat. CAP 2–5, at first convex – dome-shaped then flattened – depressed, cuticle almost completely and easily peeling, slightly sticky when wet, smooth, markedly shiny, margin usually grooved and with warty bumps, discolouring with age. STEM 2.5–6.5, fairly slender,±equal. GILLS white, fairly distant, adnexed – sinuate. SPORE PRINT white (A). TASTE hot. SMELL faint, sweet, honey. FLESH white, no red under cap cuticle. Iron salts dull green. Usually in groups,± trooping. On soil with birch trees. Summer – autumn. Widespread. Common. Poisonous. SPORES ellipsoid, ornamentation (R2–R3/R10–R11), 7.5–8×8–10. Cap cystidia elongated, cylindrical – club-shaped, 0–2 cross-walls, sulphovanillin moderately purple.

6
Russula emeticella. Cap flesh colour, taste, smell, microscopic features, habitat. CAP 2.5–6, at first convex – dome-shaped, then flattened – depressed, cuticle almost completely peeling, slightly sticky when wet, smooth, markedly shiny, margin at first smooth then usually groved, discolouring with age. STEM 2.5–7, fairly slender,±equal – club-shaped. GILLS very pale straw-coloured, slightly intervened, adnexed. SPORE PRINT white (A). TASTE very hot. SMELL faint, sweet, coconut. FLESH white, sometimes pink under cap cuticle. Iron salts±salmon-pink. Usually in groups,±trooping. On soil with broad-leaved trees. Summer – autumn. Widespread. Common. Poisonous. SPORES ellipsoid, ornamentation (R1–R2/R10–R11), 6.5–8×8–10. Cap cystidia elonga cylindrical – club-shap 0–2 cross-walls, sulpho nillin moderately purp

7
Russula mairei **Beechw Sickener**. Cap flesh col gill colour, taste, smell, microscopic features, h tat. CAP 3–6, at first con – dome-shaped, then fl tened – depressed, cuti one-third peeling, sligh sticky when wet, smooth, margin±smoo STEM 2.5–4.5, fairly stou ±equal, sometimes yel ish below. GILLS at first white with±bluish gree flush, then cream, fairly corwded, adnexed. SPO PRINT white (A). TASTE SMELL faint, sweet, cocc when young. FLESH whi pink under cap cuticle. Iron salts±salmon-pink Usually in groups,±tro ing. On soil with beech trees. Summer – autumn Widespread. Extremely common. Poisonous. SPORES ellipsoid, ornam tation (R2–R5/R12), 6– ×7–8. Cap cystidia club shaped – spindle-shape sulphovanillin purple.

8
Russula solaris. Overall colour, smell, spore pri habitat. CAP 2–7, at first convex then flattened – depressed, cuticle two-thirds peeling, slightly sticky when wet, smooth margin grooved. STEM 3 fairly slender,±equal. GILLS straw coloured, adnedex. SPORE PRINT cream-yellowish cream E). TASTE hot. SMELL m tard oil. FLESH white. Ir salts±salmon-pink. Usu in groups,±trooping. O soil with beech trees. Summer – autumn. Wi spread. Rare. Poisonou SPORES broadly ellipsoid ornamentation (R2–R6 5–7×7–8. Cap cystidia club-shaped – cylindric sulphovanillin moderate purple.

108

1
ussula atropurpurea
lack-Purple Russula.
verall colour, smell. CAP
-10, at first convex then
attened – depressed, cuti-
e one third peeling,
ightly sticky when wet,
nooth, margin at first
±otted with ochre. STEM
-5, fiarly stout, turning
reyish on aging,±equal.
LLS purple cream, adnexed.
PORE PRINT white (A–B).
STE vairbal, mild – hot.
MELL sweet, fruity, apples.
ESH white. Iron salts±
roups,±trooping. On soil
ith broad-leaved trees, us-
ally oak. Summer – aut-
mn. Widespread. Extre-
ely common. Inedible.
PORES broadly ellipsoid,
rnamentation (R1–R2/
10–R11) 6–7×7–9. Cap
ystidia club-shaped – cy-
ndrical, sometimes head-
d, sulphovanillin purple.

2
ussula aquosa. Habitat,
nell. CAP 3–9, at first con-
x then flattened –
pressed, cuticle two-
irds – completely peel-
g, slightly sticky when
et, smooth, margin at
rst±smooth, grooved and
arty-bumpy on aging.
EM 4–9.5, fairly slender,
ually flushed brownish,
ey or yellowish,±club-
aped. GILLS dirty white,
stant, adnexed. SPORE
INT white (A). TASTE
ightly hot. SMELL faint,
veet, coconuts, radish,
dine. FLESH white. Phenol
owly violet. Iron salts±
roups,±trooping. On soil
r among mosses in wet,
arshy places usually with
rch. Summer – autumn.
idespread. Uncommon.
edible. SPORES broadly
lipsoid, ornamentation
R1–R2/R8–R10) 7–8.5×
-7. Cap cystidia club-
aped, some with append-
ges, sulphovanillin mod-
rately purple.

3
Russula fragilis **Fragile
Russula.** Size, smell, spore
features, fairly fragile. CAP
2–6, at first convex then
flattened – depressed,
cuticle three-quarters peel-
ng, slightly sticky when
wet, smooth, margin at first
±smooth, later grooved.
STEM 2.5–6, fairly slender,
sometimes very slightly yellowish,±equal – club-
shaped. GILLS white – pale
cream, toothed, adnexed.
SPORE PRINT white (A–B).
TASTE very hot. SMELL
faint, sweet, fruity, apples,
pear-drops. FLESH white.
Iron salts±salmon-pink.
Usually in groups,±troop-
ing. On soil with coniferous
or broad-leaved trees. Summer – autumn. Wide-
spread. Very common. In-
edible. SPORES broadly ellipsoid – subspherical, ornamentation (R2–R3/R12)
6–8×7.5–9. Cap cystidia
club-shaped – cylindrical,
sulphovanillin purple.

4
Russula pelargonia. Size,
smell, spore features, habitat, very fragile. CAP 2–4, at
first convex then flattened –
depressed, cuticle ? peeling, slightly sticky when
wet, smooth, margin at
first±smooth, later
grooved. STEM 2–4, fairly
slender, sometimes very
slightly yellowish,±equal –
club-shaped. GILLS white –
pale cream, adnexed. SPORE
PRINT pale cream (C). TASTE
very hot. SMELL faint,
sweet, fruity, cloves,
cooked apples. FLESH
white. Iron salts±salmon-
pink. Usually in groups,±
trooping. On soil with
broad-leaved trees,
especially (always ?)
poplars. Summer –
autumn. Widespread.
Rare. Inedible. SPORES
ellipsoid, ornamentation
(R2–R3/R5) 6–8.5×7–9.
Cap cystidia ?

5
Russula violacea
(=*cavipes*). Size, smell,
spore features, fairly fragile. CAP 2–6, at first convex

then flattened – depressed,
often rather irregular and
wavy, cuticle half peeling,
slightly sticky when wet,
smooth, margin grooved.
STEM 3.5–7, fairly slender,
sometimes slightly yellowish towards base,±equal,
rather markedly lined.
GILLS cream, strongly interveined, adnexed. SPORE
PRINT white – pale cream
(B–D). TASTE fairly hot.
SMELL strong, pleasant,
pelargonium. FLESH white.
Iron salts±salmon-pink.
Usually in groups,±troop-
ing. On soil with coniferous
trees. Summer – autumn.
Widespread. Uncommon.
Inedible. SPORES broadly
ellipsoid, ornamentation
(R2–R4/R8–R10), 7–8×
8.5–10.5. Cap cystidia variable, club-shaped, cylindrical or±spindle-shaped,
some with appendages, sulphovanillin moderately
purple.

6
Russula gracillima
(=*gracilis*). Size, spore features, habitat. CAP 2–6, at
first convex then flattened –
depressed, cuticle one-
third – half peeling, slightly
sticky when wet, smooth,
margin at first±smooth,
then grooved and warty
bumpy. STEM 3–7, fairly
slender,± equal. GILLS pale
cream – yellow, adnexed.
SPORE PRINT pale ochreous –
ochreous (F–G). TASTE
slightly – moderately hot.
SMELL indistinct. FLESH
white. Iron salts±salmon-
pink. Usually in groups,±
trooping. On soil with birches. Summer – autumn.
Widespread. Uncommon.
Inedible. SPORES broadly
ellipsoid, ornamentation
(R2–R3–R8), 7–9×5–7.
Cap cystidia club-shaped –
cylindrical, sulphovanillin
moderately purple.

7
Russula versicolor. Size,
stem features, microscopic
features, habitat. CAP 1.5–
7, at first convex then
flattened – depressed, very
variable colours, cuticle at

least three-quarters peeling, slightly sticky when
wet, smooth, margin at
first±smooth, then soon
grooved. STEM 2–5, fairly
slender,±equal, often with
network of veins, often
staining yellowish brown.
GILLS pale cream, not interveined, adnexed. SPORE
PRINT yellowish cream –
pale ochreous (E–F). TASTE
very slightly – moderately
hot. SMELL indistinct. FLESH
white. Iron salts±salmon-
pink. Usually in groups,±
trooping. On soil with birches. Summer – autumn.
Widespread. Common. In-
edible. SPORES broadly ellipsoid, ornamentation variable (R1–R2/R5–R12), 4–7
×6–10. Cap cystidia mostly
±club-shaped, some cylin-
drical – spindle-shaped,
sulphovanillin purple.

8
Russula sanguinea. Stem
features, cap surface, gills,
microscopic features, habitat. CAP 4–10, at first convex
then flattened – depressed,
cuticle scarcely peeling,
very slightly sticky when
wet, minutely roughened or
wrinkled, margin±smooth.
STEM 4–10,±spindle-
shaped, often staining or
bruising yellowish brown,
rather floury and veined.
GILLS cream – pale
ochreous, narrow,
forked,±decurrent. SPORE
PRINT pale cream – pale
ochreous (C–F). TASTE
slightly – moderately hot
and bitter. SMELL faint,
fruity. FLESH white. Iron
salts±salmon-pink. Usually
in groups,±trooping. On
soil with coniferous trees,
especially pines. Summer –
autumn. Widespread.
Common. Inedible. SPORES
broadly ellipsoid, orna-
mentation (R2–R3/R6–
R8), 7–9×6–8. Cap cystidia
club-shaped – cylindrical
some headed or with
appendages, sulphovanillin
weakly purple.

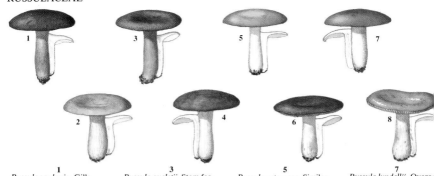

1

Russula sardonia. Gills, chemical tests, taste, habitat. CAP 4–10, at first convex then flattened – depressed, often±umbonate, cuticle peeling at margin only, slightly sticky when wet, margin±smooth. STEM 3–8,±club-shaped, often with marked lilac flush, rather floury. GILLS sulphur-yellow, slowly becoming paler, narrow, forked, branching, often weeping, adnexed – ±decurrent. SPORE PRINT pale cream – pale ochreous (C-F). TASTE not. SMELL faint, fruity. FLESH white – pale straw-coloured. Ammonia on flesh or gills, rose pink. Iron salts±salmon-pink. Usually in groups,±trooping. On soil with pines. Summer – autumn. Widespread. Common. Inedible. SPORES broadly ellipsoid, ornamentation (R2–R3/R5 –R10), 7–9×6–8. Cap cystidia narrow, often wavy, spindle-shaped – cylindrical, some with appendages, sulphovanillin purple.

2

Russula pulchella. Stem features, taste, habitat. CAP 4–10, at first convex then flattened – depressed, cuticle half peeling, slightly sticky when wet, margin± smooth. STEM 3–5, rather stout,±spindle-shaped, often with marked greyish flush, especially when wet. GILLS pale cream, adnexed. SPORE PRINT pale ochreous – ochreous (F-G). TASTE fairly hot. SMELL indistinct. FLESH white. Iron salts± salmon-pink. Usually in groups,±trooping. On soil with birch trees. Summer – autumn. Widespread. Uncommon. Inedible. SPORES ellipsoid variable, ornamentation (R1–R3/R5–R8), 6–7×8–10. Cap cystidia variable, spindle-shaped, cylindrical, ±club-shaped, sulphovanillin moderately purple.

3

Russula queletii. Stem features, taste, habitat, similar to *R. sanguinea* and *R. sardonia* but cap discolouring, gills and chemical tests especially differ. CAP 4–10, at first convex then flattened – depressed, cuticle half – two-thirds peeling, slightly sticky when wet, margin at first smooth, then grooved. STEM 3–7, fairly slender,±club-shaped, often curved, floury. GILLS pale cream, adnexed. SPORE PRINT pale cream – yellowish cream (C-E). TASTE hot. SMELL fruity, apples. FLESH white. Iron salts±salmon-pink. Ammonia – . Usually in groups,±trooping. On soil with coniferous trees. Summer – autumn. Widespread. Uncommon. Inedible. SPORES ellipsoid, ornamentation (R1–R3), 7–9×8–10. Cap cystidia cylindrical, often with appendages, sulphovanillin purple.

4

Russula firmula. Gills, spore print, taste, habitat. CAP 3–7, at first convex then flattened – depressed, cuticle half peeling, slightly sticky when wet, margin usually grooved. STEM 3–7, fairly slender,±equal, often bruising brownish. GILLS yellow, very fragile, adnexed. SPORE PRINT ochre (H). TASTE slightly – moderately hot. SMELL indistinct. FLESH white. Iron salts±salmon-pink. Usually in groups,±trooping. On soil with broad-leaved trees. Summer – autumn. Widespread. Uncommon. Inedible. SPORES ellipsoid, ornamentation (R1–R3), 8.5–10×7–8. Cap cystidia cylindrical – club-shaped, sulphovanillin purple.

5

Russula veternosa. Similar to some colour forms of *R. firmula* but smell differs. CAP 3–10, at first convex then flattened – depressed, often with rust-coloured spotting, cuticle half – three-quarters peeling, slightly sticky when wet, margin±smooth. STEM 2–7, fairly slender,±equal. GILLS ochreous, forked, interviened, adnexed. SPORE PRINT ochreous – ochre (G-H). TASTE slightly – moderately hot. SMELL sweet, honey, gingerbread. FLESH white. Iron salts±salmon-pink. Usually in groups,±trooping. On soil with beech trees. Summer – autumn. Widespread. Uncommon. Inedible. SPORES broadly ellipsoid, ornamentation (R1–R3), 7–9×6–8. Cap cystidia cylindrical – club-shaped, sulphovanillin purple.

6

Russula badia. Size, cap colour. CAP 7–11, at first convex then flattened – depressed, cuticle slight – half peeling, slightly sticky when wet, margin grooved. STEM 5–11, fairly stout,±equal or tapering upwards. GILLS ochreous, greasy, adnexed. SPORE PRINT pale ochreous – ochreous (F-G). TASTE slowly very hot. SMELL indistinct or cedarwood oil. FLESH white. Iron salts± salmon-pink. Usually in groups,±trooping. On soil with conifers. Summer – autumn. Northern, predominantly highland. Rare. Inedible. SPORES ellipsoid, ornamentation variable (R1–R3/R5/R6–R11), 6.5–8×8–11. Cap cystidia cylindrical – club-shaped, sulphovanillin moderately purple.

7

Russula lundellii. Overal[l] colour, microscopic features, habitat. CAP 9–15, first convex, then flatten depressed, cuticle one th[ird] peeling, slightly sticky when wet, shiny, margin grooved. STEM 8–10, fair[ly] stout,±equal, occasiona[l] with purple-brown flush especially after handling GILLS pale yellow-ochre, adnexed. SPORE PRINT oc[hre] (H). TASTE hot, bitter. SMELL indistinct. FLESH white. Iron salts±salmon pink. Usually in groups, trooping. On soil with birch. Summer – autumn Predominantly northern. Rare. Inedible. SPORES broadly ellipsoid, ornamentation (R3), 7–8×6.5–7.

8

Russula maculata. Overal[l] colour, taste, smell, habitat. CAP 4–10, at first con[vex] then flattened – depress often with rust spotting, cuticle peeling at margin only, slightly sticky when wet, margin smooth unti[l] very old, then grooved. STEM 3–9, fairly stout,± equal, often with pinkish flush and brownish spotting. GILLS pale ochreous forked, interviened, adnexed. SPORE PRINT ochre ous – ochre (G-H). TAST[E] usually slightly hot. SME[LL] indefinite or cedarwood FLESH white. Iron salts± salmon-pink. Usually in groups,±trooping. On so[il] with broad-leaved trees. Summer – autumn. Wid[e] spread. Uncommon. Ine[di] ble. SPORES broadly ellipsoid – subspherical, ornamentation (R1–R3/ R6–R9), 7–9×8–10. Cap cystidia cylindrical, club-shaped – spindle-shaped sulphovanillin moderate purple.

110

1

ussula gigasperma. Simi-
r to *R. firmula* but larger
nd spores much larger.
AP 5–10, at first convex
hen flattened – depressed,
uticle half peeling, slightly
cky when wet, margin
sually grooved. STEM 5–9,
irly stout,±equal, often
ruising brownish. GILLS
ellow, very fragile,
nnexed. SPORE PRINT ochre
-1). TASTE slightly –
noderately hot. SMELL
distinct. FLESH white.
on salts±salmon-pink.
sually in groups,±troop-
g. On soil with broad-
aved trees especially
aks. Summer – autumn.
Videspread. Uncommon.
nedible. SPORES ellipsoid,
rnamentation (R1–R3), 8
10×9–12. Cap cystidia
sually club-shaped, sul-
hovanillin purple.

2

ussula decipiens. Overall
olour, stem features,
ste, habitat. CAP 4–9, at
rst convex then flattened –
epressed, cuticle quarter –
ree-quarters peeling,
ightly sticky when wet,
argin usually grooved.
EM 3–10, fairly slender,±
qual, often turning greyish
nd bruising brownish.
LLS yellow, adnexed.
ASTE slightly – moderately
ot. SMELL indistinct. FLESH
hite. Iron salts±salmon-
nk. Usually in groups,±
ooping. On soil with
road-leaved trees. Sum-
er – autumn. Wide-
pread. Rare. Inedible.
ORES ellipsoid – sub-
pherical, ornamentation
R1–R3/R5/R6–R7), 7–9×
-8. Cap cystidia cylin-
rical – club-shaped, sul-
hovanillin purple.

PLEUROTACEAE

Toadstool-bracket shaped,
tough, stem usually eccentric or lateral, gills variable,
crowded – distant, decur-
rent (commonly) –
emarginate, white, cream,
yellowish, greyish or with
pink-lilac flush, flesh
usually whitish, spores
ellipsoid – cylindrical,
smooth, not amyloid, spore
print white or flushed pink-
lilac, cap surface smooth-
scaly. On wood, or rarely
(*Geopetalum*) soil, some
edible, none poisonous. A
highly artificial grouping,
constantly being revised
and changed; some allied to
Tricholomataceae, some to
'Polypores'. *Lentinus* [3],
Geopetalum [1], *Panus* [4],
Pleurotus [8].

Lentinus lepideus. Cap and
stem features, habitat. CAP
5–12, at first±dome-
shaped, later convex –
flattened or depressed,
covered with coarse, dark
scales with concentric
cracking, often grossly distorted, antler-like when in
dark (mines, cellars). STEM
3–8,±central, fairly stout,
equal, scaly, indefinite
superior ring zone, often±
rooting. GILLS at first whitish, then ochreous, broad,
distant, edge coarsely
toothed, sinuate – emarginate. SPORE PRINT white.
SMELL faint, aniseed.
FLESH yellowish white, firm,
thick. Solitary or in tufted
groups. On coniferous timber, often structural (sleep-
ers, props) especially when
part buried. Spring – autumn. Widespread. Rare,
formerly more common.
Inedible. SPORES elongated
ellipsoid – cylindrical,
smooth, 10–15×4–5, non-
amyloid.

Lentinus tigrinus. Cap and
stem features, similar to *L.
lepideus* but size and habitat differ. CAP 3–9, at first
convex – dome-shaped,
then flattened – depressed,
covered with small, dark±
hairy scales in concentric
zones. STEM 3–5, central,
fairly slender, equal or tapering slightly downwards,
finely fibrous-scaly, indefinite superior ring zone,±
rooting. GILLS at first whitish, then ochreous, fairly
narrow, fairly distant, edge
slightly toothed,±decur-
rent. SPORE PRINT white,
SMELL faint, unpleasant,
acrid, slightly rancid.
FLESH white – yellowish,
firm thick. Solitary or in
tufted groups. On broad-
leaved stumps and timber,
especially when part bur-
ied. Spring – autumn.
Widespread. Rare. Inedi-
ble. SPORES elongated ellipsoid – cylindrical, smooth,
6–8×2–3, non-amyloid.

Geopetalum carbonarium.
Overall form, gills, habitat.
CAP 1–6, at first convex –
dome-shaped, then
flattened, depressed or
umbilicate, often irregu-
larly wavy, dry, downy –
finely scaly. STEM 2–6, slender, equal, lined, rooting.
GILLS at first grey, then
paler, very narrow, thick,
distant, usually markedly
forked, decurrent. SPORE
PRINT white. SMELL indis-
tinct. FLESH whitish, thin.
In small groups,±tufted.
On soil on fire-sites.
Summer – autumn. Wide-
spread. Uncommon. Inedi-
ble. SPORES ellipsoid,
smooth, 7–11×4–5, non-
amyloid.

Panus torulosus. Cap
shape, stem features, habitat. CAP 3–7, at first±flat,
soon depressed – funnel-
shaped, margin often
markedly irregular, cracking on aging. STEM 1–2,
eccentric – lateral, tapering
downwards, at first with
pale violet down. GILLS at
first pinkish lilac, then pale
ochreous, narrow, some-
times branching, deeply
decurrent. SPORE PRINT
white, SMELL indistinct.
FLESH whitish, thin. In
groups, tufted. On wood,
branches, stumps of broad-
leaved trees. Summer –
autumn. Widespread.
Common. Inedible. SPORES
ellipsoid, 6–7×3–3.5, non-
amyloid.

Pleurotus cornucopiae. Cap
shape, overall colour, gills,
habit, habitat. CAP 4–12, at
first convex, soon depressed
– funnel-shaped, margin
often markedly irregular
and later split. STEM 2–6, usually eccentric, fairly stout,
tapering downwards, usu-
ally fused at base. GILLS
white – pale pinkish, narrow, distant, deeply decurrent. SPORE PRINT white.
SMELL floury, mushroomy,
slightly aniseed. FLESH
white. In groups, often
large, tufted. On wood,
stumps and cut trunks of
broad-leaved trees, especially on elm (after elm disease). Spring – autumn.
Widespread. Common. Ed-
ible. SPORES elongated-ellipsoid, smooth, 8–11×3–
3.5, non-amyloid.

PLEUROTACEAE

PLUTEACEAE

Pleurotus dryinus. Cap shape, cap margin, ring, habit, habitat. CAP 6–12, at first convex, soon depressed – funnel-shaped, ±oyster-shell-shaped, downy fibrous-scaly, margin with over-hanging whitish veil fragments. STEM 2–5, eccentric, stout, tapering slightly downwards, quickly disappearing superior ring zone, often fused at base. GILLS white – cream, later yellowish, narrow, fairly distant, decurrent. SPORE PRINT white. SMELL floury, mushroomy. FLESH white. Solitary or in groups, usually small, tufted. On wood, stumps and branches of broad-leaved trees, especially oak and beech. Autumn – winter. Widespread. Edible. SPORES elongated-ellipsoid, smooth, 9–14×3–5, non-amyloid.

Pleurotus lignatilis. Stem features, overall colour, habitat. CAP 2–5, at first convex, then flattened – depressed or umbilicate, ±kidney-shaped at first finely velvety, then smooth, margin often irregularly lobed. STEM 5–12, eccentric, slender, ±equal, curved, finely downy, woolly-hairy at base, rooting. GILLS white – slightly yellowish, narrow, crowded, adnate – decurrent. SPORE PRINT white. SMELL strong, mealy. FLESH white. Solitary or in small groups, ±tufted. On wood of broad-leaved trees, branches, trunks, stumps, especially beech. Autumn. Widespread. Rare. Inedible. SPORES broadly ellipsoid, smooth, 3.5–4.5×2.5–3.5, non-amyloid.

Pleurotus ulmarius Size, cap surface features, colour, season, spores. CAP 6–25, at first convex, then ±flat, smooth or very finely cracked or crazed, margin often irregularly lobed. STEM 5–12, slightly eccentric, stout, ±spindle-shaped, curved, often finely downy, especially at base. GILLS whitish-pale yellowish, broad, fairly crowded, emarginate. SPORE PRINT white. SMELL pleasant or slightly acrid. FLESH white. Usually in small-large, overlapping groups. On wood of broad-leaved trees, branches, trunks, stumps, especially elm. Summer – winter. Widespread. Rare. Edible. SPORES subspherical, smooth, 4.5–5.5×5.5–6, non-amyloid.

Pluteus pellitus. Overall colour, size, microscopic features. CAP 5–7, at first slightly convex, then flattened and broadly umbonate, finely fibrous (use hand-lens). STEM 4– fairly slender, equal or tapering slightly upward usually curved, smooth. GILLS whitish, then flesh pink, broad, crowded, fr SPORE PRINT pink. SMELL indistinct. FLESH white. Solitary or in small,±tuf groups. On wood, on or close to stumps or fallen trunks of beech. Summe autumn. Widespread. Rare. Edible. SPORES elongated-ellipsoid, smooth, 5–7.5×4–5, nor amyloid. Gill face cystid shaped with 1–4 hooked ends. Cap cuticle cells± elongated.

Pleurotus eryngii. Cap shape, habitat. CAP 3–12, at first convex, then depressed – slightly funnel-shaped, at first finely velvety, then smooth except at inrolled margin. STEM 3–10, central – slightly eccentric, stout, tapering slightly downwards,± rooting. GILLS greyish, narrow, fairly distant, decurrent. SPORE PRINT white. SMELL faint, pleasant. FLESH white. Solitary or in small groups,±tufted. On decaying roots and other debris of umbellifers, especially *Eryngium, Heracleum, Ferula, Laserpitium.* Spring – autumn. Widespread in S. Europe, not Britain. Edible. SPORES elongated-ellipsoid, smooth, 10–14× 4–5, non-amyloid.

Pleurotus ostreatus **Oyster Mushroom.** Size, cap features, colour, season. CAP 5–14, at first convex, then flattened – slightly depressed,±oyster-shell shaped, often irregularly wavy, smooth, shiny, margin usually irregularly lobed. STEM sometimes absent, usually 1–3, eccentric – lateral, stout, tapering downwards, curved, woolly-hairy at base. GILLS white – slightly yellowish, narrow, fairly crowded, decurrent. SPORE PRINT pale lilac. SMELL pleasant. FLESH white. Usually in small – large, overlapping groups. On wood of broad-leaved trees, branches, trunks, stumps, especially beech; a peacock-blue form (var. *columbinus*) occurs on poplar and willow. All year. Widespread. Common. Edible. SPORES elongated-ellipsoid – cylindrical, smooth, 7.5–11×3–4.5, non-amyloid.

PLUTEACEAE:
Toadstool-shaped, usually white or shades of pale brown, gills crowded, remote, white then pink, flesh±white, spores ellipsoid- ±spherical, smooth, non-amyloid, gill face cystidia usually present and distinctive, spore print pink, cap surface smooth and woolly – sticky. Stem with volva (*Volvariella*) or without (*Pluteus*). Smell usually indistinct. On wood (most *Pluteus*) or rich soil (most *Volvariella*), rarely otherwise. Some edible, few good, none poisonous. *Pluteus* [34], *Volvariella* [9].

Pluteus petasatus. Cap fea tures, size, microscopic fe tures. CAP 5–19, convex, very broadly umbonate, finely – coarsely scaly, slightly sticky when wet, often±lined at margin. STEM 8–20, stout, narrowi sharply downwards, usua curved, grooved and roughened towards base. GILLS white, then flesh pink, broad, crowded, fre SPORE PRINT pink. SMELL indistinct. FLESH white. Solitary or in small,±tuft groups. On sawdust or ro ting wood. Summer – autumn. Widespread. Rare. Edible. SPORES elongated – ellipsoid, smooth, 6–10×4–6, non-amyloid. Gill face cystidi with 1–4 hooked ends. Ca cuticle cells± elongated.

112

...luteus salicinus. Cap features, habitat, microscopic features. CAP 3–6, at first convex, then flattened – umbonate, finely lined, especially when moist, ...e. STEM 3–7, slender, ...qual or tapering slightly ...wards, often curved, ...ely fibrous, often slightly ...reenish blue at base. GILLS ...hite, then flesh pink, ...road, crowded, free. ...ORE PRINT pink. SMELL ...distinct. FLESH white, ...ften flushed greenish-...rey. Solitary or in small, ...tufted groups. On wood ...broad-leaved trees, ...pecially willow. Spring – ...utumn. Widespread. ...ommon. Edible. SPORES ...roadly ellipsoid, smooth, ...-8×4–6, non-amyloid. ...ill face cystidia with 1–4 ...ooked ends. Cap cuticle ...ells±elongated.

Pluteus cervinus (=*atricapillus*) **Fawn Pluteus.** Colour, cap, like *P. atromarginatus* and *P. umbrosus* but habitat and microscopic features differ. Sometimes much larger form on sawdust probably this species. CAP 3–12, at first convex – dome-shaped, then more flattened, smooth or slightly scaly at centre. STEM 5–15, fairly slender, equal, often swollen – ± bulbous at base, covered with dark fibres, especially towards base. GILLS white, then dull pink, rarely slightly brown at edge when old, broad, crowded, free. SPORE PRINT pink. SMELL indistinct or faintly radish-like. FLESH white. Solitary or in small,±tufted groups. On sawdust or rotting wood of broad-leaved, rarely coniferous trees. Spring – autumn. Widespread. Extremely common. Edible. SPORES broadly ellipsoid, smooth, 7–7.5×5–5.5, non-amyloid. Gill face cystidia with 1–4 hooked ends. Cap cuticle cells±elongated.

Pluteus umbrosus. Overall colour, cap features, gills, similar to *P. cervinus* but gills and microscopic features differ. CAP 4–9, at first convex, then more flattened, covered with tiny dark scales, often roughly hairy at margin when young. STEM 5–9, fairly slender, equal, slightly swollen-bulbous at base, finely lined or dark scaly. GILLS whitish, then pink, with markedly darker edge broad, crowded, free. SPORE PRINT pink. SMELL indistinct. FLESH white. Solitary or in small,±tufted groups. On rotting wood of broad-leaved trees. Autumn – winter. Widespread. Uncommon. Edible. SPORES broadly ellipsoid – subspherical, smooth, 6–7×4–5, non-amyloid. Gill face cystidia not hooked. Cap cuticle cells±elongated.

Pluteus depauperatus. Size, cap and stem features, microscopic features. CAP 2–5, convex – flattened or very broadly umbonate, at first finely velvety then smoother, finely cracked or crazed at centre, lined-grooved at margin. STEM 2–3.5, slender, equal; base bulbous, yellowish below, smooth-floury. GILLS pale pinkish buff, broad, crowded, free. SPORE PRINT pink. SMELL indistinct or radish-like. FLESH white – yellowish. Solitary or in small,±tufted groups. On sawdust or rotting wood of beech. Autumn. Widespread. Rare. Inedible. SPORES broadly ellipsoid – subspherical, smooth, 7–8×5.5–6, non-amyloid. Gill face cystidia not hooked. Cap cuticle cells±elongated.

...luteus atromarginatus. ...verall colour, gills, simi-...r to *P. cervinus* and *P. ...mbrosus* but habitat and ...icroscopic features differ. ...AP 5–15, at first convex, ...en flattened, at first with ...ne pointed scales, then ...ore smooth, especially ...wards margin. STEM 5–15, ...ender, equal or tapering ...wards upwards, often ...urved, covered with dark ...ores. GILLS white, then ...esh pink, edge dark brow-...sh, broad, crowded, free. ...ORE PRINT pink. SMELL ...distinct. FLESH white, ...metimes flushed brow-...ish. Solitary or in small,± ...fted groups. On sawdust ...rotting wood of conifer-...us trees. Spring – ...utumn. Widespread. ...are. Edible. SPORES ...roadly ellipsoid, smooth, ...-7.5×4.5–5.5, non-...myloid. Gill face cystidia ...ith 1–4 hooked ends. Cap ...uticle cells±elongated.

Pluteus leoninus. Overall colour, microscopic features. CAP 4–6, at first convex, then flattened-umbonate, very finely velvety, lined at margin. STEM 2–7, slender, equal, finely lined, hairy-fibrous at base. GILLS whitish, then pink, often with slightly yellowish edge, broad, crowded, free. SPORE PRINT pink. SMELL indistinct. FLESH white. Solitary or in small,±tufted groups. On rotting wood of broad-leaved trees. Autumn – winter. Widespread. Rare. Edible. SPORES broadly ellipsoid – subspherical, smooth, 6.5–7.5×5–6, non-amyloid. Gill face cystidia not hooked. Cap cuticle cells±elongated.

Pluteus hispidulus. Size, cap and stem features. CAP 0.5–2, convex – bell-shaped, covered with tiny greyish scales, often roughly hairy at margin. STEM 2–4, slender, equal, smooth but often slightly scaly at extreme base. GILLS whitish, then pink, broad, crowded, free. SPORE PRINT pink. SMELL indistinct. FLESH white, greyish below cap cuticle. Solitary or in small,±tufted groups. On stumps or rotting wood among leaf litter of beech. Autumn – winter. Widespread. Rare. Edible? SPORES broadly ellipsoid – subspherical, smooth, 5–7×4.5–6, non-amyloid. Gill face cystidia absent. Gill edge cystidia broadly club-shaped. Cap cuticle cells± elongated.

Pluteus aurantiorugosus. Colour, habitat, microscopic features. CAP 2–6, convex – flattened, smooth – finely velvety, margin finely lined. STEM 2–5, slender, equal, yellowish orange below, finely fibrous lined. GILLS dull pink, broad, crowded, free. SPORE PRINT pink. SMELL indistinct. FLESH white. Solitary or in small,±tufted groups. On stumps of broad-leaved trees, especially (always?) elm. Autumn. Widespread. Uncommon. Inedible? SPORES broadly ellipsoid, smooth, 6–6.5×4–4.5, non-amyloid. Gill face cystidia broadly spindle-shaped – flask-shaped. Cap cuticle cells±rounded.

PLUTEACEAE

Pluteus luteovirens. Colour, habitat, microscopic features. CAP 2–4, convex – flattened or very broadly umbonate, smooth – finely velvety, finely wrinkled at centre. STEM 3.5–6, slender, equal, slightly cream, especially below. GILLS white then pink, broad, crowded, free. SPORE PRINT pink. SMELL indistinct. FLESH white, flushed yellowish, especially at stem base and below cap cuticle. Solitary or in small, ±tufted groups. On stumps of broad-leaved trees, especially elm. Autumn. Widespread. Uncommon. Inedible? SPORES subspherical, smooth, 5–6×4.5–5, non-amyloid. Gill face cystidia flask-shaped with long neck. Cap cuticle cells± rounded.

Pluteus semibulbosus (=*alborugosus*). Colour, cap surface, microscopic features. CAP 1.5–3, bell-shaped – convex, wrinkled or grooved radially, finely mealy – micaceous. STEM 2–3, fairly slender, equal, bulbous, finely mealy-floury. GILLS white, then pink, broad, crowded, free SPORE PRINT pink. SMELL indistinct. FLESH white, thin, watery. Solitary or in small,±tufted groups. On sawdust or rotting wood of broad-leaved trees. Autumn. Widespread. Uncommon. Edible? SPORES broadly ellipsoid – subspherical, smooth, 5–5.5×6–7, non-amyloid. Gill face cystidia flask-shaped – cylindrical. Cap cuticle cells±rounded.

Pluteus thomsonii. Cap, stem, habitat, microscopic features. CAP 1–5, first convex then flattened-umbonate, almost depressed, often wrinkled or net-veined at centre, sometimes smooth and floury when small, lined at margin when wet. STEM 2–5, slender, equal or tapering at base or apex, finely downy-floury esp. at apex. GILLS white, then dull pink, broad, crowded, free. SPORE PRINT pink. SMELL indistinct. FLESH white – greyish brown. Usually solitary. On fallen logs and other debris of broad-leaved trees, on soil. Summer – autumn. Widespread. Uncommon. Edible? SPORES broadly ellipsoid – subspherical, smooth, 6–8×5–7, non-amyloid. Gill face cystidia absent. Gill edge cystidia club-shaped – spindle-shaped, often with appendages. Cap cuticle cells±rounded.

Pluteus phlebophorus. Ca habitat, microscopic features. CAP 2.5–6, at first convex then flattened,± covered with coarse network of raised veins, not lined when wet. STEM 2.5–9, fairly slender, equal or tapering slightly upwards finely lined – grooved. GILLS white, then pink, broad, crowded, free. SPORE PRINT pink. SMELL unpleasant, acidic. FLESH white – brownish. Solitar or in small±tufted group On stumps of broad-leav trees, or on soil nearby. Summer – autumn. Wide spread. Uncommon. Edi ble? SPORES subspherical, smooth, 4.5–6×5–7, non amyloid. Gill face cystidi flask-shaped with fairly long neck. Cap cuticle cells±rounded.

Pluteus lutescens (=*romellii*). Colour, flesh colour, habitat, microscopic features. CAP 1.5–4, convex – flattened, umbonate, smooth-finely lined, usually finely wrinkled at centre. STEM 1.5–7, fairly slender, equal, yellowish, especially below. GILLS yellow, then pink, broad, crowded, free. SPORE PRINT pink. SMELL indistinct. FLESH yellow, especially at stem base. Solitary or in small,±tufted groups. On stumps or other rotting wood of broad-leaved trees, especially beech, on soil among woody debris (then usually smaller). Spring – autumn. Widespread. Uncommon. Edible. SPORES subspherical, smooth, 5.5–6×6.5–7, non-amyloid. Gill face cystidia mostly broadly spindle-shaped – club-shaped. Cap cuticle cells±rounded.

Pluteus cinereofuscus. Colour, cap surface, habitat, microscopic features. CAP 3–5, at first convex then flattened – umbonate, barely lined, very finely mealy – micaceous (use hand-lens). STEM 3–8, slender, equal, finely silky-lined. GILLS white, then dull pink, broad, crowded, free. SPORE PRINT pink. SMELL indistinct. FLESH white. Usually in small,±tufted groups. On soil or rotting wood, among leaf litter, usually (always?) of beech. Autumn. Widespread. Rare. Edible? SPORES broadly ellipsoid – subspherical, smooth, 6–8.5×5–6.5, non-amyloid. Gill face cystidia flask-shaped with long neck. Cap cuticle cells±rounded.

Pluteus pallescens (=*satur*). Cap, stem, habitat, microscopic features. CAP 2–3, first convex then flattened, sometimes slightly umbonate and finely wrinkled or net-veined at centre, lined towards margin when wet, drying paler. STEM 3.5–5.5, slender, equal or tapering upwards, finely silky-lined, slightly downy-floury apex. GILLS white, then pink, broad, crowded, free. SPORE PRINT pink. SMELL indistinct. FLESH white – brownish. Solitary or in small±tufted groups. On soil with debris of broad-leaved trees (often ash). Summer – autumn. Widespread. Rare. Edible? SPORES subspherical, smooth, 5–6×5–7, non-amyloid. Gill face cystidia club-shaped or broadly spindle-shaped. Cap cuticle cells±rounded.

Pluteus nanus. Similar to phlebophorus but cap, st and smell differ. CAP 1–5 first convex then flattene sometimes slightly umbo ate, finely wrinkled at ce tre, not veined, very fine floury (use hand-lens), barely lined at margin wh wet. STEM 2.5–5.5, fairly slender, equal or taperin slightly upwards, silky-lined. GILLS white, then pink, broad, crowded, fr SPORE PRINT pink. SMELL indistinct. FLESH greyish brown, drying paler. Sol ary or in small±tufted groups. On stumps of broad-leaved trees, or on soil nearby. Autumn. Widespread. Uncommor Edible? SPORES subspher ical, smooth, 4.5–7×5–8, non-amyloid. Gill face cy tidia flask-shaped – spindle-shaped with long tapering neck. Cap cuticl cells±rounded.

114

Pluteus podospileus. Cap and stem features, microscopic features. CAP 1–3, at first convex then flattened, sometimes slightly umbonate, covered with small, ± flattened velvety scales, especially at centre, often lined or grooved at margin. STEM 1–4, fairly slender, equal or tapering slightly upwards, covered with small dark scales except at apex. GILLS white, then pink, broad, crowded, free. SPORE PRINT pink. SMELL indistinct or faintly acidic. FLESH whitish in cap, grey-brown in stem. Solitary or in small±tufted groups. On rotting wood of broad-leaved trees. Summer – autumn. Widespread. Rare. Edible? SPORES broadly ellipsoid – subspherical, smooth, 4–7×3.5–6, non-amyloid. Gill face cystidia broadly flask-shaped – spindle-shaped. Cap cuticle cells mixed, ± rounded and elongated.

Pluteus minutissimus. Size, cap and stem features, microscopic features. CAP 0.5–2.5, at first convex then flattened, umbonate – umbilicate, velvety, lined at margin when wet. STEM 1–2, slender, tapering upwards, very finely downy (use hand-lens) except at apex, sometimes with small dark scales at base. GILLS white, then pink, broad, crowded, free. SPORE PRINT pink. SMELL indistinct. FLESH whitish in cap, grey-brown in stem. Solitary or in small±tufted groups. On rotting wood of broad-leaved trees or on soil nearby. Autumn. Widespread. Rare. Inedible. SPORES broadly ellipsoid – subspherical, smooth, 5–7.5×4–6, non-amyloid. Gill face cystidia mostly club-shaped. Cap cuticle cells mixed, ± rounded and elongated.

Volvariella parvula. Size, volva, habitat. CAP 1–3, at first conical – convex then flattened, ± umbonate, slightly sticky when wet, finely silky when dry, ± lined at margin. STEM 1.5–4, slender, equal, silky, base±bulbous with 3–5 lobed, bag-like volva. GILLS white, then deep pink, fairly broad, fairly crowded, free. SPORE PRINT pink. SMELL indistinct. FLESH white. Solitary or in small trooping groups. On rich soil among grass, fields, gardens, open areas with trees. Spring – autumn. Widespread. Rare. Inedible. SPORES ellipsoid, smooth, 5–7.5×3–5.5, non-amyloid.

Volvariella bombycina. Size, cap and stem features, habitat. CAP 5–20, at first egg-shaped, then bell-shaped – conical and then flattened, ± broadly umbonate, densely silky-shaggy. STEM 6–15, fairly stout, tapering upwards, often curved, silky, base±bulbous with large, bag-like, ± sticky persistent volva. GILLS white, then pink, broad, crowded, free. SPORE PRINT pink. SMELL faint, pleasant, fresh. FLESH white. Solitary or in small trooping groups. On dead wood of broad-leaved trees, especially elm, often inside hollow trunks, also sawdust. Summer – autumn. Widespread. Rare. Edible. SPORES ellipsoid, smooth, 7.5–10×5–6.5, non-amyloid.

Volvariella surrecta. Cap and stem features, habitat. CAP 4–8, at first convex, then flattened, densely woolly-silky. STEM 4–10, fairly stout, tapering upwards, silky lined, base±bulbous with large, bag-like, 2–3 lobed volva. GILLS white, then pink, broad, crowded, free. SPORE PRINT pink. SMELL faint, pleasant, mild. FLESH white. Solitary or in small± trooping groups. On dead and decaying agaric fruit bodies, especially *Tricholoma* spp., *Clitocybe nebularis*. Summer – autumn. Widespread. Rare. Edible? SPORES ellipsoid, smooth, 5–7×3–5, non-amyloid.

Volvariella speciosa. Cap and stem features, habitat. CAP 5–10, at first convex, then flattened – broadly umbonate, sticky when moist. STEM 5–10, fairly stout, tapering upwards, silky lined, base±bulbous with large, bag-like volva, often deeply embedded in soil. GILLS white, then deep pink, broad, crowded, free. SPORE PRINT pink. SMELL faint, pleasant, earthy. FLESH white. Solitary or in small±trooping groups. On rich soil, manure, compost heaps, field, gardens. Summer – autumn. Widespread. Uncommon. Inedible. SPORES ellipsoid, smooth, 12–18×8–10, non-amyloid.

ENTOLOMATACEAE

ENTOLOMATACEAE: Toadstool-shaped, rarely with stem lateral, usually dull-coloured but rarely blue or bluish, gills crowded – distant, adnate – decurrent, variously coloured, usually pale, spores±angular, non-amyloid, spore print pink, rarely pink-brown. Usually on soil in grassland, sometimes on dung or with trees, rarely on wood or other fungi. *Eccilia* [8], *Entoloma* [24], *Leptonia* [47], *Nolanea* [29].

Eccilia paludicola. Cap features, gills, smell, habitat. CAP 5–25, at first convex, then soon flattened – deeply umbilicate, lined when wet, radially streaked towards margin on drying, margin inrolled and slightly toothed. STEM 2–3.5, fairly stout, equal or tapering slightly downwards, often rather wavy, smooth, downy-hairy at base. GILLS at first greyish brown, then brownish pink, fairly crowded, emarginate – decurrent. SPORE PRINT pink. SMELL indistinct or mealy. FLESH whitish. Solitary or in small±trooping groups. On wet soil, (always?) with willow. Spring – ?autumn. Widespread. Rare. Inedible. SPORES broadly ellipsoid, angular, 8–11×5.5–7, non-amyloid.

115

ENTOMATACEAE

Eccilia sericeonitida. Cap features, gills, habitat. CAP 1–3, at first convex, then soon flattened – depressed or umbilicate, silky when dry, often rather irregular – wavy. STEM 2–3, fairly stout, equal or tapering slightly downwards, often rather wavy, smooth, downy-hairy at base. GILLS at first greyish brown, then brownish pink, fairly crowded, ± decurrent. SPORE PRINT pink. SMELL mealy. FLESH whitish. Solitary or in small ± trooping groups. On wet soil, pastures, woods. Autumn. Widespread. Inedible. SPORES broadly ellipsoid, angular. 8–11×5–7, non-amyloid.

Entoloma prunuloides. Overall colour, stem features, smell, habitat. CAP 2.5–7, at first conical – convex, then flattened, rather sharply umbonate, silky-shiny, at first slightly sticky. STEM 4–8, fairly stout, equal or tapering upwards, fibrous lined. GILLS at first whitish, then pink, fairly distant, emarginate. SPORE PRINT pink. SMELL strong, mealy. FLESH whitish. Solitary or in small ± trooping groups. On wet soil, pastures, woods. Spring – autumn. Widespread. Rare, common in North. Inedible. SPORES subspherical, fairly angular, 7.5–10×7.5–8, non-amyloid.

Entoloma jubatum. Gills, cap, habitat. CAP 2–4, at first conical – convex, then flattened, rather sharply umbonate, finely fibrous – scaly. STEM 5–7, slender, tapering slightly upwards, finely fibrous-lined, white towards base. GILLS greyish brown – purple, fairly distant, ± adnexed. SPORE PRINT pink. SMELL indistinct. FLESH whitish. Solitary or in small ± trooping groups. On soil, often among mosses, woods, poor pastures, heaths. Spring – winter. Widespread. Rare. Inedible. SPORES broadly ellipsoid, angular, 9–10.5×5–6.5, non-amyloid.

Entoloma sepium. Colour changes, habitat, smell. CAP 3–6, at first conical – convex, then flattened, umbonate, at first slightly greasy, finely fibrous. STEM 4–10, fairly slender, tapering upwards, lined with reddening fibres. GILLS white, then reddish, fairly distant, adnexed. SPORE PRINT pink. SMELL mealy-floury, colouring reddish, especially in maggot tunnels. Usually in small ± trooping groups, sometimes in rings. On soil with *Prunus* spp. Spring. Widespread. Rare. Edible. SPORES subspherical, angular, 8.5–10×7.5–8.5, non-amyloid.

Entoloma nitidum. Overall colour. CAP 2–5, at first conical – convex, then flattened, rather sharply umbonate, silky. STEM 5–8, fairly slender, equal or tapering upwards, fibrous lined, white at base, rooting. GILLS at first whitish, then pink, fairly distant, emarginate. SPORE PRINT pink. SMELL faint, radish-like. FLESH whitish. Solitary or in small ± trooping groups. On wet acid soil, among mosses. Autumn. Widespread. Rare. Inedible. SPORES broadly ellipsoid – subspherical, angular, 7.5–10×6.5–7.5, non-amyloid.

Entoloma porphyrophaeum. Cap, overall stature, habitat. CAP 3–9, at first convex, then flattened, rather sharply umbonate, fibrous lined. STEM 4–8, slender, ± equal or tapering slightly upwards, fibrous lined, white downy at base. GILLS at first whitish, then pink, fairly distant, adnexed-free. SPORE PRINT pink. SMELL indistinct. FLESH whitish. Solitary or in small ± trooping groups. On soil, pastures, grassy areas, often close to trees. Spring – autumn. Widespread. Uncommon. Inedible. SPORES ellipsoid, angular, 10–12×6–8, non-amyloid.

Entoloma turbidum. Gills, spores, habitat. CAP 3–6.5, at first conical – convex, then flattened, broadly umbonate, lined, especially towards margin, rather silky, margin often split. STEM 5–12, slender, tapering slightly upwards, finely silky-fibrous, white towards base. GILLS greyish brown – pink, fairly crowded, adnexed – free. SPORE PRINT pink. SMELL indistinct. FLESH whitish. Solitary or in small ± trooping groups. On acid soil, often among mosses, usually coniferous woods. Spring – winter. Widespread. Rare. Inedible. SPORES subspherical, obscurely angular, 6.5–9×5.5–7, non-amyloid.

Entoloma clypeatum. Cap features, habitat. CAP 4–10, at first convex, then flattened, broadly umbonate, often with streaks and/or dark spotting. STEM 4–8, fairly stout, equal or tapering slightly upwards, fibrous-silky-lined. GILLS greyish then pink, fairly crowded, adnexed. SPORE PRINT pink. SMELL mealy-floury. FLESH thick, whitish. Solitary or in small ± trooping groups. On soil, with rosaceous shrubs, hedges, shrubberies. Spring – summer. Widespread. Uncommon. Inedible, poisonous? SPORES subspherical, angular, 8–11×7.5–9, non-amyloid.

ntoloma aprile. Cap fea-
ures, habitat. CAP 3–7, con-
ex, markedly umbonate,
usually finely radially
orous, lined at margin.
TEM 4–8, fairly stout, ±
qual, fibrous-lined. GILLS
reyish then pink, fairly
istant, adnexed. SPORE
RINT pink. SMELL mealy-
oury. FLESH whitish. Soli-
ary or in small ± trooping
roups. On soil, with broad-
aved shrubs and trees.
pring. Widespread. Rare.
nedible, poisonous?
PORES subspherical, angu-
r, 9–12×7.5–10, non-
myloid.

Entoloma rhodopolium.
Overall colour and form,
gills, smell, habitat, similar
to *E. nidorosum* but smell
differs. CAP 2–8, at first
convex then flattened –
±depressed, almost
umbonate, finely silky
fibrous. STEM 5–10,
slender, ±equal, fibrous
lined. GILLS whitish, then
pink, crowded, ±adnate.
SPORE PRINT pink. SMELL
faint, unpleasant, mealy-
floury – slightly rancid.
FLESH whitish. Solitary or in
small ± trooping groups. On
soil in broad-leaved woods.
Summer – autumn. Wide-
spread. Uncommon. Poiso-
nous. SPORES subspherical,
angular, 8–10.5×7–8, non-
amyloid.

Entoloma sericatum. Overall colour and form, gills,
smell, habitat, CAP 2–8, at
first conical – convex then
flattened – ±depressed,
finely silky fibrous, margin
finely lined. STEM 4–10,
slender, ±equal, fibrous
lined. GILLS whitish, then
pink, crowded, ±adnate.
SPORE PRINT pink. SMELL
acrid. FLESH whitish. Solitary or in small ± trooping
groups. On wet soil and
among *Sphagnum*, woods,
marshy places. Summer –
autumn. Widespread.
Uncommon. Inedible.
SPORES ellipsoid, angular,
7.5–10×6–8, non-amyloid.

Leptonia incana. Colour,
colour change, smell. CAP
1–3, at first convex then
flattened – depressed or
umbilicate, lined at margin.
STEM 2–5, slender, ±equal,
bruising greenish blue,
finely downy at base. GILLS
at first pale greenish, then
pink, fairly distant,
adnate – decurrent. SPORE
PRINT pink. SMELL strong,
mice. FLESH greenish. In
small ± trooping groups. On
soil among grass, especially
on chalky sites. Summer –
autumn. Widespread.
Rare. Poisonous. SPORES ±
oblong, angular, 11–14×8
–9, non-amyloid.

ntoloma sinuatum. Over-
l colour and form, gills,
nell, habitat. CAP 7–20, at
rst convex then slightly
attened, broadly umbon-
e, finely radially fibrous,
iny, ±sticky. STEM 6–10,
out, tapering upwards, ±
ılbous, silky-lined, often
ellowish-spotted. GILLS at
rst greenish yellow, then
nk, crowded, adnexed.
PORE PRINT pink. SMELL
ealy-floury, later unplea-
ınt, rancid. FLESH whitish.
olitary or in small ± troop-
g groups. On fairly rich
il, usually close to broad-
aved trees, pastures,
oadsides, hedges. Summer
autumn. Widespread.
are. Poisonous. SPORES
ıbspherical, angular, 8–11
7–8.5, non-amyloid.

Entoloma nidorosum.
Overall colour and form,
gills, smell, habitat, similar
to *E. rhodopolium* but
smell differs. CAP 2–7, at
first convex then flattened –
±depressed, finely silky
fibrous, margin finely lined.
STEM 5–10, slender, ±equal,
fibrous-lined. GILLS whitish,
then pink, crowded, ±ad-
nate. SPORE PRINT pink.
SMELL faint, ammonia-like
when fresh, then±absent.
FLESH whitish. Solitary or in
small ± trooping groups. On
soil in broad-leaved woods.
Summer – autumn. Wide-
spread. Uncommon. Poiso-
nous? SPORES subspherical,
angular, 8–10.5×7–8, non-
amyloid.

Leptonia polita. Stem
features, smell, habitat.
CAP 2–8, at first convex then
flattened – umbilicate or
funnel-shaped, markedly
lined when wet, rather
shiny when dry. STEM 4–5,
slender, ±equal, ±grooved,
smooth, shiny, finely
downy at base. GILLS whitish, then brownish pink,
fairly crowded, adnate –
sinuate. SPORE PRINT pink.
SMELL indistinct. FLESH
brownish. In ± trooping
groups. On wet soil with
willows, woods, marshy
places. Summer – autumn.
Widespread. Rare. Inedi-
ble. SPORES ± ellipsoid,
irregular, angular, 8–
10.5×7–9, non-amyloid.

Leptonia sericella. Colour,
gills. CAP 1–3, at first convex then flattened –
depressed or umbilicate,
often minutely scaly,
slightly lined at margin.
STEM 2–5, slender, ±equal,
smooth, shiny. GILLS at first
white, then pink, fairly distant, decurrent. SPORE PRINT
pink. SMELL earthy. FLESH
white. In small ± trooping
groups. On soil among
grass, woods, pastures,
roadsides, marshy areas.
Summer – autumn. Wide-
spread. Common. Inedible.
SPORES ±oblong, angular,
9–12×5–8, non-amyloid.

Leptonia pyrospila. Stem base. CAP 1–4, first convex then flattened – depressed or umbilicate, often minutely scaly, slightly lined at margin when wet. STEM 3–7, slender, ±equal, sometimes irregularly grooved, ± smooth, floury at apex, downy to base with orange flush. GILLS first bluish white, then brownish pink, fairly crowded, adnate – ± free, sometimes darker edge. SPORE PRINT pink. FLESH greyish white, sometimes flushed orange in lowest part of stem. In small± trooping groups. On soil in grass, woods, roadsides, marshy areas. Summer – autumn. Widespread. Uncommon. Inedible. SPORES ±oblong, angular, 10–12×6.5–8, non-amyloid.

Leptonia griseocyanea. Stem colour, cap features. CAP 2–3.5, at first convex – dome-shaped, then flattened, broadly umbonate, at first±smooth, then minutely scaly, especially at centre. STEM 6–8, slender, ± equal or tapering slightly upwards, downy to very finely lined (use hand lens), ±floury at apex, lilac flush towards base. GILLS at first whitish, then brownish pink, fairly crowded, emarginate. SPORE PRINT pink. FLESH whitish. In small±trooping groups. On soil among grass, woods, pastures, roadsides. Summer – autumn. Widespread. Uncommon. Inedible. SPORES±oblong, angular, 9.5–11×6.5–7.5, non-amyloid.

Leptonia euchroa. Overall colour, habitat. CAP 2–4, at first convex – dome-shaped, then flattened, broadly umbonate, finely silky. STEM 2–5.5, slender, equal or slightly swollen at base, often curved, very finely fibrous. GILLS greyish blue, fairly distant, emarginate – free. SPORE PRINT pink. SMELL indistinct. FLESH bluish white. In small±trooping groups. On wood, fallen branches, stumps of broad-leaved trees, especially alder, hazel, birch. Summer – autumn. Widespread. Uncommon. Edible. SPORES broadly ellipsoid, angular, 9–11×5–7.5, non-amyloid.

Leptonia chalybea. Over colour, cap features, gills CAP 1–2.5, at first convex then more flattened, rath± sharply umbonate,± smooth or very finely scaly. STEM 2–4, fairly sle der, equal or tapering slightly downwards,± smooth, downy at base. GILLS greyish blue, fairly distant, emarginate. SPO PRINT pink. SMELL indist inct. FLESH bluish white. small±trooping groups. soil among grass, meado pastures, often close to trees. Summer – autumn Widespread. Rare. Inedi ble. SPORES broadly ellip soid, angular, 9–10×6.5– 7.5, non-amyloid.

Leptonia lampropus. Stem, microscopic features. CAP 1.5–3.5, first convex then flattened – depressed or umbilicate, often minutely scaly at centre, slightly lined at margin when wet. STEM 3–6, slender,±equal, finely lined (hand-lens),± floury at apex, steely bluish towards base. GILLS at first bluish white, then brownish pink, fairly crowded, adnate – ±free. SPORE PRINT pink. SMELL indistinct. FLESH greyish white, sometimes bluish in parts. In small±trooping groups. On soil in grass, often with *L. griseocyanea*, woods, pastures, roadsides. Summer – autumn. Widespread. Uncommon. Inedible. SPORES ±oblong, angular, 9.5–13× 6.5–9, non-amyloid. Gill edge with sterile hairs with large±pear-shaped ends.

Leptonia lividocyanula. Stem colour, cap features. CAP 1.5–2.5, at first±convex, then flattened – deeply umbilicate,±smooth, lined at margin, especially when wet. STEM 4–5.5, slender, equal, smooth, slight bluish flush. GILLS at first greyish white, then pink, fairly crowded, adnate – ± decurrent. SPORE PRINT pink. SMELL indistinct. FLESH whitish. Trooping. On wet soil among grass, woods, pastures, roadsides. Summer – autumn. Widespread. Rare. Inedible. SPORES broadly ellipsoid, angular, 9–10×6–6.5, non-amyloid.

Leptonia serrulata. Overall colour, gills. CAP 1.5–2.5, at first convex, then flattened – depressed or umbilicate,±smooth, lined at margin. STEM 1.5–2, fairly slender, equal or tapering slightly downwards, usually with black dots at apex,±downy hairy at base. GILLS greyish blue, with irregular blackish edge, fairly distant, adnate – emarginate, often with decurrent tooth. SPORE PRINT pink. SMELL indistinct. FLESH bluish white. In small±trooping groups. On soil among grass, meadows, pastures. Summer – autumn. Widespread, predominantly northern. Uncommon. Poisonous. SPORES broadly ellipsoid, angular, 8–11×6–7, non-amyloid.

Leptonia lazulina. Overa colour, cap and stem features, gills. CAP 1.5–3, at first convex, then more flattened, covered with fine, radial fibres, lined, especially towards margi STEM 3–4, very slender, equal or tapering slightly downwards, downy at base. GILLS at fi blue – greyish blue, then pinkish, fairly distant, adnate – emarginate. SP PRINT pink. SMELL indis tinct. FLESH blue. In small±trooping groups. ↑ soil among grass, especia on acid sites, meadows, heaths. Summer – autumn Widespread, predominantly northern. Uncommon. Poisonous. SPORES broadly ellipsoid, angula 10–11.5×6.5–7.5, non-amyloid.

Leptonia corvina. Overall colour, cap and stem features contrasting with white gills. CAP 1–3.5, at first convex, then more flattened, finely fibrous. STEM 3–5, slender, equal or tapering slightly downwards, markedly paler on aging, especially at apex. GILLS pinkish, fairly distant, adnate – emarginate. SPORE PRINT pink. SMELL indistinct. FLESH greyish. In small±trooping groups. On soil among grass, meadows, pastures. Summer – autumn. Widespread. Uncommon. Poisonous? PORES broadly ellipsoid, angular, 8.5–12×6.5–7, non-amyloid.

Nolanea infula. Overall colour, cap and stem features, gills. CAP 1.5–2, at first convex, then more flattened, papillate, smooth, finely lined. STEM 5–8, very slender,±equal, smooth. GILLS at first whitish, then pink, fairly distant, adnate – emarginate. SPORE PRINT pink. SMELL indistinct? FLESH brownish. In small±trooping groups. On soil among grass, meadows, pastures. Summer – autumn. Widespread, often±highland. Uncommon. Inedible. SPORES ellipsoid, angular, 8–10×6–7, non-amyloid.

Nolanea papillata. Overall colour, cap features, gills, smell. CAP 1.5–5, at first convex, then scarcely flattened, markedly papillate or sharply umbonate, smooth, lined, especially when moist. STEM 2–6, very slender,±equal, smooth – very finely silky, floury at apex. GILLS at first pale grey, then brown-pink, fairly crowded, emarginate. SPORE PRINT pink. SMELL indistinct or very faintly mealy. FLESH brownish. In small±trooping groups. On wet soil among grass, pastures, meadows, roadsides. Summer – autumn. Widespread. Uncommon. Inedible. SPORES elongated-ellipsoid, angular, 9–12×6.5–8, non-amyloid.

Nolanea minuta. Size, overall colour, habitat. CAP 0.5–2, at first convex, then slightly flattened, barely umbonate, smooth, lined. STEM 1–3, very slender,±equal, smooth, very finely downy at base. GILLS at first whitish, then±pink, fairly distant, adnate – emarginate. SMELL faint, mealy. FLESH brownish. Trooping. On wet soil with trees, especially alder. Summer – autumn. Widespread. Uncommon. Inedible. SPORES broadly ellipsoid, angular, 8–11.5 5×6.5–8, non-amyloid.

Nolanea vernum. Overall colour, cap and stem features. CAP 2–4, at first hemispherical – bell-shaped, then more flattened but remaining umbonate, finely radially fibrous, markedly paler when dry. STEM 3–8, slender,±equal, often rather flattened and twisted, finely fibrous. GILLS greyish brown, fairly distant, adnate-emarginate. SPORE PRINT pink. SMELL indistinct. FLESH greyish brown. In small trooping groups. On soil in fairly damp places, among grass or moss, as at woodland edges. Summer – autumn. Widespread. Rare. Inedible. SPORES broadly ellipsoid – subspherical, angular, 8–10.5×6.5–8, non-amyloid.

Nolanea juncinus. Overall colour, gills, smell. CAP 1.5–2.5, at first convex, then more flattened, umbonate – papillate, smooth, rather coarsely lined. STEM 5–8, very slender,±equal, smooth. GILLS greyish brown – pink, fairly distant, adnate – emarginate. SPORE PRINT pink. SMELL mealy. FLESH brownish. In small± trooping groups. On wet soil among grass, damp woods. Summer – autumn. Widespread. Uncommon. Inedible. SPORES broadly ellipsoid, obscurely angular, 8.5–10.5×7.5–8.5, non-amyloid.

Nolanea icterina. Overall colour, cap features, gills, smell, habitat. CAP 1.5–2, convex, usually markedly papillate or sharply umbonate, smooth, lined at margin, especially when moist. STEM 2–6, slender,±equal or tapering slightly upwards, smooth – very finely silky scaly. GILLS at first yellowish white, then pinkish, fairly distant, emarginate. SPORE PRINT pink. SMELL fruity. FLESH yellowish white. In small± trooping groups. On wet soil among grass, often with trees in boggy places. Summer – autumn. Widespread. Rare. Inedible. SPORES broadly ellipsoid, angular, 10–12×6.5–8, non-amyloid.

Nolanea hirtipes. Size, smell, habitat, microscopic features. CAP 3–5, at first convex, then flattened, very sharply umbonate, smooth – silky, finely lined at margin. STEM 7–15, slender,±equal, smooth, downy at base. GILLS at first whitish, then±brownish pink, fairly distant, emarginate. SPORE PRINT pink. SMELL strong, cucumber. FLESH brownish. In small± trooping groups. On damp soil among grass, often in mixed or coniferous woods. Autumn. Widespread. Rare. Inedible. SPORES elongated-ellipsoid, angular, 11–14×7–8, non-amyloid. Gill edge cystida ±worm-like with rounded heads.

119

ENTOLOMATACEAE

CORTINARIACE/

Nolanea staurospora (=*conferundum*). Overall colour, spores. CAP 2–3.5, convex, scarcely flattened, obscurely umbonate, smooth – silky, lined, especially when wet. STEM 2–7, slender, ±equal, markedly silky-lined, downy at base. GILLS at first whitish, then pink, fairly crowded, adnexed – emarginate. SPORE PRINT pink. SMELL strong, mealy. FLESH brownish. In small±trooping groups. On soil among grass, pastures, meadows. Autumn. Widespread. Very common. Inedible. SPORES±cuboid, irregularly star-shaped, 9–11×6–9, non-amyloid.

Nolanea sericeum. Overall colour, cap and stem features. CAP 5–7, at first convex-conical, then flattened-depressed – broadly umbonate-papillate, silky, markedly paler in concentric banding on drying, margin lined especially when wet. STEM 3–6, fairly slender, ±equal, finely silky fibrous. GILLS pink – greyish white, fairly distant, emarginate-free. SPORE PRINT pink. SMELL mealy. FLESH brownish. In small±trooping groups. On soil in grassy places, lawns. Summer – autumn. Widespread. Common. Inedible. SPORES broadly ellipsoid – subspherical, angular, 7.5–10×6.5–8, non-amyloid.

Nolanea cetrata. Habitat, microscopic features, yellowish colours. CAP 1–3, convex – slightly flattened, smooth, lined, especially when wet. STEM 2–6, slender, equal or tapering slightly upwards, silky-lined, downy at base. GILLS yellowish pink, fairly crowded, emarginate – free. SPORE PRINT pink. TASTE and SMELL indistinct. FLESH brownish. In±trooping groups. On soil, often among mosses, coniferous woods. Autumn. Widespread. Common. Inedible. SPORES±subspherical, angular, 6.5–8×9–12, non-amyloid. Basidia 2-spored.

Inocybe atripes. Smell, stem features, microscop features. CAP 2.5–8, convv – broadly umbonate, ± densely covered with flattened fibres. STEM 2–7, equal, fairly slender, slightly bulbous, covered with floury coating, soon darkening, especially at base, often±lined. GILLS first whitish, then pale bu fairly distant, adnate – adnexed. SPORE PRINT snu brown. SMELL strong, acidic, unpleasant. FLESH pale whitish buff. Solitar or in small±trooping groups. On acid soil on grassland, heaths, conife ous woods. Autumn. Wi spread. Rare. Inedible. SPORES±bean-shaped, smooth, 4.5–5×8–10. Gi face cystidia broadly club shaped – pear-shaped.

Nolanea lucida. Overall colour, cap and stem features, smell, similar to *N. farinolens* but spores and habitat differ. CAP 1–5, at first convex – conical, then flattened-depressed – broadly umbonate-papillate, ±shiny-silky or streaked, lined especially when wet. STEM 2–6, slender, equal, silky-lined, ± floury at apex, downy at base. GILLS at first greyish white, then brown-pink, fairly crowded, adnate – emarginate. SPORE PRINT pink. SMELL strong, mealy. FLESH brownish. In small± trooping groups. On soil, usually among grass, pastures, meadows. Summer – autumn. Widespread. Rare. Inedible. SPORES broadly ellipsoid – subspherical, angular, 7.5–10× 5.5–7, non-amyloid.

Nolanea farinolens. Overall colour, cap and stem features, smell, similar to *N. lucida* but spores and habitat differ. CAP 1.5–3, at first convex – conical, then flattened – depressed, sometimes broadly umbonate, ±shiny-silky or streaked, cuticle rather tough, lined especially when wet. STEM 2–7, slender, equal or tapering slightly upwards, silky-lined, ±floury at apex, downy at base. GILLS at first greyish white, then brown-pink, fairly crowded, adnate – emarginate. SPORE PRINT pink. SMELL strong, mealy. FLESH brownish. In±trooping groups. On soil, often among grass in damp shady places, pastures, meadows. Summer – autumn. Widespread. Rare. Inedible. SPORES broadly ellipsoid – subspherical, angular, 6.5–9×5.5–7, non-amyloid.

CORTINARIACEAE
Extremely variable, toadstool shaped or rarely (*Crepidotus*)±kidney-shaped with stem absent, usually dull-coloured, cap surface smooth and scaly, dry – sticky, sometimes (*Cortinarius*) with±sticky cobweb-like veil stretched across young gills, stem±ring or ring zones, gills crowded – distant, decurrent – free, spores subspherical – very irregular, smooth – warty, spore print pale – dark brown, very rarely (*Leucocortinarius*) white. On soil or wood, usually with trees, most mycorrhizal, many saprotrophic, few parasitic. Few edible, several poisonous, some deadly. *Inocybe* [87], *Hebeloma* [17], *Naucoria* [21], *Gymnopilus* [9], *Cortinarius* (including at least 7 well-defined subgenera) [250], *Leucocortinarius* [1], *Rozites* [1], *Galerina* [25], *Crepidotus* [18], *Flocculina* [11], *Phaeomarasmius* [3], *Pholiota* [29], *Tubaria* [5], *Ripartites* [2], (*Phaeocollybia* [3]), (*Phaeolepiota* [1]).

Inocybe hystrix. Cap and stem features. CAP 2–4, convex – broadly umbon ate, densely covered with±upturned pointed scales. STEM 4–7, equal, fairly slender, sometimes very slightly bulbous, covered with recurved scales. GILLS at first whiti then pale buff with whitis edge, fairly distant, adna – adnexed. SPORE PRINT snuff-brown. SMELL faint indistinct. FLESH pale wh ish buff. Solitary or in sm ±trooping groups. On so in broad-leaved woods, especially with beech. Autumn. Widespread, pr dominantly northern. Uncommon. Poisonous. SPORES±almond-shaped, smooth, 4.5–6.5×9–11.5 Gill edge cystidia elonga spindle-shaped with apic crystals.

120

Inocybe agardhii. Size, habitat, stem features. CAP 2–8, at first convex then flattened and broadly umbonate, fibrous-lined. STEM 5–8, equal, rather stout, slightly bulbous, rather fibrous below indefinite superior, cottony ring zone. GILLS at first pale buff then olive-brown, fairly crowded, adnate with decurrent tooth. SPORE PRINT snuff-brown. SMELL indistinct. FLESH pale yellowish buff, sometimes with olive flush. Solitary or in small trooping groups. On soil and among plant debris in wet woods, also dunes, especially with willow. Autumn. Widespread. Uncommon. Inedible, poisonous? SPORES ellipsoid – bean-shaped, smooth, 8–10×4.5–6. Gill edge cystidia small, usually pear-shaped – club-shaped.

Inocybe patouillardii **Red-staining Inocybe.** Colour change, habitat. CAP 3–8, at first conical – bell-shaped, then convex, broadly umbonate, finely fibrous, margin usually split, bruising reddish. STEM 4–10, equal, fairly stout, usually slightly bulbous, very finely fibrous-lined, bruising reddish. GILLS at first white then olive-brown, edge white, bruising reddish, crowded adnexed. SPORE PRINT snuff-brown. SMELL faint, indefinite. FLESH white. Solitary or in small trooping groups. On soil in deciduous woods, especially beech on chalky sites. Spring – autumn. Widespread, mainly southern. Rare. Deadly poisonous. SPORES bean-shaped, smooth, 5.5–7×10–13. Gill edge cystidia club-shaped – ±cylindrical.

Inocybe cookei. Smell, habitat, bulb, flesh colours. CAP 3–5, at first conical – bell-shaped, then convex – flattened, broadly umbonate, finely fibrous, often splitting at margin. STEM 3–6, equal, fairly slender, marginate bulbous,± smooth except at extreme apex. GILLS at first white then pale reddish brown, crowded, adnexed. SPORE PRINT snuff-brown. SMELL faint, pleasant. FLESH at first white, then yellow – straw-coloured. Solitary or trooping. On soil in deciduous or mixed woods. Summer – autumn. Widespread. Common. Poisonous. SPORES bean-shaped, smooth, 4–5×7–8. Gill edge cystidia pear-shaped.

Inocybe fastigiata. Smell, habitat, cap surface, microscopic features. CAP 3–10,' at first conical – bell-shaped, then convex – flattened, rather sharply umbonate, cracked, often splitting radially from margin. STEM 4–10, equal, fairly slender, loosely fibrous-lined, white floury at apex. GILLS yellowish, edge white, crowded, adnate – adnexed. SPORE PRINT snuff-brown. SMELL faint, potatoes. FLESH white. Solitary or in small trooping groups. On soil in broad-leaved woods, especially with beech. Summer – autumn. Widespread. Very common. Poisonous. SPORES bean-shaped, smooth, 9–12×4.5–7. Gill edge cystidia club-shaped.

Inocybe dulcamara. Size, habitat, stem features. CAP 1–4, at first convex then± flattened and often broadly umbonate,±covered with flattened scales, whitish veil present when young. STEM 3–4, equal, fairly slender,± densely woolly-lined, often with indefinite superior, cottony ring zone. GILLS at first pale buff then brown, edge ragged irregular, white, fairly crowded, adnate. SPORE PRINT snuff-brown. SMELL indistinct. FLESH pale buff. Solitary or in small trooping groups. On sandy soil, roadsides, woodland edges, dunes. Autumn. Widespread. Uncommon. Inedible. SPORES bean-shaped, smooth, 7.5–10.4×5–5.5. Gill edge cystidia short, club-shaped – pear-shaped.

Inocybe jurana. Colour change, habitat, often confused with *I. patouillardii* but flesh and smell differ. CAP 2–6, at first conical – bell-shaped, then convex, broadly umbonate, finely fibrous, often turning slightly reddish. STEM 3–6, equal, fairly slender, usually very slightly bulbous, very finely fibrous-lined – almost scaly, flushed purplish. GILLS at first white then olive-brown, edge white, crowded, adnate – free. SPORE PRINT snuff-brown. SMELL mealy. FLESH white, often flushed pink in cap and stem base. Solitary or trooping. On soil in deciduous or mixed woods, especially beech on chalky sites. Autumn. Widespread. Uncommon. Inedible. SPORES bean-shaped, smooth, 5–7×10–15. Gill edge cystidia club-shaped.

Inocybe calamistrata. Smell, habitat, stem colour, microscopic features. CAP 1–5, at first conical – bell-shaped, then convex – flattened, broadly umbonate, covered with upturned pointed scales, especially in centre. STEM 3–7,±equal or tapering slightly upwards, slender, covered with recurved dark scales, blue-greenish downy at base. GILLS at first whitish, then reddish brown, edge white irregular, crowded, adnate. SPORE PRINT snuff-brown. SMELL strong, curious, sour-acidic. FLESH white, turning reddish, blue-green at stem base. Solitary or in small trooping groups. On soil in coniferous or mixed woods. Summer. Widespread. Uncommon. Inedible, poisonous? SPORES bean-shaped, smooth, 5–7×9.5–13. Gill edge cystidia broadly club-shaped – balloon-like.

Inocybe maculata. Smell, habitat, cap surface, microscopic features. CAP 2–8, at first conical – bell-shaped, then convex – flattened, broadly umbonate, at first covered with fine white fibres, then markedly dark fibrous, often splitting at margin. STEM 4–9, equal, rather stout, usually with small basal bulb, loosely fibrous-lined. GILLS at first whitish then brown, edge white irregular, crowded, adnate – emarginate. SPORE PRINT snuff-brown. SMELL pleasant, earthy-fruity. FLESH white. Solitary or in small trooping groups. On soil in broad-leaved woods, especially with beech on chalky sites. Autumn. Widespread. Common. Poisonous. SPORES bean-shaped, smooth, 9–11×4.5–5. Gill edge cystidia club-shaped.

Inocybe cervicolor. Smell, habitat, stem, microscopic features. CAP 2–5, first conical – bell-shaped, then convex – flattened, slightly umbonate, covered with upturned pointed scales, esp. in centre. STEM 4–10, equal, slender, finely fibrous-lined, floury white at apex, slightly white downy at base. GILLS first creamy, then red brown with red spotting, edge white irregular, fairly distant, adnate. SPORE PRINT snuff-brown. SMELL mouldy. FLESH white, turning reddish. Solitary or in small trooping groups. On soil in coniferous woods. Summer – autumn. Rare. Inedible, poisonous? SPORES bean-shaped – almond-shaped, smooth, 6–7.5×11–14. Gill edge cystidia cylindrical – broadly bottle-shaped.

Inocybe godeyi. Smell, colour change, microscopic features. CAP 3–5, at first conical – convex, then more flattened, slightly umbonate, silky smooth, cracking, bruising red. STEM 4–6, equal, slender, markedly marginate bulbous, fibrous, slightly floury at apex, flushing reddish. GILLS at first whitish, then reddish brown flushed olive, edge white irregular, crowded, adnexed. SPORE PRINT snuff-brown. SMELL strong, earthy, unpleasant. FLESH white, turning reddish when cut. Solitary or in small trooping groups. On soil in broad-leaved woods. Autumn. Widespread. Uncommon. Poisonous. SPORES almond-shaped, smooth, 5–7×9–11.5. Gill edge cystidia broadly bottle-shaped – pear-shaped.

Inocybe geophylla var. *lilacina*. Colour, microscopic features. CAP 1–3.5, at first ±conical, then convex – flattened, sharply umbonate, silky smooth. STEM 1–6, equal, slender, silky – fibrous. GILLS buff, crowded, adnexed. SPORE PRINT snuff-brown. SMELL earthy. FLESH lilac – whitish. Trooping. On soil, often among grass at path edges in broad-leaved, mixed or coniferous woods. Summer – autumn. Widespread. Very common. Poisonous. SPORES±almond-shaped, smooth, 5.5–6×7.5–10. Gill edge cystidia broadly spindle-shaped with apical crystals.

Inocybe sambucina. Lack of colour, stem, habitat, microscopic features. CAP 4–8, convex, broadly umbonate, silky – fibrous. STEM 2.5–5, equal or tapering slightly upwards, often slightly bulbous, stout, fibrous lined. GILLS at first cream, then buff, distant, ± sinuate. SPORE PRINT snuff-brown. SMELL strong, unpleasant. FLESH white. Solitary or in small trooping groups. On soil in coniferous woods. Summer – autumn. Widespread. Rare. Poisonous? SPORES almond-shaped, smooth, 4–6×9–12. Gill edge cystidia slender, spindle-shaped with apical crystals.

Inocybe bongardii. Smell, microscopic features. CAP 3–6, at first bell-shaped, then convex – flattened, broadly umbonate, covered with flattened fibrous scales. STEM 5–10, equal, slender, fibrous, floury at apex, flushing reddish. GILLS at first greyish olive, then brownish, edge white irregular, fairly crowded, ± sinuate. SPORE PRINT snuff-brown. SMELL strong, ripe pears. FLESH white, turning reddish. Solitary or in small trooping groups. On soil in broad-leaved or coniferous woods. Autumn. Widespread. Uncommon. Poisonous. SPORES bean-shaped, 6–7×10–12. Gills edge cystidia ± cylindrical – club-shaped.

Inocybe geophylla. Cap colour, smell, microscopic features. CAP 1–3.5, at first ±conical, then convex – flattened, sharply umbonate, silky smooth, flushed yellowish. STEM 1–6, equal, slender, silky – fibrous. GILLS at first cream, then buff, crowded, adnexed. SPORE PRINT snuff-brown. SMELL earthy. FLESH white. Trooping. On soil, often among grass in broad-leaved, mixed or coniferous woods. Summer – autumn. Widespread. Very common. Poisonous. SPORES±almond-shaped, smooth, 5–6×8–10.5. Gill edge cystidia broadly spindle-shaped with apical crystals.

Inocybe pudica. Colour, smell, habitat, microscopic features. CAP 2–5, at first conical – bell-shaped, then more flattened, fairly broadly umbonate, silky – fibrous. STEM 4–10, equal or tapering slightly upwards, fairly slender, flushed reddish. GILLS at first whitish and red-flushed, then gradually brown, fairly crowded, adnexed. SPORE PRINT snuff-brown. SMELL mealy. FLESH white, flushing red in stem. Solitary or in small trooping groups. On soil in coniferous woods. Summer. Widespread. Uncommon. Poisonous. SPORES±bean-shaped, smooth, 4.5–5.5×8–9. Gill edge cystidia spindle-shaped with apical crystals.

Inocybe corydalina. Colour, smell, stem, microscopic features. CAP 4–8, at first convex – bell-shaped, then flattened, rather sharply umbonate, smooth, later slightly fibrous towards margin. STEM 4–8, ±equal or tapering slightly upwards, often slightly bulbous, stout, fibrous-lined, sometimes greenish below. GILLS at first whitish, then brown, edge white irregular, crowded, adnate – emarginate. SPORE PRINT snuff-brown. SMELL strong fruity, ripe pears. FLESH white or very slightly pink at stem base, sometimes yellowing. Solitary or in small trooping groups. On soil in coniferous or mixed woods. Summer – autumn. Widespread. Rare. Poisonous. SPORES±ellipsoid, smooth, 5–6.5×8–10. Gill edge cystidia slender, spindle-shaped – broadly bottle-shaped with apical crystals.

Inocybe pyriodora. Colour, smell, stem, microscopic features. CAP 3–8, at first convex – bell-shaped, then more flattened, very broadly umbonate, fibrous-scaly, often splitting from margin. STEM 5–10, ±equal, stout, fibrous-lined below, floury white towards apex. GILLS at first whitish, then reddish brown, edge white irregular, crowded, adnate. SPORE PRINT snuff-brown. SMELL strong, fruity, ripe pears. FLESH white, turning slightly pink. Solitary or in small trooping groups. On soil in broad-leaved, mixed or coniferous woods. Autumn. Widespread. Common. Inedible. SPORES almond-shaped, smooth, 5–7×8–11.5. Gill edge cystidia broadly spindle-shaped with apical crystals.

Inocybe abietis. Colour, cap and stem features, habitat, microscopic features. CAP 1.5–4.5, at first convex – bell-shaped, then more flattened, ±broadly umbonate, radially fibrous lined. STEM 2–6, equal or tapering upwards, fairly stout, ±bulbous, completely floury. GILLS at first whitish, then greyish brown, rather distant, adnexed. SPORE PRINT snuff-brown. SMELL faint, ±fruity or indistinct. FLESH white. Solitary or in small trooping groups. On soil in coniferous woods, especially with firs on chalky sites. Summer – autumn. Widespread. Rare. Inedible. SPORES almond-shaped, smooth, 7.5–10×4.5–6. Gill edge cystidia spindle-shaped, usually with apical crystals.

Inocybe friesii. Cap and stem features, microscopic features, habitat. CAP 1.5–4, at first±bell-shaped, then flattened – convex, umbonate, cracked, finely fibrous. STEM 2–4, equal or tapering slightly upwards, slender, powdery at apex. GILLS whitish – olive brown, crowded, adnexed-free. SPORE PRINT brown. SMELL slightly mealy. FLESH white with pink flush, especially in stem. Solitary or in small trooping groups. On soil with coniferous trees. Autumn. Widespread. Rare. Inedible. SPORES almond-shaped – spindle-shaped, smooth, 8–10×5.5–6. Gill edge cystidia rather broadly spindle-shaped, with few apical crystals.

Inocybe flocculosa (=gausapata). Cap and stem, microscopic features. CAP 2–4, first±bell-shaped, then flattened-convex, broadly umbonate, covered with soft hairs,±finely cracked towards centre, margin with cobwebby veil. STEM 3–5,±equal or tapering slightly upwards, slender, fibrous lined, floury at apex,±downy at base. GILLS at first pale brown, then ochreous, crowded, sinuate. SPORE PRINT snuff-brown. SMELL faint, mealy. FLESH white, turning slightly reddish in stem. Solitary or in small trooping groups. On soil in broad-leaved woods, especially with oak. Autumn. Widespread. Uncommon. Inedible. SPORES±almond-shaped, smooth, 8–11×4.5–5.5. Gill edge cystidia slender, spindle-shaped, with apical crystals.

Inocybe pelargonium. Colour, cap and stem features, smell, microscopic features. CAP 2–4, at first convex – bell-shaped, then more flattened, broadly umbonate, smooth or± finely flecked, not fibrous. STEM 2–6,±equal, slender, often marginate bulbous, completely floury. GILLS at first whitish, then greyish brown, crowded, adnexed. SPORE PRINT snuff-brown. SMELL strong, pelargonium. FLESH white. Solitary or in small trooping groups. On soil in coniferous woods, especially with spruce. Autumn. Widespread. Rare. Inedible. SPORES almond-shaped, smooth, 7–11×4–5.5. Gill edge cystidia spindle-shaped with apical crystals.

Inocybe hirtella. Colour, cap and stem features, smell, habitat, microscopic features. CAP 1–3, at first convex – bell-shaped, then more flattened, broadly umbonate,±covered with small, flattened scales. STEM 2–4, equal, slightly bulbous, fairly slender, completely floury. GILLS at first straw-coloured, then brown, crowded, adnexed. SPORE PRINT snuff-brown. SMELL very faint, almonds (enclose in container to enhance). FLESH white, flushed greyish. Solitary or in small trooping groups. On soil in broad-leaved woods, especially with hazel. Autumn. Widespread. Uncommon. Inedible. SPORES almond-shaped, smooth, 10–12×6–7 (2-spored basidia) or 8.5–10×5–6 (4-spored basidia). Gill edge cystidia broadly – narrowly spindle-shaped, with apical crystals.

Inocybe brunneoatra. Cap and stem features, microscopic features. CAP 1–2, at first±bell-shaped, then flattened – convex, sharply umbonate, finely cracked, radially fibrous. STEM 2–4.5, equal, slightly bulbous, slender,±smooth. GILLS at first grey – straw-coloured, then brown, crowded, adnexed – free. SPORE PRINT snuff-brown. SMELL indistinct. FLESH white. Solitary or in small trooping groups. On soil in broad-leaved, mixed or coniferous woods. Autumn. Widespread. Common. Inedible. SPORES almond-shaped, smooth, 8–10×5–6. Gill edge cystidia slender, spindle-shaped, with apical crystals.

Inocybe tigrina. Cap and stem features, microscopic features. CAP 2–5, at first conical – bell-shaped, then flattened, barely umbonate, distinctly radially fibrous-scaly. STEM 3–6,±equal or tapering slightly upwards, slender, barely bulbous,±smooth, floury at apex, downy at base. GILLS at first white then pinkish buff, crowded, adnate. SPORE PRINT snuff-brown. SMELL indistinct. FLESH white. Solitary or in small trooping groups. On soil in broad-leaved or mixed woods. Autumn. Widespread. Rare. Inedible. SPORES almond-shaped, smooth, 8–11×4.5–5.5. Gill edge cystidia slender, spindle-shaped, apical crystals.

123

Inocybe posterula. Cap and stem features, habitat, microscopic features. CAP 2–5, at first conical – bell-shaped, then flattened, rather sharply umbonate, at first smooth, then fibrous and±cracked. STEM 3–6,±equal or tapering slightly upwards, slender, smooth – finely fibrous, floury at apex. GILLS at first white then yellowish brown, crowded, adnate – adnexed. SPORE PRINT snuff-brown. SMELL mealy. FLESH white. Solitary or in small trooping groups. On soil in coniferous woods. Autumn. Widespread. Uncommon. Inedible. SPORES almond-shaped, smooth, 7–8×4.5–5. Gill edge cystidia spindle-shaped, apical crystals.

Inocybe auricoma. Size, cap and stem features, microscopic features. CAP 1–2, at first conical – bell-shaped, then flattened, broadly umbonate, at first smooth, then finely fibrous – cracked. STEM 3–5, equal or tapering slightly upwards, slender, barely bulbous, smooth – finely fibrous, floury at apex. GILLS at first whitish then reddish brown, crowded, adnexed. SPORE PRINT brown. SMELL indistinct. FLESH white. Solitary or in small trooping groups. On soil in broad-leaved woods, often with hazel. Autumn. Widespread. Rare. Inedible. SPORES±almond-shaped, smooth, 4.5–5.5×9–10.5. Gill edge cystidia spindle-shaped, with apical crystals.

Inocybe commutabilis. Colour, cap and stem features, microscopic features. CAP 2.5–4, at first conical – bell-shaped, then flattened, broadly umbonate, at first smooth, then finely silky fibrous. STEM 3–6, tapering slightly upwards, slender, slightly bulbous, smooth – finely fibrous, floury at apex. GILLS at first whitish then greyish brown, fairly crowded, adnexed. SPORE PRINT snuff-brown. SMELL mealy. FLESH white, often flushed reddish or yellowish in stem. Solitary or in small trooping groups. On soil in coniferous woods. Autumn. Widespread, not Britain. Inedible. SPORES± ellipsoid – almond-shaped, smooth, 8–10×4–5. Gill edge cystidia spindle-shaped, with apical crystals.

Inocybe cincinnata. Size, stem, cap, microscopic features. CAP 1.5–2, at firs conical – bell-shaped, the flattened – convex, rathe sharply umbonate, covere in small, pointed scales, especially at centre. STEM 3–5, equal, slender, some times slightly bulbous, brownish fibrous – scaly towards base. GILLS at firs white – lilac with brownis edge, then brown, crowded, adnate – adnexed. SPORE PRINT snuff-brown. SMELL mealy. FLESH white lilac flush at stem apex. Solitary or in small troop ing groups. On soil among grass, in broad-leaved or coniferous woods. Autumn. Widespread. Uncom mon. Inedible, poisonous SPORES±ellipsoid, smooth 8–9.5×4.5–6. Gill edge cy tidia spindle-shaped, with apical crystals.

Inocybe lucifuga. Cap and stem features, smell, habitat, microscopic features. CAP 1–4, at first conical – bell-shaped, then flattened, broadly umbonate, at first smooth, then finely scaly – fibrous. STEM 3–4, equal or tapering slightly upwards, slender, smooth – finely fibrous, floury at apex. GILLS at first cream then olive-brown, edge white irregular, crowded, adnexed. SPORE PRINT snuff-brown. SMELL strong, unpleasant, radish. FLESH white, slightly flushed reddish. Solitary or in small trooping groups. On soil in coniferous woods. Autumn. Widespread. Rare. Inedible. SPORES ellipsoid – almond-shaped, smooth, 4.5–7×7.5–13. Gill edge cystidia slender, spindle-shaped, apical crystals.

Inocybe eutheles. Cap and stem features, microscopic features, habitat. CAP 2–4, at first conical – bell-shaped, then flattened, rather sharply umbonate, silky-fibrous, rather scaly in centre. STEM 3–9, tapering slightly upwards, slender, powdery. GILLS pale buff with whitish edge, fairly crowded, emarginate. SPORE PRINT brown. SMELL mushroomy. FLESH white. Solitary or in small trooping groups. On soil with coniferous trees. Autumn. Widespread. Common. Inedible. SPORES almond-shaped, smooth, 8.5–10× 4–5. Gill edge cystidia spindle-shaped, with very sparse apical crystals.

Inocybe griseolilacina. Size, stem colour, cap and stem features, microscopic features. CAP 2.5–4, at first conical – bell-shaped, then slightly flattened – convex, slightly umbonate, at first fibrous then±shaggy. STEM 4–7, equal, slender, sometimes slightly bulbous, covered with dense white fibres. GILLS at first whitish then brown, fairly crowded, adnate. SPORE PRINT snuff-brown. SMELL strong, mealy. FLESH lilac, turning whitish. Solitary or in small trooping groups. On soil among grass, broad-leaved woods, path edges, roadsides. Autumn. Widespread. Uncommon. Inedible. SPORES±ellipsoid – almond-shaped, smooth, 8–10×5–5.5. Gill edge cystidia spindle-shaped, with apical crystals.

Inocybe devoniensis. Habi tat, microscopic features. CAP 1.5–6.5, at first conical – convex, then more flattened, fairly sharply umbonate, radiall fibrous, then cracked or splitting towards margin. STEM 3–5, equal, slender, bulbous, brownish, fibrou lined, floury at apex. GILLS at first whitish, then gra dually brown, edge white irregular, crowded, adnate – free. SPORE PRINT snuff-brown. SMELL strong mealy. FLESH white, some times flushed brown in cen tre. Solitary or in small trooping groups. On dune slacks with *Salix repens.* Autumn. Widespread. Rare. Inedible, poisonous SPORES±cylindrical – elongated kidney-shaped, smooth, 6–7.5×11–19. Gi edge cystidia club-shaped spindle-shaped, sometime with apical crystals.

cybe lacera. Habitat, croscopic features. CAP , convex, slightly bonate, at first smooth n fibrous, often±scaly, rgin often split. STEM 2– equal or tapering slightly wnwards, slender, ghtly bulbous, fibrous. LS at first whitish, then k-buff, edge white egular, crowded, nexed. SPORE PRINT snuff-wn. SMELL mealy. FLESH ite, sometimes flushed ldish in stem. Solitary or small trooping groups. On soil in damp sandy soil, especially h pines. Autumn. Wide-read. Common. Inedible. ORES cylindrical, smooth, –6×11–15. Gill edge stidia spindle-shaped h apical crystals.

Inocybe napies. Cap, mic-roscopic features. CAP 3–5, convex – bell-shaped, sharply umbonate, at first smooth then finely fibrous. STEM 5–6, tapering upwards, slender, bulbous, fibrous. GILLS at first whit-ish, then brown, crowded, adnexed. SPORE PRINT snuff-brown. SMELL faint, inde-finite or indistinct. FLESH whitish in cap and stem base, brown in stem. Solit-ary or in small trooping groups. On soil in damp woods. Summer – autumn. Widespread. Common. Poisonous. SPORES elongated-ellipsoid, angu-lar, 5.5–6.5×9–10. Gill edge cystidia±ellip-soid with apical crystals.

Inocybe lanuginella. Cap, microscopic features. CAP 1–3, conical – bell-shaped, then flattened, sharply umbonate, finely radially fibrous – scaly, at first with fibrous veil. STEM 2–4, equal, slender, fibrous-lined, floury at apex. GILLS at first cream, then ochreous, edge white irregular, crowded, adnexed – emarginate. SPORE PRINT snuff-brown. SMELL mealy. FLESH whit-ish, often flushed brown in stem. Solitary or in small trooping groups. On soil, among grass, in coniferous and broad-leaved woods. Summer – autumn. Wide-spread. Uncommon. Inedi-ble. SPORES elongated-ellipsoid, angular, 5–6×8–9. Gill edge cystidia vari-able, pear-shaped – spherical, with apical crys-tals.

Inocybe longicystis. Cap, stem, habitat, microscopic features. CAP 3–4, at first convex, then flattened, densely shaggy fibrous, pointed scales at cente. STEM 4–7, equal, slender, shaggy fibrous. GILLS at first white, then±buff, then red-dish brown, fairly crowded, adnate – adnexed. SPORE PRINT snuff-brown. SMELL faint, unpleasant. FLESH white. Solitary or in small trooping groups. On damp, acid soil in woods, espe-cially with pine and birch. Autumn. Widespread. Common. Inedible. SPORES elongated-ellipsoid, angu-lar, 5–6×8–10. Gill edge cystidia cylindrical – broadly bottle-shaped, sometimes apical crystals.

ocybe acuta. Cap, habi-, microscopic features. e 1–4, bell-shaped, very rply umbonate, ooth – very finely rous, then cracked. STEM 3, equal, slender, bul-us, fibrous, floury at ex. GILLS at first whitish, en brown, crowded, arginate. SPORE PRINT ff-brown. SMELL faint, FLESH white, netimes brownish in m. Solitary or in small oping groups. On soil in np woods. Autumn. idespread. Rare. Inedi-. SPORES ellipsoid – angular, angular, 5.5– ×8–9.5. Gill edge cysti- cylindrical – bottle-aped, sometimes with cal crystals.

Inocybe umbrina. Cap, microscopic features. CAP 2–4, convex – bell-shaped, umbonate, finely fibrous, splitting, at first with fibrous veil. STEM 4–6, equal, slender, ±marginate bulbous, fibrous-lined. GILLS at first buff, then brown, crowded, adnate. SPORE PRINT snuff-brown. SMELL faint, indefinite. FLESH whitish, often flushed reddish brown in stem. Solitary or in small troop-ing groups. On soil in con-iferous and broad-leaved woods. Summer – autumn. Widespread. Uncommon. Inedible. SPORES elongated-ellipsoid, angular, 5–6×7–8. Gill edge cystidia±ellip-soid with apical crystals.

Inocybe lanuginosa. Cap, stem, microscopic features. CAP 1–2, at first convex, then flattened, slightly umbonate, densely fibrous, pointed scales at centre. STEM 3–4, equal, slender, barely fibrous, shaggy-fibrous towards apex. GILLS at first cream, then brown, rather distant, adnexed. SPORE PRINT snuff-brown. SMELL earthy. FLESH whit-ish, often flushed brown in stem base. Solitary or in small trooping groups. On soil, among grass, in damp broad-leaved woods. Summer – autumn. Wide-spread. Uncommon. Poiso-nous. SPORES elongated-ellipsoid, angular, 5–5.5×8–8.5. Gill edge cysti-dia variable, pear-shaped – spherical, rarely with apical crystals.

Inocybe calospora. Size, cap, stem, habitat, micro-copic features, often mis-taken for a *Naucoria.* CAP 1–2.5, first convex, then flattened, umbonate – umbilicate, small recurved concentric scales, margin fibrous. STEM 3–7, equal, slender, sometimes ±bul-bous, smooth or v. finely lined. GILLS at first± buff, then brown, edge white ir-regular, fairly crowded, ad-nexed. SPORE PRINT brown. SMELL indistinct. FLESH buff, reddish flush in stem. Solitary or in small troop-ing groups. On damp soil in plant debris. Autumn. Widespread. Uncommon. Inedible. SPORES±spherical with long blunt spines, 8.5–10×7–8. Gill edge cystidia slender, spindle-shaped with apical crystals.

125

Inocybe petiginosa. Cap, stem, microscopic features. CAP 1–2, convex – bell-shaped, broadly umbonate, at first±covered with small, whitish scales which soon disappear, then silky-fibrous. STEM 2.5–5, equal, slender, rather floury. GILLS at first yellowish cream, then brown, edge hairy (use hand-lens), fairly crowded, adnexed – emarginate. SPORE PRINT snuff-brown. SMELL indistinct. FLESH creamy with reddish flush in stem. Solitary or in small trooping groups. On soil in broad-leaved woods, especially with beech. Autumn. Widespread. Uncommon. Inedible. SPORES±ellipsoid with irregular bumps, 6.5–8.5×4–6. Gill edge cystidia slender, spindle-shaped with apical crystals.

Inocybe grammata. Cap, stem, microscopic features. CAP 1.5–4, conical – bell-shaped, sharply umbonate, ±covered with white, radial fibres. STEM 4–5, equal, fairly slender, marginate bulbous, lined, pink-tinged, rather floury. GILLS at first whitish, then grey-brown, edge white irregular, fairly crowded, adnexed. SPORE PRINT snuff-brown. SMELL strong, indefinite. FLESH white in cap centre, flushed pinkish elsewhere, pleasant. FLESH white in cap centre, flushed pinkish elsewhere, pleasant. Solitary or in small trooping groups. On soil among grass in open areas in broad-leaved or mixed woods, especially with oak. Summer. Widespread. Rare. Inedible. SPORES±irregularly ellipsoid, 7–8×5–5.5. Gill edge cystidia broadly spindle-shaped with apical crystals.

Inocybe praetervisa. Cap, habitat, microscopic features. CAP 3–5, conical – convex, barely umbonate, finely cracked radially. STEM 5–6, equal, fairly slender,±marginate bulbous, floury. GILLS at first whitish, then pale buff, crowded, adnexed. SPORE PRINT snuff-brown. SMELL mealy. FLESH white in cap, yellowish in stem. Solitary or in small trooping groups. On soil in broad-leaved or mixed woods, especially with beech. Summer – autumn. Widespread. Uncommon. Inedible. SPORES irregularly ellipsoid with lumps, 6–8×9–12. Gill edge cystidia broadly spindle-shaped with apical crystals.

Hebeloma radicosum. Stem. CAP 6–9, convex,± fibrous scaly towards ma in, slightly sticky when w STEM 5–8,±equal or narr owed at centre, fairly sto superior, double, quickl disappearing ring, floury above, scaly below, deep rooting. GILLS first pale th dark brown, crowded, ac nate – sinuate. SPORE PRI snuff-brown. SMELL alm onds. FLESH white. Solita or small trooping groups On soil in broad-leaved woods, esp. beech and o Autumn. Widespread. Rare. Inedible. SPORES ellipsoid – almond-shap finely warty, 8–9.5×5–6. Gill edge cystidia±cylin rical – hair-like.

Inocybe mixtilis. Cap, habitat, microscopic features. CAP 2–4.5, conical – bell-shaped, barely umbonate, finely cracked radially. STEM 2.5–5, equal, fairly slender, marginate bulbous, floury. GILLS at first greyish white, then pale brown, crowded, adnexed. SPORE PRINT snuff-brown. SMELL mealy. FLESH yellowish. Solitary or in small trooping groups. On soil in mixed woods. Summer – autumn. Widespread. Uncommon. Inedible. SPORES irregularly ellipsoid with 3–7 lumps, 5.5–6×7–9. Gill edge cystidia broadly spindle-shaped with apical crystals.

Inocybe asterospora. Size, cap, microscopic features. CAP 3–6,±bell-shaped, umbonate,±covered with dark, radial fibres, radially cracked. STEM 4–6, equal, fairly slender, marginate bulbous, lined, rather floury. GILLS at first greyish, then brown, edge white irregular, fairly crowded, adnexed. SPORE PRINT snuff-brown. SMELL mealy. FLESH white. Solitary or in small trooping groups. On soil in broad-leaved woods, especially with oak. Autumn. Widespread. Very common. SPORES star-shaped with 5–8 irregular rays, 8–10×9–12.5. Gill edge cystidia broadly spindle-shaped, apical crystals.

Inocybe margaritospora. Cap, habitat, microscopic features. CAP 3–5, bell-shaped,±umbonate, sparsely covered with pale, fibrous scales. STEM 4.5–9.5, equal, fairly slender, bulbous, finely fibrous-lined, floury at apex. GILLS at first whitish, then pale brown, fairly crowded, adnexed. SPORE PRINT snuff-brown. SMELL fruity. FLESH white. Solitary or in small trooping groups. On soil with hazel. Summer. Widespread. Rare. Inedible. SPORES±star-shaped with 5–6 irregular rays, 6–7.5×8.5–11. Gill edge cystidia spindle-shaped with apical crystals.

Hebeloma strophosum. Stem, smell, microscopic features. CAP 3–4, convex barely umbonate, smoot finely scaly (use hand-len STEM 2.5–5, equal, slende superior, quickly disappearing ring, floury above, scaly below. GILLS first pale buff, then darke brown with pinkish flush crowded, emarginate. SPORE PRINT buff-brown. SMELL unpleasant, radish FLESH whitish buff. Usua in small±tufted groups. soil in broad-leaved, mix or coniferous woods. Sur mer. Widespread. Rare. Inedible. SPORES ellipsoi smooth, 7.5–9×4.5–5. G edge cystidia hair-like wi swollen base.

...beloma mesophaeum.
...p with dark centre, stem,
...ell, microscopic fea-
...res. CAP 2.5–4.5, at first
...nvex, then flattened,±
...nbonate, at first rather
...rous and with veil frag-
...ents when wet. STEM 4–7.5,
...ual, slender,±fibrous,
...perior, indefinite, quick-
...disappearing ring. GILLS
...first pale buff, then dark-
...buff, crowded, emargin-
...e. SPORE PRINT buff-
...own. SMELL strong, un-
...easant, radish. FLESH
...ite. Usually in small±
...ted groups. On soil in
...oad-leaved, mixed or
...niferous woods, Summer
...autumn. Widespread.
...ncommon. Inedible.
...ORES ellipsoid, finely
...rty, 8.5–10×5–5.5. Gill
...ge cystidia short, stout,
...ir-like.

Hebeloma longicaudum.
Cap, stem, microscopic features. CAP 3–5.5, at first
convex – bell-shaped, then
more flattened, broadly
umbonate, smooth, sticky
esp. when wet. STEM 4–7,
equal, slender,±bulbous,
fibrous-lined, floury at
apex. GILLS at first whitish
then pale red-brown, fairly
crowded, adnate – sinuate.
SPORE PRINT ochre-brown.
SMELL indistinct. FLESH
white. Usually in small±
tufted groups. On soil in
broad-leaved or coniferous
woods, wet acid sites. Autumn. Widespread. Uncom-
mon. Poisonous. SPORES ellipsoid, fine warty, 11–13×5
–7. Gill edge cystidia stout,
hair-like – club-shaped.

Hebeloma pusillum. Size,
gills, habitat, microscopic
features. CAP 1–2.5, at first
conical – convex, then
more flattened, rather
sharply umbonate, smooth,
slightly sticky especially
when wet. STEM 2–4, equal,
slender, floury. GILLS at
first pale buff then darker
buff, often with pinkish
flush, with liquid drops
when wet, crowded,
adnate – emarginate. SPORE
PRINT ochre-brown. SMELL
faint, radish. FLESH whitish
buff. Usually in small±tuf-
ted groups. On damp soil
with willows. Summer –
autumn. Widespread. Rare.
Inedible, poisonous?
SPORES almond-shaped,
finely warty, 10–14×5.5–7.
Gill edge cystidia club-
shaped.

Hebeloma anthracophilum.
Gills, smell, habitat, microscopic features. CAP 2–7,
at first convex – bell-
shaped, then more
flattened,±broadly umbon-
ate, smooth, slightly sticky
especially when wet. STEM
2–5, equal, slender, silky –
scaly. GILLS at first pale
buff, then reddish buff,
edge white irregular,
crowded, adnate – sinuate.
SPORE PRINT ochre-brown.
SMELL faint, pleasant,
fruity. FLESH white. Usually
in small±tufted groups. On
burned soil, often with
mosses. Autumn. Wide-
spread. Uncommon. Inedi-
ble. SPORES almond-shaped,
finely warty, 10–13×5–7.
Gill edge cystidia
cylindrical – club-shaped?

...ebeloma fastibile. Smell,
...bitat, microscopic fea-
...res. CAP 4–6, convex,
...ooth – finely downy,
...cky especially when wet.
...EM 4–8, equal, fairly
...ut,±bulbous, fibrous
...ed, floury at apex. GILLS
...first pale buff, then dar-
...r buff, flushed pinkish,
...irly crowded, emarginate.
...ORE PRINT buff. SMELL
...rong, unpleasant, radish.
...ESH white. Usually in
...all±tufted groups. On
...il in coniferous woods.
...ring – autumn. Wide-
...read. Rare. Poisonous.
...ORES ellipsoid, smooth,
...9.5×5–6. Gill edge cysti-
...a stout, hair-like.

Hebeloma leucosarx. Gills,
habitat, microscopic fea-
tures. CAP 2–6, first convex,
then more flattened, broadly umbonate, smooth,
sticky esp. when wet, margin at first downy. STEM 2.5
–9, equal – ±club-shaped,
slender,±bulbous, at first
entirely floury then silky-
fibrous below. GILLS at first
pale buff then darker buff,
often with pinkish flush,
edge white irregular, with
liquid drops when wet,
crowded, adnate –
emarginate. SPORE PRINT
ochre brown. SMELL strong,
radish. FLESH white, flushed
ochreous in stem. Usually
in small±tufted groups. On
damp soil with willows, or
birches. Autumn. Wide-
spread. Rare. Inedible,
poisonous? SPORES lemon-
shaped, finely warty, 9–
12×5.5–6.5. Gill edge cystidia club-shaped.

Hebeloma crustuliniforme
Poison Pie. Gills, habitat,
microscopic features. CAP
4–10, at first convex, then
more flattened, rather
sharply umbonate, smooth,
slightly sticky especially
when wet. STEM 4–7, equal,
slender, sometimes
obscurely bulbous, strongly
floury, especially at apex.
GILLS pale buff, often spotted on aging, with liquid
drops when wet, crowded,
adnate – adnexed. SPORE
PRINT brown. SMELL strong,
radish. FLESH white.
Usually in small±tufted
groups. On soil in broad-
leaved or mixed woods.
Summer – autumn. Wide-
spread. Very common.
Poisonous. SPORES almond-
shaped, finely warty, 10–
12×5.5–6.5. Gill edge cystidia cylindrical – club-
shaped.

Hebeloma sacchariolens
Scented Hebeloma. Gills,
smell, microscopic fea-
tures. CAP 2–6.5, at first
convex, then more
flattened, barely umbon-
ate, smooth, slightly sticky
especially when wet. STEM
4–6, equal, slender, silky-
fibrous, floury at apex.
GILLS at first buff, then reddish brown, fairly crowded,
adnate – sinuate. SPORE
PRINT brown. SMELL strong,
sweet, fruity, sickly. FLESH
white. Usually in small
±tufted groups. On soil in
damp broad-leaved woods.
Autumn. Widespread.
Common. Inedible. SPORES
almond-shaped, finely
warty, 13–17×7–10. Gill
edge cystidia±hair-like.

127

CORTINARIACEAE

Hebeloma sinapizans. Size, smell, microscopic features. CAP 4–12, at first convex, then more flattened, barely umbonate, smooth, slightly sticky especially when wet. STEM 6–12, equal, stout, bulbous, finely scaly. GILLS at first buff, then reddish buff, crowded, sinuate. SPORE PRINT brown. SMELL strong, radish, raw potato. FLESH white, cut lengthwise, a tongue of cap flesh hangs into stem cavity. Solitary or in small±tufted groups. On soil in broad-leaved and mixed woods. Autumn. Widespread. Rare. Poisonous. SPORES almond-shaped, finely warty, 11–14.5×6–8   Gill edge cystidia broadly club-shaped.

Naucoria bohemica. Cap, habitat, microscopic features. CAP 1.5–3.5, at first convex – bell-shaped, then more flattened, broadly umbonate, smooth, slightly sticky when wet, margin slightly lined. STEM 3–6, equal, slender, finely silky-fibrous, rather floury at apex, browning from below. GILLS pale reddish brown, fairly distant, adnate – emarginate. SPORE PRINT buff. SMELL indistinct. FLESH buff. Usually in groups, tufted – trooping. On damp soil with willows or alder. Autumn. Widespread. Uncommon. Inedible. SPORES±lemon-shaped, warty, 11–13×6.5–8. Basidia 2-spored. Gill edge cystidia cylindrical – worm-like.

Naucoria escharoides. Cap, habitat, microscopic features. CAP 0.75–4, at first convex, then flattened, barely umbonate, at first minutely scaly-roughened, then smooth, at first sometimes with very few veil fragments at margin. STEM 1.5–4, equal or tapering slightly upwards, slender, finely fibrous, at first floury – scaly at apex, browning from below. GILLS yellowish ochre, fairly crowded, sinuate – emarginate. SPORE PRINT ochre brown. SMELL sweet. FLESH buff. Usually in groups, tufted – trooping. On damp soil with alder. Autumn. Widespread. Common. Inedible. SPORES ellipsoid – almond-shaped, warty, 10–13×5–6.5. Gill edge cystidia bottle-shaped with long neck.

Naucoria (=*Simocybe*) *tunculus*. Habitat, microscopic features. CAP 0.5–2 at first convex, then more flattened, barely umbonate, finely velvety, finely lined especially at margin when wet. STEM 1–3, equal or tapering slightly upwards, fairly stout, fine velvety-floury. GILLS oliv buff, fairly distant, adnate SPORE PRINT ochre brown SMELL faint, indefinite. FLESH brownish olive. Trooping. On wood, logs and twigs of broad-leave trees. Autumn. Widespread. Rare. Inedible. SPORES oliv shaped, smooth, 6.5–8× 4–5. Gill edge cystidia cylindrical – worm-like.

Hebeloma truncatum. Cap, habitat, microscopic features. CAP 4–6.5, convex – bell-shaped, barely umbonate, smooth, sticky especially when wet, margin often slightly flared. STEM 5–8, equal, stout, finely fibrous-lined, rather floury. GILLS at first whitish, then buff, crowded, adnate – sinuate. SPORE PRINT ochre brown. SMELL faint, radish. FLESH white, buff in stem. Usually in small±tufted groups. On soil among grass in coniferous woods. Autumn. Widespread. Rare. Inedible, poisonous? SPORES almond-shaped,±smooth, 7.5–11×4.5–5. Gill edge cystidia narrowly club-shaped – hair-like.

Naucoria striatula. Cap, habitat, microscopic features. CAP 0.5–3, at first convex – bell-shaped, then more flattened, barely umbonate, lined when wet, smooth – finely silky when dry, at first with few veil fragments at margin. STEM 3–7.5, equal or tapering slightly upwards, slender, slightly bulbous, finely fibrous, at first finely scaly at apex, browning from below. GILLS at first cream, then buff, fairly crowded, adnate – emarginate. SPORE PRINT buff. SMELL indistinct. FLESH buff. Usually in groups, tufted – trooping. On damp soil with alder. Autumn. Widespread. Uncommon. Inedible. SPORES almond-shaped – lemon-shaped, warty, 8.5–12×4.5–5.5. Gill edge cystidia bottle-shaped.

Naucoria scolecina. Cap, habitat, microscopic features. CAP 0.5–3, convex, smooth, finely lined at margin when wet. STEM 3–5, equal or tapering slightly upwards, slender, finely fibrous-lined, browning from below. GILLS brown – reddish brown, distant, emarginate. SPORE PRINT ochre brown. SMELL indistinct. FLESH brown – reddish brown. Usually in groups, tufted – trooping. On damp soil with alder. Autumn. Widespread. Uncommon. Inedible. SPORES almond-shaped, warty, 11–14×5–6.5. Gill edge cystidia bottle-shaped with long neck.

Gymnopilus (=*Pholiota*) *junonius* (incl. *spectabilis* Habitat, habit, microscop features. CAP 6–15, at firs convex, then more flattened, broadly umbon ate, finely fibrous or fibrous – scaly, margin incurved. STEM 5–14, tape ing downwards then nar rowed at base, stout, fibrous, superior, soon-disappearing spreading ring, shortly rooting. GILL at first yellow, then redd brown, crowded, adnate with decurrent tooth. SPC PRINT reddish brown. SME indistinct. FLESH pale yel low. Tufted. On wood, a base of trunks and on stumps of broad-leaved trees. Summer – winter. Widespread. Common. Inedible. SPORES ellipsoic almond-shaped, warty, 5 6×7–10. Gill edge cystid narrowly bottle-shaped with round head.

Gymnopilus sapineus.
Habitat, habit, microscopic features. CAP 3–10, convex, barely umbonate, finely velvety or fibrous – scaly, often cracked on aging. STEM 5–12, equal or tapering slightly downwards, slender, often rather flattened. GILLS at first yellow, then reddish brown, crowded, adnate with decurrent tooth. SPORE PRINT reddish brown. SMELL almonds. FLESH yellow. Tufted. On wood, at base of trunks and on stumps of coniferous trees. Summer – autumn. Widespread. Uncommon. Inedible. PORES ellipsoid – almond-shaped, warty, 7–10×4–5. Gill edge cystidia?

Gymnopilus hybridus.
Habitat, habit, microscopic features. CAP 2–7, convex, barely umbonate, smooth – finely fibrous. STEM 2.5–5, equal or tapering slightly upwards, slender, finely fibrous, indefinite superior ring zone, downy at base. GILLS yellow, crowded, adnate – emarginate with decurrent tooth. SPORE PRINT reddish brown. SMELL faint, pleasant. FLESH yellow in cap, reddish brown in stem. Tufted. On wood, on stumps and among debris of coniferous trees. Summer – autumn. Uncommon. Inedible. SPORES ellipsoid – almond-shaped, warty, 5.5–8.5×3.5–4.4. Gill edge cystidia bottle-shaped with rounded head.

Gymnopilus penetrans.
Habitat, habit, microscopic features. CAP 3–7, convex, barely umbonate, smooth – finely radially fibrous. STEM 4–6, equal or tapering slightly upwards, slender, often curved, finely fibrous-lined, indefinite superior ring zone at base. GILLS golden yellow, reddish brown spotted on aging, crowded, adnate with decurrent tooth. SPORE PRINT reddish brown. SMELL indistinct. FLESH yellow in cap, reddish brown in stem. Solitary or tufted. On wood, on stumps and among debris of coniferous trees. Summer – autumn. Widespread. Very common. SPORES ellipsoid – almond-shaped, warty, 7–9×4–5. Gill edge cystidia bottle-shaped with rounded head.

Gymnopilus fulgens. Habitat, habit, microscopic features. CAP 0.5–2, convex, barely umbonate, ±smooth or very finely lined at margin especially when wet. STEM 0.5–2, equal, slender, finely fibrous-lined (use hand-lens), ±floury at apex. GILLS at first yellowish, then reddish brown, fairly distant, adnate. SPORE PRINT reddish brown. SMELL? FLESH yellow. Trooping or tufted. On wet soil, boggy areas, wet woods, often among *Sphagnum*. Autumn. Widespread. Rare. Inedible. SPORES ellipsoid – almond-shaped, warty, 9–11×6–7. Gill edge cystidia cylindrical – ±worm-like, sometimes with ±rounded head.

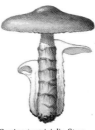

Cortinarius trivialis. Stem, habitat, spores. CAP 3–10.5, first conical – convex, then more flattened, sometimes v. broadly umbonate, very sticky, margin smooth. STEM 5–12, broad spindle-shaped, fairly stout, ±finely fibrous lined at apex, net-like – concentrically scaly below ring, sticky, rooting. GILLS first whitish buff, then darker – reddish brown, fairly crowded, edge first whitish even, adnate – emarginate. SPORE PRINT reddish brown. SMELL indistinct. FLESH whitish yellow, darkening below cap and in stem base. Trooping or ±tufted. On soil w. broad-l. trees, esp. alder and willow on wet sites. Autumn. Widespread. Uncommon. Inedible. SPORES ellipsoid – almond-shaped, warty, 6–7×10–13.

Cortinarius collinitus. Stem, habitat, spores. CAP 3.5–10, first conical – convex, then more flattened, sharply umbonate, v. sticky, margin smooth – slightly grooved, at first incurved. STEM 5–12, ±equal or tapering slightly downwards, stout, ±finely fibrous lined at apex, white – bluish concentrically scaly below ring, sticky. GILLS at first buff – greyish blue, then reddish brown, fairly distant, edge sometimes whitish, even, adnate – emarginate. SPORE PRINT reddish brown. SMELL indistinct. FLESH whitish yellow, reddish brown from stem base. Trooping or ±tufted. On soil w. conif., more rarely broad-l. trees, esp. beech. Summer – autumn. Widespread. Rare. Inedible. SPORES ellipsoid – almond-shaped, warty, 7–9×12–15.

Cortinarius mucosus. Stem, habitat, spores. CAP 4–10, first convex, then flattened, broadly umbonate, very sticky, margin smooth – slightly lined, at first incurved. STEM 5–15, ±equal or tapering slightly at base, fairly stout, ±finely lined, w. broken-up white veil towards base, silky, sticky. GILLS at first whitish, then ochre – reddish brown, fairly distant, edge toothed, adnate – emarginate. SPORE PRINT reddish brown. SMELL indistinct. FLESH whitish, flushed reddish brown below cap cuticle and in stem base. Trooping or ±tufted. On soil with conif. trees, esp. pines on sandy sites. Summer – autumn. Widespread. Uncommon. Inedible. SPORES elongated lemon-shaped, warty, 6–7×13–16.

Cortinarius pseudosalor. Cap and stem, spores. CAP 3–11, at first conical – convex, then more flattened, broadly umbonate, sticky when wet, margin smooth – slightly lined, broadly fluted, often upturned. STEM 5–10, ±spindle-shaped or tapering slightly downwards, narrowed at base, fairly stout, silky-lined at apex, silky-sticky below superior ring zone. GILLS at first ochreous buff, then darker buff, fairly crowded, edge smooth, adnate. SPORE PRINT reddish brown. SMELL indistinct. FLESH whitish, flushed yellowish in cap and stem base. Trooping or ±tufted. On soil in broad-l., mixed woods, often beech, birch. Autumn. Widespread. Very common. Inedible. SPORES almond-shaped, warty, 7–9×12–16.

CORTINARIACEAE

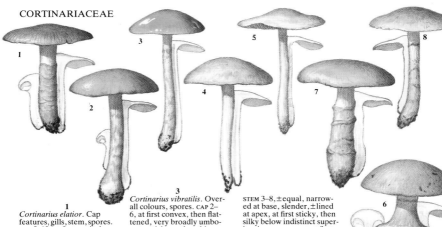

1
Cortinarius elatior. Cap features, gills, stem, spores. CAP 5–12, at first conical – convex, then more flattened, barely umbonate, very markedly wrinkled, sticky-slimy, margin often upturned. STEM 6–18, ±spindle-shaped, gradually narrowed at base, fairly slender, silky lined at apex, silky-sticky or scaly below superior ring zone. GILLS at first violet-buff, then darker reddish violet, fairly crowded, edge irregular, adnate – emarginate. SPORE PRINT reddish brown. SMELL indistinct. FLESH white or yellowish. Trooping or±tufted. On soil in broad-leaved or mixed woods, often with beech. Autumn. Widespread. Uncommon. Inedible. SPORES broadly almond-shaped, very warty, 7–9×12–17.

2
Cortinarius delibutus. Size, cap features, gills, flesh, stem, microscopic features. CAP 3–9, at first convex, then flattened – broadly umbonate, very sticky, slightly streaked or wrinkled when dry. STEM 5–10, ± club-shaped – bulbous, fairly slender, yellowish, sticky, with veil remains below superior ring zone, whitish downy at base, palish lilac flush at apex. GILLS at first violet – bluish, then paler lilac-buff, finally reddish brown, fairly distant, edge toothed – irregular, adnate – emarginate. SPORE PRINT reddish brown. SMELL indistinct or faint, radish. FLESH white, yellowish in cap, then with generally bluish flush. Trooping or often tufted. On soil in broad-leaved or mixed woods, especially with birch and beech. Autumn. Widespread. Uncommon. Inedible. SPORES broadly ellipsoid – subspherical, warty, 6–8×7–10.

3
Cortinarius vibratilis. Overall colours, spores. CAP 2–6, at first convex, then flattened, very broadly umbonate, sticky, rather shiny when dry. STEM 4–6, ±club-shaped – spindle-shaped, often sharply narrowed at base, fairly slender, sticky, especially below superior ring zone, ±floury at apex. GILLS at first cream, then reddish buff, fairly crowded, edge variable, even – irregular, adnate – emarginate. SPORE PRINT reddish brown. SMELL indistinct or faint, unpleasant. FLESH white, rather ochreous in stem. Often solitary, also trooping or±tufted. On soil in coniferous or mixed woods. Autumn. Widespread. Rare. Inedible. SPORES broadly ellipsoid, warty, 4.5–5.5×6.5–8.

4
Cortinarius ochroleucus. Cap features, overall colour, spores. CAP 3–8, at first convex, then more flattened, very broadly umbonate, usually silky and dry or very slightly sticky when very wet, margin often incurved. STEM 2.5–9, tapering downwards, narrowed at base, fairly slender, silky, superior – apical ring zone. GILLS at first whitish then ochre-buff, fairly crowded, adnate – ±free. SPORE PRINT reddish brown. SMELL indistinct. FLESH whitish. Often±tufted, also trooping. On soil in broad-leaved woods, especially with oak. Autumn. Widespread. Common. Inedible. SPORES broadly±ellipsoid,± smooth, 4–5×7–8.

5
Cortinarius causticus. Cap features, overall colour, spores. CAP 3–8, at first convex, then more flattened, very broadly umbonate – slightly depressed, silky, especially at margin, usually dry but sticky when wet. STEM 3–8,±equal, narrowed at base, slender,±lined at apex, at first sticky, then silky below indistinct superior ring zone. GILLS at first ochre-buff, then reddish brown, fairly crowded, adnate – decurrent. SPORE PRINT reddish brown. SMELL strong, unpleasant, indefinite. FLESH yellowish, ochreous in stem and below cap cuticle, whitish in centre. Trooping,±tufted and/or in rings. On soil in broad-leaved woods, especially with oak and beech. Autumn. Widespread. Rare. Inedible. SPORES broadly ellipsoid – almond-shaped, ±smooth, 4–4.5×6–8.

6
Cortinarius multiformis. Cap features, stem, chemical tests, spores. CAP 4.5–10, at first convex, then flattened, sticky, margin usually markedly incurved. STEM 4.5–7,±equal, fairly stout, marginate bulbous, silky fibrous, partial veil white, dry, white downy at base. GILLS at first whitish buff, then reddish brown, edge variable±uneven-toothed, fairly crowded, adnate – emarginate, often with tooth. SPORE PRINT reddish brown. SMELL strong, apples. NaOH on flesh, yellow, on cap cuticle, brown. FLESH white, often yellowish in centre. Trooping or±tufted. On soil in broad-leaved woods, especially with beech. Autumn. Widespread. Uncommon. Inedible. SPORES almond-shaped – lemon-shaped, warty, 5.5–6.5×9–11.

7
Cortinarius triumphans. Cap features, stem, chemical test, spores, similar to *C. crocolitus* q.v. CAP 3–12, at first convex, then flattened, small flattened scales at centre, sticky, margin usually incurved. STEM 8–12, club-shaped – bulbous, fairly slender,±lined at apex, dry, partial veil whitish leaving yellowish ring zones. GILLS at first cream, buff, then ochreous, edge variable±uneven-toothed, fairly crowded, adnate – emarginate. SPORE PRINT reddish brown. SMELL faint, indefinite. NaOH on flesh bright yellow. FLESH white – yellowish. Trooping or±tufted. On soil in coniferous woods, also broad-leaved woods, especially with birch. Summer – autumn. Widespread. Rare. Inedible. SPORES elongated±lemon-shaped – spindle-shaped, warty, 6? 7×12–15.

8
Cortinarius crocolitus. Similar to *C. triumphans* and often confused with it but cap, spores and chemical test differ. CAP 5–12, at first convex, then flattened, small flattened scales at centre, sticky, margin often with veil fragments. STEM 7–17,±equal, club-shaped bulbous, fairly slender,±lined at apex, dry, partial veil white leaving yellowish ring zones. GILLS at first creamy white, often with grey-blue flush, then buff – reddish brown, edge ±toothed, fairly crowded, adnate – emarginate. SPORE PRINT reddish brown. SMELL faint, indefinite or mouldy. NaOH on flesh – yellowish. FLESH cream – yellowish. Trooping or±tufted. On soil in broad-leaved woods, especially with birch. Summer – autumn. Widespread. Uncommon. Inedible. SPORES ellipsoid – almond-shaped, warty, 6–7×10–12.5.

Cortinarius glaucopus. Cap features, flesh colours, spores. CAP 5–12, at first convex, then flattened, ± covered in dark radial fibres, sticky, margin often markedly incurved or wavy. STEM 6–12, ±equal or tapering slightly downwards, wide – rounded marginate bulbous, fairly stout, persistently bluish at apex, dry, partial veil bluish violet. GILLS at first pale blue – lilac, then buff – reddish brown, edge ±irregular, fairly crowded, adnate – emarginate. SPORE PRINT reddish brown. SMELL indistinct or faint, indefinite or mealy. FLESH at first white, then yellowish, bluish at stem apex, yellow in bulb. Trooping or±tufted. On soil in coniferous woods, especially with beech. Autumn. Widespread. SPORES ellipsoid – ±almond-shaped, warty, 4.5–5.5 ×7–9.

Cortinarius nemorensis. Cap features, smell, chemical test, spores. CAP 3–10, at first convex, then flattened, finely fibrous, sticky, often cracked or finely scaly later. CAP 4.5–8, club-shaped, stout, often pointed at base, often floury and persistently violet at apex, dry, partial veil bluish violet. GILLS at first lilac-violet, then violet-buff, then reddish brown, edge±even, fairly crowded, adnate – emarginate. SPORE PRINT reddish brown. SMELL strong, unpleasant, earthy. Ammonia on flesh, quickly deep chrome-yellow. FLESH bluish violet, whitish in centre. Solitary or tufted. On soil in broad-leaved, mixed or coniferous woods, often with beech. Autumn. Widespread. Rare. Inedible. SPORES ellipsoid – almond-shaped, warty, 5–6.5×9–12.

Cortinarius subtortus Cap, smell, microscopic features, habitat. CAP 3–6.5, at first convex, then flattened, smooth, dull, sticky, margin often persistently inrolled. STEM 5–10,±equal but sometimes v. slightly bulbous, fairly stout, dry, partial veil yellowish white, indistinct superior yellowish ring zone. GILLS at first grey-green, then greyish brown, then red-brown, distant, adnate-emarginate. SPORE PRINT reddish brown. SMELL strong, cedar oil. FLESH pale buff. Solitary or tufted. On soil on acid sites, especially with spruce or birch. Autumn. Widespread. SPORES ellipsoid, warty, 7.5–8×6–6.5. Gill edge cystidia very large, spindle-shaped, encrusted.

Cortinarius subpurpurascens. Overall colour, stem, flesh, colour changes, spores. CAP 5–11, at first convex, then flattened – broadly umbonate or slightly depressed, often with dark streaks or spots, especially at margin, sticky. STEM 5–7, equal, club-shaped bulbous, fairly stout, at first buff with lilac flush, then pale reddish brown, bruising violet, edge±even, fairly crowded, adnate – emarginate. SPORE PRINT reddish brown. SMELL faint, pleasant or indistinct. FLESH white, bruising deep violet. Trooping or tufted. On soil in beech woods. Autumn. Widespread. Rare. Inedible. SPORES ± ellipsoid – almond-shaped, warty, 5.5–6×9–10.

Cortinarius largus. Cap features, gill colours, chemical test, spores. CAP 3–12, at first convex, then flattened, at first smooth, then sometimes finely fibrous-velvety, sticky, margin often persistently incurved. STEM 5–10, club-shaped, stout, often floury at apex, dry, partial veil white – bluish. GILLS at first pale lilac-violet, then bluish grey, then reddish brown, edge±toothed, fairly crowded, adnate – emarginate. SPORE PRINT reddish brown. SMELL indistinct or faint, fruity. Ammonia on flesh, pale yellow. FLESH at first lilac – bluish violet, then whitish. Usually tufted, also trooping. On soil in broad-leaved woods, especially with oak or beech. Autumn. Widespread. Rare. Inedible. SPORES almond-shaped – lemon-shaped, warty, 5.6–6.5×10–12.

Cortinarius varius. Cap features, gills, flesh, spores. CAP 5–10, at first convex, then flattened, smooth and shiny, sticky, margin often fringed. STEM 4–9, tapering upwards, club-shaped – bulbous, stout, dry, partial veil white, distinct superior ring zone. GILLS at first lilac-violet – bluish, then violet-buff, then reddish brown, edge±even, fairly crowded, adnate – emarginate. SPORE PRINT reddish brown. SMELL very faint, indefinite or indistinct. FLESH white, sometimes flushed yellowish cream. Trooping or tufted. On soil in coniferous woods, especially on chalky sites. Autumn. Widespread. Rare. Edible. SPORES almond-shaped, warty, 6–7×10–12.

Cortinarius purpurascens. Overall colour, colour changes, spores. CAP 5–15, at first convex, then flattened – broadly umbonate, often with dark streaks or spots, very sticky, at first margin markedly violet. STEM 5–12,±equal or tapering slightly upwards,±marginate bulbous, fairly stout, dry, partial veil purplish. GILLS at first purple-violet, then buff, then reddish brown, bruising violet, edge±irregular, fairly crowded, adnate – emarginate. SPORE PRINT reddish brown. SMELL very faint, indefinite or indistinct. FLESH pale violet, bruising deep violet. Trooping or tufted. On soil in broad-lvd or coniferous woods, especially on acid sites. Autumn. Widespread. Uncommon. Inedible. SPORES±ellipsoid – almond-shaped, warty, 5–6×8–10.

Cotinarius scaurus Overall colour, stem, habitat, spores. CAP 2–5, at first convex, then flattened, smooth, sticky, often darker spotted, especially towards margin. STEM 3–5, club-shaped, bulbous, fairly stout, dry, partial veil greenish. GILLS at first olive green with bluish flush, then grey-brown, fairly distant, emarginate. SPORE PRINT reddish brown. SMELL indistinct. FLESH greenish blue. Trooping or tufted. On soil with coniferous trees, especially spruce. Autumn. Widespread. Rare. Inedible. SPORES ellipsoid, warty, 10–13×6.5–7.

131

CORTINARIACEAE

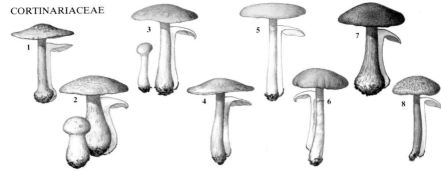

1
Cortinarius splendens.
Overall colour, flesh, chemical test, spores. CAP 3–8, at first convex, then flattened, often with scattered dark scales, sticky. STEM 2.5–6,±equal, broadly marginate bulbous, slender, dry, partial veil yellow. GILLS at first sulphur-yellow, then reddish yellow, edge±irregular, fairly crowded, adnate – emarginate. SPORE PRINT reddish brown. SMELL indistinct. NaOH on cap cuticle dark red-brown. FLESH vivid sulphur-yellow. Trooping or tufted. On soil in beech woods on chalky sites. Autumn. Widespread. Rare. Inedible. SPORES almond-shaped, warty, 5-6×10-11.

2
Cortinarius traganus. Overall colour, smell, habitat, spores. CAP 4–12, at first convex, then flattened – broadly umbonate at first±concentrically silky-scaly, then smooth – finely fibrous, often cracked, dry. STEM 6–12,±club-shaped, bulbous, fairly stout, dry, partial veil bluish violet. GILLS at first pale buff, then reddish brown, edge±irregular, fairly distant, adnate – emarginate. SPORE PRINT reddish brown. SMELL strong, unpleasant, sweet, sickly. FLESH yellow-buff in cap, yellowish in stem, turning reddish brown. Solitary or trooping and±tufted. On soil in coniferous woods. Autumn. Widespread, northern in Britain. Uncommon, locally common. Inedible. SPORES ellipsoid – almond-shaped, warty, 5–6×8–10.

3
Cortinarius malachius. Cap and stem colours, habitat, spores. CAP 4.5–11, at first convex, then flattened – barely umbonate, at first covered with silky veil, then silky-fibrous, often radially cracked, dry. STEM 4–14, at first±club-shaped, bulbous, then±equal with swollen base, fairly slender, dry, partial veil whitish violet, turning whitish from base upwards. GILLS at first deep blue-violet, then violet-buff, then reddish brown, edge±even, fairly crowded, adnate – emarginate. SPORE PRINT reddish brown. SMELL faint, indefinite, pleasant. FLESH at first deep blue-violet, then whitish. Trooping or tufted. On soil in coniferous woods, especially with pines. Autumn. Widespread. Uncommon. Inedible. SPORES ellipsoid, warty, 4.5–5×7.5–9.

4
Cortinarius hircinus (=*camphoratus*). Cap and flesh colours, smell, habitat, spores. CAP 3.5–10, at first convex, then flattened – barely umbonate, silky, dry. STEM 4–8, tapering upwards, club-shaped – bulbous, fairly slender, dry, partial veil white silky, indefinite ring zone or concentric white patches. GILLS at first deep blue-violet, then reddish lilac, then reddish brown, edge±even, fairly distant, adnate – emarginate. SPORE PRINT reddish brown. SMELL very strong, unpleasant, goats. FLESH at first whitish – bluish violet, darker above gills, then yellowish ochre throughout. Trooping or tufted. On soil in coniferous woods, especially with pines. Widespread. Rare. Inedible. SPORES±almond-shaped, finely warty, 5–6×7–8.5.

5
Cortinarius tabularis. Overall colour, cap features, spores. CAP 3.5–10, at first convex, then flattened – broadly umbonate or slightly depressed, silky-shiny or fibrous when dry, very slightly sticky when wet. STEM 3.5–12,±equal, club-shaped – bulbous at base, slender, dry, partial veil sparse white forming very indefinite ring zone, silky-lined. GILLS at first whitish buff, then paler, then reddish buff, edge± even, fairly crowded, adnate – emarginate. SPORE PRINT reddish brown. SMELL faint, pleasant or indistinct. FLESH whitish, turning slightly yellowish in stem base. Solitary or trooping and±tufted. On soil in broad-leaved woods with birch, and in coniferous woods. Autumn. Widespread. Uncommon. Inedible. SPORES broadly ellipsoid, warty, 5.5–6.5×7–9.

6
Cortinarius anomalus. Overall colour, cap features, smell, spores. CAP 3–6.5, at first convex, then flattened – broadly umbonate, finely silky-shiny, dry. STEM 6–10,±equal, club-shaped – bulbous at base, slender, dry, partial veil yellowish, very indefinite ring zone, silky lined. GILLS at first bluish violet, then grey-buff, then reddish buff, edge±even, fairly crowded, adnate – emarginate or slightly decurrent. SPORE PRINT reddish brown. SMELL faint, sweet sickly or indistinct. FLESH greyish blue in cap, creamy in stem base, turning yellowish from base upwards. Trooping or tufted. On soil in broad-leaved woods. Autumn. Widespread. Common. Inedible. SPORES broadly ellipsoid – subspherical, warty, 6–7.5×8–10.

7
Cortinarius violaceus. Overall colour, cap features, spores. CAP 3.5–15, convex, covered in velvety scales, often±cracked on aging, margin persistently incurved, dry. STEM 5–12, club-shaped, bulbous, fairly slender, dry, partial veil violet, at first±woolly but not persisting. GILLS at first very dark bluish violet, then reddish brown, sometimes with purple tinge, edge±even, often fairly thick, fairly crowded, adnate – emarginate. SPORE PRINT reddish brown. SMELL faint, pleasant or indistinct. FLESH dark bluish violet or almost black. Trooping or tufted. On soil in broad-leaved woods, especially with beech or birch, less commonly with conifers. Autumn. Widespread, predominantly northern. Uncommon. Edible. SPORES ellipsoid – almond-shaped, warty, 7–9×11–15.

8
Cortinarius bolaris. Overall colour, cap features, flesh, spores. CAP 3–7, at first convex, then more flattened – broadly umbonate or slightly depressed when old, covered with small, reddish scales, bruising reddish brown, dry. STEM 5–8,±equal – slightly spindle-shaped, bulbous, fairly stout, dry, bruising reddish. GILLS at first pale ochre-buff, then reddish buff, edge±irregular, often fairly thick, fairly crowded, adnate – ±decurrent. SPORE PRINT reddish brown. SMELL faint, pleasant or indistinct. FLESH whitish, turning yellow, especially at stem base, then reddish brown. Solitary or in small groups,±tufted. On soil in broad-leaved woods, especially with beech or birch. Summer – autumn. Widespread. Uncommon. Poisonous. SPORES subspherical, warty, 4.5–5.5×6–7.5.

132

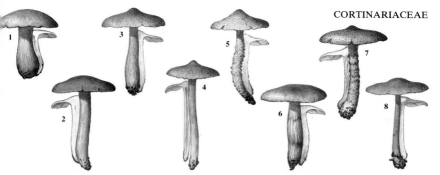

1

Cortinarius rubicundulus.
Overall colour, colour change, cap features, flesh, spores. CAP 3.5–10, at first convex, then more flattened – broadly umbonate or slightly depressed when old, finely fibrous – brous-scaly, dry. STEM 5–,±equal or tapering ownwards – slightly pindle-shaped, pointed at ase, sometimes club-haped bulbous, fairly tout, dry, bruising reddish range, partial veil yellow-sh, superior ring zone, brous-lined at apex. GILLS t first pale ochre-buff, hen reddish buff, often ruising orange-red, dge±irregular, crowded, dnate – emarginate. SPORE RINT reddish brown. SMELL aint, pleasant or indistinct. LESH pale yellow, bruising hrome-yellow. Solitary or n small groups,±tufted. On soil in broad-leaved voods, especially with oak r birch. Summer – utumn. Widespread. Jncommon. Poisonous. PORES ellipsoid – spindle-haped, warty, 3.5–.5×6.5–8.

2

Cortinarius orellanus.
Overall colour, cap fea-ures, smell, habitat, pores. CAP 3–7, at first onvex, then more attened – broadly umbon-te, finely velvety-scaly, ry. STEM 3–9,±equal or apering downwards, fairly lender, dry, fibrous lined – mooth, partial veil yellow-sh ochre, quickly dis-ppearing superior ring one. GILLS at first yellow-sh ochre, then reddish rown, edge±even, fairly istant, adnate – marginate. SPORE PRINT eddish brown. SMELL trong, radish. FLESH yel-owish, sometimes reddish rown in cap. Solitary or in mall groups,±tufted. On oil in broad-leaved woods.

Summer – autumn. Wide-spread. Rare. Deadly poisonous. SPORES ellipsoid – almond-shaped, warty, 5–7×9–12.

3

Cortinarius speciosissimus.
Overall colour, gills, smell, habitat, spores. CAP 2.5–8, at first convex, then more flattened – rather sharply umbonate, finely velvety-scaly especially towards margin, dry. STEM 5–11,±equal or tapering slightly downwards, fairly slender, dry fibrous-lined, partial veil yellowish, soon disappearing,±woolly patches towards base. GILLS at first ochre, then reddish ochre, edge±even, fairly crowded, adnate – emarginate. SPORE PRINT reddish brown. SMELL rad-ish. FLESH yellowish ochre. Solitary or in small groups,±tufted. On soil in coniferous woods, often among mosses. Autumn. Widespread, probably northern. Rare but increas-ing. Deadly poisonous. SPORES broadly ellipsoid – subspherical, warty, 6.5–8.5×9–12.

4

Cortinarius gentilis Overall colour, stem, smell, habi-tat, spores. CAP 1–3, at first convex, then more flattened, markedly and sharply umbonate, finely downy. STEM 5–10,±equal, slender, with rather obvious concentric ring-like patterns. GILLS at first red-dish yellow, then more brownish, then reddish brown, fairly distant, adnate-emarginate. SPORE PRINT reddish brown. SMELL radish. FLESH yellow-brown. Solitary or in small groups. On soil with con-iferous trees, especially pines on acid sites. Autumn. Widespread. Rare. Inedible. SPORES ellipsoid, warty, 7.5–9×5.5–6.5.

5

Cortinarius humicola. Size, cap and stem features, habitat, spores. CAP 1–5, at first conical – convex, then more flattened, sharply umbonate, covered with flattened fibrous scales, dry. STEM 3–7,±equal or tapering slightly down-wards, slender, dry, fibrous-lined at apex, fibrous-scaly below. GILLS at first whitish then ochre, then reddish ochre, edge±even, fairly distant, adnate – emarginate. SPORE PRINT reddish brown. SMELL faint or yellowish in cap, reddish brown towards stem apex. Solitary or in small groups,±tufted. On soil in beech woods. Autumn. Widespread. Rare. Inedi-ble. SPORES ellipsoid – ±almond-shaped, warty, 5–6×8–10.

6

Cortinarius limonius. Over-all colour, cap and stem features, habitat, spores. CAP 2–8, at first conical – convex, then more flattened, smooth or coarsely floury-scaly, dry. STEM 5–8,±equal or taper-ing slightly downwards, slender, dry, fibrous-lined at apex, partial veil yellow-ish, irregular±woolly scales below. GILLS at first yellow-ish ochre, then reddish ochre, edge±even, fairly distant, adnate – emarginate. SPORE PRINT reddish brown. SMELL faint or indistinct. FLESH yellowish in cap, reddish brown towards stem base. Solitary or in small groups,±tufted. On soil in coniferous woods. Summer – autumn. Wide-spread. Rare. Inedible. SPORES ellipsoid – almond-shaped, warty. 5.5–6.5×7.5–8.

7

Cortinarius pholideus. Gill colour, cap and stem fea-

tures, habitat, spores. CAP 3–10, at first conical – convex, then more flattened – depressed, usually barely umbonate, covered with small, pointed scales, dry. STEM 6–12, ±equal or tapering slightly upwards, club-shaped bulbous, slender, dry, fibrous-scaly below well defined ring zone, partial veil brownish. GILLS at first bluish violet, then violet-buff, then reddish buff, edge variable±even – irregular, fairly crowded, adnate – emarginate. SPORE PRINT reddish brown. SMELL faint, pleasant or indistinct. FLESH at first bluish violet in cap and stem apex, then whitish or ochre-buff. Solit-ary or in small groups,±tuf-ted. On soil in broad-leav-ed woods, especially (al-ways?) with birch. Autumn. Widespread. Rare. Inedi-ble. SPORES broadly ellips-oid, warty, 5–6×6.5–8.5.

8

Cortinarius uliginosus.
Overall colours, habitat, spores. CAP 1.5–4.5, at first convex, then more flattened – depressed, sometimes rather sharply umbonate, silky fibrous, often slightly fibrous scaly towards margin, dry. STEM 2.5–6.5,±equal or tapering slightly upwards, slender, dry,±fibrous-scaly at apex, fibrous-lined below, partial veil orange-yellow. GILLS at first lemon-yellow, then ochreous buff, then reddish buff, edge variable±even-irregular, fairly crowded, adnate – emarginate. SPORE PRINT reddish brown. SMELL radish. FLESH lemon-yellow, often with reddish brown flush in cap. In small groups, trooping or±tuf-ted. On wet soil in broad-leaved woods, especially with willows or alder. Aut-umn. Widespread. Uncom-mon. Inedible. SPORES ellip-soid – ±almond-shaped, warty, 5–6×8–11.

Cortinarius cinnamomeus. Gills, colours, habitat, spores. CAP 1–8, at first convex, then more flattened, usually umbonate, smooth – finely fibrous, often slightly fibrous scaly towards margin, dry. STEM 2.5–11,± equal or tapering slightly upwards, slender, dry,± fibrous lined, partial veil yellow. GILLS at first yellow, then reddish gold, edge± even, fairly crowded, adnate – emarginate. SPORE PRINT reddish brown. SMELL faint, bitter, radish. FLESH at first lemon-yellow, then paler. In small groups, trooping or±tufted. On soil in broad-leaved, mixed or coniferous woods, especially with birch. Autumn. Widespread. Uncommon. Inedible. SPORES ellipsoid – ±almond-shaped, warty, 4–5.5×6.5–8.

Cortinarius semisanguineus. Cap, gills, spores. CAP 3–8, at first convex, then more flattened, sharply umbonate, finely fibrous scaly – silky, sometimes scalier near margin, dry. STEM 2–11,±equal or swollen towards base, slender, dry, fibrous-lined esp. apex, partial veil yellowish. GILLS first deep purple-red, then dusted reddish brown, edge ±irregular, fairly crowded, adnate – emarginate. SPORE PRINT reddish brown. SMELL faint, radish. FLESH olive-buff cap, darker stem. Solitary or small groups, trooping or tufted. On soil in conif., birch woods. Autumn. Widespread. Common. Inedible. SPORES ellipsoid, warty, 4–4.5×6–7.5.

Cortinarius sanguineus. Overall colour, spores. CAP 3–6.5, at first convex, then more flattened, barely umbonate, smooth – very finely silky-fibrous (use hand-lens), dry. STEM 3–6,±equal or tapering slightly upwards, slender, dry,±silky fibrous-lined, partial veil red. GILLS at first deep blood-red, then dusted reddish brown, edge±irregular, fairly crowded, adnate – emarginate. SPORE PRINT reddish brown. SMELL faint, pleasant or indistinct. FLESH deep blood-red. Usually in small groups, trooping or±tufted. On soil in coniferous woods. Autumn. Widespread. Rare. Inedible. SPORES ellipsoid, warty, 4–5×7–9.

Cortinarius armillatus. Cap features, stem, habitat, spores. CAP 5–12, at first convex – bell-shaped, then more flattened, broadly umbonate, first±smooth, then finely scaly, paler when dry. STEM 6–14,± equal or tapering upwards, bulbous, fairly slender, dry, fibrous-lined, partial veil reddish forming ring band GILLS at first pale reddish brown, then darker, fairly distant, adnate – emarginate. SPORE PRINT reddish brown. SMELL faint, radish FLESH pale reddish brown in cap, darker in stem. Usually small groups, trooping or tufted. On acid soil with broad-leaved or coniferous trees, often in wet places. Summer – autumn Widespread. Common. Inedible. SPORES ellipsoid finely warty, 6–7×7–12.

Cortinarius malicorius. Gills, flesh colour, spores. CAP 2–6.5, at first convex, then more flattened, sometimes broadly umbonate, silky-velvety, often finely woolly scaly towards margin, dry. STEM 3.5–7,± equal, fairly slender, dry,± silky fibrous-lined, partial veil yellowish olive. GILLS at first brownish yellow, then ochre-yellow, edge± irregular, fairly crowded, adnate-emarginate. SPORE PRINT reddish brown. SMELL faint, radish or indistinct. FLESH at first deep olive-green, then paler. Trooping or±tufted. On soil in coniferous woods. Autumn. Widespread, usually northern. Uncommon. Inedible. SPORES ellipsoid – ± almond-shaped, warty, 4–5 × 6–8.

Cortinarius phoeniceus. Like *C. semisanguineus*, flesh and spores differ. CAP 3–6.5, at first convex, then more flattened, barely umbonate, finely fibrous-silky, sometimes smooth or minutely cracked and finely scaly towards centre, dry. STEM 2.5–9,±equal or tapering downwards, stout, dry,±reddish fibrous-scaly below reddish ring zone. GILLS at first deep purple-red, then dusted reddish brown, edge±irregular, fairly crowded, adnate – emarginate. SPORE PRINT reddish brown. SMELL faint, pleasant or indistinct. FLESH ochreous buff, reddish below cap cuticle and at stem apex. Usually in small groups, trooping or±tufted. On soil, conif., birch woods. Autumn. Widespread. Rare. Inedible. SPORES ellipsoid – ± almond-shaped, warty, 3.5 –4.5×6–8.

Cortinarius puniceus. Gills, flesh and partial veil colours, spores. CAP 1.5–4, at first convex, then more flattened, often rather sharply umbonate, smooth – very finely velvety fibrous, dry, sometimes finely scaly at margin. STEM 4–7,± equal, often±club-shaped at base, slender, dry, fibrous-lined, partial veil golden-brown, superior ring zone. GILLS at first deep blood-red, then reddish brown, edge±irregular, fairly crowded, adnate. SPORE PRINT reddish brown. SMELL indistinct. FLESH deep purplish red. Usually in small groups, trooping or±tufted. On soil in broad-leaved or mixed woods. Autumn. Widespread. Uncommon. Inedible. SPORES ellipsoid, smooth – very finely warty, 4–4.5×6.5–8.

Cortinarius bulliardii. Cap features, gills, stem, habitat, spores. CAP 4–8, at first convex – bell-shaped, then more flattened, barely umbonate, first±smooth, then often finely scaly, paler when dry. STEM 5–11, tapering upwards,±bulbous, fairly slender, dry, fibrous lined, partial veil reddish. GILLS at first±violet, then reddish brown, fairly distant, adnate – emarginate. SPORE PRINT reddish brown. SMELL indistinct. FLESH pale, reddish white, darker reddish at stem base. Usually in small groups, trooping or±tufted. On soil in broad-leaved woods, especially with beech. Autumn. Widespread. Rare. Inedible. SPORES ellipsoid, warty, 5–6×8.5–10.5.

CORTINARIACEAE

Cortinarius evernius. Cap, gills, stem, habitat, spores. CAP 3–9, first convex – bell-shaped, then more flattened, broadly umbonate, at first±smooth, then often finely scaly, paling when dry. STEM 8–15,±equal or tapering downwards, barely bulbous, slender, dry,±fibrous-lined, partial veil whitish, forming ring bands. GILLS first±violet, then pale buff, then reddish brown, distant, adnate – emarginate. SPORE PRINT reddish brown. SMELL indistinct. FLESH reddish brown in cap, white – pale lilac in stem. Usually small groups, trooping or±tufted. On soil in coniferous woods. Autumn. Widespread. Uncommon. Inedible. SPORES ellipsoid, warty, 5–6×9–10.5.

Cortinarius hinnuleus. Stem, distant gills, smell, habitat, spores. CAP 2–6, at first conical – convex – bell-shaped, then more flattened, sharply umbonate, first ±smooth, then often finely scaly, paling when dry. STEM 5–10,±equal or tapering slightly upwards, barely bulbous, slender, dry,±fibrous-lined, partial veil white, superior white ring zone. GILLS first±violet buff, then reddish brown, distant, adnate – emarginate. SPORE PRINT reddish brown. SMELL earthy. FLESH whitish, flushed dark buff, often±violet at stem apex. Usually in small groups, trooping or±tufted. On soil in broad-leaved woods, esp. oak. Autumn. Widespread. Rare. Inedible. SPORES ellipsoid, warty, 4.5–6.5×7–9.

Cortinarius hemitrichus. Overall colour, cap features, stem, spores. CAP 2–6, at first convex – bell-shaped, then more flattened, sharply umbonate, at first±smooth, then densely fine-scaly, later smooth, paling when dry. STEM 2–7,±equal, slightly bulbous, slender, dry, fibrous-lined, partial veil white, thick woolly white ring and bands below. GILLS at first pale buff-grey, then reddish brown, distant, adnate – emarginate. SPORE PRINT reddish brown. SMELL indistinct. FLESH greyish buff. Usually in small groups, trooping or±tufted. On soil in damp broad-leaved, mixed or coniferous woods. Autumn. Widespread. Uncommon. Inedible. SPORES ellipsoid, warty, 4–5×8–11.

Leucocortinarius bulbiger. Overall colour, spore print. CAP 5–8, convex,±broadly umbonate,±smooth with irregular woolly remains of veil. STEM 5–10, tapering upwards, very broadly bulbous, fairly slender, fibrous-lined, partial veil white, superior,±white ring zone. GILLS at first white, then buff, fairly crowded, emarginate. SPORE PRINT white. SMELL indistinct. FLESH white,± buff in stem. Usually in small groups,±trooping. On soil in coniferous woods. Autumn. Rare. Inedible. SPORES broadly ellipsoid, warty, 4–5×7–9.

Cortinarius torvus. Stem, gills, smell, habitat, spores. CAP 3–10, at first convex, then more flattened, barely umbonate, at first±smooth, then often finely scaly or marbled, paler when dry. STEM 4–7,±equal or tapering downwards, slightly bulbous, fairly slender, dry,± fibrous-lined, partial veil whitish, forming irregular bands below marked superior sheathing ring. GILLS at first±violet buff, then reddish brown, fairly distant,±adnate – emarginate. SPORE PRINT reddish brown. SMELL strong, unpleasant, camphor. FLESH buff with violet flush especially at stem apex. Usually in small groups, trooping or±tufted. On soil in broad-leaved woods, esp. beech. Autumn. Widespread. Uncommon. Inedible. SPORES ellipsoid, warty, 5–6×8–10.5.

Cortinarius paleaceus. Colour, cap, stem, smell, spores. CAP 1–3, first convex – bell-shaped, then more flattened, sharply umbonate, first±smooth, then finely scaly-fibrous, paling when dry. STEM 3–7, ±equal, slightly bulbous, slender, dry,±fibrous-lined, partial veil white,± woolly white ring and bands below. GILLS first pale buff-grey, then reddish brown, fairly distant, adnate – emarginate. SPORE PRINT reddish brown. SMELL pelargonium. FLESH greyish buff. Usually small groups, trooping or±tufted. On acid soil with broad-l. or conif. trees, heaths. Autumn. Widespread. Uncommon. Inedible. SPORES broadly ellipsoid, warty, 4–6×6.5–9.

Cortinarius obtusus. Overall colour, cap features, stem, smell, spores. CAP 1–4, at first convex – bell-shaped, then more flattened, rather sharply umbonate, at first±smooth, then lined, paler when dry. STEM 4–8,±equal,±bulbous, slender, dry, fibrous-lined, partial veil white. GILLS at first reddish buff, then reddish brown, distant, adnate – emarginate. SPORE PRINT reddish brown. SMELL strong, radish. FLESH reddish buff. Usually in small groups, trooping or ±tufted. On soil, often among moss, in coniferous woods. Autumn. Widespread. Common. Inedible. SPORES ellipsoid, warty, 4–5×8–10.

Rozites caperata. Cap colour, stem features, spore print, habitat. CAP 5–9, at first ellipsoid – convex, then flattened, broadly umbonate, often±finely wrinkled, shiny, finely scaly. STEM 5–11, equal or tapering upwards, slightly bulbous with fragmentary volva, fairly slender, fibrous-lined,±superior or median persistent fleshy ring. GILLS at first whitish buff, then reddish buff, crowded, adnate. SPORE PRINT brownish ochre. SMELL mild, pleasant. FLESH white-buff. Solitary or in small groups,±trooping. On acid soil with coniferous trees, heather. Autumn. Widespread, northern, Scotland in Britain. Uncommon. Edible. SPORES ellipsoid, warty, 7–9×11–14.

135

Galerina heimansii. Size, cap and stem features, habitat, spores. CAP 0.5–1, at first conical – bell-shaped, then convex, rather sharply umbonate, rather coarsely lined – grooved, paler when dry. STEM 1–2, equal, slender, floury at apex, sparsely fibrous below. GILLS reddish ochre, fairly distant, adnate – ±decurrent. SPORE PRINT reddish brown. SMELL indistinct. FLESH reddish ochre. Usually in small groups,± trooping. On wet soil or wet, rotten wood, with alder, birch or willow. Summer – autumn. Widespread. Rare. Inedible. SPORES elongated-ellipsoid, warty, 5–6×8–10.5.

Galerina praticola. Size, cap features, habitat, spores. CAP 1–3, at first convex, then more flattened, barely umbonate, finely lined at edge, greasy sticky when wet, paler when dry. STEM 2–6, equal, slender, superior fairly persistent spreading ring, floury at apex, silky-lined below. GILLS at first yellowish buff, then reddish brown, fairly distant, adnate – ±decurrent. SPORE PRINT reddish brown. SMELL mealy. FLESH reddish buff. Solitary or in small groups, trooping or±tufted. On wet soil with mosses, among grass, on wet rotten wood, woods, dunes. Autumn. Widespread. Uncommon, commoner northwards. Inedible, poisonous. SPORES almond-shaped, warty, 5.5–7×9-11, with small germ pore.

Galerina paludosa. Habitat, stem, spores. CAP 1–3, first conical then convex, sharply umbonate, lined to ½-way, smooth – coarsely floury, esp. when young. STEM 5–10, equal, v. slender, silky, superior white woolly quickly-disappearing ring, finely floury at apex, deeply rooted. GILLS first pale yellowish ochre, then reddish brown, fairly distant, adnate. SPORE PRINT reddish brown. FLESH red-ochre. Solitary or trooping. In *Sphagnum*, marshy places. Summer – autumn. Widespread. Common. Inedible. SPORES ellipsoid – ±lemon-shaped, warty, 6–7×9.5–11.

Galerina tibiicystis. Habitat, stem, spores, very similar to *G. sphagnorum* but no smell and stem differs. CAP 1.5–3.5, at first conical – bell-shaped, then convex, sometimes umbonate, lined at margin, smooth – coarsely floury, especially when young. STEM 5–15, equal, very slender, minutely bristly, deeply rooted in substrate. GILLS at first pale yellowish ochre, then reddish brown, fairly distant, adnate – emarginate. SPORE PRINT reddish brown. SMELL indistinct. FLESH reddish ochre. Solitary or trooping. In *Sphagnum*, bogs, marshy places. Summer – autumn. Widespread. Uncommon. Inedible. SPORES ellipsoid – ±almond-shaped, warty, 5–6×8.5–12.

Galerina sphagnorum. Habitat, stem, spores, very like *G. paludosa* but no ring. CAP 1.5–3.5, first conical – bell-shaped, then convex, rather sharply umbonate, lined, smooth – coarsely floury, esp. when young. STEM 4–10, equal, very slender, silky-fibrous, finely floury at apex, deeply rooted. GILLS first pale yellowish ochre, then reddish brown, fairly distant, adnate – decurrent. SPORE PRINT reddish brown. SMELL mealy. FLESH reddish ochre. Solitary or trooping. In *Sphagnum*, marshy places. Summer – autumn. Widespread. Uncommon. Inedible. SPORES ellipsoid – ±almond-shaped, very finely warty, 5–7×8.5–12.

Galerina nana. Size, cap features, spores. CAP 0.5–2.5, at first conical – ellipsoid, then convex, rather coarsely lined – grooved, paler when dry. STEM 1–4, equal, slender, finely woolly-scaly at apex, sparsely fibrous below. GILLS reddish ochre, fairly distant, adnate – ±decurrent. SPORE PRINT reddish brown. SMELL indistinct. FLESH reddish ochre. Usually in small groups,± trooping. On soil, sometimes among grass, woods, paths in gardens and greenhouses. Summer – autumn. Widespread. Rare. Inedible. SPORES elongated-ellipsoid, warty, 5–6.5× 6.5–11, some basidia 2-spored.

Galerina unicolor (*=marginata*). Size, stem features, habitat, smell, spores. CAP 1.5–3, at first convex, then more flattened – ±umbonate, finely lined, paler when dry. STEM 2–8, equal, slender, superior fairly persistent spreading ring, darker below. GILLS reddish brown, fairly distant, adnate. SPORE PRINT reddish brown. SMELL mealy. FLESH reddish buff. Solitary or in small tufted groups. On wet rotten wood of coniferous trees. Autumn. Widespread. Uncommon. Poisonous. SPORES elongated-ellipsoid, warty, 5–7.5×8–10.5, often with outer wall separating.

Galerina salicicola. Size, cap features, habitat, spores. CAP 1–2.5, at first convex, then more flattened, rather sharply umbonate, lined when wet, paler when dry. STEM 1.5–3.5, equal or tapering slightly upwards slender, superior quickly disappearing ring zone,± floury at apex, silky-lined or loosely woolly-scaly below, darkening from base. GILLS at first yellowish but then reddish ochre, fairly distant, adnate – ±decurrent. SPORE PRINT reddish brown. SMELL mealy. FLESH reddish buff. Usually in small groups, trooping or tufted. On and close to rotting willow stumps. Autumn. Widespread. Rare. Inedible, poisonous. SPORES almond-shaped, warty, 4.5–5×7.5–9, sometimes with small germ pore.

Galerina badipes. Size, stem features, habitat, spores. CAP 1–2, at first convex, then more flattened, rather broadly umbonate, lined, paler when dry. STEM –4, equal, slender, rarely with superior quickly disappearing ring zone, ± floury at apex, silky lined or barely loosely woolly-scaly below, darkening from base. GILLS at first yellowish brown, then reddish ochre, fairly distant, adnate. SPORE PRINT reddish brown. SMELL mealy. FLESH reddish buff. Usually in small groups, trooping or ±tufted. On twigs and needles in coniferous woods. Autumn. Widespread. Rare. Inedible, poisonous? SPORES almond-shaped, pitted, 5.5–7×10–13. At least some basidia 2-spored.

Galerina cinctula. Size, stem features, habitat, spores. CAP 0.5–1.5, at first conical – convex, then more flattened, broadly umbonate, lined when moist, paler when dry. STEM 0.5–2.5, equal, sometimes barely bulbous, slender, floury at apex, densely fibrous-silky below. GILLS at first pale yellowish, then reddish ochre, fairly distant, adnate. SPORE PRINT reddish brown. SMELL mealy. FLESH reddish buff. Usually in small groups, trooping or ±tufted. On wet rotten wood, especially of coniferous trees, also wet soil, often with mosses. Autumn. Widespread. Rare. Inedible. SPORES almond-shaped, pitted, 5–6×10–13. Basidia 2-spored.

Galerina sideroides (=*stylifera*). Size, stem features, habitat, spores. CAP 2–3.5, at first conical – bell-shaped, then convex, sharply umbonate, finely lined at margin, sticky-slimy, peelable skin, paler when dry. STEM 4–7, equal, slender, ±floury at apex, sparsely white fibrous below, extremely sparse superior ring zone. GILLS at first yellowish ochre, then reddish ochre, fairly crowded, adnate – decurrent. SPORE PRINT reddish brown. SMELL floury-rancid. FLESH yellowish buff. Usually in small groups, trooping or ±tufted. On wet rotten wood and other debris of coniferous trees. Summer – autumn. Widespread. Uncommon. Inedible. SPORES ellipsoid, smooth, 4–6×6–8.5.

Galerina embolus. Stem, habitat, spores. CAP 0.5–1.5, first convex, then flattened, sometimes barely papillate, lined esp. when wet, silky, paler when dry. STEM 1–2.5, tapering downwards, slender, ±floury at apex, finely silky-lined, darkening from base. GILLS at first yellowish ochre, then reddish ochre, fairly distant, adnate – ±decurrent. SPORE PRINT reddish brown. SMELL indistinct. FLESH yellowish buff. Usually small groups,±trooping. On soil, peat, sand, in moss, lichens, dunes, heaths. Autumn. Widespread. Rare. Inedible. SPORES ellipsoid – ± almond-shaped, smooth, 4.5–6×9–11. Basidia usually 2-spored.

Galerina vittaeformis. Size, stem features, habitat, spores. CAP 0.5–1, at first conical – bell-shaped, then convex, sometimes ±papillate, lined, paler when dry. STEM 2–3.5, equal, slender, minutely bristly. GILLS at first yellowish brown, then reddish ochre, fairly distant, adnate. SPORE PRINT reddish brown. SMELL? FLESH reddish buff. Usually in small groups, trooping or ±tufted. On wet soil among mosses and plant debris, woods. Autumn. Widespread. Rare. Inedible. SPORES ellipsoid – almond-shaped, warty, –7×8–11.

Galerina ampullaceocystis. Size, stem features, habitat, spores. CAP 1–1.5, at first conical – convex, then more flattened, papillate – sharply umbonate, lined when moist, paler when dry. STEM 2–4, equal, sometimes barely bulbous, slender, floury at apex, superior whitish ring zone, irregularly woolly-scaly below. GILLS at first ochre-cream, then reddish ochre, fairly crowded, adnate – decurrent. SPORE PRINT reddish brown. SMELL mealy. FLESH yellowish buff. Usually in small groups, trooping or ±tufted. On wet rotten wood, especially of coniferous trees. Summer – autumn. Widespread. Rare. Inedible. SPORES ellipsoid – almond-shaped, smooth, 5–6× 9–11.5. Basidia 2-spored.

Galerina mycenopsis. Stem features, habitat, spores. CAP 1–2, at first hemispherical, then bell-shaped, then convex, lined to half way, slightly sticky-slimy, paler when dry. STEM 3–8, equal, slender, ±floury at apex, sparsely white fibrous. GILLS yellowish ochre, fairly distant, adnate. SPORE PRINT ochreous. SMELL indistinct. FLESH yellowish. Trooping. In moss, usually close to coniferous woods. Autumn. Widespread. Uncommon. Inedible. SPORES ellipsoid, smooth, 5–6×9.5–13.

Galerina mycenoides. Stem features, habitat, spores. CAP 0.25–2, at first conical – bell-shaped, then convex, sometimes rather sharply umbonate, lined, paler when dry. STEM 3–8, equal, slender, prominent superior ring zone, darkening from base. GILLS reddish ochre, fairly distant, adnate. SPORE PRINT reddish brown. SMELL indistinct. FLESH yellowish buff. Trooping. In *Sphagnum* or other mosses, in plant debris, marshy places. Autumn. Widespread. Uncommon. Inedible. SPORES ellipsoid, smooth, 5–7×9–13. Basidia 2-spored.

137

CORTINARIACEAE

Galerina mniophila. Cap colours, stem features, habitat, spores. CAP 1-2, at first conical – bell-shaped, then convex, lined when wet, paler when dry. STEM 3.5–7, equal, slender, floury at apex, finely fibrous-lined – woolly below. GILLS at first ochre, then darker, fairly crowded, adnate. SPORE PRINT reddish brown. SMELL indistinct. FLESH yellowish buff. Trooping. In deep mosses (not *Sphagnum*) in damp woods. Autumn. Widespread. Uncommon. Inedible. SPORES almond-shaped, very finely warty, 5.5–6.5×10–12.

Galerina (= *Kuehneromyces*) *mutabilis*. Habit, habitat, stem features, spores. CAP 3–6, at first convex, then flattened and broadly umbonate, smooth, much paler when dry. STEM 3–8, equal, slender, scaly below superior – apical spreading ring. GILLS at first pale ochre, then reddish brown, crowded, adnate. SPORE PRINT reddish ochre. SMELL indistinct. FLESH whitish buff. Densely tufted. On wood, stumps or fallen branches of broad-leaved trees. Spring – winter. Widespread. Very common. Edible. SPORES ellipsoid – almond-shaped, smooth, 4–5×6–7, germ pore.

Crepidotus calolepis. Very similar to *C. mollis* but smaller and cap and flesh differ slightly. CAP 0.5–1.5,±kidney-shaped, smooth, slightly sticky, very soft, often with rather dense minute scales, lined towards margin. STEM absent or rudimentary. GILLS first greyish brown, then reddish brown, crowded, decurrent to base. SPORE PRINT brown. SMELL indistinct. FLESH whitish, rather brittle. Solitary or usually in small overlapping groups. On wood, twigs, branches. Summer – autumn. Widespread. Uncommon. Inedible. SPORES broadly ellipsoid, smooth, 5–6.5×7–10.

Crepidotus wakefieldiae. Spore print, habitat, spores. CAP 0.25–0.5,± shell-shaped, smooth, ofte slightly incurved at margin STEM absent, hairy at cap base. GILLS at first whitish then buff-brown, distant, remote. SPORE PRINT buff-brown. FLESH whitish buff. Solitar or in small± overlapping groups. On rotting wood and bark of broad-leaved trees. Autumn – winter. Widespread. Rare. Inedible. SPORES spherical, warty, 5–6.5.

Galerina hypnorum. Overall form, habitat, spores. CAP 0.5–1, at first conical – bell-shaped or±spherical, then convex, lined when wet, paler when dry. STEM 2–4, equal, extremely slender, floury at apex, very finely fibrous-lined – woolly below. GILLS at first pale ochre, then darker, fairly distant, adnate. SPORE PRINT reddish brown. SMELL indistinct. FLESH yellowish buff. Trooping. Among mosses, on rotting tree-stumps and on damp soil nearby. Autumn. Widespread. Very common. Inedible. SPORES ellipsoid, very finely warty, 5–7×9–12.

Crepidotus mollis. Cap features, size, spores. CAP 1.5–7,±kidney-shaped, smooth, sticky, very soft, often with few scattered scales, lined towards margin; gelatinous pellicle can be stretched, although the flesh splits. STEM absent or very short. GILLS at first greyish brown, then reddish brown, crowded, decurrent to base. SPORE PRINT pale snuff-brown. SMELL indistinct. FLESH whitish, watery. In small or large overlapping groups. On wood, stumps or fallen branches of broad-leaved trees, especially ash. Summer – autumn. Widespread. Very common. Inedible. SPORES broadly ellipsoid, smooth, 5–6.5×7–10.

Crepidotus applanatus. Spores. CAP 0.5–4.5,±kidney-shaped, smooth, often lined at margin. STEM absent or very short. GILLS at first whitish, then buff, crowded, decurrent to base. SPORE PRINT pale snuff-brown. FLESH whitish. Solitary or in small± overlapping groups. On wood, twigs, branches. Autumn. Widespread. Uncommon. Inedible. SPORES spherical, minutely spiny, 5–6.

Crepidotus haustellaris. Cap features, spore print microscopic features. CAP <0.5,±kidney-shaped, very finely downy-velvety margin smooth – very finely lined. STEM 0.25–0. lateral, tapering upwards slender, curved, with downy white base. GILLS a first ochre-buff, then ochr brown, fairly crowded,± decurrent. SPORE PRINT ochre-brown. SMELL indisinct. FLESH whitish buff, watery. Solitary or in sma scattered groups. On twig and dead branches of broad-leaved trees. Summer – autumn. Wide spread. Rare. Inedible. SPORES broadly ellipsoid, smooth, 5–6×8–10. Basic 2-spored.

Crepidotus pubescens Cap features, spore print, spores. CAP 0.5–2.5, ±kidney-shaped, very finely downy-velvety, margin smooth-very finely lined. STEM absent or very short. buff-brown, fairly crowded, ±decurrent. SPORE PRINT pale snuff-brown. SMELL indistinct. FLESH whitish buff, watery. Solitary or in small, scattered groups. On twigs, herbaceous plant debris, fern remains. Summer – autumn. Widespread, Rare. Inedible. SPORES ellipsoid – ±almond-shaped, smooth, 5–6× 8.5–12.

Crepidotus herbarum (=*Pleurotellus hypnophilus*). Cap features, spore print, spores. CAP 0.5–1, ±kidney-shaped – rounded, very finely downy-velvety, margin±smooth. STEM absent or, when young, extremely short. GILLS at first white, then yellowish buff, fairly crowded, decurrent to base. SPORE PRINT ochre-buff. SMELL indistinct. FLESH whitish buff, watery. Solitary or in small, scattered groups. On twigs, grass remains, herbaceous plant debris. Summer – autumn. Widespread. Uncommon. Inedible. SPORES elongated ellipsoid – spindle-shaped, smooth, 2.5–3.5×7–9.

Flocculina granulosa. Cap and stem features, spores. CAP 0.5–1.5, convex, coarsely mealy, often± scaly, especially in centre. STEM 1–2.5, ±equal, slender, downy-fibrous with± woolly base. GILLS ochre-brown, fairly distant, adnate – adnexed. SPORE PRINT dull reddish brown. SMELL indistinct. FLESH pale reddish brown. Solitary or trooping. On soil, especially on wet, clayey sites, often in woods or near to trees especially with sycamore. Autumn. Widespread. Rare. Inedible. SPORES ellipsoid – almond-shaped, smooth, 4.5–5.5×8–10.

Pholiota squarrosa. Cap and stem features, habit, habitat. CAP 3–10, at first convex, then flattened, densely covered with±concentric rings of coarse upturned scales, dry. STEM 5–14, tapering slightly downwards, fairly slender, often curved, covered in coarse upturned scales below superior – apical ragged ring, smooth at apex, dry. GILLS at first yellowish, then reddish ochre, crowded, adnate. SPORE PRINT reddish brown. SMELL unpleasant, radish. FLESH yellowish, reddish brown in stem base. Densely tufted. On wood at trunk base of broad-leaved (or rarely coniferous) trees. Autumn. Widespread. Common. Inedible. SPORES ellipsoid, smooth, 3.5–5×6–9.

Crepidotus variabilis. Cap features, spore print, spores. CAP 1–3.5, ±kidney-shaped, resupinate, very finely downy-velvety, margin±smooth. STEM absent or extremely short. GILLS at first whitish, then buff-brown, fairly distant, decurrent to base. SPORE PRINT pinkish buff. SMELL indistinct. FLESH whitish buff, watery. Solitary or in small, scattered groups. On twigs, straw, grass-stalks or herbaceous plant debris. Summer – autumn. Widespread. Common. Inedible. SPORES elongated – ellipsoid, minutely warty, 3–3.5×5–7.

Crepidotus (=*Melanotus*) *phillipsii*. Cap features, spore print, spores. CAP 0.25–1, kidney-shaped – ±rounded, smooth, very finely lined. STEM 0.25–0.5, eccentric–lateral,±equal, smooth. GILLS pinkish brown, fairly crowded, decurrent. SPORE PRINT pale purplish buff. SMELL indistinct. FLESH whitish buff, watery. Solitary or in small, scattered groups. On herbaceous plant debris, especially of grasses or other monocotyledonous plants. Summer – autumn. Widespread. Uncommon. Inedible. SPORES ellipsoid, smooth, 3–4×5–7.

Phaeomarasmius erinaceus. Cap and stem features, habitat. CAP 1–1.5, at first convex, soon flattened – umbilicate, covered with small pointed scales, margin at first fringed. STEM 1–2, ±equal or tapering slightly upwards, slender, often curved, rather coarsely hairy-scaly. GILLS reddish ochre, fairly distant, adnate. SPORE PRINT dull reddish brown. SMELL indistinct. FLESH reddish brown. Solitary or trooping. On wood, twigs, small branches especially of willow. All year. Widespread. Uncommon. Inedible. SPORES ellipsoid – lemon-shaped, smooth, 6–8×9–11.

Pholiota flammans. Cap and stem features, habit, habitat, spores. CAP 2–7, at first convex, then flattened, densely covered with±concentric rings of coarse upturned scales, dry. STEM 4–8, equal or tapering slightly upwards, fairly slender, covered in coarse upturned scales below superior – apical±ragged ring, smooth at apex, dry. GILLS at first yellowish, then reddish yellow, crowded, adnate – emarginate. SPORE PRINT reddish brown. SMELL indistinct. FLESH yellowish. Solitary or tufted. On wood. stumps or fallen branches of coniferous trees. Summer – autumn. Widespread, predominantly northern and highland. Uncommon, locally common. Inedible. SPORES ellipsoid, smooth, 2–2.5×4–4.5.

139

Pholiota tuberculosa. Cap and stem features, habit, habitat, spores. CAP 2–4, at first convex–±spherical, then flattened, at first± smooth, then covered with small, flattened scales, especially towards margin, dry. STEM 5–8, equal or tapering slightly upwards, almost bulbous, rather stout, sparsely scaly below quickly disappearing superior – apical ring, smooth at apex, dry. GILLS at first yellow, then spotted reddish brown, crowded, adnate. SPORE PRINT reddish brown. SMELL faint, earthy. FLESH yellowish, bruising reddish brown. Tufted. On wood, stumps, fallen branches, sawdust of broad-leaved (and coniferous?) trees. Summer – autumn. Widespread. Rare. Inedible. SPORES ellipsoid – kidney-shaped, smooth, 4–5×6.5–8.

Pholiota adiposa. Cap and stem features, habit, habitat, spores. CAP 5–10, at first convex, then flattened, covered with small, flattened scales, especially towards centre, sticky-slimy. STEM 2–5.5, equal or tapering slightly upwards, fairly slender, often curved, covered with±concentric bands of upturned scales below quickly disappearing superior – apical ring, smooth at apex, sticky-slimy. GILLS at first yellow, then reddish brown, crowded, adnate. SPORE PRINT reddish brown. SMELL faint, indefinite, pleasant. FLESH at first yellowish, then reddish brown. Tufted. On wood, at base of beech trunks. Summer –

autumn. Widespread. Rare. Inedible. SPORES ellipsoid, smooth, 3–4×5.5–6.5.

Pholiota aurivella. Cap and stem features, habit, habitat, spores. CAP 5–12, at first convex, then flattened – very broadly umbonate, covered with±concentric bands of large flattened scales, very sticky-slimy. STEM 2–5.5, equal or tapering slightly upwards, fairly slender, often curved, covered with±concentric bands of small, upturned, slightly sticky scales below quickly disappearing superior – apical ring, smooth at apex, not slimy. GILLS at first yellowish, then reddish brown, crowded, adnate–emarginate. SPORE PRINT reddish brown. SMELL faint, indistinct. FLESH at first yellowish, then reddish brown. Tufted. On wood, on upper branches of living or dead broad-leaved trees. Autumn. Widespread. Common, rarer in North. Inedible. SPORES ellipsoid, smooth, 5–6×7–9.

Pholiota lenta. Cap and stem features, habit, habitat, spores. CAP 5–9, at first convex, then flattened, sparsely covered with pale, quickly disappearing scales, sticky-slimy. STEM 7–9, equal or tapering slightly upwards, almost bulbous, fairly stout, covered with coarse scales below indefinite superior – apical ring zone, floury at apex, dry. GILLS at first yellowish, then reddish brown, crowded,± decurrent. SPORE PRINT red-

dish brown. SMELL faint, pleasant, fruity. FLESH white. Solitary or in small groups,±tufted. On woody debris of broad-leaved or coniferous trees, or on soil from buried debris. Autumn. Widespread. Rare. Inedible. SPORES ellipsoid, smooth, 3–4×6–7.5.

Pholiota gummosa. Cap, habitat, spores. CAP 3–6, at first convex, then flattened – slightly depressed, at first sparsely covered with rather large scales, then smooth, sticky peelable skin. STEM 4–8, equal, fairly slender, fibrous silky. GILLS at first yellowish white, then reddish brown, crowded, adnate. SPORE PRINT reddish brown. SMELL indistinct. FLESH yellowish white. Usually in small, tufted groups. On soil (from buried wood?) among grass close to trees and from debris of coniferous and broad-leaved trees. Autumn. Widespread. Uncommon. Inedible. SPORES ellipsoid, smooth, 3–4×5–7.

Pholiota highlandensis (=*carbonaria*). Habitat, cap, spores. CAP 2–5, at first convex, then flattened – slightly depressed, smooth, sticky. STEM 3–7, equal or tapering slightly downwards, slender, finely fibrous-scaly below indefinite superior ring zone. GILLS at first buff, then reddish buff, crowded, adnate. SPORE PRINT reddish brown. SMELL indistinct. FLESH yel-

lowish white. Usually in large±tufted groups. Or soil on fire sites, especia in woods. Summer – winter. Widespread. Co mon. Inedible. SPORES el soid, smooth, 4–5×6–8.

Pholiota spumosa Cap fe tures, spores, habitat, ca 2–6, at first convex, then flattened-slightly depressed, smooth, very sticky. STEM 3–7, equal or tapering slightly downwards, slender, finely fibrous. GILLS at first brig yellow, then brownish gre crowded, adnate. SPORE PRINT brown. SMELL indis tinct. FLESH greenish yel low, more reddish in stem Usually in small tufted groups. On soil with con iferous trees. Autumn. Widespread. Rare. Inedi ble. SPORES ellipsoid, smooth, 7–8×3–4.

Pholiota scamba. Cap fea tures, habitat, spores. CAP 1–4, at first convex, then flattened – slightly depressed, often umbon ate, rather silky, at first sticky when wet, then dry STEM 1–3, equal, fairly sle der, usually curved,±fine woolly or sparsely scaly, densely downy at base. GILLS at first yellowish buf then darker buff, crowde adnate – ±decurrent. SPORE PRINT pale reddish ochre. SMELL indistinct? FLESH yellowish. Usually i small tufted groups. On rotten wood, stumps, falle branches of coniferous trees, especially pine and larch. Autumn. Widespread. Uncommon. Inedi ble. SPORES ellipsoid, smooth, 4.5–5.5×8.5–9.5.

140

oliota alnicola. Cap,
ell, habitat, spores. CAP
8, first convex, then flat-
ed – slightly depressed,
en umbonate, smooth,
easy-slimy. STEM 3–8,
ual, fairly slender, often
ghtly curved,±fibrous,±
v. GILLS first pale yellow-
, then reddish buff, fairly
wded, adnate. SPORE
NT reddish brown. SMELL
asant, sweet, fruity.
SH yellowish, reddish
wn in stem base. Solit-
y or small tufted groups.
wood of broad-leaved
es, esp. birch, alder, wil-
v in wet places. Autumn.
despread. Uncommon.
edible. SPORES ellipsoid,
ooth, 4.5–5.5×8.5–10.5.

Pholiota myosotis. Habitat,
spores, stem. CAP 2–3.5, at
first convex, then flattened,
barely umbonate, smooth,
often slightly lined at margin, snakeskin-like, sticky.
STEM 7–12, equal, slender,
fibrous or finely scaly, rooting. GILLS olive-buff, edge
paler, fairly distant,
adnate with decurrent
tooth. SPORE PRINT dull
brown. SMELL mealy. FLESH
yellowish white. Solitary or
trooping. On wet soil or
peat, among *Sphagnum*,
marshes, bogs. Autumn.
Widespread. Uncommon.
Inedible. SPORES ellipsoid –
almond-shaped, smooth, 7–
8×13–18.

Tubaria autochthona.
Habitat, spores, overall
colour. CAP 0.5–2, at first
convex, then flattened –
depressed, very finely
velvety, lined at margin.
STEM 1.5–2.5, tapering
downwards, often curved
or wavy, fairly stout,±
floury, downy at base.
GILLS yellowish buff, then
darker buff, fairly crowded, adnate with decurrent
tooth. SPORE PRINT ochre-
brown. SMELL indistinct.
FLESH whitish. Usually in
small groups,±trooping.
On soil, especially under
hedges, with hawthorn.
Summer – autumn. Wide-
spread. Uncommon (prob-
ably overlooked). Inedi-
ble. SPORES ellipsoid, very
finely warty, 3–4.5×5–7.5.

Tubaria furfuracea. Habitat, cap features, season,
gills. CAP 1–4, at first convex, then flattened –
depressed, fibrous scaly
and lined – grooved at
margin, paler when dry.
STEM 1.5–4,±equal or
tapering slightly upwards,
fairly slender, fibrous,
downy at base, barely evident superior ring zone.
GILLS reddish brown, fairly
distant,±decurrent. SPORE
PRINT ochre-brown. SMELL
indistinct. FLESH reddish
buff. Trooping or±tufted.
On wood, twigs and other
woody debris. All year.
Widespread. Very com-
mon. Inedible. SPORES
ellipsoid – almond-shaped,
smooth, 4–6×6–8.5.

oliota ochrochlora. Cap,
ls, spores. CAP 2–5, first
nvex, then flattened –
ghtly depressed, some-
es slightly umbonate,
vered in small, flattened
les, esp. at centre, first
ghtly sticky, then dry
cy. STEM 2–5, equal or
pering slightly upwards,
rly slender, often slight-
rved, fibrous-scaly below
perior quickly disappear-
g ring zone, sometimes
olly-fibrous at apex.
LS first pale yellowish,
en olive-greenish, fairly
wded, adnate. SPORE
NT reddish brown. SMELL
distinct. FLESH yellowish
ite, reddish brown in
all tufted groups. On
od of broad-leaved
es. Summer – autumn.
idespread. Uncommon.
edible. SPORES ellipsoid,
ooth, 4.5–5.5×8.5–10.5.

Tubaria confragosa. Habitat, spores, stem, overall
colour. CAP 1–6, at first
convex, then flattened,
smooth – fibrous, at first
often with ragged fibrous
veil remains at margin,
paler when dry. STEM 3–10,
equal or tapering upwards,
slender, fibrous, superior
fairly persistent ring. GILLS
reddish brown, fairly distant, adnate. SPORE PRINT
ochre-brown. SMELL indis-
tinct. FLESH pale reddish
brown. Usually in small
tufted groups. On rotten
wood of broad-leaved
trees, especially birch and
poplar. Autumn. Predomi-
nantly northern. Rare.
Inedible. SPORES ellipsoid,
smooth, 4.5–5×6.5–7.5.

Tubaria conspersa. Size,
habitat, cap features,
spores, gills, overall colour.
CAP 1–2.5, at first convex,
then flattened – depressed,
covered with remains of
veil, silky – fibrous-scaly,
ragged at margin. STEM 2–
4,±equal or tapering
slightly upwards, almost
bulbous, slender, fibrous,
downy at base. GILLS red-
dish buff, edge white
irregular, fairly distant,±
decurrent. SPORE PRINT
ochre-brown. SMELL indistinct. FLESH reddish buff.
Trooping or±tufted. On
soil or rotten woody debris.
Summer – autumn. Wide-
spread. Uncommon. Ined-
ible. SPORES ellipsoid –
lemon-shaped, smooth, 4–
6×7–10.

Ripartites tricholoma.
Overall form, colour, spore
print. CAP 1.5–3.5,
at first convex, then
flattened and depressed –
funnel-shaped,±smooth-
finely fibrous, hairy at margin. STEM 3–4,±equal or
tapering slightly upwards,
fairly stout, smooth – finely
scaly. GILLS at first whitish,
then brownish buff,
crowded, decurrent. SPORE
PRINT pale ochre-buff.
SMELL indistinct. FLESH
white. Solitary or trooping.
On soil in broad-leaved,
mixed or coniferous woods.
Autumn. Widespread.
Uncommon. Inedible.
SPORES subspherical, warty,
3.5–4×4–5.

CORTINARIACEAE

BOLBITIACEAE

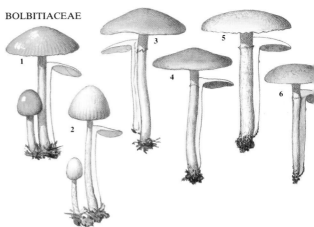

Ripartites metrodii. Overall form, colour, spore print, habitat, spores. CAP 1.5–4.5, at first convex, then flattened and ±depressed, at first±smooth-finely velvety, then often cracked. STEM 3–4, ±equal or tapering upwards, fairly stout, ± smooth, granular at apex. GILLS at first pale buff, then brownish buff, often with pink flush, crowded, decurrent. SPORE PRINT pale ochre-buff. SMELL indistinct. FLESH whitish buff. Usually in small groups, ± trooping. On soil in coniferous woods, especially with spruce. Autumn. Widespread, not Britain? Rare? Inedible. SPORES subspherical, warty, 4–5×5–6.5.

BOLBITIACEAE
Toadstool-shaped, sometimes very fragile and in *Bolbitius* rapidly disintegrating, usually dull-coloured but yellow or pinkish in *Bolbitius*, often much paler when dry, gills crowded – distant, adnate – free, variously-coloured but generally darker on maturing, stem sometimes with ring, flesh usually coloured as fruit body, spores ellipsoid – almond-shaped, usually smooth and with±evident germ-pore, spore print brown – reddish brown. Usually on soil, typically humus-rich, or dung, few on wood, all saprotrophic. Some edible, few good but at least one cultivated, some poisonous or hallucinogenic. *Bolbitius* [5], *Agrocybe* [17], *Conocybe* [58].

1
Bolbitius vitellinus **Yellow Cow-pat Toadstool**. Habitat, fragility, spores. CAP 1–5, at first convex – bell-shaped, then more flattened, often slightly umbonate, sticky with peelable skin, margin at first lined, then markedly grooved, fragile. STEM 3–6, tapering slightly upwards, slender, finely mealy, especially at apex, very fragile, quickly disintegrating when handled. GILLS at first pale straw-coloured, then reddish brown, fairly crowded, free. SPORE PRINT reddish brown. SMELL indistinct. FLESH whitish. Usually in groups, trooping or tufted. On manure, compost, well-manured soil, fields, gardens, farmland. Summer – autumn. Widespread. Very common. Inedible. SPORES ellipsoid, smooth, large germ pore, 6–7×12–13.

2
Bolbitius lacteus. Habitat, fragility, spores. CAP 0.25–1, at first convex – bell-shaped, then more flattened, often slightly umbonate, sticky with peelable skin, margin at first lined, then markedly grooved or folded, fragile. STEM 5–6, tapering slightly upwards, slender, finely mealy, fragile. GILLS at first pale straw-coloured, then reddish brown, fairly crowded, free. SPORE PRINT reddish brown. SMELL indistinct. FLESH whitish. Usually in groups, trooping or tufted. On soil, fields, path-sides, open areas in woods. Summer – autumn. Widespread. Rare. Inedible. SPORES ellipsoid, smooth, large germ pore, 6–6.5×10.5–11.5.

3
Agrocybe paludosa. Habitat, stem features, season. CAP 1.5–3, at first convex, then flattened – slightly depressed, often slightly umbonate, smooth, at first slightly sticky. STEM 4–7, equal or tapering slightly upwards, slender, silky-lined, especially above superior – apical spreading ring. GILLS at first buff, then ochreous, then brown, crowded, adnate – emarginate. SPORE PRINT hazel-brown. SMELL mealy. FLESH whitish in cap, brownish in stem. Usually in groups, ±trooping. On soil in wet fields and marshy places. Spring – summer. Widespread. Uncommon. Inedible. SPORES broadly ellipsoid, smooth, prominent germ pore, 4.5–6×7–9.5.

4
Agrocybe praecox. Habitat, stem features, season. CAP 2–6, at first convex, then flattened, sometimes slightly umbonate, smooth or slightly cracked or wrinkled. STEM 4–9, equal, swollen at base, fairly slender, fibrous-lined, rather floury at apex above superior±spreading white ring, mycelial cords at base. GILLS at first whitish buff, then brown, crowded, adnate – adnexed. SPORE PRINT hazel-brown. SMELL indefinite, pleasant. FLESH whitish in cap, buff in stem. Usually in groups, trooping – ±tufted. On soil, often among grass in fields and woods. Spring – summer. Widespread. Uncommon. Edible. SPORES ellipsoid, smooth, large prominent germ pore, 5–6×8.5–10.

5
Agrocybe molesta (=dur Habitat, stem features, s son. CAP 3–7, at first con vex, then flattened, bare umbonate, smooth or slightly wrinkled, margir often with persistent vei remnants. STEM 5–8, equ or tapering slightly dowr wards, fairly slender, fibrous-lined, floury at apex above quickly co lapsing superior±spread white ring, mycelial corc at base. GILLS at first wh ish buff, then dark buff-brown, fairly crowded, adnate. SPORE PRINT haze brown. SMELL faint, inde finite, pleasant. FLESH w ish, darkening in stem. Usually in groups, troop ing. On soil, often amon grass in fields and woods Spring – summer. Wide spread. Uncommon. Ed ble. SPORES ellipsoid, smooth, prominent germ pore, 7–8×11–14.

6
Agrocybe semiorbicular Habitat, cap and stem fe tures, microscopic featu CAP 1–3.5, at first subsph ical, then convex or sligt flattened, smooth or ver slightly wrinkled at cent slightly sticky-greasy. ST 3–5, ±equal, slender, at first floury, then smooth shiny. GILLS at first pale brown, then darker, fair distant, adnate. SPORE PI hazel-brown. SMELL stro mealy. FLESH whitish, wi buff areas. Usually in groups, trooping. On so often among grass in fiel lawns and woods. Sprin autumn. Widespread. Common. Inedible. SPOR broadly ellipsoid, smoot large germ pore, 7–8×10.5–14, very thick-walled.

142

1

rocybe arvalis. Stem fea-
res, microscopic features.
p 1–2, at first convex,
en flattened – slightly
pressed, sometimes
oting, usually from black-
oadly umbonate, at first
inkled when dry, greasy
en wet. STEM 5–11,±
ual or tapering slightly
wards, slender, floury,
oting, usually from black-
pea-sized sclerotium.
LS at first buff, then red-
own, fairly distant,
nate – adnexed. SPORE
NT hazel-brown. SMELL
distinct. FLESH buff in
p, paler in stem. Usually
small groups, trooping.
soil, often among grass
fields and woods. Spring
autumn. Widespread.
ncommon. Inedible.
ORES ellipsoid, smooth,
all germ pore, 5–6×9–
. Gill face cystidia club-
aped with finger-like
tensions.

2

rocybe cylindracea
aegerita). Habit, habitat,
m features, microscopic
tures. CAP 2.5–10, at first
nvex, then flattened –
y slightly depressed, at
t silky smooth but later
inkled or cracked. STEM
5, variable,±equal,
metimes very slender and
vy, fibrous, rather floury
apex, superior, fairly
rsistent spreading ring.
LS at first buff, then
own, crowded, adnate
h tooth – decurrent.
ORE PRINT hazel-brown.
ELL pleasant, mealy.
ESH white, brownish in
centre and stem base.
ups. On soil or wood, at
se of stumps of broad-
ved trees, especially
plar, willow, elm, alder.
l year. Widespread, pre-
minantly southern.
common. Edible.
dely cultivated in S.
rope. SPORES ellipsoid,
ooth, small, indistinct
m pore, 5–6.5×8–11.

3

Agrocybe erebia. Size, stem
features, microscopic features. CAP 2.5–6, at first
convex, then slightly
flattened, usually broadly
umbonate, slightly sticky
when wet, drying paler,
wrinkled and lined at margin on aging. STEM 2–7,
equal or tapering slightly
upwards, fairly slender,
silky-fibrous below, lined
above into gills, superior,
white, quickly disappearing
ring. GILLS at first buff, then
brown, fairly distant, adnate
with tooth – ±decurrent.
SPORE PRINT hazel-brown.
SMELL pleasant. FLESH pale
brown, darker in stem
base. Usually trooping. On
soil, often among litter in
woods, copses, hedgerows
and other shady places.
Autumn. Widespread.
Common. Inedible. SPORES
elongated – ellipsoid,
smooth, no germ pore, 6–
7×9–13. Basidia 2-spored.

4

Conocybe dunensis. Habitat, cap features. CAP 1–3,
at first conical – convex,
then convex, sometimes
slightly umbonate, smooth.
STEM 4–10,±equal or tapering slightly upwards, slender, fibrous-lined or
grooved, usually deeply
inserted in sand. GILLS at
first whitish, then yellowish
cream, then reddish brown,
fairly crowded, adnate.
SPORE PRINT reddish brown.
SMELL indistinct. FLESH
buff. Usually trooping. On
sand in dunes and stable
grassland, often with marram. Autumn. Wide-
spread, coastal. Rare.
Inedible. SPORES ellipsoid,
smooth, large germ pore,
7–8×12–14. Gill edge cystidia skittle-shaped.

5

Conocybe subovalis. Size,
cap features, stem features.
CAP 1.5–3, at first conical –
bell-shaped or subspher-
ical, then flattened convex,
markedly paler and matt
when dry, smooth, usually
lined at margin when fresh
and moist. STEM 5–11,±
equal or tapering slightly
upwards, very slender, bulbous, fibrous-lined, very
finely woolly-floury at apex.
GILLS at first buff, then reddish brown, fairly crowded,
adnate. SPORE PRINT reddish
brown. SMELL indistinct.
FLESH buff. Usually trooping. On soil among grass,
fields, woodland edges,
pathsides. Autumn. Wide-
spread. Rare. Inedible.
poisonous? SPORES ellips-
oid, smooth, large germ
pore, 6.5–8×11.5–13.5.
Gill edge cystida skittle-
shaped.

6

Conocybe tenera. Overall
form and colour, microscopic features. CAP 1–2, at
first conical – bell-shaped,
then convex, paler and
glistening when dry,
smooth, markedly lined.
STEM 3–7.5,±equal or
tapering slightly upwards,
very slender, slightly bulbous, finely floury-lined.
GILLS at first pale reddish
brown, then darker,
crowded, adnate – free.
SPORE PRINT reddish brown.
SMELL indistinct. FLESH
buff. Usually trooping. On
soil among grass, fields,
woodland edges, path-
sides, gardens. Spring –
autumn. Widespread.
Common. Inedible. SPORES
ellipsoid, smooth, large
germ pore, 5.5–6×10–12.
Gill edge cystidia skittle-
shaped.

7

Conocybe rickeniana.
Overall form and bright
colour, microscopic fea-
tures. CAP 1–3, at first
conical – bell-shaped, then
convex, paler and matt when
dry, smooth, lined when
wet. STEM 2.5–10,±equal,
very slender, slightly bulbous, finely floury-lined.
GILLS at first pale ochreous,
then reddish brown, fairly
crowded, adnate. SPORE
PRINT reddish brown. SMELL
indistinct. FLESH buff.
Usually trooping. On soil
among grass, lawns, fields,
woodland edges, path-
sides. Spring – autumn.
Widespread, not Ireland.
Uncommon. Inedible.
SPORES ellipsoid, smooth,
small germ pore, 4–5.5×7–
9.5. Gill edge cystidia
skittle-shaped with very
large heads.

8

Conocybe pubescens. Cap
features, microscopic features, habitat. CAP 0.5–1.5,
conical – bell-shaped, paler
and markedly hairy when
dry, lined when wet. STEM
7–12,±equal or tapering
slightly upwards, very slender, slightly bulbous, finely
floury-woolly-lined. GILLS
at first ochreous, then reddish brown, fairly distant,
adnate. SPORE PRINT reddish
brown. SMELL faint, inde-
finite. FLESH pale ochre,
darker at stem base.
Usually trooping. On well-
manured soil or dung, often
in deep shade in coniferous
woods. Spring – autumn.
Widespread. Uncommon.
Inedible. SPORES ellipsoid,
smooth, large germ pore,
7–9×14–17.5. Gill edge
cystidia skittle-shaped with
small heads.

143

BOLBITIACEAE

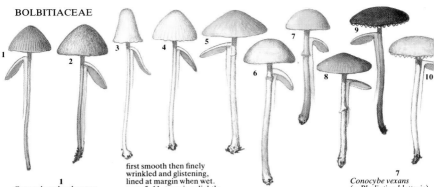

1

Conocybe subpubescens. Cap features, microscopic features, habitat. CAP 1–2.5, conical – convex, sometimes slightly umbonate, paler and finely velvety-hairy when dry, lined when wet. STEM 3–9, equal, very slender, slightly bulbous, finely floury-velvety, lined. GILLS at first cream, then reddish ochre, fairly crowded, adnate. SPORE PRINT reddish brown. SMELL indistinct. FLESH pale ochre in cap, darker in stem. Usually trooping. On soil in damp, shady places, woods, copses. Spring – autumn. Widespread. Rare. Inedible. SPORES ellipsoid, smooth, large germ pore, 6–8×11–13. Gill edge cystidia skittle-shaped.

2

Conocybe rickenii. Cap features, microscopic features, habitat. CAP 0.5–2.5, conical – convex – bell-shaped, barely flattening, paler when dry, smooth or finely wrinkled, at first lined at margin. STEM 3–10, equal or tapering slightly upwards, very slender, slightly bulbous, finely floury, especially at apex. GILLS at first cream, then pale ochreous, then reddish brown, fairly distant, adnate. SPORE PRINT reddish brown. SMELL indistinct. FLESH pale cream or whitish. Usually trooping, often in very large numbers. On well-manured soil on grassland. Summer – autumn. Widespread. Uncommon. Inedible. SPORES ellipsoid, smooth, large germ pore, 7–10×12.5–16.5. Basidia 2-spored. Gill edge cystidia skittle-shaped.

3

Conocybe lactea. Size, cap features, microscopic features. CAP 1–1.5, elongated bell-shaped, barely flattening, not paler when dry, at first smooth then finely wrinkled and glistening, lined at margin when wet. STEM 5–11, tapering slightly upwards, very slender, slightly bulbous, finely downy-lined. GILLS at first pale reddish brown, then darker, crowded, adnexed – free. SPORE PRINT reddish brown. SMELL indistinct. FLESH pale cream or whitish. Trooping. On soil among grass, lawns, pastures, parks. Summer – autumn. Widespread. Uncommon. Inedible. SPORES broadly ellipsoid, smooth, large germ pore, 7.5–8.5×11-14. Gill edge cystidia skittle-shaped.

4

Conocybe (=*Pholiotina*) *coprophila.* Habitat, cap features, stem colour, microscopic features. CAP 0.5–2.5, convex, barely flattening, at first smooth and sticky, powdery-mealy when dry, lined at margin only when mature. STEM 1–3, equal or tapering slightly upwards, very slender, often markedly curved, silky-fibrous towards base, floury at apex. GILLS at first whitish or pale ochreous, then reddish brown, fairly crowded, adnate. SPORE PRINT reddish brown. SMELL faint, pleasant or indistinct. FLESH pale cream-buff in cap, white in stem. Usually in small groups,±trooping. On dung, on chalky pastures, mountainous areas, also sand dunes. Summer – autumn. Widespread. Uncommon. Inedible. SPORES broadly ellipsoid, smooth, large germ pore, 7–8×11.5–14. Gill edge cystidia very broadly and irregularly bottle-shaped.

5

Conocybe blattaria (=*Pholiotina teneroides*). Cap and stem features, microscopic features. CAP 0.5–1.5, conical – bell-shaped,±smooth, markedly paler when dry, at first lined at margin, then smooth. STEM 4–5, equal or tapering slightly upwards, very slender, at first silvery-fibrous, floury at apex, small thick superior ring, often slipping down stem. GILLS reddish brown, irregular white edge, fairly crowded, adnexed. SPORE PRINT yellowish brown, flushed reddish. SMELL indistinct or faint, unpleasant. FLESH dark reddish brown in cap, paler in stem and towards base. Usually in small groups,± trooping. On soil, woodland edges, path-sides. Summer – autumn. Widespread. Uncommon. Inedible. SPORES ellipsoid, smooth, inevident germ pore, 5.5–6.5×11.5–13. Basidia 2-spored. Gill edge cystidia cylindrical – club-shaped.

6

Conocybe (=*Pholiotina*) *filaris.* Cap size, stem features, microscopic features. CAP 0.5–1.5, at first conical – bell-shaped, then convex, umbonate, markedly paler when dry,±smooth, lined at margin when wet. STEM 1–3.5, equal or tapering slightly upwards, slender, silky-fibrous, lined towards base, floury at apex, small felty median ring, often slipping down stem. GILLS yellowish brown, irregular white edge, fairly distant, adnexed. SPORE PRINT reddish brown. SMELL indistinct or faint, unpleasant. FLESH yellowish brown in cap, darker towards stem base. Solitary or in small groups,±trooping. On soil, especially wet, clayey and chalky sites, woodland edges, path-sides. Autumn. Widespread. Uncommon. Poisonous. SPORES ellipsoid, smooth, inevident germ pore, 4.5–5×7–8.5. Gill edge cystidia bottle-shaped.

7

Conocybe vexans (=*Pholiotina blattaria*). Cap and stem features, microscopic features. CAP 0.5–2, at first conical – convex, then more flattened, umbonate, pal[e] when dry,±smooth-fine[ly] wrinkled, barely lined at margin when wet. STEM 3.5–7, equal or tapering slightly upwards, slende[r], often rather wavy, silky-fibrous, lined towards ba[se], floury at apex, rather irregular superior – apic[al] ring, sometimes slipping down stem. GILLS at first buff, then reddish brow[n], irregular whitish edge, fairly crowded, adnate. SPORE PRINT reddish brow[n] SMELL indistinct or faint, unpleasant. FLESH±ochr[e]ous in cap, darker towar[ds] stem base. Solitary or in small groups,±trooping On soil, usually among mosses, in broad-leaved mixed woods, path-sides Spring – autumn. Widespread. Uncommon. Ine[di]ble. SPORES ellipsoid, smooth, large germ pore 5.5–6.5×10–12. Gill edg[e] cystidia±bottle-shaped with long curved neck.

8

Conocybe (=*Pholiotina*) *aporos.* Season, microsc[o]pic features. CAP 1–3, at first convex – bell-shape[d] subspherical, then conve[x] flattened, rather sharply umbonate, paler when dry,±smooth – finely wrinkled, very slightly sticky when fresh, lined [at] margin when wet. STEM 2–[?] 5, equal or tapering sligh[t]ly upwards, slender, silky-fibrous, lined towards ba[se] floury at apex, median,±fra[?]gile ring, often slipping down stem and breaking up. GILLS at first pale yel[l]owish brown, then redd[ish] brown, irregular white edge, crowded, adnexed SPORE PRINT yellowish brown. SMELL faint, unpleasant. FLESH reddis[h] brown in cap, yellowish brown in stem. Solitary o[r]

144

small groups, ±trooping. soil, especially on yey chalky sites, woods, ds, parks, path-sides. ring. Widespread. Common. Inedible. SPORES ellip-d, smooth, no germ re, 4.5–5.5×8–10. Gill ge cystidia ±cylindrical – ttle-shaped, often irregu-.

9
nocybe (=*Pholiotina*) *unnea*. Cap margin, micscopic features. CAP 1–5, at first conical – convex, then more flattened, ghtly umbonate, paler en dry, lined when wet, eth-like veil fragments at argin. STEM 2.5–4, equal tapering slightly wards, slender, very ely woolly-scaly. GILLS ddish brown, irregular itish edge, crowded, nate. SPORE PRINT pale ddish brown. SMELL faint idic. FLESH buff, darker low cap cuticle and in em base. Solitary or in all groups, ±trooping. soil, especially on alky sites, often among rbaceous plant debris, ods, path-sides. Summer autumn. Widespread. are. Inedible. SPORES ipsoid – kidney-shaped, looth, small germ pore, 5–4.5×6.5–8. Gill edge stidia skittle-shaped.

10
nocybe (=*Pholiotina*) *pendiculata*. Cap margin, croscopic features. CAP 2.5, at first conical – nvex, then more ttened, broadly umbon-e, paler when dry, slightly ed when wet, irregular eth-like veil fragments at argin. STEM 2.5–3.5, equal tapering slightly wards, slender, silky rous towards base, floury apex, scattered irregular il fragments, sometimes rming indistinct ring ne. GILLS reddish buff, en reddish brown, irregu-r whitish edge, fairly owded, adnate. SPORE NT reddish brown. SMELL int, acidic or indistinct. ESH pale buff, darker in em base. Solitary or in all groups, ±trooping. n soil, often with mosses, pecially on chalky sites, ten among herbaceous ant debris, woods, pses. Summer – autumn. idespread. Rare. Inedi-e. SPORES ellipsoid, looth, small germ pore, 5×6.5–8.5. Gill edge cys-lia irregularly elongated ttle-shaped – irregularly air-like.

PAXILLACEAE

PAXILLACEAE
Toadstool or bracket-shaped, generally stout, cap at first downy-velvety, sometimes sticky, often becoming rather wavy, gills decurrent, often branched, flesh usually firm – hard, stem stout, sometimes lateral or absent, sometimes rooting, spores ±ellipsoid, smooth, spore print reddish brown. On soil or wood, with trees, most mycorrhizal and some causing serious decay. None edible, some poisonous, possibly deadly. *Paxillus* [5], (*Phylloporus* [1]).

Paxillus atrotomentosus. Overall form, habitat, stem features. CAP 12–27, at first convex, then flattened – funnel-shaped, very finely downy-velvety, inrolled at margin. STEM 3–9, eccentric, equal, stout, at first downy, then coarsely velvety, rooting. GILLS at first olive-buff, then ochre and often reddish brown spotted, branched, crowded, decurrent. SPORE PRINT reddish brown. SMELL indistinct. FLESH cream-buff. Solitary or in small ± tufted groups. On wood, on stumps of coniferous trees. Summer – autumn. Widespread. Common. Inedible. SPORES ellipsoid, smooth, 3–4.5×5–6.5.

Paxillus involutus **Brown Roll-Rim.** Cap margin, gill features. CAP 5–12, at first convex, then soon flattened – depressed, at first very finely downy-velvety, then smoother towards margin, sticky when wet, persistently inrolled and downy at margin. STEM 3–7.5, sometimes slightly eccentric, tapering downwards, stout, smooth – fibrillose. GILLS pale ochre, bruising reddish brown, branched, crowded, decurrent. SPORE PRINT reddish brown. SMELL acidic. FLESH pale ochre-buff, more yellowish in stem base, bruising reddish brown. Usually in groups, trooping. On soil in mixed and broad-leaved woods, especially on acid sites. Summer – autumn. Widespread. Common. Poisonous. SPORES ellipsoid, smooth, 5–6×8–10.

Paxillus panuoides. Overall form and habitat, habitat features. CAP 1–6, broadly tongue- or oyster-shell-shaped, at first finely downy-velvety, then coarser and ±scaly, usually inrolled at margin. STEM lateral, rudimentary or absent. GILLS buff – pale yellowish brown, bruising slightly darker, branched, crowded, decurrent. SPORE PRINT ochre – reddish brown. SMELL indistinct. FLESH ochreous. Usually in large overlapping groups. On wood, fallen logs and stumps of coniferous trees causing wood to turn soft and bright yellow. Summer – autumn. Widespread, predominantly northern. Uncommon. Inedible. SPORES ellipsoid, smooth, 3–4×4–5.5.

AGARICACEAE

AGARICACEAE
Toadstool-shaped, usually fairly large, often white or brown, cap smooth-scaly, stem with ring, gills crowded, free, at first white – pink, then chocolate-brown, flesh usually white, sometimes changing characteristically red or yellow, spores ellipsoid, smooth, spore print dark brown. Smell sometimes characteristic. Habitat often characteristic, woods or fields. Many edible, one widely cultivated, few poisonous. *Agaricus* [40].

Agaricus bisporus (=*brunnescens*). Cap and flesh features, habitat, microscopic features. CAP 2.5–15, at first convex, then more flattened, smooth – radially fibrous or scaly. STEM 2.5–8, ±equal, fairly stout, at first bulbous, then slightly tapered at base, smooth-silky, bruising reddish pink, superior fairly persistent single ring. GILLS at first whitish, then pink, then chocolate brown, often white-edged, crowded, free. SPORE PRINT chocolate-brown. SMELL mushroomy-earthy. Schaeffer – . FLESH white, quickly bruising reddish pink, then brown. Usually in small groups, trooping or ±tufted. On well-manured soil, manure, compost. Spring – autumn. Widespread. Uncommon. Edible, widely cultivated. SPORES broadly ellipsoid, smooth, 4.5–7×6–9. Basidia 2-spored.

145

1
Agaricus bitorquis. Cap and stem features, habitat, spores. CAP 4–8, at first convex, then more flattened – slightly depressed, smooth – very finely scaly-flaky. STEM 4–6,±equal or tapering slightly upwards, fairly stout, tapered at base, rooting, smooth-silky, superior persistent double rings, upper rigid spreading lined above, lower thin, erect. GILLS at first pale pink, then very dark brown, paler-edged, very crowded, free. SPORE PRINT chocolate-brown. SMELL pleasant, sometimes almond-like. Schaeffer – or slightly +. FLESH white, bruising very slightly pink. Usually in large groups, trooping or±tufted. On manured or sandy soil, often in gardens or near roads, sometimes emerging through tarmac. Spring – autumn. Widespread. Rare. Edible. SPORES subspherical, smooth, 4–5×5–6.

2
Agaricus devoniensis. Habitat, cap and stem features, spores. CAP 2–7, at first convex, then flattened – slightly depressed, silky smooth. STEM 3–4,±equal or tapering slightly upwards, fairly stout, bruising reddish, covered with irregular ring-like veil remnants, sometimes with superior, narrow, quickly disappearing ring. GILLS at first pale pink, then very dark brown, irregular white-edged, very crowded, free. SPORE PRINT chocolate-brown. SMELL indistinct. Schaeffer ? FLESH white, bruising brownish towards stem base. Solitary or in small groups,±trooping. In sand, usually deeply buried with only cap emerging. Autumn. Widespread, coastal. Rare. Edible. SPORES broadly ellipsoid – subspherical, smooth, 4.5–5×6.5–7.

3
Agaricus litoralis. Habitat, cap and stem features, spores. CAP 7–8, at first convex, then slightly flattened – slightly depressed, at first fibrous but soon covered with± fibrous scales. STEM 3–4,± equal, fairly stout, lined above superior-median ring. GILLS at first pale pink-buff, then very dark brown – black with purple flush, irregular white-edged, very crowded, free. SPORE PRINT chocolate-brown. SMELL faint, indefinite, bitter almonds? Schaeffer? FLESH white in cap, reddish brown in stem. Solitary or in small groups, ±trooping. On soil in short turf close to the sea. Spring – autumn. Widespread, coastal. Rare. Edible? SPORES ellipsoid, smooth, 4.5–5×6–8.

4
Agaricus bernardii. Habitat, cap and stem features, flesh colour change, spores. CAP 8–15, at first±sub-spherical, then convex – flattened or slightly depressed, bruising slightly reddish, at first silky-fibrous but soon covered with fairly large coarse scales, margin often markedly in-rolled and shaggy. STEM 5–7,±equal – broadly spindle-shaped, stout, usually pointed at base, silky, lined below and irregularly scaly, superior – apical thin ring, rarely with indefinite second inferior ring. GILLS at first greyish pink, then dark brown – black, irregular whitish edge, crowded, free. SPORE PRINT chocolate-brown. SMELL unpleasant, fishy. Schaeffer – . FLESH white, turning orange-red when cut. Usually in small groups, trooping or rings. On sand or soil, dunes, coastal meadows, sometimes in shallow standing pools, also road-sides exposed to winter salting. Autumn. Widespread, predominantly coastal. Rare. Edible. SPORES broadly ellipsoid – subspherical, smooth, 5–6×5.5–7.

5
Agaricus lanipes. Cap and stem features, habitat, spores. CAP 5–10, at first±subspherical, then convex – flattened and slightly depressed, at first silky fibrous but soon covered with large coarse scales, especially towards margin, centre±woolly-velvety. STEM 4–6, tapering upwards, very stout, markedly bulbous, usually pointed at extreme base and tapering into rooting strand, lined, scaly-woolly below, superior thin rather spreading ring. GILLS at first pale pink, then dark brown – black, irregular whitish edge, crowded, free. SPORE PRINT chocolate-brown. SMELL faint, pleasant, earthy-mushroomy or slightly of bitter almonds. Schaeffer –. FLESH white, turning pink-ish at stem apex when young, yellow at stem base when old. Usually in groups,±trooping or tufted. On soil in broad-leaved woods, especially with beech. Summer – autumn. Widespread. Rare. Edible. SPORES ellipsoid, smooth, 3.5–4×5.5–6.

6
Agaricus langei. Flesh colour change, cap and stem features, spores. CAP 6–12, at first±subspherical, then convex – flattened, very broadly umbonate, covered with fibrous scales. STEM 7–12, equal or tapering slightly upwards, fairly stout, bruising reddish, finely woolly-scaly below superior rather thick ring. GILLS at first rose-pink, then dark brown – black, barely irregular whitish edge, crowded, free. SPORE PRINT chocolate-brown. SMELL faint, pleasant, earthy-mushroomy. Schaeffer – . FLESH white, quickly turning bright red when cut. Usually in groups,±trooping or tufted. On soil in coniferous or mixed woods. Summer – autumn. Widespread. Uncommon. Edible. SPORES elongated-ellipsoid, smooth, 4–5×7–8.

7
Agaricus haemorrhoidarius. Flesh colour change, cap and stem features, habitat, spores. CAP 8–12, at first±subspherical, then convex – flattened, very broadly umbonate,± smooth in centre, fibrous – flattened scaly towards margin. STEM 8–12, equal or tapering slightly upwards, broadly bulbous, fairly slender, bruising reddish below superior rather thick sometimes±toothed ring, deeply inserted in soil. GILLS at first rose-pink, then dark brown – black, irregular whitish edge, bruising slightly reddish, crowded, free. SPORE PRINT chocolate-brown. SMELL faint, indefinite or acidic. Schaeffer – . FLESH white, sometimes ochreous at stem base, quickly turning bright red when cut, especially at stem apex. Usually in large groups, trooping or±tufted. On soil in broad-leaved woods. Summer – autumn. Widespread. Rare. Edible. SPORES ellipsoid, smooth, 3–3.5×4.5–6.

8
Agaricus silvaticus. Habitat, spores, otherwise very variable. CAP 5–10, at first convex, then flattened, broadly umbonate,±covered with fibrous, flattened scales. STEM 6–10, equal or tapering slightly upwards, broadly bulbous, fairly slender, finely woolly-scaly below superior rather thick ring, sometimes rather deeply inserted in soil. GILLS at first rose-pink, then reddish, then dark chocolate-brown, irregular whitish edge, crowded, free. SPORE PRINT chocolate-brown. SMELL faint, indefinite or acidic. Schaeffer – . FLESH white, quickly turning bright red in patches when cut, especially at stem apex and above gills. Usually in large groups, trooping or±tufted. On soil in coniferous woods. Summer – autumn. Widespread. Uncommon. Edible. SPORES ellipsoid, smooth, 3–3.5×4.5–6.

...garicus variegans. Habi-
...t, cap and stem features,
...ores. CAP 5–10, at first
...onvex, then flattened, ±
...overed with ± concentric,
...brous, flattened scales,
...specially towards centre.
...TEM 8–13, equal – slightly
...ub-shaped, bulbous,
...airly slender, smooth to-
...ards apex, ± fibrous-scaly
...elow superior rather thick
... ng. GILLS at first pale pink,
...hen dark chocolate-brown,
...arely irregular whitish
...dge, crowded, free. SPORE
...RINT chocolate-brown.
...MELL strong, unpleasant,
...adishy. Schaeffer – .
...LESH white, barely turning
...inkish when cut, espe-
...ially at stem apex. Usually
... n large groups, trooping
...r ± tufted. On soil in con-
...erous woods. Summer –
...utumn. Widespread.
...Jncommon. Edible.
...PORES ellipsoid, smooth,
...–3.5×5–6.

Agaricus campestris **Field
Mushroom.** Very variable,
but habitat, flesh, spores
distinctive. CAP 5–8, at
first ± subspherical, then
slowly convex, finally
flattened, smooth – finely
downy-scaly. STEM 3–6,
equal or tapering down-
wards, rather slender,
smooth towards apex, ±
woolly-scaly below super-
ior barely thin fragile soon
disappearing ring. GILLS at
first rose-pink, then dark
brown – black, crowded,
free. SPORE PRINT chocolate-
brown. SMELL pleasant,
mushroomy or slightly acidic. Schaeffer – . FLESH
white, sometimes barely
pinkish when cut. Usually
in groups, trooping. On
soil, among grass in fields,
pastures. Summer – aut-
umn. Widespread. Com-
mon. Edible. SPORES ellipsoid, smooth, 4–5×7–8.

Agaricus augustus **The
Prince.** Size, chemical test,
smell. CAP 10–20, at first
subspherical – egg-shaped,
then convex, sometimes ±
umbonate, w. concentric
rings of fibrous scales. STEM
10–20, tapering slightly upwards, fairly slender, often
deep in substrate, bruising
yellowish, ± silky smooth
towards apex, woolly-scaly
towards base, superior
broad ring, often flushed
yellow. GILLS at first pale,
then darker pink, then
brown – black, crowded,
free. SPORE PRINT chocolate-
brown. SMELL bitter alm-
onds. Schaeffer + . FLESH
whitish, pinkish flush esp.
stem base. Usually groups,
trooping or ± tufted. On
soil, often in grass or plant
debris, with broad-leaved
or coniferous trees.
Summer – autumn. Wide-
spread. Uncommon. Edi-
ble. SPORES ellipsoid,
smooth, 4.5–5×7–8.

Agaricus abruptibulbus
(=*essettii*). Habitat, stem
base, smell, chemical test.
CAP 8–12, at first ± egg-
shaped, then convex –
flattened, slightly umbonate, smooth, bruising yellow. STEM 10–12, equal or
tapering slightly upwards,
fairly slender, broadly marginate bulbous, smooth,
shiny, superior – apical
broad ring with cog-wheel
pattern beneath. GILLS at
first greyish, then brown,
crowded, free. SPORE PRINT
chocolate-brown. SMELL
aniseed. Schaeffer + . FLESH
whitish or pinkish, espe-
cially in stem. Usually in
small groups, usually ± tufted. On soil, among needle
litter with spruce. Summer
– autumn. Widespread.
Rare. Edible. SPORES ellipsoid, smooth, 4–5×6–6.

... garicus vaporarius. Cap
...eatures, habit, habitat,
...pores. CAP 10–15, at first ±
...ubspherical, then convex-
...attened, ± covered with ±
...oncentric, large, fibrous,
...attened scales. STEM 6–12,
...qual or tapering down-
...vards, stout, smooth to-
...vards apex, ± fibrous-lined
...nd very coarsely scaly be-
...ow superior very thick
...ing. GILLS at first pink,
...hen dark brown – black,
...regular whitish edge,
...rowded, free. SPORE PRINT
...hocolate-brown. SMELL
...trong, indefinite, acidic-
...nushroomy. Schaeffer – .
...LESH white, barely reddish
...vhen cut. Usually in large
...roups, trooping or tufted,
...ap often ± covered with
...oil. On soil in broad-
...eaved woods. Autumn.
...Videspread. Rare. Edible.
...PORES ellipsoid, smooth,
...–3.5×5–6.

Agaricus bresadolianus.
Habitat, stem, spores. CAP
3.5–9, at first convex, then
more flattened – depres-
sed, fibrous scaly except at
centre and later at margin.
STEM 4–6.5, equal or tapering slightly upwards, fairly
stout, ± silky-smooth,
flushed yellow at base,
tapering at base into rooting strand, superior thin
fragile ring, soon collapsing
onto stem. GILLS at first
pale pink, then dark
brown – black, crowded,
free. SPORE PRINT chocolate-
brown. SMELL faint,
pleasant or indistinct.
Schaeffer ?. FLESH whitish
with brownish flush below
cap cuticle. Usually in
groups, trooping. On soil,
among grass, lawns, open
areas in woods. Summer.
Widespread. Rare. Edi-
ble? SPORES ellipsoid,
smooth, 3.5–4×5.5–6.5.

Agaricus silvicola **Wood
Mushroom.** Cap, stem
base, colour changes, smell.
CAP 5–8, first ± subspherical
– egg-shaped, then convex,
smooth, bruising ochre.
STEM 6–10, ± equal, fairly
slender, bulbous, often w.
rooting mycelial strands,
silky-smooth, superior
broad ring. GILLS first pale
pink, then brown – black,
crowded, free. SPORE PRINT
chocolate-brown. SMELL
strong, aniseed. Schaeffer
+ . FLESH whitish or pinkish,
esp. in stem. Usually small
groups, trooping or ± tufted. On soil, in broad-l. or
conif. woods. Autumn.
Widespread. Uncommon.
Edible. SPORES ellipsoid,
smooth, 3–4×5–6.

Agaricus nivescens. Habit,
habitat, cap, smell, chemical test. CAP 10–15, at first ±
egg-shaped, then convex –
flattened, smooth – very
slightly scaly, bruising yellow. STEM 8–10, ± equal or
tapering slightly down-
wards, fairly stout, smooth
– v. finely scaly, shiny, superior – apical broad ring.
GILLS first pale pink, then
brown – black, crowded,
free. SPORE PRINT chocolate-
brown. SMELL bitter alm-
onds. Schaeffer + . FLESH
white, sometimes yellowish
spotting. Usually in large
rings. On soil, among grass,
lawns, meadows, pastures.
Summer – autumn. Wide-
spread. Rare. Edible?
SPORES broadly ellipsoid,
smooth, 4–4.5×5–6.

147

AGARICACEAE

Agaricus arvensis. Habitat, cap and stem features, smell, chemical test. CAP 7–15, at first±egg-shaped, then convex – flattened, sometimes very broadly umbonate, smooth – very slightly scaly, bruising yellow. STEM 8–13,±equal but swollen towards base or± bulbous, slender, silky-smooth or finely scaly towards base, superior broad rather pendulous ring with cog-wheel pattern beneath. GILLS at first whitish then greyish pink, then brown – black, crowded, free. SPORE PRINT chocolate-brown. SMELL bitter almonds. Schaeffer+. FLESH white, sometimes turning ochreous. Usually in groups,±trooping or in rings. On soil, among grass, lawns, meadows, pastures. Autumn. Widespread. Common. Edible. SPORES broadly ellipsoid, smooth, 4.5–5×7–8.

Agaricus macrosporus. Overall colour, cap and stem features, spores. CAP 10–15, at first subspherical, then convex – flattened, densely covered with tiny woolly scales, bruising yellow. STEM 5–10,±broadly spindle-shaped, stout,± rooting, coarsely scaly, superior rather fragile ring with irregular teeth beneath. GILLS at first whitish then pink, then brown – black, crowded, free. SPORE PRINT chocolate-brown. SMELL faint, at first bitter almonds, then ammonia. Schaeffer+/−. FLESH white, flushed pinkish towards stem base when cut. Usually in rings. On soil among grass, pastures, meadows, often close to the sea. Summer – autumn. Widespread. Uncommon. Edible. SPORES broadly ellipsoid, smooth, 5.5–6× 8–12.

Agaricus porphyrizon. Stem, habitat, cap features. CAP 6–8, at first subspherical, then convex – flattened or slightly depressed, silky-smooth,±covered w. flattened fibrous scales. STEM 5 –6, tapering upwards – ± club-shaped, fairly stout, usually ±rooting mycelial strand, silky smooth, often flushing yellow, bruising deep yellow at base, superior-median narrow spreading – pendulous ring. GILLS at first greyish, then faintly flushed reddish, then brown – black, crowded, free. SPORE PRINT chocolate-brown. SMELL faint, bitter almonds. Schaeffer+. FLESH at first whitish, turning deep yellow at stem base. Usually in small groups,±trooping. On soil with trees, open grassy places in woods, hedges, parkland. Summer – autumn. Widespread. Rare. Inedible. SPORE broadly ellipsoid, smooth, 3–3.5×4.5–5.5.

Agaricus purpurellus. Stem flesh colour, habitat, cap and stem features, spores. CAP 2.5–3.5, at first subspherical, then convex – flattened, densely radially fibrous-scaly. STEM 3– 4,±equal, slender, base club-shaped – bulbous, silky-smooth, bruising yellow, superior – median, thin fragile ring. GILLS at first whitish, then greyish pink, then brown – black, crowded, free. SPORE PRINT chocolate-brown. SMELL bitter almonds. Schaeffer +. FLESH at first whitish, turning yellow at stem base. Usually in small groups, tufted or±trooping. On soil among plant debris with coniferous trees, especially spruce. Summer – autumn. Widespread. Rare. Inedible – poisonous. SPORES broadly ellipsoid, smooth, 3–4× 4–5.

Agaricus excellens. Overall colour, cap and stem features, spores. CAP 10–15, at first subspherical, then convex – flattened, densely covered with tiny woolly scales, bruising yellow. STEM 10–14,±equal or tapering upwards, slender, ±rooting, silky-smooth at apex, coarsely scaly below, lined close to superior – apical rather fragile thick ring. GILLS at first whitish then pink, then brown – black, crowded, free. SPORE PRINT chocolate-brown. SMELL faint bitter almonds. Schaeffer+. FLESH white, dull reddish pink when cut. Usually in groups,±trooping. On soil in coniferous or more rarely broad-leaved woods. Autumn. Widespread. Rare. Edible. SPORES broadly ellipsoid, smooth, 5–6.5×9–11.

Agaricus comtulus. Size, overall colour, cap and stem features, spores. CAP 2–3, at first subspherical, then convex – flattened, smooth. STEM 3–4, tapering slightly upwards, silky-smooth, superior – apical thin fragile ring. GILLS at first pink, then brown – black, crowded, free. SPORE PRINT chocolate-brown. SMELL faint, bitter almonds. Schaeffer−? FLESH white, flushed slightly yellow at stem base. Usually in small groups,±trooping. On soil among grass, pastures, meadows. Summer – autumn. Widespread. Rare. Edible. SPORES broadly ellipsoid, smooth, 3–3.5×4.5–5.5.

Agaricus semotus. Stem, habitat, cap, spores. CAP 3 –5, at first subspherical, then convex – flattened, often broadly umbonate, silky smooth, then±covered with small, lilac scales and darker fibres. STEM 4– 6, tapering upwards, fairly sharply bulbous, slender, silky-smooth, bruising yellow at base, superior – apical narrow spreading – pendulous ring. GILLS at first whitish, then greyish pink, then brown – black, crowded, free. SPORE PRINT chocolate-brown. SMELL indistinct or very faint, bitter almonds. Schaeffer+. FLESH at first whitish, turning ochre-yellow at stem base. Usually in small groups,±trooping. On soil with trees, open grassy places in woods, hedges, parkland. Summer – autumn. Widespread. Rare. Inedible – poisonous. SPORES broadly ellipsoid, smooth, 2.5–3.5×4–5.

Agaricus xanthodermus. Size, stem flesh colour, habitat, stem features, spores. CAP 5–15, at first subspherical, then convex flattened, bruising bright yellow, at first±smooth, then very finely cracked or minutely scaly. STEM 6– 17,±equal or tapering upwards, moderately bulbous, fairly slender, silky-smooth, bruising yellow, superior rather broad spreading ring. GILLS at first whitish, then purplish pink then purplish brown, crowded, free. SPORE PRINT chocolate-brown. SMELL unpleasant, ink. Schaeffer −. FLESH at first whitish, turning chrome-yellow in stem base. Usually in small groups,±trooping. On soil among grass, woods, pastures, fields, gardens. Summer – autumn. Widespread. Uncommon. Poisonous. SPORES broadly ellipsoid, smooth, 3–4×5–6.5.

148

garicus placomyces. Stem
esh colour, cap features,
ores. CAP 5–12, at first
bspherical, then convex –
ttened, often very
oadly umbonate, densely
vered with small
ttened scales. STEM 6–
,±equal or tapering
ghtly upwards, bulbous,
rly slender, silky-
100th, bruising yellow,
pecially at base, sparsely
aly towards base, super-
r large rather fragile
reading – pendulous
1g, rapidly bruising yel-
w. GILLS at first whitish,
en pink, then black –
own, crowded, free.
ORE PRINT chocolate-
own. SMELL strong,
pleasant, ink. Schaeffer
, FLESH at first whitish,
en flushed yellow and
rning yellow in stem base.
ually in groups,±troop-
g. On soil, often among
ass in woods. Summer –
tumn. Widespread. Un-
mmon. Poisonous.
ORES broadly ellipsoid,
100th, 3–4×4–5.

Hypholoma capnoides.
Habit, habitat, gills. CAP 4–
9, convex, broadly umbon-
ate, smooth, slightly sticky
when wet, paler at margin.
STEM 3–9, ±equal or tapering upwards, slender, darker at base,±smooth at least
towards apex. GILLS at first
whitish, then greyish lilac,
fairly crowded, adnate –
marginate. SPORE PRINT
choc-brown. SMELL indis-
tinct. FLESH whitish or pale
yellow. Densely tufted. On
wood, conif. stumps. Sum-
mer – autumn. Wide-
spread. Uncommon. Edi-
ble. SPORES ellipsoid,
smooth, germ pore,
4–5×7–9.

Hypholoma sublateritium
Brick-Red Hypholoma.
Size, colour, habit, habitat,
gills. CAP 4–9, convex,
smooth, paler towards margin. STEM 5–12,±equal or
tapering slightly down-
wards, fairly slender, darker and fibrous scaly
towards base, usually with
indefinite superior ring
zone. GILLS at first yellowish, then yellowish – olive-
green, crowded, adnate.
SPORE PRINT chocolate-
brown. SMELL faint, earthy-
mushroomy. FLESH pale
yellowish, more reddish
brown in stem. Densely
tufted. On wood or sawdust
of broad-leaved trees.
Autumn. Widespread.
Common. Inedible. SPORES
ellipsoid, smooth, germ
pore, 3–4×6–7.

Hypholoma radicosum.
Habit, habitat, stem, gills.
CAP 4–8, first convex, then
more flattened – slightly
umbonate, smooth, greasy
when wet. STEM 5–15,±
equal or tapering down-
wards, fairly slender,
deeply rooting, fibrous-
scaly, often with indefinite
superior ring zone. GILLS at
first yellowish white, then
olive – purplish brown,
crowded, adnate – emarginate. SPORE PRINT purple-
brown. SMELL strong, unp-
leasant, acrid. FLESH whitish
in cap, yellowish in stem,
darker at base. Solitary or
in small tufts. On rotting
wood, stumps of conif.
Spring – autumn. Wide-
spread. Rare. Inedible.
SPORES ellipsoid, smooth,
germ pore, 4–4.5×6.5–7.5.

Hypholoma epixanthum.
Habit, habitat, cap fea-
tures, gills. CAP 1.5–5, at
first convex, then more
flattened, sometimes
slightly umbonate or later
depressed, smooth at cen-
tre, finely fibrous-scaly at
margin. STEM 1.5–7,±equal
or slightly club-shaped,
fairly slender, at first silky-
fibrous-scaly, then fibrous-
lined, downy at apex,
sometimes with indefinite
ring zone. GILLS at first
whitish, then buff with
violet flush, crowded,
adnate – emarginate, often
with decurrent tooth. SPORE
PRINT choc-brown. SMELL
faint, acidic or indistinct.
FLESH pale ochre-buff, more
red-brown in stem. Densely
tufted. On wood or saw-
dust of broad-l. trees. Autumn. Widespread. Uncom-
mon. Inedible? SPORES ellipsoid, smooth, germ pore,
4–4.5×7–8.

Hypholoma fasciculare **Sulphur Tuft.** Colour, habit,
habitat, season, gills. CAP
2–7, at first convex, then
more flattened – slightly
umbonate. smooth, often
with veil remnants at margin. STEM 4–12,±equal or
tapering slightly down-
wards, fairly slender,
usually curved, fibrous,
often with indefinite superior ring zone. GILLS at first
yellow, then yellowish –
olive-green, then dark
brown, crowded, adnate.
SPORE PRINT choc-brown.
SMELL faint, earthy-mush-
roomy. FLESH yellow,
browner towards stem base.
Densely tufted. On wood,
stumps of broad-leaved or
conif. trees. All year. Widespread. Extremely com-
mon. Inedible. SPORES ellipsoid, smooth, germ pore,
4–4.5×6–7.

Hypholoma marginatum.
Habit, habitat, stem, gills.
CAP 1–4, convex – bell-
shaped, broadly umbonate,
smooth, shiny, dry, paler at
margin, often dark veil
remnants. STEM 3–6, equal
or tapering slightly downwards, slender, silky-fib-
rous-scaly, bruising darker.
GILLS first yellowish, then
greenish – olive-brown,
crowded, adnate – emarginate. SPORE PRINT choc-
brown. SMELL ? FLESH whitish in cap, brownish in
stem. Usually in small
groups, tufted. On soil, rotting wood near conif. trees.
Summer – autumn. Wide-
spread. Common. Inedible.
SPORES ellipsoid, smooth,
germ pore, 4–5×7–9.

'ROPHARIACEAE
adstool-shaped, usually
all – medium, usually
ll but sometimes
rropharia) cap±covered
th green-blue slime, cap
smooth, usually sticky –
easy, gills±crowded, ad-
xed – decurrent, at first
le, then dark. Spores±
ipsoid, smooth, with
rm pore, spore print usu-
y chocolate-brown, some-
nes with lilac flush. Smell
riable, sometimes chara-
eristic. On soil, dung,
ood, plant debris. Not
ycorrhizal. Few edible,
me poisonous/hallucino-
nic. *Hypholoma* [13], *Psi-
cybe* [2], *Deconica* [7],
rropharia [15].

1
Hypholoma polytrichi.
Habitat, stem, gills. CAP 1–
2.5, convex – bell-shaped,
broadly umbonate, smooth
and shiny at centre, markedly fibrous and paler in
margin. STEM 5–8,±equal,
slender, usually wavy, often twisted, smooth-silky.
GILLS at first pale yellow,
then greenish with yellowish edge, then olive-brown,
crowded, adnate – emargi-
nate. SPORE PRINT chocolate-
brown. SMELL indistinct.
FLESH whitish in cap, brownish in stem. Usually in
small groups, tufted. Am-
ong mosses, especially *Polytrichum*. Spring – aut-
umn. Widespread. Rare.
Inedible. SPORES ellipsoid,
smooth, germ pore, 4–
5.5×7–9.

2
Hypholoma ericaeum. Habitat, gills, cap features. CAP
2–3, at first convex, then
more flattened, broadly umbonate, smooth, slightly
sticky, especially when wet.
STEM 7–10,±equal, slender,
smooth-silky. GILLS at first
greyish white, then dark
brown, crowded, adnate –
emarginate. SPORE PRINT
chocolate-brown. SMELL
indistinct. FLESH yellowish.
Usually in large groups,
trooping. On damp peat,
heathland. Spring –
autumn. Widespread.
Uncommon. Inedible.
SPORES ellipsoid, smooth,
germ pore, 7–8×12–14.

3
Hypholoma udum. Habi-
tat, gills, cap features. CAP
1–2, at first convex – bell-
shaped, then more
flattened, smooth and shiny
at centre, slightly sticky,
especially when wet. STEM
4–10,±equal, very slender,
usually wavy, smooth-silky.
GILLS at first greyish olive-
green, then dark brown,
crowded, adnate –
emarginate. SPORE PRINT
chocolate-brown. SMELL
earthy-mushroomy. FLESH
brownish buff. Usually in
large groups, trooping. On
wet peat or among *Sphag-
num* moss. Summer –
autumn. Widespread.
Uncommon. Inedible.
SPORES ellipsoid, smooth,
germ pore, 6–7×13–15.

4
Hypholoma elongatum
(*=elongatipes*). Habitat,
stem, gills, cap features.
CAP 1–2, at first convex –
bell-shaped, then more
flattened, smooth and shiny
at centre, lined at margin,
especially when wet. STEM
5–10,±equal, very slender,
usually wavy, smooth-silky,
downy at base. GILLS at first
greyish lilac-buff, then
greyish brown, crowded,
adnate. SPORE PRINT dull
snuff-brown. SMELL earthy-
mushroomy. FLESH yellow-
ish white. Usually in large
groups, trooping. Among
mosses, especially *Sphagnum* and *Polytrichum*.
Autumn. Widespread.
Common. Inedible. SPORES
ellipsoid, smooth, germ
pore, 6–6.5×9–12.

5
Psilocybe semilanceata
Liberty Caps. Cap, gills,
spores. CAP 0.5–1.5, con-
ical, very sharply umbon-
ate, paler when dry, sticky
when wet, lined – wrinkled
at margin. STEM 3–8, equal,
very slender, often wavy,
smooth, often bluing at
base. GILLS at first pale
buff, then dark purple-
brown, white edge, fairly
distant, adnate –
emarginate. SPORE PRINT
purple brown. SMELL indistinct. FLESH whitish cream.

Usually in groups, troop-
ing. On soil, among grass,
lawns, path edges, road-
sides. Summer – autumn.
Widespread. Common.
Poisonous – halluci-
nogenic. SPORES ellipsoid,
smooth, germ pore, 7–
9×11.5–14.

6
Deconica (=*Psilocybe*)
coprophila. Habitat, cap
features, gills, spores. CAP
0.5–2.5, at first subspherical – bell-shaped, often
broadly umbonate, with
peelable sticky skin, barely
lined at margin. STEM 3–4,
equal or tapering slightly
downwards, slender, often
wavy,±irregularly woolly-
scaly below. GILLS at first
brownish grey, then dark
purple-brown, fairly dis-
tant, adnate. SPORE PRINT
purple-brown. SMELL
mealy. FLESH whitish. In
small groups, trooping. On
dung. Summer – autumn.
Widespread. Uncommon.
Inedible. SPORES lemon-
shaped, smooth, germ
pore, 6.5–8×12–14.

7
Deconica (=*Psilocybe*)
inquilina. Size, habitat, cap
features, spores. CAP 0.5–
1.5, at first convex, then
more flattened, broadly
umbonate, markedly paler
when dry, with peelable
sticky skin, lined. STEM 1–2,
equal or tapering slightly
upwards, slender, often
slightly wavy, at first finely
silky-fibrous, then±
smooth. GILLS at first whitish, then dark brown, fairly
crowded, adnate. SPORE
PRINT reddish brown. SMELL
? FLESH yellowish buff,
darker in stem. In small
groups, trooping. On dead
grasses. Summer – autumn.
Widespread. Rare. Inedi-
ble. SPORES ellipsoid –
lemon-shaped, smooth,
germ pore, 5–6×8–10.5.

shaped, smooth, germ
pore, 5–6×8–10.5.

8
Deconica (=*Psilocybe*)
montana. Size, habitat, c
features, spores. CAP 1–1
at first convex, then more
flattened, umbonate –
papillate, markedly paler
when dry, lined when we
STEM 0.5–1, equal or tape
ing slightly downwards,
very slender, often slight
wavy,±smooth. GILLS da
reddish brown, fairly
crowded, adnate. SPORE
PRINT purple-brown. SME
? FLESH reddish buff. In
small groups, trooping. C
sandy soil, often with mo
ses. Summer – autumn.
Widespread. Rare, com-
moner northwards. Inedi
ble. SPORES ellipsoid –
lemon-shaped, smooth,
germ pore, 4–5×6–8.

9
Stropharia squamosa. Ste
features, size, habitat. CA
2–5, at first subspherical –
convex, then more flatten
ed, v. slightly sticky when
wet,±concentrically dis-
persed triangular flattene
scales, margin often rathe
irregular. STEM 10–15,±
equal, very slender, often
slightly wavy, with bands
of dark fibrous scales belo
superior, fragile±spread-
ing ring, pale±smooth ab
ove. GILLS at first greyish,
then dark purple-brown,
fairly crowded, adnate.
SPORE PRINT purple-brown
SMELL indistinct. FLESH
greyish white, sometimes
w. reddish flush. In small
groups,±trooping. On so
usually from fragments of
buried twig or wood chips
wood, heaths. Autumn.
Widespread. Rare. Edible
SPORES ellipsoid, smooth,
germ pore, 6–7×11–15.

groups,±trooping. On soil,
usually from fragments of
buried wood, also some-
times stumps and rotting
wood, woods, heaths, pas-
tures. Spring – autumn.
Widespread. Common.
Poisonous. SPORES ellip-
soid, smooth, germ pore,
4–5×7.5–9.

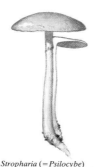

*Stropharia (= Psilocybe)
merdaria.* Habitat, cap and
stem. CAP 2–5, first convex
– bell-shaped, then more
flattened, slightly umbonate, sticky when wet, usually veil remnants at margin. STEM 3–7,±equal or
tapering slightly upwards,
slender,±rooting, downy
white towards base,
superior – apical often
rather indefinite ring zone.
GILLS at first whitish, then
purple-brown, fairly
crowded, adnate. SPORE
PRINT purple-brown. SMELL
indistinct. FLESH white,
darkening in stem on aging.
In small groups,±trooping
or tufted. On dung, espe-
cially horse, sewage beds.
Summer – autumn. Wide-
spread. Rare. Inedible.
SPORES broadly ellipsoid –
±lemon-shaped, smooth,
germ pore, 7.5–9×10–14.

Stropharia semiglobata
Dung Roundhead. Habitat,
cap, stem, spores. CAP 1–4,

ropharia hornemannii.
ıp and stem features,
ıe, habitat. CAP 5–13, at
st subspherical – convex,
ən more flattened, sticky,
ıooth. STEM 8–14,±equal
tapering downwards,
ther stout, coarsely
ınular-scaly below super-
r fairly thick±spreading
ıg, pale±smooth above.
ıLLS at first greyish, then
rk purple-brown, fairly
ɔwded, adnate. SPORE
ɪNT purple-brown. SMELL
ʼong, indefinite, unpleas-
t. FLESH greyish white. In
ıall groups,±trooping or
ʼted. On soil, usually
ɔm fragments of buried
ɔod, also stumps and rot-
ıg wood in coniferous
ɔods. Autumn. Wide-
'read, predominantly
ʼthern. Rare. Inedible.
ɔRES ellipsoid, smooth,
'rm pore, 5.5–7×10.5–13.

ropharia aeruginosa. Cap
ıd stem features. CAP 3–8,
first convex – bell-shap-
, then convex – flatten-
, slightly umbonate, cov-
ːd with thick blue-green
ıcous, often with±woolly
ıite scales. STEM 4–10,±
ıal or tapering slightly
wards, fairly slender,
her coarsely white scaly
low superior±spreading
ıg. GILLS at first white,
en buff-brown, then dark
ɔwn, fairly distant,
ınate. SPORE PRINT purple-
ɔwn. SMELL indistinct.
ᴇsʜ bluish white. In small

hemispherical, sometimes
very slightly umbonate,
sticky. STEM 5–9,±equal or
tapering slightly upwards,
very slender, scaly-sticky
below superior – apical
often rather indefinite ring
zone. GILLS dark brown,
often black flecked, fairly
crowded, adnate. SPORE
PRINT purple-brown. SMELL
indistinct. FLESH whitish. In
groups, trooping or
tufted. On dung. Summer –
autumn. Widespread. Very
common. Inedible, (poiso-
nous ?). SPORES ellipsoid,
smooth, germ pore, 8–
11×14–18.

COPRINACEAE
Toadstool-shaped, usually
dull-coloured, cap surface
smooth, scaly – hairy-
downy, dry-sticky,
stem±ring zones, gills
crowded – distant,
adnate – free, characteristically changing from pale
to dark and then usually
deliquescing to form black
ink-like mass (*Coprinus*) or
not. Spores variably
shaped, usually smooth and
with germ pore. Spore
print usually dark brown –
black, rarely paler. Usually
on soil or dung. Apparently
all saprotrophic. Some edible and good, few poiso-
nous. *Coprinus* [92], *Lacrymaria* [2], *Panaeolina* [1],
Panaeolus [12], *Psathyrella*
[57].

Coprinus comatus **Shaggy
Ink Cap, Lawyer's Wig.**
Cap features, habitat. CAP
at first 5–15 and elongated
egg-shaped – ±cylindrical,
then conical – bell-shaped

with upturned margin,
soon±covered with shaggy
buff scales. STEM 10–37,
equal, slightly swollen at
base – bulbous, often±
rooting, fairly stout, at first
smooth and shiny, then
coarsely fibrous, superior,
fragile ring, often slipping
down stem. GILLS at first
white, then±pink, then
black, deliquescing, crowded, adnexed – free. SPORE
PRINT black-brown. SMELL
faint, indistinct, pleasant.
FLESH whitish when young.
In groups,±tufted. On soil,
sometimes among grass,
often on disturbed sites,
roadsides, garden beds.
Spring – autumn. Wide-
spread. Very common.
Edible. SPORES ellipsoid –
almond-shaped, smooth,
germ pore, 6.5–8×10–13.

Coprinus erythrocephalus.
Cap features, size, habitat,
spores. CAP at first 1–2 and
elongated egg-shaped – ±
cylindrical, then conical –
bell-shaped, then flattened
with upturned torn margin,
first±fibrous-scaly, then
smooth, grooved-wrinkled
at margin. STEM 3–8.5,
equal or tapering slightly
upwards, slender, at first
fibrous-scaly, then±
smooth. GILLS first white,
then dark brown, then
black, deliquescing, crowded, adnexed. SPORE PRINT
black. SMELL indistinct.
FLESH whitish when young.
Solitary or in small groups,
±tufted. On soil, rubbish
dumps, fire sites. Autumn.
Predominantly southern.
Uncommon. Inedible.
SPORES ellipsoid, smooth,
germ pore, 4.5–5.5×8–10.

151

COPRINACEAE

1

Coprinus atramentarius.
Size, stem features, spores.
C. acuminatus is similar
with narrower spores and is
sometimes included in this
sp. CAP at first 3–6.5, and ±
egg-shaped, then conical –
convex, then flattened with
upturned margin, at first ±
fibrous-scaly, then smooth
towards margin. STEM 7–18,
±equal, swollen at base –
±bulbous, slender, smooth
or ±floury at apex, ring
mark above base. GILLS at
first white, then brown,
then black, deliquescing,
crowded, adnexed – free.
SPORE PRINT dark purple-
brown. SMELL indistinct or
faint, indefinite, pleasant.
FLESH whitish when young.
Solitary or in small groups, ±
tufted. On wood, often
from buried twigs or other
woody debris. Spring – autumn. Widespread. Very
common. Edible, but un-
pleasant with alcohol (anta-
buse effect). SPORES ellipsoid – ±almond-shaped,
smooth, germ pore, 5–6×8
–11.

2

Coprinus picaceus **Magpie
Fungus.** Size, cap features,
spores. CAP at first 5–8 and
elongated egg-shaped –
cylindrical, then conical –
bell-shaped, then flattened
with upturned margin, at
first covered with felty coat,
then irregularly woolly-
scaly. STEM 9–30, tapering
upwards, bulbous, slender,
at first downy-woolly, then
smooth, downy at base.
GILLS at first white, then
pink-buff, then black, deliquescing, crowded,
adnexed – free. SPORE
PRINT black. SMELL strong,
indefinite, unpleasant.
FLESH whitish when young.
Solitary or in small groups, ±
tufted. On soil, often among leaf litter, woods, especially with beech on chalky
sites. Summer – autumn.
Widespread. Uncommon.
Poisonous? SPORES ellips-
oid, smooth, germ pore,
10–12×13–17.

3

Coprinus cinereus. Size,
stem features, spores. CAP
at first 1–5 and elongated
egg-shaped – cylindrical,
then conical – bell-shaped,
then ±flattened with
upturned margin, at first
felty then densely fibrous-
scaly, then smooth with
lined margin. STEM 4–12,
equal or tapering slightly
upwards, slender, bulbous-
rooting, smooth-floury at
apex, fibrous-woolly-scaly
below, then smooth. GILLS
at first white, then greyish
buff, then black, deliquescing, crowded, adnexed –
free. SPORE PRINT black.
SMELL indistinct or strong,
pleasant. FLESH whitish
when young. Solitary or in
groups, ±tufted. On dung,
especially when heating
through decomposition. All
year. Widespread. Com-
mon. Inedible. SPORES ellipsoid, smooth, germ pore,
6–7×9–12.

4

Coprinus radiatus. Size,
habitat, spores. CAP at first
2–6 and elongated egg-
shaped – cylindrical, then
conical – bell-shaped, then
flattened with upturned
margin, at first sparsely
fibrous-scaly, then smooth
and lined. STEM 2–5, equal
or tapering slightly up-
wards, very slender, ±root-
ing, sparsely fibrous then
smooth except at base.
GILLS at first whitish, then
black, deliquescing, distant
– sparse, free. SPORE PRINT
black. SMELL indistinct.
FLESH whitish when young.
Usually in large groups, ±
trooping. On dung, espe-
cially horse. Spring – autumn. Widespread. Uncom-
mon. Inedible. SPORES ellipsoid – kidney-shaped,
smooth, germ pore, 6–
7×11–14.

5

Coprinus pseudoradiatus.
Size, habitat, very similar
to *C. radiatus* and probably
confused with it but spores
differ. CAP at first 3–5 and
elongated egg-shaped –

cylindrical, then conical –
bell-shaped, then flattened
with upturned margin, at
first fibrous-scaly, then
smooth and lined. STEM
1.5–5, equal or tapering
slightly upwards, very slender, sparsely fibrous then
smooth except at base.
GILLS at first whitish, then
black, deliquescing,
distant-sparse, free. SPORE
PRINT black. SMELL indis-
tinct. FLESH whitish when
young. Usually in large
groups, ±trooping. On
dung. Spring – autumn.
Widespread. Rare. Inedi-
ble. SPORES ellipsoid,
smooth, germ pore, 4.5–
5.5×7.5–8.5.

6

Coprinus macrocephalus.
Size, cap and stem features,
habitat, spores. CAP at first
1–3 and elongated egg-
shaped – cylindrical, then
conical – bell-shaped, then
flattened with upturned
margin, at first ±coarsely
fibrous-scaly, then smooth
and lined. STEM 4–19, equal
or tapering slightly up-
wards, sometimes ±rooting,
very slender, sparsely fibrous then smooth except at
base. GILLS at first whitish,
then grey, then black, deliquescing, fairly distant,
free. SPORE PRINT black.
SMELL indistinct. FLESH
whitish when young. Solitary or in large groups, ±
trooping. On manured
straw or old dung. Spring –
autumn. Widespread.
Rare. Inedible. SPORES ellipsoid, smooth, germ pore,
7.5–8.5×11–14.

7

Coprinus lagopides. Cap
features, habitat, spores.
CAP at first 1.5–5.5 and
conical – cylindrical, then
convex – flattened, margin
often rolled, at first densely
covered with small
upturned fibrous scales
then smooth and lined.
STEM 3–11, equal or tapering slightly upwards, slender, at first fibrous woolly

then smooth, downy at
base. GILLS greyish then
quickly turning black, de-
quescing, fairly crowded,
adnexed – free. SPORE
PRINT black. SMELL indis-
tinct. FLESH whitish when
young. Usually in groups
trooping or tufted. On so
on old fire sites, also
burned wood or plaster.
Autumn. Widespread.
Common. Inedible. SPOR
ellipsoid – subspherical,
smooth, germ pore, 5–
7×6–9.

8

Coprinus lagopus. Habita
cap features, spores. CAP
first 1–3.5 and conical –
cylindrical, then convex -
flattened or ±depressed a
with reflexed margin, at
first densely covered with
small upturned fibrous
scales then smooth and
lined, margin often finall'
upturned. STEM 6.5–13,
equal or tapering slightly
upwards, slender, some-
times slightly swollen at
base, at first fibrous-wool
then smooth. GILLS white
then greyish then black,
deliquescing, fairly
crowded, adnexed – free
SPORE PRINT black. SMELL
indistinct. FLESH whitish
when young. Often solita
but sometimes in small
groups, trooping or tufted
On soil, among plant
debris, usually in woods.
Summer – autumn. Wide
spread. Common. Inedibl
SPORES ellipsoid – almonc
shaped, smooth, germ
pore, 6–7×11–13.5.

9

Coprinus extinctorius.
Habitat, cap features,
spores. CAP at first 1.5–2.5
and conical – cylindrical,
then convex – flattened
with markedly rolled mar-
gin, at first ±covered with
small pointed fibrous scale
then smooth and lined,
especially at margin. STEM
3.5–5.5, equal or tapering
slightly upwards, ±bulbou
slender, floury at apex, at
first fibrous-scaly then
smooth, downy at base.
GILLS white, then greyish

152

en black, deliquescing, irly crowded, adnexed – ee. SPORE PRINT black. MELL indistinct. FLESH hitish when young. Solit-ry or in small groups, ± ooping or tufted. On ood, stumps or stem and ranch wounds on broad-aved trees. Summer – utumn. Widespread. Un-ommon. Inedible. SPORES mon-shaped – almond-naped, smooth, germ ore, 6.5–7.5×8–10.

10

oprinus urticaecola *=brassicae*). Habitat, ores. CAP at first 3–8 sub-herical or egg-shaped, en conical bell-shaped nd flattened, with torn argin, at first covered ith small woolly-silky orous scales, then smooth. EM 2–4, equal or tapering ghtly upwards, very slen-r, base swollen, disc-like, first floury then smooth. LLS white, then purplish own, deliquescing, fairly stant, adnexed – free. ORE PRINT dark purplish own. SMELL indistinct. ESH whitish when young. sually in small groups, ± ooping. On rotting plant bris, especially of gras-s, rushes, sedges, nettles damp places. Summer – utumn. Widespread. Rare. edible. SPORES ellipsoid, nooth, germ pore, 4.5–5×6.5–8.5.

11

oprinus truncorum. Habi-t, extremely similar to *C. icaceus* and often con-sed with it, only spores ffer reliably. CAP at first -2 and convex – conical, en more flattened, at first tirely mealy-granular, en smooth from margin nd deeply-grooved or rinkled except at centre. EM 4.5–8.5, ±equal, slen-r, at first finely velvety-owny, then smooth and iny above, downy at ase. GILLS white-cream, en violet-buff, then pur-ish brown, deliquescing,

fairly crowded, adnexed – free. SPORE PRINT black. SMELL indistinct. FLESH whitish when young. Tufted. On wood, logs, stumps. Summer – autumn. Widespread, perhaps southern. Rare. Edible? SPORES ellipsoid – almond-shaped, smooth, germ pore, 5–6.5×6.5–8.5.

12

Coprinus micaceus. Habi-tat, extremely similar to *C. truncorum* and often con-fused with it, only spores differ reliably. CAP at first 1–3.5 and elongated egg-shaped – cylindrical, then bell-shaped, then more flattened – convex, some-times umbonate, at first entirely mealy-granular, then smooth from margin and deeply grooved or wrinkled. STEM 4–10, ± equal, fairly slender, at first finely velvety-downy, then smooth and shiny, downy at base. GILLS white, then pur-plish brown, then black, del-iquescing, fairly crowded, adnexed – free. SPORE PRINT very dark brown. SMELL indistinct. FLESH whit-ish when young. Tufted, often densely. On wood, logs, stumps. Spring – win-ter. Widespread. Very com-mon. Edible. SPORES bis-hop's hat-shaped (mitri-form), smooth, germ pore, 4.5–6×7–10.

13

Coprinus ellisii. Stem fea-tures, spores, habitat. CAP at first 0.5–3.5 and ± elong-ated egg-shaped – cylindri-cal, then bell-shape, then more flattened – convex, at first entirely scurfy-scaly, then smooth from rolled margin and lined-grooved. STEM 4.5–9, tapering up-wards, very slender, bulb-ous, at first finely velvety-downy, then smooth and shiny, volva-like veil zone at base, with reddish or-ange mycelial growth.

GILLS white, then buff, then purplish brown, deli-quescing, fairly crowded, adnexed – free. SPORE PRINT dark brown. SMELL indistinct. FLESH whitish when young. Solitary or in small groups, ± trooping. On wood, logs, twigs, other woody debris. Summer – autumn. England, but probably widespread. Rare. Inedible? SPORES cylindrical – kidney-shaped, smooth, inevident germ pore, 3–4.5×6.5–8.5.

14

Coprinus domesticus. Cap features, spores, habitat. CAP at first 1–3 and ± elon-gated egg-shaped – cylind-rical, then convex – bell-shaped, then more flatten-ed, split at margin, at first entirely scurfy-scaly, then smooth from rolled margin and lined-grooved. STEM 4–15, tapering upwards, slen-der, ± bulbous, smooth – finely silky-lined, some-times ± finely velvety-dow-ny at base, with reddish orange mycelial growth. GILLS white, then purplish brown, then black, deli-quescing, fairly crowded, adnexed – free. SPORE PRINT dark brown. SMELL indistinct. FLESH whitish when young. Solitary or in small groups, trooping or ± tufted. On wood, logs, twigs, other woody debris of broad-leaved trees. Spring – summer. Wide-spread. Uncommon. Inedi-ble. SPORES cylindrical – ellipsoid – ± kidney-shaped, smooth, germ pore, 4–5×7.5–10.

15

Coprinus xanthothrix. Cap features, spores, habitat. CAP at first 1.5–2 and el-ongated egg-shaped – con-ical, then more flattened, sometimes ± umbonate, split at margin, at first sparsely scurfy-scaly, then smooth from margin and

lined-grooved. STEM 6–9, ±equal, fairly slender, slightly bulbous, finely lined, at first minutely floury (use hand-lens), sometimes sparsely scaly at base. GILLS creamy grey-buff, then dark brown, deli-quescing, fairly crowded, adnexed – free. SPORE PRINT dark brown. SMELL indistinct. FLESH whitish when young. Solitary or in small groups, trooping or ± tufted. On wood, logs, stumps, other woody debris of broad-leaved trees. Spring – summer. Probably widespread. Uncommon. Inedible. SPORES ellipsoid – ± almond-shaped, smooth, germ pore, 4.5–5×7–9.

16

Coprinus radians. Spores, stem features, habitat. CAP at first 2–4 and ± elongated egg-shaped – conical, then more flattened, split at margin, at first entirely scurfy-scaly, then smooth from margin and lined-grooved. STEM 3–8, ± equal, fairly slender, slightly bulb-ous, finely floury-lined, downy-felty and sometimes sparsely scaly at base, often arising from reddish brown mycelial mat. GILLS white – creamy, then dark purplish brown, then black, deli-quescing, fairly crowded, adnexed – free. SPORE PRINT black. SMELL indis-tinct. FLESH whitish when young. Solitary or in small groups, trooping or ± tuft-ed. On wood, logs, stumps, other woody debris of broad-leaved trees. Spring – summer. Widespread? Uncommon. Inedible. SPORES ellipsoid – kidney-shaped, smooth, germ pore, 5–6.5×8.5–11.

1

Coprinus ephemeroides.
Cap and stem features,
spores, habitat. CAP at first
2–6 and ±elongated egg-
shaped – cylindrical,
then ± flattened with
upturned margin, at first
entirely mealy-scaly, then
lined-grooved – ± smooth
towards margin. STEM 1–
3, ±equal or tapering
slightly upwards, very slender, slightly bulbous,
smooth but downy-silky at
base, inferior – ± median ±
woolly fragile ring. GILLS
whitish, then black, deliquescing, fairly distant,
adnate – free. SPORE PRINT
black. SMELL indistinct.
FLESH whitish when young.
Usually in small groups, ±
trooping. On dung. Spring
– autumn. Widespread.
Uncommon. Inedible.
SPORES very broadly ellipsoid – subspherical,
smooth, germ pore, 6.5–8
×6–9.

2

Coprinus niveus. Size, cap
colour and features, habitat.
CAP at first 1.5–3
and ±elongated egg-
shaped – cylindrical, then
bell-shaped, then ± flattened with split or rolled margin, at first entirely mealy-
scurfy, rubbing off onto
fingers on handling, then ±
smooth and lined. STEM 3–
9, ±equal or tapering
slightly upwards, fairly
slender, barely bulbous, at
first mealy scurfy, rather
silky at apex, ±downy at
base. GILLS whitish, then
grey, then black, deliquescing, fairly crowded, ad-
nate – free. SPORE PRINT
black. SMELL indistinct.
FLESH whitish when young.
Usually in small groups, ±
trooping. On cow or horse
(or rarely other) dung.
Spring – winter. Wide-
spread. Common. Inedi-
ble. SPORES ellipsoid,
smooth, germ pore, 11–
13×15–19.

3

Coprinus patouillardii.
Size, stem features, spores,
habitat. CAP at first 0.75–
1.25 and ±egg-shaped, then
convex – flattened or
slightly depressed, at first
mealy-granular-scaly,
coarser in centre, then ±
smooth and wrinkled-lined.
STEM 2.5–3.5, ±equal, very
slender, slightly bulbous,
smooth but at first mealy
scaly at base. GILLS whitish,
then grey, then black, deliquescing, fairly distant,
adnexed – free. SPORE
PRINT black. SMELL indis-
tinct. FLESH whitish when
young. Usually in small
groups, trooping or ±tufted.
On strawy dung, compost,
straw, domestic waste.
Spring – winter. Probably
widespread. Common. In-
edible. SPORES very broadly
ellipsoid – subspherical,
smooth, germ pore, 7–
8×7–9.

4

Coprinus cortinatus. Habitat, stem features, spores.
CAP at first 0.5–1 and ±egg-
shaped, then flattened, at
first entirely finely mealy-
scurfy, margin at first with
veil remnants then
grooved-lined. STEM 1–5,
equal, very slender, at first
finely woolly, then smooth,
often rather hairy at base,
quickly disappearing apical
ring zone. GILLS whitish,
then very dark purple-
brown, then black, deli-
quescing, fairly crowded,
adnexed – free. SPORE
PRINT black. SMELL indis-
tinct. FLESH whitish when
young. Usually in small
groups, ±trooping. On soil
in shady woods, sometimes
on wood. Autumn. Prob-
ably widespread. Uncom-
mon. Inedible. SPORES
almond-shaped, smooth,
germ pore, 5–6×9.5–11.

5

Coprinus laanii. Habitat,
spores, size. CAP at first
0.5–2 and ±egg-shaped –
conical, then convex –
bell-shaped, then flattened
with upturned margin, at
first entirely mealy with
granular scaly margin, then
grooved-lined at margin.
STEM 2–5.5, equal or tapering slightly upwards, slender, at first mealy woolly,
then fibrous-silky. STEM
whitish grey, then pinkish
buff, then black, deliquescing, fairly distant,
adnexed – free. SPORE
PRINT black. SMELL indis-
tinct. FLESH whitish when
young. Usually in small
groups, ±trooping. On
wood chips, sawdust, moss
on wet stumps or logs, also
algal scum. Spring –
autumn. Probably wide-
spread. Rare. Inedible.
SPORES ±ellipsoid, smooth
but with wavy outer coat,
germ pore, 5–6×10–11.5
(minus coat).

6

Coprinus narcoticus. Habitat, smell, spores, probably
includes more than one
species. CAP at first 0.75–1.5
and ±egg-shaped then
convex – conical, then
more flattened with split
margin, at first entirely
mealy-scaly, then more
coarsely in centre and
grooved-lined at margin.
STEM 1.5–6, equal or tapering at apex, slender, sometimes swollen or ±rooting
at base, at first densely
woolly-hairy, especially at
base. GILLS white, then
grey, then black, deliquescing, fairly crowded,
adnate – free. SPORE PRINT
black. SMELL strong, gas.
FLESH whitish when young.
Usually in small groups, ±
trooping. On dung or well-
manured soil. Autumn.
Probably widespread.
Rare. Inedible. SPORES ellipsoid – ±almond shaped,
smooth but with dotted
outer coat, germ pore, 5–6
×10–11.5 (minus coat).

7

Coprinus stercoreus. Habitat, spores, smell. CAP at
first 0.25–1.25 and ±egg
shaped, then convex –
flattened with split or rolled
margin, at first entirely
mealy-scaly, then ±smooth
and grooved lined. STEM
1–4, equal or tapering
slightly upwards, extremely
slender, at first silky-mealy
scaly, then ±smooth, sometimes woolly-hairy at base.
GILLS white, then dark
brown, then black, deli-
quescing, fairly distant,
adnate-free. SPORE PRINT
black. SMELL indistinct or
faint, excremental. FLESH
whitish when young. Solitary or in small groups, ±
trooping. On dung (cow,
deer, horse, rabbit, sheep)
Spring – autumn. Wide-
spread. Uncommon. Inedi-
ble. SPORES elongated
ellipsoid – ±kidney
shaped, smooth, germ
pore, 3.5–4×7–8.

8

Coprinus heptemerus. Size,
habitat, spores. CAP at first
0.1–1 and ±elongated egg
shaped, then convex –
flattened with split or rolled
margin, at first minutely
granular-scaly, especially in
centre, then wrinkled-
lined, margin toothed. STEM
0.5–5, equal, extremely
slender, ±smooth. GILLS
white – greyish, then
black, deliquescing, fairly
distant, adnexed – free.
SPORE PRINT black. SMELL
indistinct. FLESH whitish
when young. Solitary or in
small groups, ±trooping.
On dung (cow, deer, rab-
bit, sheep). Spring –
autumn? Widespread.
Rare. Inedible. SPORES
ellipsoid, smooth, large
eccentric germ pore, 6–
7.5×11.5–14.5.

1

Coprinus disseminatus
Fairies' Bonnets. Habit,
habitat, cap features,
spores. CAP at first 0.5–1.5
and ±egg-shaped, then
convex – bell-shaped, at
first entirely minutely
velvety-scurfy, then smooth
towards margin and
wrinkled-lined. STEM 1.5–4,
equal or tapering slightly
upwards, slender, at first
minutely velvety, downy at
base. GILLS white – greyish,
then dark violet-brown,
then black, fairly crowded,
adnate – adnexed. SPORE
PRINT very dark brown.
SMELL indistinct. FLESH
whitish when young.
Usually in large – huge
groups, ±tufted. On wood,
old stumps or on soil
nearby. Spring – autumn.
Widespread. Common.
Inedible. SPORES ellipsoid,
smooth, germ pore, 4–
5×7–9.5.

2

Coprinus silvaticus. Spores,
habitat, cap features,
resembling *C. micaceus*.
CAP at first 1.25–3 and egg
shaped – subspherical,
then convex – conical, then
more flattened, at first
entirely minutely velvety
(use hand-lens), then
deeply grooved-lined. STEM
3–8.5, ±equal, slender,
silky-lined, floury-velvety
at apex, later smooth
towards base. GILLS white –
greyish, then black, barely
deliquescing, fairly
crowded, adnexed – free.
SPORE PRINT black. SMELL
indistinct. FLESH whitish
when young. Usually in
groups, ±tufted. On rotten
wood (usually oak), also
apparently on soil or
among litter but from
buried woody debris.
Autumn. Widespread.
Uncommon. Inedible.
SPORES almond-shaped –
lemon shaped, smooth –
ornamented with minute
ridges, germ pore, 8–
10×11–15.

3

Coprinus ephemerus.
Spores, habitat, cap fea-
tures. CAP at first 0.5–1.5
and ±egg shaped – cylind-
ical, then convex – coni-
cal, then ±flattened with
torn or rolled margin,
lined-grooved towards margin. STEM 4–7, ±equal or
tapering slightly upwards,
slender, at first finely
velvety, then smooth, ±
downy-hairy at base. GILLS
greyish, then black, deliquescing, fairly distant, adnexed – free. SPORE PRINT
black. SMELL indistinct.
FLESH whitish when young.
Usually in groups, ±troop-
ing. On old cow or horse
dung or manured straw.
All year. Widespread. Un-
common. Inedible. SPORES
ellipsoid – almond-shaped,
eccentric germ pore, 6–7.5
×11.5–15.5.

4

Coprinus stellatus. Spores,
habitat, cap features. CAP at
first 0.5–1 and cylindrical –
conical, then ±flattened
with torn or rolled margin,
splitting star-like into 12–16
rays, minutely bristly (use
hand lens). STEM 4–7, tapering upwards, slender, very
finely floury. GILLS white
then greyish, deliquescing,
fairly distant, adnexed –
free. SPORE PRINT black.
SMELL indistinct. FLESH
whitish when young.
Usually in groups, ±troop-
ing. On dung. All year.
Widespread? Rare. Inedi-
ble. SPORES ellipsoid,
smooth, germ pore, 4–
5×8–10.

5

Coprinus congregatus.
Habit, habitat, spores. CAP
at first 0.5–2 and elongated
egg-shaped – cylindrical,
then ±flattened and con-
vex, minutely velvety (use
hand-lens), then ±smooth
and lined-grooved. STEM 2–
8, tapering upwards, slender, often rooting and ±
fused, at first very finely
velvety then smooth. GILLS
pale buff, then brown, then
black, deliquescing, fairly
distant, adnexed – free.
SPORE PRINT black. SMELL
pleasant. FLESH whitish
when young. Usually in
groups, ±tufted. On rotten
straw, domestic waste, sil-
age, manured soil. All
year. Widespread? Rare.
Inedible. SPORES
elongated – ellipsoid,
smooth, slightly eccentric
germ pore, 6–7×12–14.

6

Coprinus bisporus. Microscopic features, habit, habitat. CAP at first 0.5–1.5 and
elongated egg shaped –
convex, then ±flattened,
minutely velvety (use hand-
lens), then hoary and lined-
grooved towards margin.
STEM 3–8, tapering
upwards, slender, slightly
swollen at base, often rooting and ±fused, at first very
finely velvety. GILLS white –
pale buff, then black, deliquescing, fairly distant,
adnexed – free. SPORE
PRINT black. SMELL indis-
tinct or faint, pleasant.
FLESH whitish when young.
Usually in groups, ±tufted.
On dung or manured straw
or soil. All year. Wide-
spread. Uncommon. Inedi-
ble. SPORES ellipsoid –
almond-shaped, smooth,
eccentric germ pore, 5.5–
7.5×9.5–14.5. Basidia 2-
spored.

7

Coprinus angulatus. Habitat, cap features, spores.
CAP at first 0.5–1.5 and
elongated egg-shaped,
then ±flattened – convex or
conical, minutely velvety
(use hand-lens), then
wrinkled and lined-grooved
from ±toothed margin.
STEM 2.5–6.5, equal or
tapering upwards, slender,
at first very finely velvety,
hairy-downy at base. GILLS
white – greyish, then dark
brown, barely deliquescing,
distant, free – remote.
SPORE PRINT dark brown.
SMELL indistinct. FLESH
whitish when young.
Usually in groups, trooping
or ±tufted. On soil or plant
debris in wet places, pond
margins, ditches. All year.
Widespread. Uncommon.
Inedible. SPORES ellipsoid –
±almond shaped, smooth,
eccentric germ pore, 5–
6×9–11.

8

Coprinus impatiens. Size,
habit, habitat, spores. CAP
at first 2–4 and convex –
egg-shaped, then flattened-
slightly umbonate,
grooved, lined when wet.
STEM 7–10, equal or tapering slightly upwards, very
slender, at first very finely
floury, then silky-
lined, ±finely woolly at
apex. GILLS pale buff, then
greyish brown, barely deliquescing, fairly distant,
adnexed – free. SPORE
PRINT dark brown. SMELL
indistinct. FLESH whitish
when young. Solitary or in
small groups, ±trooping.
On soil or among leaf litter,
shady woods, especially
with beech. Autumn.
Widespread. Rare. Inedi-
ble. SPORES ellipsoid –
±almond shaped, smooth,
germ pore, 5–6×9–12.

COPRINACEAE

Coprinus hiascens. Habit, habitat, spores. CAP at first 0.5–25 and convex – egg-shaped, then flattened-convex, minutely velvety (use hand-lens), then wrinkled-lined. STEM 2–6, equal,±bulbous, slender, at first very finely floury, downy at base. GILLS white – greyish, then purplish brown, then black, slowy deliquescing, fairly distant, adnexed – free. SPORE PRINT dark brown. SMELL indistinct. FLESH whitish when young. Solitary or in small groups,± tufted. On soil, often among grass, path edges, open grassy places in woods. Spring – autumn. Widespread. Rare. Inedible. SPORES ellipsoid – almond-shaped, smooth, eccentric germ pore, 4.5–5.5×9–11.

Coprinus auricomus. Habit, habitat, colours, microscopic features, season. CAP at first 1.25–1.5,±egg-shaped, then convex, then±flattened, sometimes±papillate, first smooth, then grooved lined, margin sometimes toothed. STEM 4.5–7.5,± equal or tapering slightly upwards, slender, sometimes slightly swollen base, ±fibrous-silky, white downy at base. GILLS whitish then buff, then dark brown-black, slowly deliquescing, fairly crowded, adnate – adnexed. SPORE PRINT black. SMELL indistinct. FLESH whitish when young. Solitary or in small groups,±tufted. On soil. Spring – summer. Widespread. Uncommon. Inedible. SPORES ellipsoid – ±almond shaped, smooth, germ pore, 7–7.5×10–13. Long brown setae in cap.

Coprinus hemerobius. Habitat, cap, gills, spores, v. like *C. plicatilis* but mature cap and spores differ. CAP at first 0.75–1 and± egg-shaped, then convex, smooth, mealy when dry, deeply grooved, finally split at margin. STEM 1.5–5,± equal or tapering slightly downwards, slender, smooth. GILLS greyish, then black, barely deliquescing, fairly distant, adnexed – free. SPORE PRINT dark brown. SMELL indistinct. FLESH whitish when young. Solitary. On soil, in grass, path edges, woods, shady places. Spring – autumn. Widespread. Uncommon. Inedible. SPORES ellipsoid – almond-shaped, smooth, germ pore, 7–8×11.5–12.5.

Panaeolina foenisecii **Brown Hay Cap.** Gills, cap features, habitat, spores. CAP 1–2, convex – bell-shaped, paler when dry, smooth. STEM 4–7, equal, slender, often slightly wavy, smooth. GILLS at first pale brown, then with chocolate-brown spotting, fairly crowded, adnate. SPORE PRINT very dark brown. TASTE and SMELL indistinct. FLESH buff-brown. Usually in small groups, trooping. On soil, among short grass, lawns, path edges. Summer – autumn. Widespread. Very common. Inedible, hallucinogenic, poisonous? SPORES ellipsoid – lemon-shaped, warty, germ pore, 7–8×12–16.

Coprinus miser. Size, cap and stem features, habitat, spores. CAP at first 0.25–0.5 and±egg-shaped, then convex, then±flattened, smooth, then wrinkled-lined. STEM 0.5–4, equal, extremely slender – hair-like, smooth but often minutely velvety at base (use hand-lens). GILLS pale grey, then black, barely deliquescing, fairly crowded, adnate – adnexed. SPORE PRINT black. SMELL indistinct. FLESH whitish when young. Solitary or in small groups, ±tufted. On cow or horse dung. Spring – autumn. Widespread. Common. Inedible. SPORES very broadly ellipsoid – subspherical, smooth, germ pore, 6–8× 7–9.

Coprinus plicatilis **Little Japanese Umbrella Toadstool.** Habitat, cap, gills, spores. CAP first 0.5–1.25, ±egg shaped, then convex, then±flattened – depressed, smooth, deeply grooved-lined. STEM 3–7,±equal, slightly bulbous, v. slender, smooth. GILLS buff-grey, then black, barely deliquescing, fairly distant, remote to distinct collar. SPORE PRINT black. SMELL indistinct. FLESH whitish when young. Solitary or small groups,±trooping. On soil, in grass, fields, path edges. Spring – autumn. Widespread. V. common. Inedible. SPORES ellipsoid – ±almond shaped, smooth, eccentric germ pore, 8.5– 10.5×10–13.

Lacrymaria (= *Psathyrella*) *velutina* **Weeping Widow.** Cap features, gills, spores. CAP 1.5–10, at first convex and broadly umbonate, then more flattened, at first entirely fibrous-woolly, then±smooth, margin fringed with veil remnants. STEM 4–10,±equal or tapering slightly upwards, fairly slender, fibrous-scaly below superior irregular ring zone. GILLS purple-brown with black spotting, then black, edge whitish, often weeping, fairly crowded, adnate – adnexed. SPORE PRINT black. SMELL indistinct. FLESH buff-brown. Solitary or in small groups,±tufted. On soil, among grass, path edges, woods. Spring – autumn. Widespread. Very common. Edible. SPORES lemon-shaped, warty, germ pore, 5–7×8–11.

Panaeolus papilionaceus. Gills, cap features, habitat, spores. CAP 2–4, convex – subspherical, smooth or finely cracked, margin often±irregular-toothed from veil remnants. STEM 5–10, equal or tapering slightly upwards, base± swollen, slender, often rather wavy, especially towards base,±smooth – finely floury. GILLS at first greyish, then with black spotting, then black, white edge, fairly crowded, adnate. SMELL indistinct. FLESH buff-brown. Usually in small groups, trooping. On well-manured soil or horse dung, fields, pastures. Summer – autumn. Widespread. Uncommon. Inedible. SPORES±lemon-shaped, smooth, germ pore, 7–8×12–14.

1
…aeolus campanulatus.
…s, cap features, habitat,
…es. CAP 1.5–3,
…spherical – dome-
…ed, smooth, slightly
…y when wet, margin
…n or slightly irregular-
…hed from veil rem-
…s. STEM 7–10, equal or
…ring slightly upwards,
… barely swollen, slen-
…sometimes slightly
…y,±smooth – finely
…ry. GILLS at first greyish,
…with black spotting,
…n black, white edge,
…y crowded, adnate.
…RE PRINT black. SMELL
…t, indefinite. FLESH
…-brown. Usually in
…ll groups, trooping. On
…g, fields, pastures.
…mer – autumn. Wide-
…ead. Uncommon. Inedi-
SPORES±lemon-
…ed, smooth, germ
…e, 7–8×12–14.

2
…aeolus sphinctrinus.
…s, cap features, habitat,
…es. CAP 2–3,
…spherical – dome-
…ed or bell-shaped,
…tly umbonate, paler
…n dry, smooth – radially
…ed, margin rather
…ly toothed from veil
…nants. STEM 7–12,
…al, slender,±smooth –
…y floury. GILLS at first
…ish, then with black
…ting, then black, white
…e, fairly crowded,
…ate. SPORE PRINT black.
…LL indistinct. FLESH
…-brown. Usually in
…ll groups, trooping. On
…-manured soil or dung,
…ls, pastures. Spring –
…mn. Widespread. Very
…mon. Hallucinogenic.
…RES lemon-shaped,
…ooth, germ pore, 10–
…5×14–18.

3
Panaeolus rickenii. Gills,
cap features, habitat,
spores. CAP 2–3, conical –
convex – elongated bell-
shaped, rather sharply
umbonate, paler when dry,
smooth, lined at margin
when wet. STEM 5–10,
equal, slender, finely
floury. GILLS at first greyish,
then with black spotting,
then black, white edge,
fairly crowded, adnate.
SPORE PRINT black. SMELL
earthy-mushroomy. FLESH
buff-brown. Usually in
small groups, trooping. On
soil, fields, pastures.
Summer – autumn. Wide-
spread. Very common.
Inedible. SPORES lemon-
shaped, smooth, germ
pore, 9.5–11×13–16.

4
Panaeolus acuminatus.
Gills, cap features, habitat,
spores. CAP 2–2.5, elon-
gated bell-shaped, sharply
umbonate, paler when dry,
smooth, margin very
slightly irregular-toothed.
STEM 3.5–5, tapering
slightly upwards, slender,
often slightly wavy, especially towards base, finely
floury. GILLS at first greyish,
then with black spotting,
then black, white edge,
fairly crowded, adnate.
SPORE PRINT black. SMELL
indistinct. FLESH buff-
brown. Usually in small
groups, trooping. On soil,
fields, pastures, near
woods. Summer – autumn.
Widespread. Uncommon.
Inedible. SPORES lemon-
shaped, smooth, germ
pore, 9–11×12–15.

5
Panaeolus subbalteatus.
Cap features, gills, habitat,
spores. CAP 3–5, at first
convex – conical, then
more flattened and broadly
umbonate, paler when dry
with marked marginal
zone, smooth. STEM 6–9,
equal, slender, often
slightly wavy, silky-fibrous,
sometimes blue at base.
GILLS at first pinkish buff,
then with black spotting,
then black, fairly crowded,
adnate. SPORE PRINT black.
SMELL mushroomy. FLESH
buff-brown. Usually in
small groups,±tufted. On
well-manured soil, manure
hills, compost-heaps.
Summer – autumn. Wide-
spread. Uncommon. Poiso-
nous, hallucinogenic.
SPORES lemon-shaped,
smooth, germ pore, 7.5–
8.5×12–14.

6
Panaeolus ater. Gills, cap
features, habitat, spores.
CAP 1.5–4.5, subspherical –
convex, barely umbonate,
paler when dry, smooth –
very slightly roughened.
STEM 2–8.5, equal, slender,
often slightly wavy,±
smooth-floury, downy at
base. GILLS at first greyish,
then with black spotting,
then black, whitish edge,
fairly crowded, adnate.
SPORE PRINT black. SMELL
indistinct. FLESH buff-
brown. Usually in small
groups,±trooping. On soil
on lawns, among grass,
close to trees. Spring –
autumn. Widespread. Un-
common. Inedible. SPORES
±lemon-shaped, smooth,
oblique germ pore, 7–8×
10–14.

7
Panaeolus fimicola. Gills,
cap features, habitat,
spores, very similar to *P.
ater.* CAP 1.5–3,
subspherical – convex,
barely umbonate, paler
when dry, smooth – very
slightly roughened. STEM 4–
8, equal, slender, often
slightly wavy, smooth but
floury at apex, downy at
base. GILLS at first greyish,
then with black spotting,
then black, whitish edge,
fairly crowded, adnate.
SPORE PRINT black. SMELL
indistinct. FLESH buff-
brown. Usually in small
groups,±trooping. On soil
among grass, close to trees.
Spring – autumn. Wide-
spread. Uncommon. Inedi-
ble. SPORES ellipsoid –
±lemon-shaped, flattened
on one side, smooth, germ
pore, 7–8×11–14.

8
Panaeolus (=*Anellaria*)
semiovatus. Size, cap features, habitat, spores. CAP
2–6, subspherical – ±egg-
shaped, sticky when wet,
smooth, shiny, cracked
when dry, veil remnants
forming irregular edge.
STEM 5–15, slightly tapering
upwards, slender, smooth
below median – superior
persistent fragile ring. GILLS
at first whitish, then mottled brownish black,
then±black, often with
whitish edge, fairly
crowded, adnate. SPORE
PRINT black. SMELL indis-
tinct. FLESH whitish, straw-
coloured in stem. Solitary
or in small groups, trooping. On dung and dung/
straw mixtures. Spring –
autumn. Widespread. Com-
mon. Inedible. SPORES ellipsoid, smooth, germ pore,
9–12×16–20.

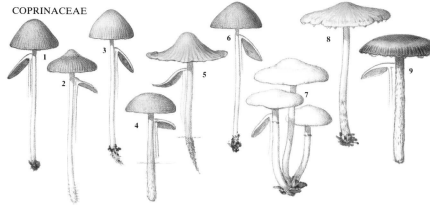

1

Psathyrella conopilea. Cap features, spores, microscopic features. CAP 1.5–4, conical – bell-shaped, smooth – minutely floury, often cracked. STEM 10–15,±equal, very slender, smooth, silvery shiny. GILLS at first grey – pinkish brown, then very dark brown, fairly crowded, adnate – adnexed. SPORE PRINT black. SMELL indistinct. FLESH pinkish-brown. Usually in groups,±tufted, close to trees. Autumn. Widespread. Uncommon. Edible. SPORES ellipsoid, smooth, eccentric germ pore, 7.5–8×12.5–16. Brown setae in cap.

2

Psathyrella corrugis. Cap and stem features, spores. CAP 2–3.5, at first±conical, then bell-shaped, markedly wrinkled. STEM 5–13,± equal, very slender, smooth, silvery-shiny, shortly rooting, downy at base. GILLS greyish brown with violet flush, fairly crowded, adnate – adnexed. SPORE PRINT black. SMELL indistinct. FLESH pinkish-brown. Usually in groups,±tufted. On soil, among plant debris, open places in woods. Autumn. Widespread. Rare. Edible? SPORES ellipsoid, smooth, germ pore, 6.5–7×11–13.

3

Psathyrella gracilis. Size, cap and stem features, spores. CAP 1–3.5, at first±conical, then bell-shaped, then more flattened, slightly umbonate, paler when dry, lined to half way when wet. STEM 4–10, equal, very slender, smooth, silvery-shiny, shortly rooting, downy at base. GILLS greyish black, edge pinkish, fairly crowded, adnate. SPORE PRINT black. SMELL indistinct. FLESH pinkish-brown. Usually in groups, trooping or±tufted. On soil, usually among grass, often with plant debris, open places in woods. Summer – autumn. Widespread. Uncommon. Edible. SPORES ellipsoid, smooth, germ pore, 6.5–7×11–13.

4

Psathyrella ammophila. Habitat, stem features, spores. CAP 1–2.5, at first convex, then more flattened, paler when dry, smooth. STEM 4–5, equal, slender, smooth, silvery-shiny, very downy at base. GILLS at first greyish-brown, then brown-black, fairly distant, adnate. SPORE PRINT black. SMELL indistinct. FLESH buff-brown. Usually in groups, trooping or±tufted. On sand, attached to roots of marram. Dunes. Summer – autumn. Widespread, coastal. Uncommon. Inedible. SPORES ellipsoid, smooth, germ pore, 6–7×10–11.

5

Psathyrella caudata. Stem and cap features, spores. CAP 3–5, at first bell-shaped, then more flattened and conical with upturned margin, paler when dry, grooved-lined. STEM 6–8, equal, slender, smooth, silvery-shiny, very deeply rooting, often± fused, downy at base. GILLS at first greyish, then black, white edge, fairly distant, adnate – adnexed. SPORE PRINT dark brown. SMELL indistinct. FLESH buff-brown. Tufted, often in dense groups. On soil, usually close to trees or stumps. Summer – autumn. Widespread. Rare.

Inedible? SPORES ellipsoid – ±kidney-shaped, smooth, germ pore, 6.5–7.5×11.5–13.5.

6

Psathyrella atomata. Cap features, spores. CAP 1–2.5, at first convex – bell-shaped, then convex, scarcely paler and glistening finely granular-mealy when dry, sometime becoming lined-grooved. STEM 4–8, equal, slender, often slightly wavy towards base, smooth,±translucent. GILLS at first greyish, then black, paler edge, fairly distant, adnate – adnexed. SPORE PRINT dark brown-black. SMELL indistinct. FLESH greyish. Solitary or in small groups,± trooping. On soil, among grass, lawns, path sides, field edges. Autumn. Widespread. Uncommon. Inedible? SPORES elongated ellipsoid, smooth, germ pore, 7–7.5×14–17.

7

Psathyrella leucotephra. Size, cap and stem features. CAP 6–7, at first convex – bell-shaped, then flattened – depressed, very finely lined-wrinkled (use hand-lens). STEM 8–11, equal or tapering slightly upwards, fairly slender, lined at apex, rather woolly-scaly below superior – apical pendulous rather fragile ring. GILLS at first whitish buff, then grey, then black, white edge, crowded, adnate – adnexed. SPORE PRINT dark brown-black. SMELL indistinct. FLESH greyish buff. Solitary or in small groups,±tufted. On soil in broad-leaved woods. Autumn. Widespread. Uncommon. Inedible? SPORES ellipsoid, smooth, germ pore, 5–6×8–9.

8

Psathyrella candolleana. Size, habitat, cap and ste features. CAP 2–6.5, at fi convex – bell-shaped, t flattened, at first sparse and finely scaly, then smooth – minutely glist ing floury when dry, ofte with veil fragments at m gin. STEM 3–8.5, equal o tapering slightly upward fairly slender,±smooth, sometimes±rooting. GII at first greyish with lilac flush, then dark brown, white edge, crowded, adnate – adnexed. SPOR PRINT dark brown-black. SMELL earthy-mushroom FLESH whitish. Tufted. On wood, stumps and other rotting parts of broad-leaved trees, also on tub barrels and other old cu timber. Spring – autumn Widespread. Common. Edible. SPORES ellipsoid smooth, germ pore, 3.5–4.5×6–8.

9

Psathyrella spintrigera. Habitat, cap and stem fe tures. CAP 2–5, a first convex – dome-shaped, then convex-flattened, paler when dr margin lined and with thick, woolly veil remna STEM 6–7,±equal, fairly slender, lined at apex, woolly-scaly below supe ior, often rather indefini ring zone. GILLS at first greyish with lilac flush, t dark greyish brown, whi edge, fairly crowded, adnate – adnexed. SPOR PRINT dark brown-black. SMELL indistinct. FLESH whitish. Usually in small groups,±tufted. On soil among leaf and needle li ter, woods. Summer – autumn. Widespread. Rare. Inedible? SPORES ellipsoid – bean-shaped smooth, germ pore, 4.5–5×6–7.5.

ble. SPORES ellipsoid, smooth, germ pore, 4–5.5×8.5–9.5.

...athyrella caput-medusae. .bit, habitat, cap and m features, smell. CAP ..7, at first convex – bell ..iped, then more ..ttened, broadly ..bonate, ±covered with ..ncentric pattern of hairy ..les but smoother at cen-.. STEM 5–7, ±equal or ..ering slightly upwards, ..rly stout, ±smooth at ..ex, covered with coarse ..turned scales below ..perior, spreading± ..uble ring. GILLS at first ..eyish, then dark brown, ..rly crowded, adnexed. ..ORE PRINT dark brown. ..ELL strong, sweet. FLESH ..itish buff. Tufted. On ..mps of coniferous trees. ..utumn. Widespread. ..re. Inedible. SPORES nar-..wly ellipsoid, smooth, ..rm pore, 4–5.5×10–11.5.

...athyrella squamosa. ..abitat, cap and stem fea-..res. CAP 2.5–3.5, at first ..ongated egg-shaped – ..ll-shaped, then convex – ..ttened, umbonate, ..ghtly paler when ..y, ±covered with silky ..res, slightly lined ..ooved at margin. STEM 4-..±equal, slender, lined at ..ex, fibrous-scaly below ..regular, superior fibrous ..ng zone. GILLS at first ..itish, then buff-brown, ..en dark purple-brown, ..irly crowded, adnate. ..ORE PRINT dark purple-..own. SMELL indistinct. ..ESH yellowish buff. ..sually in small groups, ± ..fted. On soil in beech ..oods. Autumn. Wide-..·read. Common. Inedi-

Psathyrella multipedata. Habit, cap and stem features. CAP 1–3, at first convex – conical, then slightly flattened, barely umbonate, paler when dry, smooth, finely lined to half way. STEM 7–10, equal, slender, often rather wavy, smooth – fibrous. GILLS dark purple-brown, crowded, adnate – adnexed. SPORE PRINT dark purple-brown. SMELL indistinct. FLESH whitish. Densely tufted, in large – huge groups. On soil among grass, open grassy places in woods. Summer. Widespread. Rare. Inedible. SPORES ellipsoid, smooth, germ pore, 3.5–4×6.5–8.

Psathyrella gossypina. Cap and stem features, spores. CAP 2–3.5, at first bell-shaped, then flattened, paler when dry, very coarsely grooved, at first rather loosely fibrous, then markedly irregular fibrous toothed at margin. STEM 3–4, equal, fairly stout, very densely downy-fibrous. GILLS dark purple-brown, white edge, crowded, adnate. SPORE PRINT dark purple-brown. SMELL indistinct. FLESH whitish. Usually in small groups, ±tufted. On soil among plant debris, open grassy places in broad-

leaved woods. Summer – autumn. Widespread. Rare. Inedible. SPORES ellipsoid – ±bean-shaped, smooth, germ pore, 3.5–4×6–8.

Psathyrella pennata. Habitat, cap and stem features, spores. CAP 1–2.5, at first bell-shaped, then convex – flattened, ± densely downy-fibrous or scaly, especially towards lined margin. STEM 3–5, ±equal, fairly slender, silky-fibrous-lined, sometimes±slightly rooting. GILLS at first greyish, then greyish purple, crowded, adnate. SPORE PRINT dark purple-brown. SMELL indistinct. FLESH brownish white, darker in cap. Usually in small groups, trooping or±tufted. On soil on old fire sites. Summer – autumn. Widespread. Uncommon. Inedible. SPORES ellipsoid – ± bean-shaped, smooth, germ pore, 4–4.5×8–9.

Psathyrella fusca. Habit, habitat, cap features. CAP 3–7.5, at first±subspherical, then convex, ±densely fibrous-lined, margin at first with overhanging white fibres. STEM 6–10, equal, fairly slender, smooth – silky-fibrous lined. GILLS at first grey-brown, then darker violet-brown, edge whitish, fairly crowded, adnate. SPORE PRINT very dark brown. SMELL indistinct. FLESH

whitish buff. Usually solitary. On soil among plant debris in beech woods. Spring – autumn. Widespread. Uncommon. Inedible. SPORES ellipsoid, smooth, germ pore, 3.5–4.5×7.5–10.

Psathyrella hydrophila. Habit, habitat, cap features. CAP 2–4, at first±bell-shaped, then convex – flattened, paler when dry, smooth, then often cracking, margin at first with overhanging veil remnants. STEM 4–10, equal, fairly slender, often rather wavy, smooth – silky-fibrous lined. GILLS at first buff brown, then dark brown, edge whitish, fairly crowded, adnate – adnexed. SPORE PRINT very dark brown. SMELL indistinct. FLESH whitish buff. Densely tufted. On soil, usually close to stumps of broad-leaved trees. Spring – autumn. Widespread. Very common. Inedible. SPORES ellipsoid, smooth, germ pore, 3–4×4.5–7.

COPRINACEAE

Psathyrella spadiceogrisea.
Habit, habitat, cap, stem.
CAP 3–5, at first conical –
bell-shaped, then convex –
flattened, umbonate, paler
when dry, lined when wet,
smooth. STEM 6–10, equal,
fairly slender, smooth,
shiny. GILLS at first whitish,
then greyish, then dark
violet brown, edge whitish,
fairly crowded, adnate –
adnexed. SPORE PRINT very
dark brown. SMELL indis-
tinct. FLESH greyish buff.
Usually in small groups,
trooping. On soil, usually
close to stumps of broad-
leaved trees. Autumn.
Widespread. Common.
Inedible. SPORES ellipsoid,
smooth, germ pore, 4–
5×7–10.

Psathyrella vernalis. Sea-
son, cap and stem features,
habitat. CAP 1.5–2.5, at
first±conical, then convex
– flattened, slightly sticky,
smooth. STEM 6–7, equal or
tapering slightly upwards,
fairly slender, smooth,
sometimes slightly floury at
apex, shiny. GILLS at first
whitish, then±buff, then
dark brown, fairly crowded,
adnate – adnexed. SPORE
PRINT dark greyish brown.
SMELL indistinct. FLESH
greyish buff. Usually in
small groups, trooping. On
soil, among plant debris in
broad-leaved woods.
Spring. Widespread. Un-
common. Inedible. SPORES
ellipsoid, smooth, germ
pore, 4–5×7.5–9.5.

Psathyrella obtusata. Cap
and stem features, habitat.
CAP 1.5–4, at first±conical,
then convex, lined towards
margin, especially when
wet, markedly paler and
very finely wrinkled when
dry, smooth. STEM 6–7,
equal or tapering slightly
upwards, fairly slender,
silky-smooth, sometimes
slightly floury at apex,
shiny. GILLS at first whitish,
then±buff, then dark
brown, fairly crowded,
adnate – adnexed. SPORE
PRINT dark greyish brown.
SMELL indistinct. FLESH
whitish buff. Usually in
small groups, trooping. On
soil, among plant debris in
broad-leaved woods.
Spring – autumn. Wide-
spread. Uncommon. Inedi-
ble. SPORES ellipsoid,
smooth, germ pore, 4–
5.5×7.5–10.

Psathyrella subnuda. Cap
and stem features, season,
spores. CAP 2–3, at first
conical, then convex, finely
lined at margin, paler when
dry, smooth, finely granular when dry. STEM 6–9,
equal or tapering slightly
upwards, slender, often
slightly wavy, silky smooth,
sometimes slightly floury at
apex, shiny. GILLS at first
purplish brown, then dark
brown, fairly crowded,
adnate – adnexed. SPORE
PRINT purplish black. SMELL
indistinct. FLESH greyish
buff. Solitary or in small
groups, trooping. On soil,
among grass or plant debris
in woods. Spring – autumn.
Widespread. Rare. Inedi-
ble. SPORES ellipsoid – ±
lemon shaped, smooth,
germ pore, 5–5.5×8–9.5.

AURISCALPIACEAE

APHYLLOPHORALES
Fruit body with spore-
bearing surface exposed
during development,
usually flattened against
substrate, effused, stem-
less or short stemmed, disc,
cup, club shaped or coral or
bracket like, rarely
toadstool-shaped. Spore-
bearing surface one or two-
sided, smooth, folded,
toothed or tubular with
tubes structurally separate
from or fused with woody
or±corky flesh. Spores
variously shaped, often
white but sometimes
variously coloured, smooth
or ornamented, sometimes
amyloid or cyanophilous,
rarely septate. Basidia non
septate, 2-several spored.
Hyphal system mono-, di-,
or trimitic, colourless or
coloured. Mostly saprot-
rophic on wood, soil or
plant debris, some biot-
rophic causing important
tree diseases. Few edible,
few poisonous. Divided
into about twenty one families, all represented in
Europe, largely on basis of
basidial and other microscopic characters although
these often correlate fairly
well with macroscopic features.

AURISCALPIACEAE
Fruit body±toadstool-
shaped (Auriscalpium),
bracket-like with stem
central – eccentric
or±lateral (Lentinellus), or
completely resupinate
(Gloiodon), dull-coloured,
brown – whitish, smooth –
very hairy. Spores borne on
spines or on distant, decurrent notched gills,
subspherical – ellipsoid,
smooth or minutely spiny,
amyloid. Flesh brown –
whitish, usually tough.
Spore print white. Hyphal
system dimitic. Smell not
usually distinctive. On
wood or fallen conifer
cones. Apparently all saprotrophic. Some edible,
none good, none poiso-
nous.

Auriscalpium vulgare Ear
Pick Fungus. Habitat, cap
and stem features. CAP 1–
kidney-shaped, slightly
convex, ±covered with
coarse downy hairs, then
often±smooth, margin
usually wavy. STEM 2–6,
eccentric, tapering
upwards, slender, dense
bristly, more downy
towards base. SPINES 0.1–
0.3, at first dark pinkish
brown, then greyish brow
conical. SPORE PRINT whit
whitish, tough. Solitary
in small groups, sometim
±tufted. On±buried pin
cones. Autumn. Wide-
spread. Common. Inedib
SPORES broadly ellipsoid
minutely spiny, 3.5–4.5×
4.5–5.5, amyloid. HYPHA
SYSTEM dimitic.

Lentinellus cochleatus.
Habit, gills, stem feature
smell, spores. CAP 2–6, ir
gularly ear or funnel
shaped, smooth, shiny.
STEM 2–5, usually eccentr
– lateral, tapering down-
wards, fairly stout, usual
±rooting. GILLS pale pin
ish, fairly distant, deeply
decurrent. SPORE PRINT
white. SMELL strong, anis
eed. FLESH pinkish, toug
Tufted. On stumps of
broad-leaved trees. Sum-
mer – autumn. Wide-
spread. Uncommon. Edi
ble. SPORES subspherical,
minutely spiny. 3.5–4×4
5, amyloid. HYPHAL SYSTE
dimitic.

entinellus tridentinus.
ze, habitat, habit, spores.
AP 0.5–1, irregularly ear or
unnel-shaped, minutely
rinkled radially. STEM
.25–0.5, usually eccentric
lateral, ±equal or taper-
g downwards, fairly
out. GILLS pale pinkish,
irly distant, deeply dec-
rrent. SPORE PRINT white.
MELL indistinct. FLESH
ough, pinkish. Solitary or
small groups. On wood
broad leaved trees, esp-
cially rowan, and on herb-
ceous stems. Summer –
utumn. Highland. Rare.
edible. SPORES ellipsoid,
nooth, 4–5×5–6.5, amy-
oid. HYPHAL SYSTEM
imitic.

CANTHARELLACEAE

ANTHARELLACEAE
uit body±toadstool-
aped or funnel-shaped –
bular, with stem central –
ccentric, often brightly-
oloured, yellow-orange,
nooth – minutely scaly-
urfy. Spores borne on dis-
nt, decurrent wrinkles or
ranching folds, subspher-
al – ellipsoid, smooth,
on-amyloid. Flesh white –
ellowish, sometimes with
nkish flush. Hyphal sys-
m monomitic. Smell
ometimes distinctive. On
oil or rotten wood.
.pparently all saprotrophic
nd mycorrhizal. Some edi-
e and good, none poiso-
ous.

Cantharellus friesii. Size,
habit, colour, spores. CAP
1–3, at first±convex, then
soon irregularly funnel-
shaped, ± umbilicate, margin irregularly wavy,
smooth-shiny. STEM 1–
3, ±equal, fairly stout,
smooth – very finely
velvety. FOLDS yellowish,
sometimes with pink flush,
irregularly forked, bran-
ched, distant, decurrent.
SPORE PRINT pale straw-
yellow. SMELL faint, indefinite, pleasant. FLESH pale
orange in cap, whitish yellow in stem. Solitary or in
small±tufted groups. On
soil in broad-leaved woods,
often with beech, especially
among moss at path edges.
Summer – autumn. Wide-
spread. Rare. Edible.
SPORES ellipsoid, smooth,
4–5×8.5–10.5, non-
amyloid. HYPHAL SYSTEM
monomitic.

Cantharellus cibarius **Chanterelle.** Size, habit, colour,
spores. CAP 3–10, at
first±subspherical, then
convex, then soon irregu-
larly funnel-shaped, margin
irregularly wavy, smooth-
shiny. STEM 3–8, tapering
downwards, fairly stout,
smooth – very finely
velvety. FOLDS ochre-
yellow, irregularly forked,
branched, distant, decur-
rent. SPORE PRINT pale
ochreous. SMELL faint,
slightly fruity but often
absent. FLESH yellowish,
fading to almost white.
Usually in groups, trooping
and often widely dispersed
or±tufted. On soil in
woods, especially with
broad-leaved trees.
Summer – autumn. Wide-
spread. Very common.
Edible. SPORES ellipsoid,
smooth, 4.5–6.5×8–10,
non-amyloid. HYPHAL SYS-
TEM monomitic.

*Cantharellus infundibuli-
ormis.* Colour, overall
form, cap and stem fea-
tures. CAP 3–8, at first±
convex, then funnel
shaped, margin irregularly
wavy, smooth – very
slightly scaly. STEM 3–8, ±
equal, fairly slender, often
flattened or twisted,
smooth – very finely
velvety. FOLDS at first yellowish, then grey, irregularly forked, branched, distant, decurrent. SPORE PRINT
pale yellowish. SMELL faint,
pleasant, indefinite. FLESH
yellowish. In groups, ±tuft-
ed. On soil in broad-leaved
or coniferous woods on acid
sites. Autumn. Wide-
spread. Uncommon. Edi-
ble. SPORES ellipsoid,
smooth, 6.5–8×7.5–10,
non-amyloid. HYPHAL SYST-
EM monomitic.

Cantharellus lutescens.
Habitat, cap and stem colours. CAP 1.5–8, at first±
convex, then funnel-
shaped, slightly umbilicate,
margin irregularly wavy,
finely fibrous-scaly, wrinkled. STEM 3–10, ±equal,
fairly stout, often flattened
or twisted, smooth – very
finely velvety. FOLDS at first
yellowish, then reddish or
pinkish orange, irregularly
forked, branched, distant,
decurrent. SPORE PRINT
white – pale yellowish.
SMELL strong, pleasant,
fruity. FLESH yellow. In
groups, ±tufted. On soil in
coniferous or rarely broad
leaved woods. Summer –
autumn. Widespread, pre-
dominantly highland. Rare.
Edible. SPORES ellipsoid,
smooth, 6–8×10–12, non-
amyloid. HYPHAL SYSTEM
monomitic.

Cantharellus tubaeformis.
Folds, overall form, cap
and stem features. CAP 2–6,
at first±convex, then
funnel-shaped, umbilicate,
margin irregularly wavy,
smooth – very slightly
scaly. STEM 2–8, ±equal,
fairly slender, usually
flattened or twisted and
grooved, smooth – very
finely velvety. FOLDS at first
yellowish, then greyish,
irregularly forked, bran-
ched, distant, decurrent.
SPORE PRINT white – pale
yellowish. SMELL faint,
indefinite. FLESH pale yellowish white. In groups, ±
tufted. On soil in coniferous or broad-leaved woods.
Summer – autumn. Wide-
spread. Uncommon. Edi-
ble. SPORES ellipsoid,
smooth, 6–7.5×9–11, non-
amyloid. HYPHAL SYSTEM
monomitic.

Craterellus cornucopiodes
Horn of Plenty. Overall
shape and colour. FRUIT
BODY 2–10, at first±convex
and depressed, then deeply
funnel-shaped – tubular or
trumpet-shaped, margin
irregularly wavy, lined-
grooved, ±finely scaly-
scurfy, outer surface grey,
at first smooth, then±wavy.
STEM absent. FOLDS absent.
SPORE PRINT white. SMELL
faint, indefinite, pleasant.
FLESH greyish, tough. In
groups, trooping or±tuft-
ed. On soil, among leaf litter in broad-leaved woods.
Summer – autumn. Wide-
spread. Common. Edible.
SPORES ellipsoid, smooth,
6–7×10–16, non-amyloid.
HYPHAL SYSTEM monomitic.

161

CANTHARELLACEAE

Craterellus sinuosus. Cap form, habit. CAP 1–4, at first±convex – depressed, then soon funnel-shaped, often with irregular outgrowths, margin irregularly wavy, radially wrinkled, outer surface greyish brown, distantly wrinkled. STEM 3–6, tapering downwards, fairly slender, flattened, twisted, grooved, smooth. FOLDS indefinite, see CAP. SPORE PRINT white. SMELL faint, indefinite, pleasant. FLESH greyish, tough. Solitary or in groups, trooping or±tufted, sometimes with two or more caps from each stem. On soil, among leaf litter in broad-leaved woods, especially with beech. Summer – autumn. Widespread. Uncommon. Edible? SPORES ellipsoid, smooth, 7–8×9.5–12, non amyloid. HYPHAL SYSTEM monomitic.

CLAVARIACEAE
Fruit body usually erect, usually with stem, unbranched and finger to pencil-like or variously branched, horn or antler like, usually circular in cross-section, white, greyish or brightly-coloured. Outer spore-bearing surface smooth – wrinkled, sometimes absent at fruit body apex. Spores variable in shape, smooth or rarely spiny-warty, almost always non-amyloid. Flesh soft and brittle – ±gelatinous or tough, variously coloured. Spore print white – pale yellowish. Hyphal system monomitic or rarely dimitic. Taste and smell not usually distinctive. Usually terrestrial or on plant debris, more rarely on rotten wood. Apparently almost all saprotrophic, some mycorrhizal. Few edible, some poisonous.

CLAVARIACEAE

Clavaria fumosa. Colour, habit. FRUIT BODY 2–12, unbranched, at first club like, then spindle-shaped – worm like, slender, circular – very slightly flattened in cross-section, smooth, tips at first pointed, then rounded. STEM absent or vestigial. SPORE PRINT white. SMELL indistinct. FLESH white, brittle. Tufted, often in large groups. On soil, usually among grass at path edges, open grassy places in woods. Summer – autumn. Widespread. Uncommon. Inedible. SPORES ellipsoid, smooth, 3–4×5–7.5, non-amyloid. HYPHAL SYSTEM monomitic.

Clavaria rosea. Colour, habit. FRUIT BODY 2–5, unbranched, at first club-like, then spindle-shaped, slender – rather stout, at first circular in cross-section, then±flattened, paler at base, smooth, tips at first pointed, then rounded or blunt. STEM absent or vestigial. SPORE PRINT white. SMELL indistinct. FLESH pinkish white, brittle. Solitary or in small groups,±tufted. On soil, usually among grass at path edges, open grassy places in woods. Summer – autumn. Widespread. Rare. Inedible. SPORES ellipsoid, smooth, 2.5–3.5×5–8, non-amyloid. HYPHAL SYSTEM monomitic.

Clavaria acuta. Colour, overall form, habit. FRUIT BODY 1–6, unbranched or rarely forked, worm-like – club-shaped, slender, at first circular in cross-section, then sometimes slightly flattened, smooth, shiny, tips at first pointed, then rounded below. STEM 0.5–2, paler than fruit body, finely woolly-downy at base. SPORE PRINT white. SMELL indistinct. FLESH white, brittle. Solitary or in small groups,±trooping, tufted. On soil, sometimes among grass or leaf litter, path edges, field boundaries, open grassy places in woods, in plant pots in greenhouses, cold frames. Summer – autumn. Widespread. Uncommon. Inedible. SPORES broadly ellipsoid, smooth, 5.5–8×7–10, non-amyloid. HYPHAL SYSTEM monomitic.

Clavaria argillacea Moor Club. Habitat, overall form, habit. FRUIT BODY 3–5, unbranched, at first± worm-like, then markedly club-shaped, rather stout, at first circular in cross-section, then markedly flattened and grooved, smooth, floury, tips markedly blunt – almost bifurcated, narrowed below. STEM 0.5–1.5, darker than fruit body, smooth-floury. SPORE PRINT white. SMELL indistinct. FLESH yellowish white, fairly brittle. Solitary or in small groups,±tufted. On soil, usually with mosses, on heaths, moors, other acid sites. Summer – autumn. Widespread. Uncommon. Edible. SPORES ellipsoid – cylindrical, smooth, 4–6×8–11, non-amyloid. HYPHAL SYSTEM monomitic.

Clavaria vermicularis Wⁱ **Spindles.** Colour, overal form, habitat. FRUIT BODⅠ 3–11, unbranched,±woⁱ like, slender, at first circ lar in cross-section, then slightly flattened and grooved, smooth, shiny, tips pointed – blunt, nar rowed below. STEM abseⁱ SPORE PRINT white. SMELⅠ faint, mealy. FLESH whitⁱ brittle. Usually in smal groups,±tufted. On soil usually among grass in fields but close to trees. Autumn. Widespread. Uncommon. Edible. SPORES ellipsoid, smooth 3.5–5×5–8, non-amyloiⁱ HYPHAL SYSTEM monomⁱ

Clavaria zollingeri. Colⁱ overall form, habitat. FR BODY 4–8, 2–3 branched, coral-like, rather stout, ⁱ first blunt, then grooved with blunt pincer-like tiⁱ at first±circular in cross-section, then flattened, wrinkled and finely, tips often paler. STEM 0.5–1, sometimes±absent, smooth – wrinkled, palⁱ than rest of fruit body. SPORE PRINT white. SMELⅠ faint, indefinite, pleasanⁱ FLESH pale lilac, brittle. Solitary or in small grouⁱ trooping or±tufted. On soil, usually on poor aciⁱ sites, with grass, mosses, trees. Summer – autumⁱ Widespread. Rare. Inedⁱ ble? SPORES broadly ellipsoid – subsphericaⁱ smooth, 4.5–5.5×5.5–7, non-amyloid. HYPHAL SYⁱ TEM monomitic.

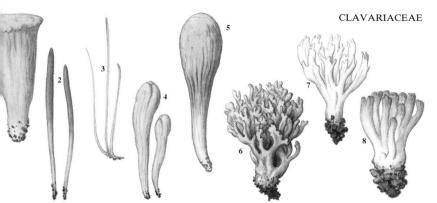

1
Clavariadelphus truncatus.
Overall form, habitat,
smell. FRUIT BODY 5–15,
unbranched, at first nar-
rowly club-shaped, then
much broader – inverted
wrinkled head, stout, ±cir-
cular in cross-section, wrinkled and lined. STEM barely
distinct from rest of fruit
body but whole paler and
smoother towards base.
SPORE PRINT yellowish
white. SMELL faint, indefinite, pleasant. FLESH white,
turning slightly lilac-brown
when cut, spongy. Solitary
in small groups, troop-
ing or±tufted. On chalky
soil, among leaf and needle
litter in coniferous and
mixed woods. Summer –
autumn. Widespread, pre-
dominantly highland,
southern in Britain. Rare.
Edible. SPORES ellipsoid,
smooth, 6–7.5×10–13,
non-amyloid. HYPHAL SYS-
TEM monomitic.

2
Clavariadelphus fistulosus.
Overall form, habitat, variable and now considered
several separate species.
FRUIT BODY 8–25, unbran-
ched, narrowly cylindrical
– needle-like, very slender,
often curved towards base,
at first sharp at tip, then
very slightly blunted,
smooth – very finely granular. STEM barely distinct
from rest of fruit body but
whole paler and smoother
towards base. SPORE PRINT
white. SMELL indistinct?
FLESH yellowish, firm. Solitary or in small groups, trooping. On wood, among leaf
litter on fallen twigs of
broad-leaved trees, especially beech. Autumn. Wide-
spread. Rare (but var. con-
torta locally common on
alder). Inedible. SPORES±
spindle-shaped, smooth, 5
–8×10–18, non-amyloid.
HYPHAL SYSTEM monomitic.

3
Clavariadelphus junceus.
Overall form, habitat,
taste. FRUIT BODY 3–15,
unbranched, very narrowly
cylindrical – needle-like,
extremely slender, barely
narrowed towards base, at
first sharp at tip, then very
slightly blunted, smooth –
very finely granular. STEM
barely distinct from rest of
fruit body but whole hairy
towards base. SPORE PRINT
white. SMELL indefinite,
unpleasant. FLESH yellow-
ish, firm. Solitary or in
small groups, trooping. On
wood or other plant debris,
among leaf litter in broad-
leaved woods. Autumn.
Widespread. Rare. Inedi-
ble. SPORES ellipsoid –
almond-shaped, smooth,
3.5–5.5×6–12, non-
amyloid. HYPHAL SYSTEM
monomitic.

4
Clavariadelphus ligula.
Habitat, habit, overall
form. FRUIT BODY 3–8,
unbranched, narrowly club
shaped – cylindrical, fairly
slender, slightly flattened,
tapering towards base,
blunt – flattened at tip,
smooth – finely wrinkled or
grooved. STEM barely dis-
tinct from rest of fruit body
but whole hairy towards
base. SPORE PRINT white.
SMELL faint, indefinite.
FLESH white, spongy.
Usually in large – very
large trooping groups,
sometimes±tufted. On soil
among needle litter in coniferous woods. Summer –
autumn. Widespread, pre-
dominantly northern.
Rare. Inedible. SPORES
elongated – ellipsoid,
smooth, 3–4.5×10–14, non
amyloid. HYPHAL SYSTEM
monomitic.

5
Clavariadelphus pistillaris.
Size, overall form, habitat,
habit. FRUIT BODY 8–30,
unbranched, rather nar-
rowly cylindrical – broadly
club-shaped, stout, bruising
violet-brown, barely
flattened, tapering towards
base, smoothly rounded at
tip, smooth – finely wrinkled or grooved. STEM often
barely distinct from rest of
fruit body but whole more
wrinkled and hairy toward
base. SPORE PRINT yellowish
white. SMELL faint,
unpleasant, sickly. FLESH
white, spongy, turning
violet-brown when cut.
Solitary or in small trooping groups. On chalky soil
among leaf litter in beech
woods. Autumn. Wide-
spread. Uncommon. Inedi-
ble. SPORES elongated –
ellipsoid, smooth, 6–
10×11–16, non amyloid.
HYPHAL SYSTEM monomitic.

6
Clavulina cinerea **Grey
Coral Fungus.** Overall
form, colour. FRUIT BODY
3–11, many times bran-
ched, branches rather narrowly cylindrical, slender,
often parasitised by *Hel-
minthosphaeria clavar-
iarum*, often rather wavy,
often slightly flattened,
usually blunt and not
forked at tips, finely
grooved. STEM 0.5–3, rather
stout, usually±flattened,
paler than rest of fruit
body. SPORE PRINT white.
SMELL unpleasant. FLESH
whitish, soft, rather tough.
Solitary or in small groups,
trooping or±tufted. On soil
and among leaf litter or
other plant debris in
woods. Summer – autumn.
Widespread. Very com-
mon. Edible. SPORES
broadly ellipsoid –
subspherical, smooth, 6–
9×7–10, non-amyloid.
Basidia 2-spored. HYPHAL
SYSTEM monomitic.

7
Clavulina cristata **Crested
Coral Fungus.** Overall
form, colour. FRUIT BODY
2–8, 1 – many times bran-
ched especially towards
acute tips, branches club-
shaped, circular – flattened
in cross-section, fairly slender, forked many times and
paler at tips to become
fringed or toothed, smooth,
finely grooved. STEM 0.5–3,
rather stout, usually±flat-
tened. SPORE PRINT white.
SMELL indistinct. FLESH
whitish, soft, rather tough.
Solitary or in small groups,
trooping or±tufted, some-
times in small rings. On soil
and among leaf litter or
other plant debris in woods,
especially with coniferous
trees. Summer – autumn.
Widespread. Very com-
mon. Edible. SPORES
broadly ellipsoid – sub-
spherical, smooth, 6–7.5×
7–9, non-amyloid, Basidia
2-spored. HYPHAL SYSTEM
monomitic.

8
Clavulina amethystina. Colour, overall form. FRUIT
BODY 2–8, 1 – many times
branched especially to-
wards tips, branches±cyl-
indrical, fairly stout, usu-
ally±forked – finger-like at
tips, smooth – finely wrinkled. STEM 0.5–3, rather
stout, usually±cylindrical,
paler than rest of fruit body.
SPORE PRINT white. SMELL ?
FLESH whitish with violet
flush, soft, rather fragile.
Solitary or in small groups,
trooping or±tufted. On soil
and among leaf litter or
other plant debris in woods,
especially with broad-
leaved trees. Autumn.
Widespread. Rare. Inedi-
ble? SPORES broadly
ellipsoid – subspherical,
smooth, 6–8×7–12, non-
amyloid. Basidia 2-spored.
HYPHAL SYSTEM monomitic.

163

CLAVARIACEAE

Clavulina rugosa **Wrinkled Coral Fungus.** Habit, overall form. FRUIT BODY 5–10, unbranched or 1 – few times branched towards tips, branches club-shaped, ±flattened in cross-section, fairly slender, usually± twisted, blunt at tips, grooved, wrinkled. STEM barely distinct from rest of fruit body. SPORE PRINT white. SMELL indistinct. FLESH whitish, soft-elastic, rather fragile. Solitary or in small groups,±tufted. On soil and among leaf litter in woods. Summer – autumn. Widespread. Common. Edible. SPORES broadly ellipsoid – subspherical, smooth, 7.5–11×9–14, non-amyloid. Basidia 2-spored. HYPHAL SYSTEM monomitic.

Clavulinopsis corniculata. Habit, colour, smell. FRUIT BODY 1.5–7, unbranched or 1-few branched especially towards tips (highly branched in the commonest form var. *pratensis*), circular – slightly flattened in cross-section, fairly slender, often twisted, usually tapering downwards – ± spindle shaped, blunt and sometimes incurved at tips, smooth. STEM 0.5–4, paler than rest of fruit body, white downy. SPORE PRINT white. SMELL mealy-rancid, unpleasant. FLESH yellowish, firm, tough. Solitary or tufted. On soil, especially among grass, on lawns, in woods and fields. Summer – autumn. Widespread. Common. Edible. SPORES subspherical, smooth, 4.5–6×4–7, non-amyloid. HYPHAL SYSTEM monomitic.

Clavulinopsis fusiformis **Golden Spindles.** Habit, colour, habitat. FRUIT BODY 5–12, unbranched, spindle-shaped, circular – slightly flattened in cross-section, often grooved, slender, often slightly wavy or twisted,±pointed at tips, smooth. STEM absent. SPORE PRINT white. SMELL indistinct. FLESH yellowish, rather fibrous, fragile. Tufted. On soil, especially among grass and mosses on poor, acid sites, woods, heaths, fields. Summer – autumn. Widespread. Uncommon. Inedible. SPORES broadly ellipsoid – subspherical, smooth, 4.5–7.5×5–8, non-amyloid. HYPHAL SYSTEM monomitic.

Clavulinopsis pulchra (=*laeticolor*). Habit, colour, size, often confused with *C. helvola* but spores differ. FRUIT BODY 2–4, unbranched, cylindrical – spindle-shaped – narrowly club-shaped, usually±circular in cross-section, slender, often slightly wavy, fairly blunt at tips,± smooth. STEM absent. SPORE PRINT white. SMELL indistinct. FLESH pale yellow, soft. Solitary or trooping, rarely±tufted. On soil among leaf litter and other plant debris in woods. Summer – autumn. Widespread. Rare. Inedible. SPORES broadly ellipsoid – subspherical, smooth, 3.5–5×4.5–6, non-amyloid. HYPHAL SYSTEM monomitic.

Typhula quisquiliaris. Size, habitat, habit. FRUIT BODY 0.2–0.4, unbranched, cylindrical – club-shaped, usually±circular in cross section, rather stout, blunt at tip,±smooth. STEM 0.2–0.4, circular in cross-section, slender, smooth, arising from yellowish sclerotium embedded in substrate. SPORE PRINT white. SMELL indistinct. FLESH white – colourless, very soft, fragile. Trooping usually in±straight lines. On dead stalks of bracken (*Pteridium*), on the ground or still standing. Autumn. Widespread. Rare. Inedible. SPORES elongated-ellipsoid – cylindrical, often concave on one side, smooth, 3.5–5×9–11.5, non-amyloid. HYPHAL SYSTEM monomitic.

Clavulinopsis luteoalba. Habit, colour, FRUIT BODY 3–6, unbranched, circular – slightly flattened in cross-section, fairly slender, usually tapering downwards – ±club shaped, blunt – very slightly forked at tip,± smooth. STEM barely distinct from rest of fruit body. SPORE PRINT white. SMELL musty. FLESH yellow, soft, fairly fragile. Solitary or in small groups, trooping or± tufted. On soil, especially among grass, on lawns, in woods and fields. Autumn. Widespread. Rare. Inedible. SPORES ellipsoid, smooth, 2.5–4×5–8, non-amyloid. HYPHAL SYSTEM monomitic.

Clavulinopsis cinerioides. Habit, colour, spores. FRUIT BODY 2–7, 1–few branched, circular – very slightly flattened in cross section, fairly slender,±equal, blunt at tips, smooth. STEM barely distinct from rest of fruit body. SPORE PRINT white. SMELL? FLESH whitish, fairly firm, tough. Tufted. On soil in woods. Autumn. Widespread. Rare. Inedible. SPORES spherical, smooth, 4–6, non-amyloid. HYPHAL SYSTEM monomitic.

Clavulinopsis helvola. Habit, colour, size, often confused with *C. fusiformis* but smaller and spores especially differ. FRUIT BODY 2–7, unbranched, spindle-shaped – narrowly club-shaped, usually flattened in cross-section, often grooved, slender, often slightly wavy or twisted, fairly blunt and occasionally±forked at tips,±smooth. STEM absent. SPORE PRINT white. SMELL indistinct. FLESH pale yellow, fibrous, firm. Solitary or trooping – ±tufted. On soil, especially among grass and mosses, in woods and fields. Summer – autumn. Widespread. Common. Inedible. SPORES broadly ellipsoid – subspherical, warty-angular, 4–6×4–7, non-amyloid.

amariopsis kunzei. Over-
| form, colour, spores.
ʁUIT BODY 4–12, 1–many
nes branched, cylindrical,
ʌtward curving – spread-
g, usually±circular –
ɡhtly flattened in cross-
ction, fairly slender,
unt at tip, ±smooth. STEM
·5, ±circular – slightly
ʌttened in cross-section,
ender, smooth. SPORE
ɪNT white. SMELL ? FLESH
hite, fairly firm, fragile.
SPORES spherical,
e. SPORES spherical,
ooping – ±tufted. On soil
ɒlitary or in groups,
ɒooping – ±tufted. On soil
ɩong grass, fields, pas-
res, open grassy places in
ɒods. Summer – autumn.
′idespread. Rare. Inedi-
e. SPORES spherical,
ɩooth, 3.5–5, non-
ɩyloid. HYPHAL SYSTEM
ɒnomitic.

CONIOPHORACEAE

CONIOPHORACEAE
Very similar to some mem-
bers of Corticiaceae (q.v.)
but saprotrophic with
spores brown and walls
strongly cyanophilic.

Coniophora puteana. Overall form, colour, habitat,
microscopic features. FRUIT
BODY irregular, resupinate,
tightly attached to subs-
trate, smooth – irregularly
warty, lumpy or wrinkled,
floury, margin paler,
broad, fringed. SPORE PRINT
pale buff-brown. FLESH
whitish, very thin, soft,
fibrous. On wood, dead
trunks and branches of
standing trees, fallen logs,
structural timber in buildings as the major cause of
wet rot. All year. Wide-
spread. Common. SPORES
broadly ellipsoid, smooth,
7–9×10–15. Strongly
cyanophilic. Basidia 60–75,
club-shaped – urn-shaped,
4–spored. Cystidia absent.
HYPHAL SYSTEM monomitic.

CORTICIACEAE
Fruit body resupinate,
effused – effuso-reflexed,
rarely otherwise and/or
with stem, surface membranous, delicately hairy, cottony, waxy or gelatinous,
rarely tubular, usually
smooth but sometimes
granular, toothed or otherwise ornamented. Usually
white or dull-coloured.
Smell usually indistinct.
Spores variously shaped,
usually regular in outline,
smooth – sparsely
ornamented, not or weakly
cyanophilic, usually non-
amyloid. Spore print white,
pink, lilac or rarely other
colours. Basidia with 2, 4,
6, or 8 spores. Cystidia,
when present, variable.
Typically on wood, but also
on soil or plant debris.
None edible. Saprotrophic
or biotrophic. Hyphal system monomitic or more
rarely dimitic.

Botryobasidium pruinatum.
Overall form, colour, habitat, microscopic features.
FRUIT BODY irregular,
resupinate, loosely
attached to substrate,
smooth – finely net-
patterned – delicately
hairy, margin narrow.
SPORE PRINT white. FLESH
whitish, very thin, soft,
cottonwool-like. On dead
wood, especially of broad-
leaved trees. Spring –
autumn. Widespread.
Uncommon. SPORES
broadly ellipsoid, smooth,
2.5–3.5×5.5–8, weakly
cyanophilous, non-
amyloid. Basal hyphae
broad, rather straight,
roughened. Basidia 15–
22, ±cylindrical, con-
stricted, 4–8-spored. Cystidia absent. HYPHAL SYSTEM
monomitic.

*Botryobasidium subcorona-
tum.* Overall form, colour,
habitat, microscopic fea-
tures. FRUIT BODY irregular,
resupinate, tightly attached
to substrate, at first loosely
downy, then densely
velvety-smooth, margin
narrow. SPORE PRINT white.
FLESH whitish, very thin,
soft, cottonwool-like. On
dead wood, especially of
beech. Summer – autumn.
Widespread. Common.
SPORES ellipsoid – boat-
shaped, smooth, 3–3.5×6–
9, weakly cyanophilous,
non-amyloid. Basal hyphae
fairly broad, rather
straight, smooth. Basidia
12–18, ±cylindrical, often
constricted, 6–8-spored.
Cystidia absent. HYPHAL
SYSTEM monomitic.

CORTICIACEAE

*Botryohypochnus isabelli-
nus.* Microscopic features,
overall form, colour. FRUIT
BODY irregular, resupinate,
loosely attached to subs-
trate, densely velvety, margin narrow, finely fringed.
SPORE PRINT yellowish.
FLESH yellowish, very thin,
soft, cottonwool-like. On
dead wood of broad-leaved
and coniferous trees.
Summer – autumn. Wide-
spread. Uncommon.
SPORES subspherical, spiny,
5.5–9×6–10.5 (excluding
spines), weakly cyanophi-
lous, non-amyloid. Basal
hyphae with markedly
right-angled branches,
smooth. Basidia 15–20,
cylindrical, 4–spored. Cystidia absent. HYPHAL SYSTEM
monomitic.

Sistotrema brinkmannii.
Microscopic features, habitat, overall form, colour.
FRUIT BODY irregular,
resupinate, tightly attached
to substrate, smooth –
warty or delicately hairy-
downy, margin indefinite,
floury-mealy. SPORE PRINT
white. FLESH whitish, very
thin, soft, waxy-powdery.
On dead wood of broad-
leaved and coniferous
trees, fungal fruit bodies,
plant debris, soil. All year.
Widespread. Uncommon.
SPORES ellipsoid, sometimes
concave on one side or
slightly boat-shaped,
smooth, 2–2.5×3.5–5.5,
non-amyloid. Basidia 10–
22, urn-shaped, 6–8-
spored. Cystidia absent.
HYPHAL SYSTEM monomitic.

CORTICIACEAE

Amphinema byssoides.
Margin features, overall texture, habitat, microscopic features. FRUIT BODY usually very irregular and patchy, resupinate, loosely attached to substrate, delicately and loosely hairy-downy, margin irregular, fringed, usually with long yellowish rhizomorphs, floury-mealy. SPORE PRINT white. FLESH whitish, very thin, loosely fibrous. On dead wood of broad-leaved and coniferous trees, especially on underside of fallen logs, also debris of ferns, mosses and other plants. All year. Widespread. Rare. SPORES ellipsoid, smooth, 2–3×4–5, non-amyloid. Basidia 15–23, club-shaped, 2–4-spored. Cystidia cylindrical, slightly encrusted at tip. HYPHAL SYSTEM monomitic.

Gloeoporus dichrous.
Overall form, similar to 'true' polypores (pp. 177–184) but pore mouths spore-bearing. FRUIT BODY 1–3, annual, resupinate, effuso-reflexed or bracket-like, tightly attached to substrate, at first densely flattened velvety above, then smoother, barely zoned, margin sharp and slightly wavy. PORE SURFACE (beneath) at first pale reddish, then dark purple, then brownish, white floury when young, margin white and ±downy. Tubes 0.5–1 deep, gelatinous. Pores 4–6/mm, round-angular. SPORE PRINT white. FLESH 2–4 thick, white, loose – ±woolly. Usually in large, overlapping and fused groups. On dead wood of broad-leaved trees causing white soft rot, also on dead

fruit bodies of polypores. Spring – autumn. Widespread. Rare. SPORES cylindrical – sausage-shaped, smooth, 0.5–1.5×3.5–5.5, non-amyloid. Pore mouths spore-bearing. HYPHAL SYSTEM monomitic.

Cristella candidissima (= *Trechispora mollusca*). Microscopic features, fruit body surface, flesh. FRUIT BODY irregular, resupinate, thin, effused, loosely attached to substrate, membranous-waxy, margin irregular, fringed, usually with long white rhizomorphs, porous with pores 1–4/mm, angular. SPORE PRINT white. FLESH white, thin, downy, fragile. On dead wood of broad-leaved and coniferous trees, especially on underside of fallen logs and leaves. All year. Widespread. Uncommon. SPORES broadly ellipsoid – subspherical, finely spiny, 2.5–4×3.5–5.5, non-amyloid. Basidia 12–14, cylindrical, slightly constricted, 4–spored. Cystidia absent. HYPHAL SYSTEM monomitic.

Cristella (= *Trechispora*) *farinacea.* Microscopic features, very variable in fruit body surface. FRUIT BODY irregular, resupinate, effused, tightly attached, at first mealy – delicately hairy, then warty – shortly spiny, margin fringed, often with white rhizomorphs. SPORE PRINT white. FLESH white, thin,±downy. On very rotten wood of broad-leaved and coniferous trees, especially on underside of fallen logs. All year. Widespread. Uncommon. SPORES broadly ellipsoid – subspherical, finely spiny, 2.5–3×3–4, non-amyloid. Basidia 10–15, elongated – club-shaped, 4–spored. Cystidia absent. HYPHAL SYSTEM monomitic.

Cristella sphaerospora (= *Trechispora microspora*). Fruit body form, microscopic features. FRUIT BODY discontinuous, resupinate, effused, loosely attached to substrate, mealy-granular or finely net-like (use hand-lens), margin irregularly fringed, hairy. SPORE PRINT white. FLESH white, thin, softly downy. On very rotten wood of broad-leaved and coniferous trees. Summer – autumn. Widespread. Rare. SPORES broadly ellipsoid – subspherical, irregularly warty, 2.5–3×3–3.5, non-amyloid. Basidia 8–15, shortly cylindrical – ±club-shaped, 2–4-spored. Cystidia absent. HYPHAL SYSTEM monomitic.

Cristella sulphurea (= *Trechispora vaga*). Overall colour, fruit body surface, microscopic features. FRUIT BODY irregular, resupinate, tightly attached to substrate,±granular at centre, delicately hairy-fibrous, branching net-patterned towards fan-like margin, later±covered with branching yellow rhizomorphs. SPORE PRINT white. FLESH yellow, thin, softly fibrous. On rotten wood of broad-leaved and coniferous trees, especially on undersides of fallen logs, also on other plant debris. Summer-autumn. Widespread. Uncommon. SPORES ellipsoid, spiny-warty, 3–4×4–5, non-amyloid. Basidia 12–22, club-shaped, 4–spored. Cystidia absent. HYPHAL SYSTEM monomitic.

Athelia epiphylla. Fruit body surface, flesh, microscopic features. FRUIT BODY irregular, resupinate, effused, loosely attached to substrate, membranous-smooth, cracking irregularly when dry into detachable pieces, thinning markedly and almost fibrous at margin. SPORE PRINT white. FLESH whitish ochre, very thin, softly fibrous. On wood, dead branches, fallen logs, also leaf litter and other plant debris. All year. Widespread. Uncommon. SPORES elongated ellipsoid, smooth, 3–3.5×6–7.5, non-amyloid. Basidia 12–18, club-shaped, 4-spored. Cystidia absent. HYPHAL SYSTEM monomitic.

Athelia (= *Corticium*) *sublaeve* (= *Ceraceomyces sublaevis*). Fruit body surface, flesh, microscopic features. FRUIT BODY irregular, resupinate, effused, loosely attached to substrate, membranous-smooth – rather puckered, often cracking when dry, thinning markedly towards delicately hairy margin. SPORE PRINT white. FLESH whitish cream, thin, waxy, soft. On rotten wood and dead branches of coniferous trees. Summer – autumn. Widespread. Uncommon. SPORES subspherical, smooth, 2–3×3–4, non-amyloid. Basidia 18–28, elongated club-shaped, 4-spored. Cystidia sparse, cylindrical, blunt. HYPHAL SYSTEM monomitic.

iloderma byssinum. Fruit
ody surface, flesh, micros-
opic features. FRUIT
ODY ± discontinuous,
esupinate, effused, loosely
tached to substrate,
embranous-smooth, very
ely warty or porous (use
and-lens), margin
elicately hairy-downy with
e white rhizomorphs.
PORE PRINT white. FLESH
hite, thin, downy, soft.
n rotten wood, leaf litter
nd other plant debris.
ummer – autumn. Wide-
pread. Uncommon.
PORES broadly ellipsoid –
pread, 2.5–
5×3.5–4, non-amyloid.
asidia 10–18, club-
aped, rather markedly
alked, 2–4-spored. Cysti-
ia absent. HYPHAL SYSTEM
onomitic.

lyphoderma argillaceum.
verall fruit body form and
urface, flesh, microscopic
eatures. FRUIT BODY irregu-
ar, resupinate, effused,
ather loosely attached to
ubstrate, waxy-smooth,
ery finely downy or porous
use hand-lens), margin
ealy-floury. SPORE PRINT
hite. FLESH white, thin,
axy, soft. On rotten wood
f broad-leaved or conifer-
us trees, especially on
nderside of fallen logs.
pring – autumn. Wide-
pread. Uncommon.
PORES broadly ellipsoid,
mooth, 3.5–4.5×8–10,
on-amyloid. Basidia 15–
0, elongated-club-shaped,
-spored. Cystidia±spin-
le-shaped – cylindrical,±
mooth. HYPHAL SYSTEM
onomitic.

Hyphoderma puberum.
Overall fruit body form and
surface, microscopic fea-
tures. FRUIT BODY irregular,
resupinate, effused, tightly
attached to substrate,
membranous-smooth, very
finely downy (use hand-
lens), margin indefinite,
mealy-floury. SPORE PRINT
white. FLESH white, thin,
membranous-waxy, soft.
On rotten wood of broad-
leaved or coniferous trees.
Spring – autumn. Wide-
spread. Uncommon.
SPORES elongated-ellipsoid,
slightly concave on side-
almost boat-shaped,
smooth, 4–5×8–11, non-
amyloid. Basidia 22–35,
cylindrical – club-shaped,
4-spored. Cystidia spindle-
shaped – cylindrical,
strongly incrusted from
half-way. HYPHAL SYSTEM
monomitic.

Hyphoderma radula. Overall fruit body form and surface, microscopic features.
FRUIT BODY at first 2–
4,±circular, then irregular,
resupinate, effused, tightly
attached to substrate, at
first irregularly wrinkled-
warty, then irregularly
spiny, margin usually
rather sharp – slightly
fibrous. SPORE PRINT
white. FLESH white, fairly
thin, waxy-fleshy, soft. On
rotten wood of broad-
leaved or less commonly
coniferous trees. All year.
Widespread. Uncommon.
SPORES cylindrical, smooth,
3–3.5×8–13, non-amyloid.
Basidia 16–30, cylindrical –
club-shaped, 4-spored.
Cystidia±worm-like, not
emerging. HYPHAL SYSTEM
monomitic.

*Hyphoderma praetermis-
sum (=tenue).* Overall fruit
body form and surface,
microscopic features. FRUIT
BODY irregular, resupinate,
effused, loosely attached to
substrate, smooth or
slightly warty, margin
usually rather sharp –
slightly fibrous. SPORE PRINT
white. FLESH white, fairly
thin, waxy, soft. On rotten
wood of broad-leaved or
coniferous trees. All year.
Widespread. Uncommon.
SPORES elongated ellipsoid
– cylindrical, sometimes
slightly flattened on one
side, smooth, 3.5–4.5×8–
10, non-amyloid. Basidia
25–30, club-shaped, 4-
spored. Cystidia±cylindri-
cal, some slightly incrusted,
mixed with swollen vesicu-
lose cells. HYPHAL SYSTEM
monomitic.

Hyphoderma setigerum.
Microscopic features. FRUIT
BODY irregular, resupinate,
effused, tightly attached to
substrate, finely hairy,
smooth – warty, sometimes
slightly toothed, margin
rather hairy and delicately
hairy-downy. SPORE PRINT
white. FLESH white, thin,
waxy, soft. On rotten wood
of broad-leaved or coniferous trees. All Year. Widespread. Common. SPORES
elongated-ellipsoid –
cylindrical, smooth, 4–
6×9–13, non-amyloid.
Basidia 40–45, elongated-
club-shaped – cylindrical,
2–4-spored. Cystidia
elongated-cylindrical,
smooth or incrusted.
HYPHAL SYSTEM monomitic.

*Hyphodontia (=Grandinia)
alutaria.* Microscopic features, fruit body surface,
habitat. FRUIT BODY
discontinuous – irregular,
resupinate, effused, tightly
attached to substrate, at
first smooth, then warty,
sometimes slightly toothed,
margin indefinite, mealy.
SPORE PRINT white. FLESH
whitish, thin, waxy-crusty,
soft. On rotten wood of
coniferous trees. Summer –
autumn. Widespread.
Rare. SPORES broadly
ellipsoid – subspherical,
smooth, 3.5–4.5×5–5.5,
non-amyloid. Basidia 20–
25, club-shaped –
cylindrical, 4-spored. Cystidia (1) cylindrical –
worm-like, often with small
head, smooth, (2) tapering,
spindle-to awl-shaped,
usually with incrusted tips.
HYPHAL SYSTEM monomitic.

*Hyphodontia (=Grandinia)
crustosa.* Microscopic features, fruit body surface,
habitat. FRUIT BODY irregular, resupinate, effused,
tightly attached to sub-
strate, at first smooth, then
warty and irregularly
toothed, cracked when dry,
margin fairly sharp-fringed.
SPORE PRINT white. FLESH
whitish, thin, waxy-crusty,
soft. On rotten wood of
broad-leaved (or rarely
coniferous?) trees. Spring.
Widespread. Rare. SPORES
elongated-ellipsoid,
smooth, 2–3.5×5.5–7, non-
amyloid. Basidia 15–30,
club-shaped – cylindrical,
2–4-spored. Cystidia tapering, spindle-shaped,
smooth. HYPHAL SYSTEM
monomitic.

CORTICIACEAE

Hyphodontia (=*Grandinia*) *pallidula*. Microscopic features, fruit body surface, habitat. FRUIT BODY irregular, resupinate, effused, fairly tightly attached to substrate, mealy-smooth – warty, margin fairly sharp-fringed. FLESH whitish, thin, waxy, soft. On rotten wood of coniferous or rarely broad-leaved trees. Summer – autumn. Widespread. Uncommon. SPORES ellipsoid, smooth, 2.5–3×3.5–5, non-amyloid. Basidia 10–15, club-shaped – cylindrical, 4-spored. Cystidia cylindrical – worm-like. HYPHAL SYSTEM monomitic.

Hyphodontia papillosa (=*Grandinia nespori*). Microscopic features, fruit body surface. FRUIT BODY irregular, resupinate, effused, tightly attached to substrate, granular-mealy, densely warty, margin fairly sharp-fringed. SPORE PRINT white. FLESH whitish, thin, waxy, soft. On rotten wood of coniferous or broad-leaved trees. Summer – autumn. Widespread. Uncommon. SPORES elongated-ellipsoid – cylindrical, smooth, 2.5–3×4.5–5, non-amyloid. Basidia 10–18, elongated-club-shaped – cylindrical, slightly constricted, 2–4-spored. Cystidia barely differentiated from hyphae, worm-like, sometimes irregularly and coarsely incrusted. HYPHAL SYSTEM monomitic.

Hyphodontia (=*Grandinia*) *breviseta*. Microscopic features, habitat, fruit body surface. FRUIT BODY irregular, resupinate, effused, tightly attached to substrate, at first densely woolly-velvety, then warty or toothed (use hand-lens), margin at first indefinite, then sharp. SPORE PRINT white. FLESH whitish, thin, crusty-chalky. On dead wood of coniferous (or broad-leaved?) trees. All year. Widespread. Rare. SPORES ellipsoid, smooth, 3–4×5.5–6.5, non-amyloid. Basidia 15–25, elongated-club-shaped, 2–4-spored. Cystidia barely differentiated from hyphae, worm-like, sometimes with small swollen head and liquid drops. HYPHAL SYSTEM monomitic.

Hyphodontia (=*Lyomyces*) *sambuci*. Habitat, fruit body surface. FRUIT BODY irregular, resupinate, effused, tightly attached to substrate, smooth, membranous, like white emulsion paint, margin variable, indefinite – sharp. SPORE PRINT white. FLESH white, thin, crusty-chalky. On dead wood of broad-leaved trees and shrubs, especially *Sambucus nigra*, (also coniferous trees?) All year. Widespread. Common. SPORES ellipsoid, smooth, 4–5×5–7, non-amyloid. Basidia 15–25, elongated-club-shaped – cylindrical, 2–4-spored. Cystidia narrowly cylindrical – spindle-shaped often with head, sparsely incrusted. HYPHAL SYSTEM monomitic.

Hypochnicium punctulatum. Microscopic features, fruit body surface. FRUIT BODY discontinuous – irregular, resupinate, effused, tightly attached to substrate, smooth – porous, slightly warty, margin variable indefinite – sharp. SPORE PRINT white. FLESH whitish, thin, waxy, soft. On dead wood of broad-leaved and coniferous trees. Autumn. Widespread. Rare. SPORES broadly ellipsoid, densely warty, 7–8×9–10, cyanophilic, non-amyloid. Basidia 30–50, narrowly club-shaped, 2–4-spored. Cystidia sparse, narrowly cylindrical – worm-like, smooth. HYPHAL SYSTEM monomitic.

Plicaturopsis (=*Plicatura*) *crispa*. Overall form and colour, superficially similar small bracket-like fungi have wrinkles beneath. FRUIT BODY 0.5–3, bracket-like, semi-circular – shell-shaped, upper surface densely and minutely downy, often±concentrically zoned, margin paler, wavy – ±toothed, often slightly inrolled, lower surface white – bluish grey, with forked folds, almost gill-like, sometimes with rudimentary stem. SPORE PRINT white. FLESH whitish, soft, elastic when fresh, hard and brittle when dry. Usually in very large, overlapping groups. On wood, dead branches and trunks of broad-leaved trees, especially beech. All year. Widespread. Rare. SPORES sausage-shaped, smooth, 1–1.5×3.5–4, weakly amyloid. Basidia 12–15, club-shaped, 4-spored. Cystidia absent. HYPHAL SYSTEM monomitic.

Phlebia (=*Phlebiopsis*= *Peniophora*) *gigantea*. Fruit body surface, microscopic features. FRUIT BODY irregular, often very large (>1m.), resupinate, effused, tightly attached to substrate but peeling at margin when dry, smooth – finely warty, margin sharp and distinct, greasy. SPORE PRINT white. FLESH whitish, thin, waxy, soft, tough and brittle when dry. On dead wood of coniferous trees, artificially introduced to pine stumps in managed forests as antagonistic control for *Heterobasidion annosum*. Summer – autumn. Widespread. Uncommon, locally common when introduced. SPORES ellipsoid, smooth, 2.5–3.5×5–7, non-amyloid. Basidia 12–25, elongated-club-shaped, 4-spored. Cystidia broadly spindle-shaped, incrusted from half-way. HYPHAL SYSTEM monomitic.

Phlebia hydnoides (=*Scopuloides rimosa*). Fruit body surface, microscopic features. FRUIT BODY irregular, resupinate, effused, tightly attached to substrate, smooth, waxy, with scattered tufts of slender bristly teeth, margin indistinct. SPORE PRINT white. FLESH whitish, thin, waxy, soft. On dead wood of broad-leaved trees, especially on fallen twigs and small branches and in cavities in stumps. Spring – autumn. Widespread. Common. SPORES elongated-ellipsoid-cylindrical with depression on one side, smooth, 1.5–2.5×3–4, non-amyloid. Basidia 10–15, club-shaped, 2–4-spored. Cystidia spindle-shaped, awl-shaped or cylindrical, strongly incrusted. HYPHAL SYSTEM monomitic.

...lebia merismoides (incl.
...diata). Fruit body sur-
...ce, colour, microscopic
...atures. FRUIT BODY irregu-
...r, resupinate, effused,
...htly attached to subs-
...te, markedly and
...dially folded-puckered,
...er warty, margin
...nged – slightly toothed.
...ORE PRINT white. FLESH
...itish pink, fairly thin,
...latinous, soft, tough
...hen dry. On dead wood of
...oad-leaved trees, espe-
...ally beech, birch, alder,
...lso coniferous trees?) All
...ar. Widespread. Com-
...on. SPORES elongated-
...lindrical – sausage-
...aped, smooth, 1.5–
...5×3.5–6, non-amyloid.
...asidia 15–25, elongated
...ub-shaped, 4-spored.
...ystidia sparse, club-
...aped – spindle-shaped,
...ooth. HYPHAL SYSTEM
...onomitic.

Phlebia rufa. Fruit body
surface, flesh colour, microscopic features, very
similar to *P. merismoides*
but often paler and puckering differs. FRUIT BODY
irregular, resupinate,
effused, tightly attached to
substrate, irregularly
folded-puckered – porous,
margin fringed-fibrous,
paler. SPORE PRINT white.
FLESH reddish white, thin,
gelatinous, soft, tough
when dry. On dead wood of
broad-leaved trees, espe-
cially oak. Autumn –
spring. Widespread.
Uncommon. SPORES
elongated-cylindrical –
sausage-shaped, smooth,
1.5–2×4.5–6.5, non-
amyloid. Basidia 15–25,
elongated-club-shaped, 4-
spored. Cystidia club-
shaped, smooth. HYPHAL
SYSTEM monomitic.

Mycoacia stenodon. Fruit
body surface, colour, microscopic features. FRUIT
BODY irregular, resupinate,
effused, tightly attached to
substrate, densely covered
with±blunt awl-shaped
spines (0.5–2mm), margin
fibrous-floury. SPORE PRINT
white. FLESH yellowish
white, fairly thin, waxy,
soft, brittle when dry. On
rotten wood of broad-
leaved trees, especially on
underside of fallen logs.
Summer – autumn. Wide-
spread. Uncommon.
SPORES ellipsoid – sausage-
shaped, smooth, 1–2×3–
5.5, non-amyloid. Basidia
8–10, club-shaped, 2–4-
spored. Cystidia absent.
HYPHAL SYSTEM monomitic.

Resinicium bicolor. Fruit
body surface, microscopic
features. FRUIT BODY irregular, resupinate, effused,
tightly attached to subs-
trate, densely warty-
toothed, greenish flushed
from embedded algae, mar-
gin floury-mealy. SPORE
PRINT white. FLESH whitish,
thin, waxy, soft, brittle
when dry. On dead wood of
coniferous (and broad-
leaved?) trees. All year.
Widespread. Common.
Inedible. SPORES elongated-
ellipsoid, often slightly
curved, smooth, 3–3.5×
5.5–7.5, non-amyloid. Basidia 10–20, club-shaped, 4-
spored. Cystidia (1) worm-
like with markedly swollen
tip, smooth (2) sharply
pointed with star-like apical incrustation. HYPHAL
SYSTEM monomitic.

...lebia roumeguerii. Fruit
...ody surface, flesh, micros-
...pic features. FRUIT BODY
...egular, resupinate,
...fused, tightly attached to
...bstrate, waxy-smooth,
...ery finely velvety-hairy
...se hand-lens), margin±
...ury but sharp and dist-
...ct. SPORE PRINT white.
...ESH whitish, thin, waxy,
...ft, hard and porcelain-
...ke when dry. On dead
...ood, especially fallen logs
... broad-leaved trees.
...oring. Widespread. Un-
...mmon. SPORES elong-
...ed-ellipsoid, smooth, 2.5
...×5–7, non-amyloid. Basi-
...a 10–25, club-shaped, 2–
...spored. Cystidia spindle-
...aped – conical, incrust-
...d, especially from half-
...ay. HYPHAL SYSTEM mono-
...itic.

Mycoacia fuscoatra. Fruit
body surface, colour, colour change, microscopic
features. FRUIT BODY irregular, resupinate, effused,
tightly attached to
substrate,±covered with
blunt awl-shaped spines
(0.5–2mm), markedly turn-
ing dark brown when dry,
margin fibrous-floury.
SPORE PRINT white. FLESH
greyish white, fairly thin,
waxy, soft, brittle when
dry. On rotten wood of
broad-leaved trees.
Summer – autumn. Wide-
spread. Rare. SPORES nar-
rowly ellipsoid –
cylindrical, smooth, 2–
3×4.5–6, non-amyloid.
Basidia 15–20, elongated-
club-shaped, 4-spored.
Cystidia spindle-shaped,
incrusted. HYPHAL SYSTEM
monomitic.

Mycoacia uda. Fruit body
surface, colour, chemical
test, microscopic features.
FRUIT BODY irregular,
resupinate, effused, tightly
attached to substrate,±
covered with pointed awl-
shaped spines (0.5–2mm),
margin±smooth, fibrous-
floury. SPORE PRINT white.
FLESH yellowish white,
fairly thin, waxy, soft.
KOH on fruit body reddish
purple. On rotten wood of
broad-leaved trees, espe-
cially on underside of fallen
logs. Spring – autumn.
Widespread. Common.
SPORES ellipsoid, smooth,
2.5–3.5×4–6.5, non-
amyloid. Basidia 10–20,
club-shaped, 4-spored.
Cystidia sparse, spindle-
shaped, smooth. HYPHAL
SYSTEM monomitic.

Phanaerochaete velutina.
Fruit body surface, mic-
roscopic features, very
variable in colour. FRUIT
BODY irregular, resupinate,
effused, loosely attached to
substrate, smooth-waxy –
slightly warty, very finely
velvety (use hand-lens),
margin fringed-fibrous,
often with white rhizo-
morphs. SPORE PRINT white.
FLESH whitish, thin, waxy,
soft, often cracked when
dry. On dead wood of
broad-leaved or rarely coniferous trees. All year.
Widespread. Rare. SPORES
ellipsoid, flattened on one
side, smooth, 3–4×5–8,
non-amyloid. Basidia 30–
40, elongated-club-shaped,
2–4-spored. Cystidia cylindrical – ±spindle-shaped,
incrusted, especially
towards apex. HYPHAL
SYSTEM monomitic.

CORTICIACEAE

Gloeocystidiellum porosum. Fruit body surface, microscopic features. FRUIT BODY irregular, resupinate, effused, tightly attached to substrate, smooth – slightly warty, pox-marked, margin fibrous distinct. SPORE PRINT white. FLESH whitish, thin, waxy, soft, cracked when dry. On dead wood of broad-leaved trees, especially on underside of fallen logs. Spring – autumn. Widespread. Common. SPORES ellipsoid, slightly flattened on one side, smooth, 2.5–3×4–5, amyloid. Basidia 15–25, elongated-club-shaped, 2–4-spored. Cystidia broadly spindle-shaped – cylindrical, sharply narrowed at base, with granular contents. HYPHAL SYSTEM monomitic.

Serpula himantioides. Habitat, fruit body surface, microscopic features. FRUIT BODY irregular, resupinate, effused, loosely attached to substrate and silky beneath, velvety-greasy, warty-puckered – pseudoporous, margin distinct, downy. SPORE PRINT orange-yellow. FLESH whitish, thin, silky-fibrous, soft. On dead wood of coniferous trees. Autumn. Widespread. Rare. SPORES ellipsoid, smooth, 5.5–6.5×8–11. Basidia? Cystidia ± spindle- or worm-shaped, smooth. HYPHAL SYSTEM dimitic.

Leucogyrophana mollusca. Fruit body surface, habitat, microscopic features. FRUIT BODY irregular, resupinate, effused, loosely attached to substrate and often with brown sclerotia beneath, at first smooth then complexly folded into net-like or pseudo-porous pattern, margin distinct. SPORE PRINT yellowish. FLESH whitish, rather thick, soft, fragile when dry. On dead coniferous wood, especially on underside of fallen logs, also other woody debris, such as plant boxes in gardens. Autumn. Widespread. Rare. SPORES broadly ellipsoid, some ± irregular, smooth, 3.5–4.5 ×5–7. Basidia 15–25, club-shaped, 4-spored. Cystidia absent? HYPHAL SYSTEM monomitic.

Meruliopsis corium. Habit, overall form, fruit body surface, microscopic features. FRUIT BODY irregular, resupinate, effused, fairly tightly attached to substrate, fibrous-downy, slightly zoned, or ± bracket-like with lower surface at first whitish, then brownish, warty – net-like – pseudo-porous, margin hairy-fibrous. SPORE PRINT white. FLESH whitish, thin, leathery, tough. On dead wood, especially on underside of small fallen twigs. All year. Widespread. Common. SPORES elongated-ellipsoid – cylindrical, smooth, 2.5–3.5×5–6, non-amyloid. Basidia 25–30, elongated club-shaped, 4-spored. Cystidia absent. HYPHAL SYSTEM monomitic.

Vuilleminia comedens. Habit, habitat, microscopic features. FRUIT BODY irregular, resupinate, effused, tightly attached to substrate, smooth-waxy or gelatinous-greasy, often inconspicuous when dry, margin ± velvety. SPORE PRINT white. FLESH whitish thin, waxy, soft, cracked when dry. On dead wood of broad-leaved trees, either standing or fallen, typically appearing on exposed wood from which bark has peeled away. All year. Widespread. Common. SPORES broadly cylindrical sausage-shaped, smooth, 5.5–6.5×15–20, weakly amyloid. Basidia 50–100, very narrowly club-shaped 2–4-spored. Cystidia absent. HYPHAL SYSTEM monomitic.

Serpula lacrymans. Habitat, fruit body surface, microscopic features. FRUIT BODY irregular, resupinate, effused, loosely attached to substrate, velvety-greasy, warty-puckered, margin distinct, downy also often ± bracket-like, underside net-like irregularly porous – net-like, pores yellow-reddish brown. SPORE PRINT orange-red. SMELL strong, mushroomy. FLESH whitish, lilaceous, rather thick, spongy, soft, tough. On structural timber in buildings, causing dry rot, spreading by strands over plaster, bricks, carpets and other non-living substrates. All year. Widespread. Common. SPORES ellipsoid, smooth, 5.5–8×8–11. Basidia 45–70, elongated-club-shaped, 4-spored. Cystidia ± spindle-shaped – worm-like, smooth. HYPHAL SYSTEM dimitic.

Merulius tremellosus. Habit, overall form, fruit body surface, microscopic features. FRUIT BODY sometimes irregular, resupinate, effused, tightly attached to substrate, downy-hairy, rubbery-gelatinous, but more usually bracket-like with lower surface yellowish pink-orange, folded-puckered and net-like or pseudo-porous, margin wavy, translucent. SPORE PRINT white. FLESH whitish, rather thick, gelatinous, tough, hard when dry. Usually in large, overlapping – ± fused masses. On dead wood, especially rotten stumps of broad-leaved and coniferous trees. Autumn-spring. Widespread. Common. SPORES cylindrical – sausage-shaped, smooth, 1–1.5×4–4.5, non-amyloid. Basidia 20–25, elongated-club-shaped, 4-spored. Cystidia narrowly cylindrical, sparsely incrusted. HYPHAL SYSTEM monomitic.

Meruliopsis (=Merulioporia) taxicola. Overall colour, fruit body surface, microscopic features. FRUIT BODY irregular, resupinate, effused, tightly attached to substrate, smooth – irregularly porous, especially towards centre, pores 2–5/ mm, ± rounded, tubes <1mm deep, at first ± whitish, bruising reddish brown, margin distinct, paler, velvety. SPORE PRINT white. FLESH whitish, thin, waxy. On dead wood of coniferous trees. All year. Widespread. Rare. Inedible. SPORES cylindrical – sausage-shaped, smooth, 1–1.5×3.5–5, non-amyloid. Basidia 15–25, club-shaped, 4-spored. Cystidia awl-shaped, smooth. HYPHAL SYSTEM monomitic.

abit, habitat, microscopic
atures. FRUIT BODY irregu-
r, resupinate, effused,
htly attached to subs-
ate, film-like, smooth-
ury, very finely velvety
d porous (use hand-
ns), very inconspicuous
en dry, margin indis-
ct. SPORE PRINT white.
ESH greyish, extremely
in, membranous, soft,
rd when dry. On rotten
ood of coniferous trees,
pecially spruce. Autumn.
idespread. Rare. SPORES
oadly ellipsoid, smooth,
3.5×4–5.5, non-amyloid.
asidia 10–15, cylindrical –
ub-shaped, 2–4-spored.
ystidia elongated-
lindrical with small swol-
n head. HYPHAL SYSTEM
onomitic.

Tubulicrinis subulatus.
Fruit body surface, habitat,
microscopic features. FRUIT
BODY irregular – discontinuous, resupinate, effused,
tightly attached to sub-
strate, smooth – finely
woolly, finely warty, margin finely hairy – indistinct.
SPORE PRINT white. FLESH
whitish, thin, waxy, soft.
On rotten wood of coniferous trees, especially on fallen logs. Autumn – spring.
Widespread. Uncommon.
SPORES cylindrical –
sausage-shaped, smooth,
1–2×7–9, non-amyloid.
Basidia 15–25, elongated-
club-shaped, 4-spored.
Cystidia conical – awl-
shaped, with very thick
walls and solid apex, often
incrusted towards apex.
HYPHAL SYSTEM monomitic.

Peniophora incarnata.
Overall form, colour, spore
print, flesh colour, microscopic features. FRUIT BODY
irregular, resupinate,
effused, tightly attached to
substrate, smooth – crusty,
irregularly warty, margin
fairly sharp, at first±fib-
rous. SPORE PRINT pink,
FLESH reddish orange, thin,
waxy and soft when wet,
hard and crusty when dry.
On dead wood of broad-
leaved or rarely coniferous
trees, especially on hazel
and gorse. All year. Widespread. Common. SPORES
elongated-ellipsoid – cylindrical, smooth, 3–4.5×8–
10, non-amyloid. Basidia
30–40, cylindrical – club-
shaped, 4-spored. Cystidia
(1)±spindle-shaped,
incrusted from half-way,
(2)±irregularly worm-like
with granular contents.
HYPHAL SYSTEM monomitic.

Peniophora cinerea. Overall form, spore print, microscopic features. FRUIT
BODY irregular, resupinate,
effused, tightly attached to
substrate, smooth – crusty-
warty, margin at first paler,
fairly sharp, more distinct
when older. SPORE PRINT
pinkish white. FLESH
greyish, thin, waxy and soft
when wet, hard and crusty
when dry. On dead wood of
broad-leaved (or rarely
coniferous?) trees, espe-
cially on fallen logs. All
year. Widespread. Com-
mon. SPORES cylindrical –
±sausage-shaped, smooth,
2–3.5×8–10, non-amyloid.
Basidia 30–50, elongated-
club-shaped, 4-spored.
Cystidia very numerous,
elongated-cylindrical –
broadly spindle-shaped,
incrusted towards apex.
HYPHAL SYSTEM monomitic.

Tubulicrinis glebulosus.
uit body surface, habitat,
icroscopic features. FRUIT
ODY irregular, resupinate,
fused, tightly attached to
bstrate, smooth-waxy,
ery finely bristly (use
nd-lens), margin±fib-
ous – net-like. SPORE PRINT
hite. FLESH whitish, thin,
embranous, waxy, soft.
n rotten wood of conifer-
us trees, especially on
llen logs. Autumn. Wide-
pread. Rare. SPORES cylin-
rical – sausage-shaped,
nooth, 1.5–2.5×6–9, non-
myloid. Basidia 15–25,
ub-shaped, 4-spored.
ystidia±cylindrical with
ick walls markedly thin-
ing at apex. HYPHAL SYS-
EM monomitic.

*Subulicystidium longis-
porum.* Overall form, microscopic features. FRUIT
BODY irregular – ± discontinuous, resupinate,
effused, tightly attached to
substrate, membranous-
waxy, markedly thin,
smooth – finely hairy-
floury, margin indistinct.
SPORE PRINT white. FLESH
whitish, extremely thin,
soft. On dead, (barkless?)
wood of coniferous and
broad-leaved trees.
Autumn. Widespread.
Uncommon. SPORES
elongated-cylindrical –
spindle-shaped, smooth,
1.5–2.5×10–15, non-
amyloid. Basidia 10–15,
club-shaped – urn-shaped,
4-spored. Cystidia±elong-
ated cylindrical, irregularly
incrusted. HYPHAL SYSTEM
monomitic.

Peniophora limitata. Fruit
body surface, margin fea-
tures, spore print, microscopic features. FRUIT BODY
irregular, resupinate,
effused, tightly attached to
substrate but gradually
peeling back from margin,
smooth – irregularly warty,
margin markedly darker,
fairly sharp. SPORE PRINT
pink. FLESH greyish, thin,
waxy and soft when wet,
hard and crusty when dry.
On dead wood of broad-
leaved trees, especially on
ash. All year. Widespread.
Uncommon. SPORES
elongated-ellipsoid –
cylindrical – ±sausage-
shaped, smooth, 2.5–4×8–
10, non-amyloid. Basidia
35–45, cylindrical – club-
shaped, 4-spored. Cystidia
club-shaped – spindle-
shaped, densely incrusted
from half-way. HYPHAL SYS-
TEM monomitic.

Peniophora lycii. Overall
form, spore print, cystidia.
FRUIT BODY irregular,
resupinate, effused, tightly
attached to substrate,
smooth – crusty-warty,
margin fairly sharp. SPORE
PRINT pink. FLESH greyish,
thin, waxy and soft when
wet, hard and crusty when
dry. On dead wood of
broad-leaved (or rarely
coniferous?) trees, espe-
cially on fallen twigs and
logs. All year. Widespread.
Common. SPORES
cylindrical – ±sausage-
shaped, smooth, 3–4.5×8–
12, non-amyloid. Basidia
20–30,±club-shaped, 4-
spored. Cystidia broadly
club-shaped, markedly
incrusted, often barely
emergent, and intermixed
with swollen buried cystidia. HYPHAL SYSTEM
monomitic.

171

CORTICIACEAE

Peniophora rufomarginata. Fruit body surface, habitat, spore print, microscopic features. FRUIT BODY irregular, resupinate, effused, at first tightly attached to substrate but then looser and rolling back at margin to reveal brownish underside, smooth – irregularly warty, finely cracked or crazed when dry, margin rather sharp. SPORE PRINT pink. FLESH greyish pink, thin, waxy and soft when wet, hard and crusty when dry. On dead wood of lime (*Tilia*). All year. Widespread. Uncommon. SPORES cylindrical – ±sausage-shaped, smooth, 2.5–3.5×7.5–9, non-amyloid. Basidia 30–45, cylindrical – club-shaped, 4-spored. Cystidia rather sparse, cylindrical – conical, incrusted from half-way. HYPHAL SYSTEM monomitic.

Peniophora violaceolivida. Fruit body surface, habitat, spore print, microscopic features. FRUIT BODY irregular, resupinate, effused, tightly attached to substrate, smooth – irregularly warty, finely cracked or crazed when dry, margin rather sharp. SPORE PRINT pink. FLESH greyish lilac-pink, thin, waxy and soft when wet, hard and crusty when dry. On dead wood of broad-leaved trees, especially poplar and willow. All year. Widespread. Uncommon. SPORES cylindrical – ±sausage-shaped, smooth, 2.5–3.5×7.5–9, non-amyloid. Basidia 30–45, cylindrical, often rather wavy, 4-spored. Cystidia (1) conical, incrusted from half-way, (2) club-shaped – broadly spindle-shaped with granular contents. HYPHAL SYSTEM monomitic.

Peniophora nuda. Fruit body surface, spore print, microscopic features. FRUIT BODY irregular, resupinate, effused, tightly attached to substrate, smooth – slightly irregular, finely cracked or crazed when dry, margin indistinct – fairly sharp. SPORE PRINT pink. FLESH greyish, thin, waxy and soft when wet, hard and crusty when dry. On dead wood of broad-leaved trees, especially ash. All year. Widespread. Common. Inedible. SPORES cylindrical – ±sausage-shaped, smooth, 2.5–3.5×8–10, non-amyloid. Basidia 25–35, cylindrical – club-shaped, 4-spored. Cystidia (1) conical, dark, incrusted from half-way, (2) club-shaped with swollen apex and granular contents. HYPHAL SYSTEM monomitic.

Peniophora quercina. Fruit body surface, habitat, spore print, microscopic features. FRUIT BODY irregular, resupinate, effused, at first tightly attached to substrate but then looser and rolling back at margin to reveal dark underside, smooth – slightly irregular, finely cracked when dry, margin indistinct – fairly sharp. SPORE PRINT pink. FLESH whitish, thin, waxy and soft when wet, hard and crusty when dry. On dead wood of broad-leaved trees, especially oak or beech. All year. Widespread. Common. SPORES cylindrical – ±sausage-shaped, smooth, 3–4×9–12, non-amyloid. Basidia 25–35, cylindrical – club-shaped, 4-spored. Cystidia conical, incrusted from half-way. HYPHAL SYSTEM monomitic.

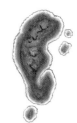

Pulcherricium caeruleum. Overall colour. FRUIT BODY irregular, resupinate, effused, tightly attached to substrate but sometimes looser at margin, smooth – irregularly warty, usually finely velvety, margin paler and rather sharp. SPORE PRINT bluish white. FLESH bluish violet, waxy and soft when wet, hard and crusty when dry. On dead wood of broad-leaved trees, especially ash and hazel. All year. Widespread. Rare. SPORES ellipsoid, smooth, 4.5–6×6.5–9, non-amyloid. Basidia 30–50, elongated-club-shaped, sometimes with short sterile braches, 4-spored. Cystidia absent. HYPHAL SYSTEM monomitic.

Cylindrobasidium evolvens. Overall fruit body form, habitat, microscopic features. FRUIT BODY irregular, resupinate, effused, tightly attached to substrate but peelable when old and dry, irregularly and rather coarsely warty, ±shiny, margin fibrous-sharp. SPORE PRINT white. FLESH whitish buff, soft, fragile, cracking. On dead wood of broad-leaved or coniferous trees, especially on cut surfaces, log piles. All year. Widespread. Common. SPORES broadly ellipsoid – pear-shaped, smooth, granular contents, often sticking together, 5–7×8–11, non-amyloid. Basidia 45–65, elongated-club-shaped, 2–4-spored. Cystidia spindle-shaped, smooth. HYPHAL SYSTEM monomitic.

GOMPHACEAE

GOMPHACEAE
Fruit body usually with stem, either with distinct fan, top or funnel-shaped cap or branched and coral-like, rarely effused. Spore-bearing surface smooth, wrinkled, folded or toothed. Often brightly-coloured. Flesh usually thin and±soft, rarely gelatinous. Smell often distinctive. Spores ellipsoid or almond-shaped – ±cylindrical, usually warty or spiny, strongly cyanophilic, non-amyloid. Spore print ochreous brown, yellowish or cream. Basidia 2–4-spored, cystidia rare. On soil, usually on and among plant debris. Few edible, few poisonous. Mycorrhizal. Hyphal system monomitic or more rarely dimitic.

Gomphus clavatus. Overall fruit body form, colour, habitat. FRUIT BODY 4–10, top-shaped, at first with±flat, smooth top, then wrinkled and slightly funnel-shaped, outer surface longitudinally wrinkled-folded with branching folds,± smooth – woolly-downy at base. SPORE PRINT yellowish. FLESH white with irregular marbling, soft, fragile. Solitary or in small groups, trooping or±tufted, often in rings. On soil in coniferous or more rarely mixed woods. Summer. Widespread, predominantly montane, southern in Britain. Rare. Edible. SPORES ellipsoid, coarsely warty, 4.5–5.5×10–14, cyanophilic, non-amyloid. Basidia 50–65, elongated-club-shaped, 4-spored. Cystidia absent. HYPHAL SYSTEM monomitic.

172

...maria eumorpha
(=invalii). Overall fruit
...dy form, colour, habitat,
...veral other similar spe-
...es but chemical test diag-
...ostic. FRUIT BODY 3–5, sev-
al times branched, coral-
...ke, fairly slender, ±circul-
in cross-section, smooth,
...ps ±pointed, forked. STEM
...5–1, paler than fruit
...ody, white woolly-downy.
...ORE PRINT yellow. SMELL
...int, indefinite or fruity.
...LESH whitish, fibrous,
...ough. KOH on flesh pink-
...h orange. Solitary or in
...nall groups, trooping
...r ±tufted, often in rings.
...n soil in coniferous
...oods. Summer – autumn.
...Videspread. Rare. Inedi-
...e. SPORES ellipsoid, spiny-
...arty, 3.5–4.5×7–9,
...yanophilic, non-amyloid.
...asidia 30–40, elongated-
...ub-shaped, 4-spored.
...ystidia absent. HYPHAL
...YSTEM monomitic.

...amaria formosa. Overall
...uit body form, colour,
...abitat. several other simi-
...r species but chemical test
...iagnostic. FRUIT BODY 5–
...5, several times branched,
...oral-like, very stout,
...attened in cross-section,
...nooth, tips ±pointed,
...orked. STEM 1–5, paler
...an fruit body, very
...out, ±white woolly-
...owny. SPORE PRINT yellow.
...MELL faint, indefinite.
...LESH white, bruising brow-
...ish, soft, firm. Iron salts
...n flesh greenish blue.
...olitary or in small groups,
...rooping or ±tufted. On soil
...mong leaf litter in broad-
...eaved woods, especially
...eech. Summer – autumn.
...Videspread. Rare. Poiso-

nous. SPORES elongated-
ellipsoid – cylindrical,
warty, 5–6×9–13,
cyanophilic, non-amyloid.
Basidia 40–50, elongated-
club-shaped, 4-spored.
Cystidia absent. HYPHAL
SYSTEM monomitic.

Ramaria aurea. Overall
fruit body form, colour,
habitat, microscopic fea-
tures. FRUIT BODY 5–12,
several times branched,
coral-like, stout, circular –
flattened in cross-section,
smooth, tips ±pointed,
forked. STEM 1–3, paler
than fruit body, stout, ±
white woolly-downy.
SPORE PRINT ochre-yellow.
SMELL faint, indefinite,
pleasant. FLESH white,
marbled, soft, firm. Solitary or in small groups,
trooping or ±tufted. On soil
among leaf litter in broad-
leaved woods, especially
beech. Summer – autumn.
Widespread. Rare. Inedi-
ble. SPORES elongated-
ellipsoid, warty, 3.5–5×8–
13, cyanophilic, non-
amyloid. Basidia 40–50,
elongated club-shaped, 4-
spored. Cystidia absent.
HYPHAL SYSTEM monomitic.

Ramaria botrytis. Overall
fruit body form, colour,
habitat, microscopic fea-
tures. FRUIT BODY 8–15,
many times branched,
cauliflower-like, stout,
circular-flattened in cross-
section, smooth, tips ±
pointed, forked, darker
than branches. STEM 2–4,
paler than fruit body, very
stout, ±white velvety. SPORE
PRINT yellowish. SMELL
faint, indefinite, pleasant.
FLESH white, soft, firm. Sol-

itary or in small groups,
trooping or ±tufted. On
soil in leaf litter in broad-
leaved woods, esp. beech.
Summer–autumn. Wide-
spread. Uncommon. Edi-
ble. SPORES elongated ellipsoid, longitudinally lined,
4.5–8×14–17, cyanophilic,
non-amyloid. Basidia 45–
60, elongated club-shaped,
4-spored. Cystidia absent.
HYPHAL SYSTEM monomitic.

Ramaria stricta. Overall
fruit body form, colour,
habitat, microscopic fea-
tures. FRUIT BODY 4–10,
many times branched,
densely coral-like, fairly
stout, ±circular in cross-
section, smooth, tips ±
pointed, forked. STEM 1–2,
paler than fruit body, very
stout, ±white velvety, with
white cords. SPORE PRINT
yellowish. SMELL unpleas-
ant, earthy-slightly ani-
seed. FLESH white, elastic,
tough. Solitary or in small
groups, trooping or ±tuft-
ed. On soil in leaf litter and
plant debris in broad-
leaved woods, esp. beech.
Summer – autumn. Wide-
spread. Uncommon. Edi-
ble. SPORES broadly ellipsoid, warty, 4–5×7.5–10,
cyanophilic, non-amyloid.
Basidia 25–35, elongated
club-shaped, 4-spored.
Cystidia absent. HYPHAL
SYSTEM monomitic.

HYDNACEAE

Fruit body ±toadstool
shaped with distinct cap
and stem. Spore-bearing
surface toothed. Often
fairly brightly coloured.
Flesh usually ±soft. Smell
sometimes distinctive.
Spores ellipsoid-
subspherical, smooth or
not. Amyloid or non-
amyloid. Spore print
white – brownish. Basidia
2–4-spored, cystidia absent.
On soil, usually on and
among plant debris. Few
edible, few poisonous.
Mycorrhizal. Hyphal sys-
tem monomitic.

Hydnum repandum. Fruit
body form, habitat, microscopic features. CAP 3–10,
first convex, then flattened
– slightly depressed,
smooth – very finely vel-
vety, sometimes wrinkled
on aging, margin often persistently inrolled. STEM 2–6,
often slightly eccentric,
stout, spindle-shaped,
smooth. SPINE SURFACE
salmon pink – whitish,
decurrent, spines <6mm,
fairly crowded. SPORE PRINT
white. SMELL faint,
indefinite, pleasant. FLESH
white, soft. Solitary or
small groups. On soil in
broad-leaved or coniferous
woods. Summer – autumn.
Widespread. Common.
Edible. SPORES broadly
ellipsoid – subspherical,
smooth, 5–6.5×6–9, non-
amyloid. Basidia 35–55,
elongated-club-shaped, 4-
spored. Cystidia absent.
HYPHAL SYSTEM monomitic.

Hydnum repandum var.
rufescens. Fruit body form,
habitat, microscopic fea-
tures, v. like *H. repandum*
but colour, spine surface
and spores differ slightly.
CAP 2–6, at first convex, then
flattened – slightly depres-
ed, smooth – very finely velvety, sometimes wrinkled
on aging, margin often persistently inrolled. STEM 1.5–
4, often slightly eccentric,
stout, spindle-shaped,
smooth. SPINE SURFACE salmon-pink – whitish, ad-
nate, spines <6mm, fairly
crowded. SPORE PRINT white.
SMELL faint, indefinite,
pleasant. FLESH white, soft.
Solitary or small groups.
On soil in broad-l. or conif.
woods. Summer – autumn.
Widespread. Uncommon.
Edible. SPORES broadly
ellipsoid – subspherical,
smooth, 6–7×8–10, non-
amyloid. Basidia 35–55,
elongated club-shaped, 4-
spored. Cystidia absent.
HYPHAL SYSTEM monomitic.

HYDNACEAE

Phellodon tomentosus. Overall fruit body form, habitat, microscopic features. CAP 2–6, flattened – depressed, markedly radially zoned, finely velvety, margin markedly paler and often slightly wavy and lobed. STEM 1–3, sometimes eccentric, ± equal, rather wavy, fairly stout, smooth – finely fibrous, often fused into common base. SPINE SURFACE at first white, then greyish, decurrent, spines <3mm, fairly crowded. SPORE PRINT white. SMELL faint, indefinite, pleasant, spicy when dry. FLESH buff-brown in cap, darker brown in stem, tough, corky. Tufted and/or in rings, often with individual bases fused. On soil in coniferous or mixed woods on acid sites, often with *Vaccinium myrtilus* Summer – autumn. Widespread. Rare. Inedible. SPORES subspherical, spiny, 2.5–3.5×4.5–5.5, non-amyloid. Basidia 20–25, elongated-club-shaped, 4-spored. Cystidia absent. HYPHAL SYSTEM monomitic.

Hericium erinaceus. Overall fruit body form, habitat, microscopic features. FRUIT BODY 3–8, cushion-like, solid, with pendulous white – yellowish spines <60mm, elongated-conical, smooth – floury, crowded. STEM not distinct from rest of fruit body. SPORE PRINT white. SMELL strong, indefinite, unpleasant. FLESH whitish, soft, tough, elastic. Solitary or in small groups. On wood, from wounds on living broad-leaved trees, especially beech. Summer-autumn. Widespread. Rare. Edible. SPORES subspherical, finely warty-spiny, 4–5.5×6–6.5, amyloid. Basidia 25–30, club-shaped, 4-spored. Cystidia worm-like with granular contents. HYPHAL SYSTEM monomitic.

Sarcodon (= Hydnum) *imbricatum.* Overall fruit body form, habitat, microscopic features. CAP 8–20, at first convex, then flattened – slightly depressed, at first smooth – very finely velvety, then cracking into ± concentrically-zoned, dark upturned scales. STEM 3–7, stout, spindle-shaped, paler towards base. SPINE SURFACE at first white, then dark purple-brown, decurrent, spines <10mm, fairly crowded. SPORE PRINT brown. SMELL faint, indefinite, pleasant. FLESH white, soft. Solitary or in small groups, trooping – ±tufted. On soil in coniferous woods. Summer – autumn. Predominantly northern. Rare. Edible. SPORES±subspherical, very irregularly warty, 5–6×6.5–8. Basidia 30–45, elongated club-shaped, 4-spored. Cystidia absent. HYPHAL SYSTEM monomitic.

Bankera fuligineo-alba. Overall fruit body form, habitat, microscopic features. CAP 5–12, at first convex, then flattened – slightly depressed, smooth – very finely hairy scaly, margin markedly paler and often slightly wavy and lobed. STEM 2–5, sometimes eccentric, ±equal, stout, finely fibrous, marked ring zone towards apex. SPINE SURFACE at first white, then reddish brown, decurrent, spines <5mm, fairly crowded. SPORE PRINT white. SMELL faint, indefinite, pleasant spicy when dry. FLESH white – pinkish, soft. Solitary or in small groups, trooping – ± tufted. On soil in coniferous woods on dry sites. Summer – autumn. Widespread. Rare. Inedible. SPORES elongated-ellipsoid – subspherical, spiny, 2.5–3.5×4.5–5.5, non-amyloid. Basidia 25–30, club-shaped, 4-spored. Cystidia absent. HYPHAL SYSTEM monomitic.

HYMENOCHAETACEAE

HYMENOCHAETACEAE Fruit body stemmed or stem-less, bracket-shaped or coral-like, more rarely resupinate, effused, annual or perennial. Spore-bearing surface smooth, warty, toothed or porous – ±concentrically gill-like. Usually whitish, brown or otherwise dull-coloured. Flesh variable, soft and fibrous or leathery to hard and corky or woody, almost always darkening with KOH. Smell rarely distinctive. Spores variously shaped, usually smooth, usually non-amyloid. Spore print white, yellow, greenish yellow or brown. Basidia 2–4-spored, cystidia occasional but characteristic setae usually present. On wood or rarely other plant material or soil. Saprotrophic or biotrophic, most causing white rot of timber. Few edible, none poisonous. Hyphal system monomitic or dimitic.

1
Hymenochaete cinnamomea. Fruit body surface, colour, habitat, microscopic features. FRUIT BODY perennial, irregular, resupinate, effused, tightly attached to substrate, smooth – velvety, margin thin,±fibrous. SPORE PRINT white. FLESH reddish buff, thin, soft, tough. On dead wood of broad-leaved (or very rarely coniferous?) trees, especially hazel. All year. Widespread. Uncommon. Inedible. SPORES elongated-ellipsoid – cylindrical, smooth 2–3×5–7.5, non-amyloid. Basidia 12–20, elongated-club-shaped, 2–4-spored. Cystidia absent. Setae 55–90, elongated-conical, brown. HYPHAL SYSTEM monomitic.

2
Hymenochaete corrugata. Fruit body surface, habitat, microscopic features. FRUIT BODY perennial, irregular, resupinate, effused, tightly attached to substrate, irregularly warty, cracked when mature, drying paler, margin at first thin, ±fibrous, then sharp. SPORE PRINT white. FLESH greyish, hard, brittle. On dead wood of broad-leaved trees, especially hazel. Summer – autumn. Widespread. Uncommon. Inedible. SPORES elongated-ellipsoid – ±sausage-shaped, smooth 1.5–2×4–6.5, non-amyloid. Basidia 10–15, elongated-club-shaped, 4-spored. Cystidia absent. Setae 40–70,

elongated-cylindrical – awl-shaped, brown. HYPHA SYSTEM monomitic.

3
Hymenochaete rubiginosa. Overall form, habitat, microscopic features. FRUIT BODY perennial, irregular, 1–4,±bracket-shaped, at least in upper part, finely downy-smooth,±concentrically zoned, margin sharp, paler, wavy, sometimes with rudimentary stem and smooth, dull orange below at first. SPORE PRINT white. SMELL indistinct. FLESH brown, leathery, tough. On dead, usually unbarked wood of oak and sweet chestnut. All year. Widespread. Rare. Inedible. SPORES ellipsoid, smooth, 4.5–6×2.5–3, non amyloid. Basidia 20–25, cylindrical – club-shaped, 4-spored. Cystidia absent. Setae 40–60,±awl-shaped dark brown. HYPHAL SYSTEM monomitic.

4
Hymenochaete fuliginosa. Overall form, habitat, microscopic features. FRUIT BODY 1–4, perennial, resupinate – ±bracket-shaped, attached at centre to substrate, upper surface smooth – very finely velvety, rather wavy and concentrically ridged, lower surface smooth – warty, at first orange-brown, then dark brown, margin paler, wavy. STEM rudimentary or absent. SPORE PRINT white. FLESH greyish brown, leathery, tough. On dead wood of broad-leaved trees, especially oak, usually barkless All year. Widespread. Very common. Inedible. SPORES ellipsoid, smooth 2.5–3×4.5–6, non-amyloid. Basidia 20–25, elongated-club-shaped, 4-spored. Cystidia absent. Setae 40–60, awl-shaped, dark brown. HYPHAL SYSTEM monomitic.

5
Coltricia perennis. Overall form, habitat, microscopic features. CAP 3–8, annual (but persisting when dead), flat but depressed at centre at first finely velvety, then±smooth, markedly concentrically zoned, margin wavy, sometimes indented. STEM 2–4,±central, fairly stout,±equal but swollen at base, often flattened, smooth – velvety. PORE SURFACE at first±white floury, then reddish brown, decurrent Tubes 0.5–3 deep, brown Pores 2–4/mm, irregularly

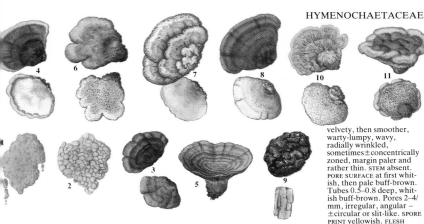

und – angular. SPORE
PRINT ochreous brown.
FLESH brown, soft, corky,
hard when dry. On soil, in
woods, at path edges, especially on sandy, acid sites.
All year. Widespread.
Common. Inedible. SPORES
ellipsoid, smooth 4–4.5×6–
5, cyanophilic, non-
amyloid. Basidia 13–25,
club-shaped, 2–4-spored.
Cystidia absent. Setae
present. HYPHAL SYSTEM
mitic.

6
Inonotus cuticularis. Microscopic features of fruit
body surface, overall colour. FRUIT BODY 8–18,
annual, bracket-like,
broadly attached, convex –
flattened above, at first
velvety, then±hairy-
bristly, then often smooth,
radially lined or irregularly
pitted, margin usually paler
and often incurved. STEM
absent. PORE SURFACE at
first yellowish, then brown.
Tubes 5–15 deep, yellowish
brown. Pores 2–3/mm, irregularly round – angular.
PORE PRINT brown. FLESH
reddish brown, soft,
porous, hard when dry.
Solitary or in overlapping
and±fused groups. On
wood of broad-leaved
trees, especially arising
from wounds on living
trees. Autumn. Wide-
spread. Rare. Inedible.
SPORES broadly ellipsoid,
smooth 4.5–6×6–8. Cysti-
dia absent. Setae 15–30,
broadly awl-shaped, dark
brown. Setae-like struc-
tures on fruit body surface
with barbed hooks, dark
brown. HYPHAL SYSTEM
monomitic.

7
Inonotus dryadeus. Habitat, fruit body surface features, microscopic features.

FRUIT BODY 5–25, annual,
bracket-like, broadly
attached, convex above,
very irregularly warty-
lumpy, at first finely
velvety, then±smooth,
darkening on aging, exud-
ing reddish liquid drops
when in active growth and
more generally at margin.
STEM absent. PORE SURFACE
at first whitish – yellow
brown, then reddish
brown, then dark brown.
Tubes 1–3 deep, dull
brown. Pores 3–5/mm,
round – angular. SPORE
PRINT yellowish white.
FLESH yellowish-reddish
brown, soft, fibrous. Solitary or in small overlapping
and±fused groups. On
wood of broad-leaved
trees, especially oak at base
of trunk, causing soft white
rot, mainly in heartwood.
All year. Widespread, predominantly central and
southern. Rare. Inedible.
SPORES subspherical,
smooth 6.5–8×7–8.5. Cys-
tidia absent. Setae 20–35,
awl-shaped with hooked
tip, swollen at base, dark
brown. HYPHAL SYSTEM
monomitic.

8
Inonotus hispidus. Fruit
body surface, flesh, habitat.
FRUIT BODY 5–25, annual,
bracket-like, broadly
attached, convex above,
markedly and densely
downy-hairy, then±bristly,
sometimes turning smooth
and dark when old. STEM
absent. PORE SURFACE at
first pale buff-brown, then
reddish brown, then±
black. Tubes 1–4 deep,
ochreous-reddish brown.
Pores 2–3/mm, angular.
SPORE PRINT pale reddish
brown. FLESH reddish
brown, soft, spongy, hard
when dry. Usually solitary.
On wood of broad-leaved

trees, especially ash, causing limited but serious
white – yellowish decay.
All year. Widespread, predominantly central and
southern. Common. Inedi-
ble. SPORES subspherical,
smooth 7–9×8–11. Cystidia
absent. Setae 20–30,
broadly awl-shaped, dark
brown. HYPHAL SYSTEM
monomitic.

9
Inonotus obliquus. Habitat,
overall form, tubes, microscopic features. FRUIT BODY
irregular, annual, resupinate, effused, at first whitish,
then±brown, smooth,
porous. Tubes <0.1, obli-
quely slanting, whitish.
Pores 3–5/mm, angular-
elongated. SPORE PRINT
white. FLESH whitish, soft,
corky, hard when dry. On
wood of broad-leaved
trees, especially birch,
causing serious white heart
rot. All year. Predomi-
nantly northern, especially
Scotland in Britain. Rare.
Inedible. SPORES ellipsoid,
smooth 5–7.5×8–10. Cysti-
dia absent, cystidia-like
cells±awl-shaped, barely
visible in dried material.
Setae 25–45, narrowly awl-
shaped, dark brown.
HYPHAL SYSTEM monomitic.
[Usually found as con-
spicuous asexual form in
same habitat, preceding
formation of above,±
irregularly hemispherical,
crusty, coal-like, fruit
bodies with 1–2-celled,
smooth, brown conidia 3.5–
5.5×7–10.]

10
Inonotus radiatus. Fruit
body surface, habit, habitat, flesh, microscopic features. FRUIT BODY 3–8,
annual, bracket-like,
broadly attached,±flat
above, at first finely

velvety, then smoother,
warty-lumpy, wavy,
radially wrinkled,
sometimes±concentrically
zoned, margin paler and
rather thin. STEM absent.
PORE SURFACE at first whitish, then pale buff-brown.
Tubes 0.5–0.8 deep, whit-
ish buff-brown. Pores 2–4/
mm, irregular, angular –
±circular or slit-like. SPORE
PRINT yellowish. FLESH
brown – reddish brown,
shiny, soft, watery-spongy,
hard and woody when dry.
Usually in small – large,
overlapping and±fused
groups. On wood of broad-
leaved trees, especially
alder causing serious white-
buff, flaky decay.
Summer – winter. Wide-
spread. Common. Inedible.
SPORES ellipsoid, smooth
3.5–4.5×4.5–7. Cystidia
absent. Setae 20–30, awl-
shaped, sometimes
hooked, usually with swollen base, dark brown.
HYPHAL SYSTEM monomitic.

11
Phaeolus schweinitzii.
Habitat, habit, overall colour, microscopic features.
FRUIT BODY 10–20, annual,
fan-shaped – bracket-
like,±flat-depressed above,
at first velvety-hairy, then
irregularly warty-hairy,
then smoother, wavy, con-
centrically zoned, margin
paler. STEM 2–6, fairly
stout, tapering downwards,
circular – flattened in
cross-section, finely
velvety, often fused. PORE
SURFACE at first yellowish,
bruising brown, then
brown. Tubes 0.5–1 deep,
yellowish brown. Pores
0.5–4 mm diam, irregular-
angular. SPORE PRINT yel-
lowish white – reddish brown,
soft. Usually in small –
large,±fused groups. On
soil from buried roots or on
stumps of conif. trees, causing brown cubical decay,
esp. old trees. Summer –
autumn. Widespread. Com-
mon. Inedible. SPORES ellipsoid, smooth 3.5–4.5×5–7,
non-amyloid. Cystidia club-
shaped – conical, often
with brown liquid drop.
Setae absent. HYPHAL SYS-
TEM monomitic.

175

HYMENOCHAETACEAE

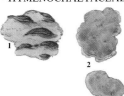

1

Phellinus conchatus. Habit, habitat, microscopic features. FRUIT BODY irregular, perennial, resupinate or 1–5,±bracket-like and broadly attached,±flat above, at first finely velvety, then smooth but concentrically zoned, often cracked when old and supporting mosses and algae, margin paler, at first sharp, then rounded. STEM absent. PORE SURFACE at first reddish brown, then greyish brown, rather wavy and warty. Tubes 0.5–1 deep, greyish. Pores 5–6/mm, round. SPORE PRINT yellowish white. FLESH reddish brown, hard, tough. Usually in large masses comprising resupinate and bracket-like components. On wood of broad-leaved trees, especially on living trunks of willows. All year, mature summer – autumn. Widespread. Uncommon, locally common. Inedible. SPORES subspherical, smooth 4.5–5×5–6, non-amyloid. Cystidia absent. Setae 15–20, irregularly awl-shaped, often with irregular tips, dark brown. HYPHAL SYSTEM dimitic.

2

Phellinus ferreus. Overall fruit body form and colour, habitat, microscopic features. FRUIT BODY irregular, perennial, resupinate, effused, smooth or irregularly wavy (contoured with substrate), porous. Tubes layered, each <3mm deep, brown. Pores 4–5/mm, round – angular. SPORE PRINT white. FLESH reddish brown – golden yellow, thin, soft, fluffy. On wood of broad-leaved trees, especially on dead or living trunks and branches of oak. All year. Widespread. Common. Inedible. SPORES cylindrical, smooth 2–2.5×6–7.5, non-amyloid. Cystidia absent. Setae 25–30, irregularly awl-shaped, usually with swollen±rooting base, dark brown. HYPHAL SYSTEM dimitic.

3

Phellinus ferruginosus. Overall fruit form body and colour, habitat, microscopic features. FRUIT BODY irregular, annual – perennial, resupinate, effused,±warty, porous. Tubes weakly layered, each 1–3mm deep, brown. Pores 4–5/mm, rounded. SPORE PRINT white. FLESH reddish brown, fairly thin, loose, soft,±woolly, rather hard and corky when old. On wood of broad-leaved trees, especially on underside of fallen logs of ash, beech, hazel, alder and willow. All year. Widespread. Common. Inedible. SPORES broadly ellipsoid, smooth 3–3.5×4–5, non-amyloid. Cystidia absent. Setae 20–40,±narrowly cylindrical, blunt, dark brown. HYPHAL SYSTEM dimitic.

4

Phellinus igniarius. Very variable, overall fruit body form, habitat, microscopic features. FRUIT BODY 5–30, perennial, bracket-like – hoof-like, flat – irregularly convex above, at first very finely velvety, then smooth, broadly grooved or wrinkled, cracked and crazed when older, often supporting mosses and algae, margin usually paler and distinct. STEM absent. PORE SURFACE yellowish brown – dark brown, sometimes greyish. Tubes indistinctly layered, each 2–5mm deep, reddish brown. Pores 4–6/mm, rounded. SPORE PRINT white. FLESH reddish brown, hard, brittle. On wood of broad-leaved trees, especially on willow, causing soft yellowish white rot. All year. Widespread, predominantly central and northern. Uncommon. Inedible. SPORES subspherical, smooth 4.5–6×5.5–7, non-amyloid. Cystidia absent. Setae 12–20, very broadly awl-shaped, dark brown. HYPHAL SYSTEM dimitic.

5

Phellinus laevigatus. Fruit body surface features and colour, microscopic features. FRUIT BODY irregular, perennial, resupinate, or, on vertical substrates, shortly bracket-like, smooth, often slightly grooved, cracked when older, porous. Tubes indistinctly layered, each 1–4mm deep, dark brown. Pores 5–8/mm, rounded. SPORE PRINT white. FLESH reddish brown, thin, corky, tough. On wood of broad-leaved trees, especially dead stems and branches of birch. All year. Widespread. Rare. Inedible. SPORES broadly ellipsoid, smooth, 3–4×4–5, non-amyloid. Cystidia absent. Setae 10–20, very irregular, usually with sharp tips and swollen base, dark brown. HYPHAL SYSTEM dimitic.

6

Phellinus pini. Habitat, overall fruit body form, microscopic features. FRUIT BODY 5–20, perennial, bracket-like, broadly attached, irregularly convex above, at first finely velvety, then±hairy, then smooth except at margin, rather markedly radially grooved, often supporting mosses, lichen and algae. STEM absent. PORE SURFACE yellowish – reddish brown, sometimes greyish brown. Tubes indistinctly layered, each 4–7mm deep, light brown. Pores 1–2/mm, angular. SPORE PRINT white – yellowish. FLESH deep reddish brown, fairly thin, woody, hard. On wood of living pines or, outside Britain, also larch, often very high on trunk, causing serious decay, at first reddish then white and pocketed. All year. Widespread, predominantly northern in Britain. Rare. Inedible. SPORES subspherical, smooth, 4–5×4.5–5.5, non-amyloid. (Slightly larger, spherical dark brown conidia also occur). Cystidia absent. Setae 40–80, broadly awl-shaped, dark brown. HYPHAL SYSTEM dimitic.

7

Phellinus pomaceus (=*tuberculosus*). Habitat, overall fruit body form, microscopic features. FRUIT BODY 3–10, perennial, variable,±resupinate – bracket-like or hoof-like, broadly attached – decurrent onto substrate, irregularly bulbous – convex above, at first fine velvety, then finely cracked-crazed, except at smooth grooved margin, often supporting algae. STEM absent. PORE SURFACE brown – dark brown, margin paler. Tubes indistinctly layered, each 2–3mm deep, brown. Pores 5–6/mm, rounded – angular. SPORE PRINT white – yellowish. FLESH bright reddish brown, sometimes yellowish, thick, corky, tough. On wood of living or dead *Prunus* spp. especially on plum, causing white, crumbly heartwood decay. All year. Widespread. Common. Inedible. SPORES subspherical, smooth, 4.5–5×5.5–6.5, non-amyloid. Setae 12–20, awl-shaped, with broadly swollen base, dark brown. HYPHAL SYSTEM dimitic.

FISTULINACEAE

Fruit body with short or very short rooting stem, bracket or tongue-shaped, annual. Spore-bearing surface densely porous with free tubes, each constricted at the base. Usually predominantly brownish. Flesh coarsely fibrous or softly corky, juicy. Smell very strong, unpleasant when fresh. Spores subspherical – broadly ellipsoid, smooth, non-amyloid. Spore print white or very faintly reddish brown. Basidia 4-spored, cystidia absent, setae absent. On wood. Saprotrophic or biotrophic. Some edible, none poisonous. Hyphal system monomitic.

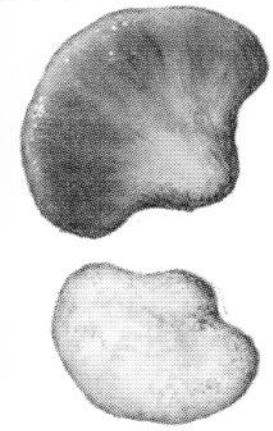

ılina hepatica **Beefsteak gus**. Overall fruit body ı, colours, habitat, mic- opic features. FRUIT ʏ 6–20, annual, tongue- bracket-like, ±convex, ⁄ finely spiny-warty, ally grooved or owed, ±sticky. STEM mentary. PORE SURFACE rst white-yellowish, sing reddish brown, ı reddish brown. Tubes ly separable, <12mm p, white-yellowish. es 2–3/mm, rounded. ʀE PRINT white- owish. FLESH at first te-yellowish, then red- pink, mottled, like raw ıt, soft, fleshy. Often tary. On wood of living lead oaks or sweet stnut, (or rarely other ad-leaved trees) usually ower part of trunk, sing 'brown oak' stain- and sometimes then ay. Late summer – ımn. Widespread. Very ımon. Edible. SPORES adly ellipsoid – spherical, smooth, 3.5– ×5–6, non-amyloid. ıtidia absent. HYPHAL ᴛEM monomitic.

NODERMATACEAE
it body stemmed or nless, ±bracket-shaped, ual or perennial. Spore- ring surface densely ous, pores small – very ıll, tubes narrow, often ɜred. Usually predomi- tly brownish. Flesh iable. Smell not usually inctive. Spores spher- – ellipsoid, smooth or arently spiny because of nplex structure of cell ls. Spore print brown. ıidia 4–spored, cystidia ent, setae absent. On od. Saprotrophic or trophic. Some edible, ıe poisonous. Hyphal ɜem trimitic.

1
ıoderma adspersum ıustrale). Overall fruit ly form, very similar to *ıpplanatum* but pore face features, flesh and re size differs. FRUIT ʏ 10–50, perennial, cket-like, broadly ıched, ±flat but wavy ve, smooth or slightly

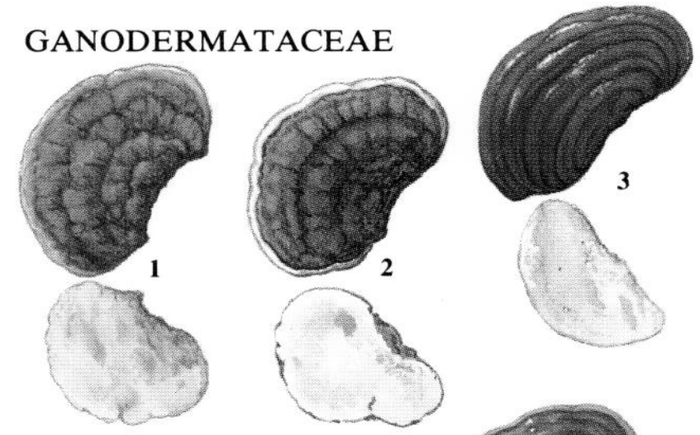

warty, ±zoned, often fairly regularly grooved, usually coloured reddish brown from deposited spores, margin pale and slightly swollen. STEM absent. PORE SURFACE at first cream-whitish, bruising brownish, then greyish brown. Tubes layered, each <12mm deep, brown, never affected by insect galls. Pores 4–5/mm, rounded. SPORE PRINT brown. FLESH dark reddish brown, thicker than tube layer, concentrically zoned, fibrous. Solitary or in small, overlapping groups. On wood of living broad-leaved trees, usually on lower part of trunk, especially in gardens and parks, less usually on wild trees, causing white, soft rot. All year. Widespread. Extremely common. Inedible. SPORES ellipsoid, flattened at one end, apparently warty, 6–8×9–11.5. Cystidia absent. Setae absent. HYPHAL SYSTEM trimitic.

2
Ganoderma applanatum **Artist's Fungus**. Overall fruit body form, very similar to *G. adspersum* but pore surface features and spore size differs. FRUIT BODY 10–50, perennial, bracket-like, broadly attached, ±flat but wavy above, smooth or slightly warty, ±zoned, often fairly regularly grooved, usually coloured reddish brown from deposited spores, margin pale and slightly swollen. STEM absent. PORE SURFACE at first cream-whitish, bruising brownish, then greyish brown. Tubes layered, each <12mm deep, brown, often affected by cone-shaped insect galls. Pores 4–5/mm, rounded. SPORE PRINT brown. FLESH dark reddish brown, concentrically zoned, fibrous. Solitary or in small, overlapping groups. On wood of living or dead broad-leaved trees, especially beech. All year. Widespread. Uncommon. Inedible. SPORES ellipsoid, flattened at one end, apparently warty, 5–6.5×6.5–8.5. Cystidia

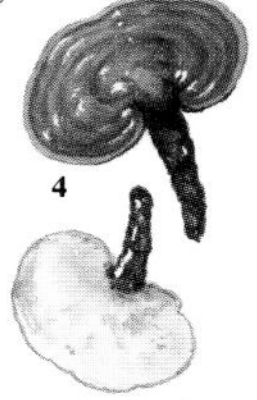

absent. Setae absent. HYPHAL SYSTEM trimitic.

3
Ganoderma resinaceum. Fruit body upper surface, spores. FRUIT BODY 10–40, perennial, bracket-like, narrowly – broadly attached, sometimes ±stem-like, semicircular, ±flat but wavy above, smooth, at first shiny and resinous, then dull, broadly zoned. STEM absent. PORE SURFACE at first white – pale yellowish, then pale brown. Tubes barely layered, <20mm deep, reddish brown. Pores 3–4/mm, rounded. SPORE PRINT brown. FLESH pale brown, soft, fibrous. Solitary or in small, overlapping groups. On wood of living or dead broad-leaved trees, especially oak, sometimes causing serious heartwood rot. All year. Widespread. Rare. Inedible. SPORES ellipsoid, flattened at one end, apparently warty, 4.5–7×9–11.5. Cystidia absent. Setae absent. HYPHAL SYSTEM trimitic.

4
Ganoderma lucidum. Fruit body form, habit, habitat. FRUIT BODY 10–20, annual, cap kidney-shaped, wavy, grooved or lumpy above, smooth, shiny, marked crust (easily dented with finger-nail), margin wavy, first pale, then darker. STEM 5–25, stout, irregularly wavy, shiny, circular – flattened in cross-section, sometimes ±rudimentary. PORE SURFACE at first white-cream, then ochreous. Tubes not layered, <30mm deep, ochreous. PORES 4–6/mm, rounded. SPORE PRINT reddish brown. FLESH cream-white-ochreous, soft, fibrous. Solitary or in small, ±tufted groups. On soil from buried roots or on wood of stumps of broad-l., more rarely conif. trees. All year. Widespread. Rare. Inedible. SPORES ellipsoid, flattened one end, apparently warty, 6–8×7–12. Cystidia absent. Setae absent. HYPHAL SYSTEM trimitic.

POLYPORACEAE
[In the broad sense: the family is often now subdivided in several different ways]. Fruit body annual or perennial, very variable, stemmed or stem-less, from effused to distinctly capped, (commonly ±stem-less and bracket-shaped), never branched or coral-like. Spore-bearing surface always one-sided, porous or rarely gill-like or with flattened teeth or ridges, tubes when present never free, pore mouths not spore-bearing. Usually brownish or otherwise dull-coloured. Flesh v. variable, soft and fleshy to hard and woody. Smell sometimes distinctive. Spores variable in shape, usually smooth, usually non-amyloid. Spore print white or slightly cream-coloured. Basidia 2–4-spored, cystidia sometimes present, rarely with granular contents, setae absent. On wood, soil or plant debris. Saprotrophic or biotrophic. Few edible, none (?) poisonous. Hyphal system monomitic, dimitic or trimitic.

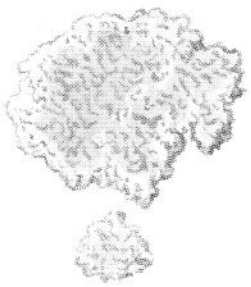

Schizopora paradoxa. Fruit body form, surface, microscopic features. FRUIT BODY irregular, resupinate, annual, effused, tightly attached to substrate, usually ± porous, also irregularly maze-like or toothed, margin usually distinct, coarsely granular. Tubes 0.1–0.3 deep, whitish. Pores 1–3/mm, angular. SPORE PRINT white. FLESH white, soft, hard when dry. On dead wood of broad-l. (rarely conif.) trees. All year. Widespread. Extremely common. Inedible. SPORES broadly ellipsoid, smooth, 3–4×5–6.5, non-amyloid. Cystidia-like structures club-shaped, spindle-shaped or broadly swollen. HYPHAL SYSTEM dimitic.

Amyloporia xantha. Overall fruit body form and surface, microscopic features. FRUIT BODY irregular, resupinate, (or shortly ± hoof-like on vertical substrates), annual, rarely perennial, effused, tightly attached to substrate, porous, ± smooth. Tubes 0.3–0.5 deep, cream. Pores 3–5/mm, irregular, rounded – angular. SPORE PRINT white. FLESH cream white, soft, brittle-chalky when dry, amyloid. On dead wood of broad-leaved or coniferous trees, often on greenhouse staging. Spring – autumn. Widespread. Uncommon. Inedible. SPORES cylindrical – ± sausage-shaped, smooth, 3–4×5–6.5, non-amyloid. Cystidia absent. HYPHAL SYSTEM dimitic.

Antrodia albida. Overall fruit body form and surface, microscopic features, very similar to *A. serpens* but pores differ. FRUIT BODY irregular, resupinate – shortly bracket-like (on vertical substrates), annual, effused – reflexed, tightly attached to substrate when fresh but peelable when dry, porous, ± smooth. Tubes<1.5 deep, cream. Pores 1–3/mm, rounded – angular. SPORE PRINT white. FLESH white, rather hard, corky. On dead wood of broad-leaved trees, often bracket-like on fence posts. Spring – autumn. Widespread, predominantly southern. Rare. Inedible. SPORES cylindrical – elongated-ellipsoid, smooth, 3.5–5×9.5–14, non-amyloid. Cystidia absent. HYPHAL SYSTEM dimitic.

Antrodia serialis. Overall fruit body form and surface, habitat, microscopic

features. FRUIT BODY irregular, resupinate – shortly bracket-like (on vertical substrates), annual – perennial, effused – reflexed, often elongated along grain of wood, loosely attached to substrate, often spotted pinkish or otherwise coloured by mould growth, porous, ± smooth. Tubes<0.8 deep, white. Pores 2–4/mm, rounded – angular. SPORE PRINT white. FLESH white, fairly soft, corky, tough. On dead wood of coniferous trees, often on structural timber. All year. Widespread. Uncommon. Inedible. SPORES cylindrical – ± boat-shaped, smooth, 2–3.5×6–9, non-amyloid. Cystidia absent. HYPHAL SYSTEM dimitic.

Antrodia serpens. Overall fruit body form and surface, microscopic features, very similar to *A. albida* but pores differ. FRUIT BODY irregular, resupinate – shortly bracket-like (on vertical substrates), annual, effused – reflexed, tightly attached to substrate when fresh but peelable when dry, porous, ± smooth. tubes<1.5 deep, cream. Pores 0.5–2/mm, rounded – angular. SPORE PRINT white. FLESH white, rather hard, corky. On dead wood of broad-leaved trees, often bracket-like on fence posts. Spring – autumn. Widespread, predominantly southern. Rare. Inedible. SPORES cylindrical – elongated-ellipsoid, smooth, 3.5–5×9.5–14, non-amyloid. Cystidia absent. HYPHAL SYSTEM dimitic.

Datronia mollis. Overall fruit body form, microscopic features. FRUIT BODY irregular, resupinate – shortly bracket-like, annual, effused – reflexed, loosely attached to substrate, ± flat and at first finely velvety-downy above, then ± smooth,

bruising darker, porous but often with pore-less patches, margin wavy-lobed. Tubes<0.5 deep, ochreous. Pores 1–2/mm, ± angular on horizontal surfaces, slit-like – irregular when sloping. SPORE PRINT white. FLESH cream – pale buff with black line below fruit body surface, leathery, hard and brittle when dry. When bracket-like, in fairly large overlapping groups. On dead wood of broad-leaved trees, especially beech. All year. Widespread. Very common. Inedible. SPORES cylindrical, smooth, 2.5–4×7.5–10, non-amyloid. Cystidia absent. HYPHAL SYSTEM dimitic.

Coriolus (= *Trametes*) *hirsutus*. Fruit body surface. FRUIT BODY 3–10, annual, bracket-like and broadly fan-shaped, broadly attached, ± flat above, densely downy-hairy, then often ± velvety, concentrically grooved and zoned, margin wavy, distinct, sharp. PORE SURFACE at first white, then cream, then greyish, slightly shiny. Tubes 0.1–0.4 deep, white-cream. Pores 2–4/mm, angular. SPORE PRINT white. FLESH white, leathery, tough. Occasionally solitary, usually in small – large, overlapping groups. On dead wood of broad-leaved (or rarely coniferous?) trees. All year. Widespread. Common. Inedible. SPORES cylindrical – sausage-shaped, smooth, 1.5–2×5–6.5, non-amyloid. Cystidia absent. HYPHAL SYSTEM trimitic.

Coriolus (= *Trametes*) *versicolor*. Fruit body surface, very variable, probably several distinct varieties exist. FRUIT BODY 3–8,

annual, bracket-like and ± kidney-shaped, broadly attached, ± flat above, finely velvety, then often ± smooth, markedly concentrically grooved and zoned, margin wavy, distinct, sharp. PORE SURFACE at first white-cream, then buff. Tubes 0.05–0.1 deep white-cream. Pores 3–5/mm, ± angular. SPORE PRINT white – very pale yellowish. FLESH white, leathery tough. Usually in small – large, densely overlapping groups. On dead wood of broad-leaved trees, and also structural softwoods All year. Widespread. Extremely common. Inedible. SPORES cylindrical – sausage-shaped, smooth, 1.5–2×5–6, non-amyloid. Cystidia absent. HYPHAL SYSTEM trimitic.

Pseudotrametes (= *Trametes*) *gibbosa*. Pores, habitat. FRUIT BODY 5–20, annual, bracket-like and ± semicircular, broadly attached, ± flat above, at first finely velvety, then ± smooth, often supporting algal growth margin thick, even, distinct. PORE SURFACE white-cream or buff. Tubes<1.5 deep, white-cream. Pores 1–2/mm, variable, usually elongated radially – ± maze-like. SPORE PRINT white. FLESH white-cream, at first slightly soft, tough, very hard when dry. Solitary or in small overlapping groups. On dead wood of broad-leaved trees, especially beech. All year. Widespread. Common. Inedible. SPORES cylindrical – elongated-ellipsoid or slightly sausage-shaped, smooth, 2–2.5×4–5, non-amyloid. Cystidia absent. HYPHAL SYSTEM trimitic.

1

Trametes suaveolens. Colour, smell, habitat. FRUIT BODY 3–12, annual, bracket like and ± semicircular, broadly attached, flat – convex above, at first finely velvety, then ± smooth warty, sometimes rather

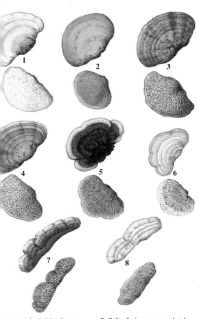

y, margin fairly sharp,
n, distinct. PORE SUR-
E white-cream or buff.
es <1.5 deep, white.
es 1–2/mm, angular but
gated where pore sur-
angled. SPORE PRINT
te. SMELL strong,
eed. FLESH white,
se, tough. Solitary or in
ll overlapping groups.
dead or living wood of
ow or rarely poplar. All
r. Widespread, pre-
inantly southern.
e. Inedible. SPORES
ndrical – slightly
sage-shaped, smooth,
×7–9.5, non-amyloid.
stidia absent. HYPHAL
TEM trimitic.

2

noporus cinnabarinus.
erall colour. FRUIT BODY
, annual, bracket-like
±kidney-shaped,
adly attached, flat
ve, at first very finely
vety, then smooth –
htly warty or wrinkled,
ely zoned, margin
rp, even, distinct. PORE
RFACE orange-red. Tubes
.7 deep, orange-red.
res 2–3/mm, angular.
RE PRINT white. FLESH
nge-red, fibrous, tough.
itary or in small±over-
ping – fused groups. On
d wood of broad-leaved
es, especially birch.
mmer – autumn. Wide-
read, predominantly
stern. Rare. Inedible.
RES cylindrical – slight-
sausage-shaped, smooth,

2–2.5×5–6, non-amyloid.
cystidia absent. HYPHAL
SYSTEM trimitic.

3

Daedalea quercina **Maze-Gill.** Pore surface, habitat.
FRUIT BODY 5–20, perennial,
bracket-like and semicircular, broadly and very firmly
attached, flate – slightly
convex above, smooth –
finely velvety, sometimes
rather warty-lumpy, margin
sharp, even, distinct. PORE
SURFACE ochreous. tubes
<4 deep, pale – dark
ochreous. Pores 1–3mm
diameter, elongated –
maze-like or almost thickly
gill-like. SPORE PRINT white.
FLESH buff-brown, corky,
tough. Usually solitary or
in small overlapping
groups. On dead wood of
broad-leaved trees, espe-
cially (and in some areas
exclusively) oak. Spring –
winter. Widespread. Very
common. Inedible. SPORES
often sparse, cylindrical –
ellipsoid, smooth, 2.5–
3.5×5.5–7, non-amyloid.
Cystidia spindle-shaped.
HYPHAL SYSTEM trimitic.

4

Daedaleopsis confragosa
Blushing Bracket. Pore surface, habitat. FRUIT BODY
5–20, annual, bracket-like
and±kidney-shaped, fairly
broadly attached,±flat
above, often basally
umbonate, smooth – finely
velvety, concentrically
zoned and grooved, margin
sharp, rather wavy. PORE

SURFACE whitish ochreous,
bruising darker, often reddish. Tubes 0.5–1 deep,
white – ochreous. Pores 1–
2/mm, variable, elongated
– almost maze-like. SPORE
PRINT white. FLESH ochre-
ous, then darkening, corky,
tough. Solitary or in small
overlapping groups. On
dead wood of broad-leaved
trees, especially birch,
beech and willow. All year.
Widespread. Very com-
mon. Inedible. SPORES
cylindrical – slightly
sausage-shaped, smooth,
2–3×7–11, non-amyloid.
Cystidia absent. HYPHAL
SYSTEM trimitic.

5

Gloeophyllum sepiarium.
Spore-bearing surface,
overall fruit body form.
FRUIT BODY 5–12, annual –
perennial, bracket-like
and±rosette-shaped, nar-
rowly attached, several to a
common base,±flat above,
at first finely velvety, then
±hairy, then becoming
smooth but with concentric
grooved zones, margin oft-
en slightly indented, rather
wavy. SPORE-BEARING SUR-
FACE gill-like with±crowd-
ed, branching, maze-like
gills, brown with pale golden
brown edges, sometimes
with irregularly rounded –
elongated porous areas,
pores 1–2/mm. SPORE PRINT
white. FLESH dark brown,
fibrous, tough. Usually in
groups, linear or overlapping. On dead wood of coniferous (or rarely broad-
leaved?) trees, especially
spruce, often when used as
structural timber. All year.
Widespread. Uncommon.
Inedible. SPORES cylindrical,
smooth, 3–5×9–13, non-
amyloid. Cystidia broadly
awl-shaped, not projecting
from spore-bearing surface.
HYPHAL SYSTEM trimitic.

6

Lenzites betulina. Spore-
bearing surface, habitat,
overall fruit body form.
FRUIT BODY 3–8, annual,
bracket-like and±semicir-
cular, narrowly – broadly
attached, sometimes
with±resupinate portion,
flat above, velvety-hairy in
concentric grooved pattern,
margin even or slightly
indented. SPORE-BEARING
SURFACE±gill-like with±
crowded, branching, maze-
like gills, at first white, then
cream – ochreous. SPORE
PRINT white. FLESH white,
fibrous, tough. Usually solitary but also in small, scattered – overlapping groups.
On dead wood of broad-
leaved (or very rarely coniferous) trees, especially
birch and willow. All year.
Widespread. Uncommon.

Inedible. SPORES cylindrical
– slightly boat-shaped,
smooth, 2–3×5–6, non-
amyloid. Cystidia absent.
HYPHAL SYSTEM trimitic.

7

Hirschioporus
(=*Trichaptum*) *abietinus*.
Habit, habitat, microscopic
features. FRUIT BODY 2–5,
annual (but new layers may
be added to dead fruit
bodies), bracket-like –
shortly stemmed or±resup-
inate,±fan-shaped, broadly
attached, flat – convex above, at first velvety-hairy in
concentric grooved pattern,
then smooth, margin wavy
and indented. PORE SUR-
FACE at first violet, then light
– dark brown. tubes 0.5–1
deep, violet-brown. Pores
3–5/mm, at first±rounded
in net-pattern, then maze
or slit-like. SPORE PRINT
white. FLESH white above,
darker close to tubes,
elastic-resinous, tough. In
large, overlapping-
resupinate and fused
groups. On dead wood of
coniferous (or very rarely
broad-leaved) trees, especially spruce. All year.
Widespread. Very com-
mon. Inedible. SPORES
cylindrical – slightly
sausage-shaped, smooth,
2–3×6–8, non-amyloid.
Cystidia club-shaped – awl-
shaped, incrusted towards
apex. HYPHAL SYSTEM dimi-
tic.

8

Hirschioporus (=*Trichaptum*) *fuscoviolaceus*. Identical to *H. abietinus* except
for spore-bearing surface.
FRUIT BODY 2–5, annual (but
new layers may be added to
dead fruit bodies), bracket-
like – shortly stemmed or±
resupinate,±fan-shaped,
broadly attached, flat-convex above, at first velvety-
hairy in concentric grooved
pattern, then smooth, margin wavy and indented.
SPORE BEARING SURFACE at
first violet, then grey-
brown, spiny-toothed –
almost porous, spines 0.01–
0.5, SPORE PRINT white.
FLESH white above, darker
close to tubes, elastic-resinous, tough. In large, over-
lapping-resupinate and
fused groups. On dead
wood of coniferous (or very
rarely broad-leaved) trees,
especially spruce. All year.
Widespread. Uncommon.
Inedible. SPORES cylindrical
– slightly sausage-shaped,
smooth, 2–3×6–8, non-
amyloid. Cystidia club-
shaped – awl-shaped, in-
crusted towards apex.
HYPHAL SYSTEM dimitic.

179

POLYPORACEAE

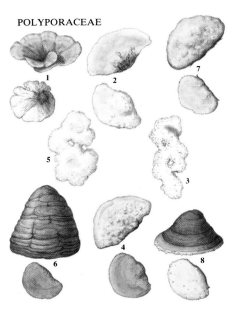

1

Heteroporus biennis.
Habit, habitat. FRUIT BODY
1–2, annual, variable, often
stemmed, cap-like and ±
funnel-shaped or bracket-
like, semi-circular, broadly
attached, almost smooth –
very finely downy-velvety
above, margin wavy, blunt.
STEM (when present) 5–7,
central, eccentric or lateral, stout, downy, soft outside but with hard core, ±
rooting. PORE SURFACE at
first white, then brownish
grey or pinkish, often ± decurrent. Tubes <0.7 deep,
white – greyish. Pores 1–3/
mm, irregular, angular –
maze-like. SPORE PRINT
white. FLESH white, soft
above, hard close to tubes.
In groups, tufted or ± overlapping. On soil from buried dead wood of broad-
leaved or rarely coniferous
trees. Summer – autumn.
Predominantly western and
southern. Uncommon. In-
edible. SPORES ellipsoid –
subspherical, smooth, 3.5–
4.5×4–7, non-amyloid.
(Similarly-sized slightly yellowish conidia also often
present). Cystidia
cylindrical-wavy, with
granular contents. HYPHAL
SYSTEM monomitic.

2

Oxyporus populinus. Fruit
body surface, habitat, pore
surface. FRUIT BODY 3–10,
perennial, bracket-like,
fan-shaped but often irregular when growing in cracks,
broadly attached, ± flat above, usually finely warty, at
first velvety, then smooth,
often supporting mosses
and algae at base, margin
wavy, fairly sharp. PORE
SURFACE white-cream,
shiny, distinct sterile margin. Tubes layered, each
layer 0.1–0.4 deep, at first
whitish, then darker. Pores
5–7/mm rounded – angular.
SPORE PRINT white. FLESH
cream, soft and elastic
when fresh, hard when dry.
Solitary or in small, overlapping groups. On wood
of broad-leaved trees, especially from wounds or
knot-holes. All year. Widespread. Common. Inedible.
SPORES spherical, smooth, 4
–5, non-amyloid. Cystidia
club-like, incrusted at apex.
HYPHAL SYSTEM monomitic.

3

*Rigidoporus sanguinolen-
tus.* Colour change, pore
surface, habitat. FRUIT
BODY irregular, resupinate,
mostly elongated with
grain of wood, fairly tightly
attached to substrate,
quickly bruising reddish
then brown, very dark
when dry, porous. Tubes
<0.2 deep, at first white-
cream, then brown. Pores
3–4/mm, round – angular,
slit-like when on sloping
surface. SPORE PRINT white.
FLESH white-cream, soft,
watery, red-brown and hard
when dry. On very rotten,
wet woody debris of broad-
leaved and coniferous
trees, often when on or in
soil. Summer – autumn.
Widespread. Common. In-

edible. SPORES spherical,
smooth, 5–6, non-amyloid.
Cystidia absent. HYPHAL
SYSTEM monomitic.

4

Rigidoporus ulmarius.
Habitat, pore surface colours, distribution. FRUIT
BODY 15–45, perennial,
bracket-like, broadly
attached, ± flat above, very
irregularly warty-knobbly,
at first finely velvety, then
smooth, concentrically
ridged, margin thick,
rounded, often supporting
algal growth. PORE SURFACE
at first pink-orange, then
brownish. Tubes layered,
each layer <0.5, pinkish
brown – brown. Pores 5–8/
mm, rounded – angular.
SPORE PRINT white. FLESH at
first cream-buff, tough,
fibrous, then very hard,
woody. Solitary or in small,
overlapping groups. On
wood of broad-leaved
trees, especially elm, at
base of trunk causing dark
brown, angular decay. All
year. Western and south-
ern. Common. Inedible.
SPORES spherical, smooth,
6–7.5, non-amyloid. Cystidia absent. HYPHAL SYSTEM
monomitic.

5

Rigidoporus vitreus. Very
similar to *R. sanguinolentus*
but colour change differs.
FRUIT BODY irregular,
resupinate, effused, with
knob-like lateral growths
when on vertical substrate,
fairly tightly attached to
substrate, bruising brow-
nish very slowly or not all,
porous. Tubes 0.2–0.4
deep, whitish. Pores 3–5/
mm, rounded, slit-like
when on sloping surface.
SPORE PRINT white. FLESH
white-cream, waxy, hard
when dry. On dead wood of
broad-leaved and conifer-
ous trees, often on structural timber. Summer –
autumn. Widespread.
Rare. Inedible. SPORES
spherical, smooth, 4–5,
non-amyloid. Cystidia-like
structures cylindrical,
incrusted at apex. HYPHAL
SYSTEM monomitic.

6

Fomes fomentarius. Habitat, distribution, microscopic features. FRUIT BODY 10–
25, perennial, hoof-like,
broadly attached, steeply
convex – semiconical
above, concentrically
grooved, very finely
velvety-smooth, margin
blunt, at first finely downy,
then smooth. PORE SURFACE
at first pale ochreous, then
greyish brown. Tubes
layered by thin brown
zones, each layer <0.10

deep, pale ochreous. Por
2–4/mm, rounded. SPORE
PRINT white. FLESH pale
brown, tough, leathery.
Solitary or in small, ± fus
groups. On wood of broa
leaved trees, especially
birch in Britain, also bee
elm, maple and sycamore
All year. Predominantly
northern. Common. Ine
ble. SPORES elongated-
ellipsoid – cylindrical,
smooth, 4.5–7×15–20, n
amyloid. Cystidia absent
HYPHAL SYSTEM trimitic.

7

Fomitiporia cytisina
(= *Perenniporia fraxinea*
Habitat, distribution, mi
roscopic features. FRUIT
BODY 10–20, perennial,
bracket-like, broadly
attached, convex above,
irregularly undulating,
warty, at first finely velve
then smooth, margin ±
blunt, wavy. PORE SURFA
buff. Tubes layered, eac
layer <0.5 deep, greyish
Pores 1–5/mm, rounded
angular. SPORE PRINT whi
FLESH pale brown, tough
corky. Usually in groups
often fused in large mass
On wood of broad-leave
trees, especially ash, caus
ly at base of trunk, causi
white, felt-like decay. A
year. Predominantly cen
tral and southern. Uncor
mon. Inedible. SPORES su
spherical, smooth, germ
pore, 5–6×6–7, dextrino
cyanophilic. Cystidia
absent. HYPHAL SYSTEM
dimitic.

8

Fomitopsis pinicola. Frui
body surface, smell. FRU
BODY 5–25, perennial,
bracket-like – hoof-like,
broadly attached, steeply
convex – semiconical ab
ove, broadly concentrica
grooved-wrinkled, smoo
crustose from resinous
covering which melts in
heat (use a lighted match
margin blunt, exuding
drops when actively grov
ing. PORE SURFACE at first
buff – pale yellow, then
brownish, grey-violet wh
scratched. Tubes layered
each layer <0.1 deep, pa
ochre. Pores 3–4/mm,
rounded. SPORE PRINT
white. SMELL very strong
acidic. FLESH cream-ochi
tough, hard. Solitary or i
small groups. On wood c
broad-leaved or conifero
trees. All year. Wide-
spread. Rare. Inedible.
SPORES elongated-ellipso
– cylindrical with beak,
smooth, 3.5–4×6–8, non
amyloid. Cystidia absent
HYPHAL SYSTEM trimitic.

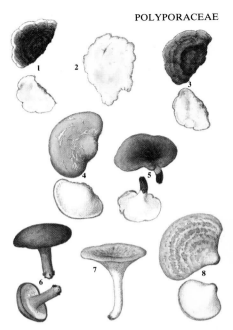

1

erobasidion annosum.
it body surface, pore
face, habit, habitat.
IT BODY 5–15, perennial,
cket-like – resupinate,
▸adly attached, flat –
▸vex above, concentri-
y and irregularly
▸oved-wrinkled, at first±
▸vety, then smooth, mar-
±rounded, often wavy.
▸E SURFACE white-cream,
▸n rather warty. Tubes
▸ered, each layer <0.4
▸p, white-cream. Pores 2
▸mm, rounded – angular.
▸RE PRINT white. FLESH
▸te-cream, fibrous,
▸ky. Usually in small,±
▸rlapping groups. On
▸ng trunks of coniferous
▸es and many species of
▸ub, usually very close to
▸und and±obscured by
▸getation, causing very
▸ious white pocketed
▸cay. All year. Wide-
▸ead. Extremely com-
▸n. Inedible. SPORES
▸adly ellipsoid – sub-
▸herical, very finely warty,
▸.5×4.5–6, non-amyloid,
▸nophilic. Cystidia
▸sent. HYPHAL SYSTEM
▸nitic.

2

▸ria (= *Perenniporia*)
▸dulla-panis*. Overall fruit
▸ly form, habitat, micros-
▸ic features. FRUIT BODY
▸egular, resupinate,
▸used, with knob-like
▸eral growths when on
▸tical substrate, fairly
▸htly attached to subs-
▸te, often slightly wavy,
▸rous. Tubes stratified,
▸ch layer <0.4 deep, whit-
▸buff. Pores 4–5/mm,
▸nded,±elongated when
▸sloping margin. SPORE
▸NT pale yellow. FLESH
▸ite-cream, tough, rather
▸hery. On dead wood of
▸ad-leaved and conifer-
▸s trees, especially oak.
▸l year. Widespread.
▸re. Inedible. SPORES
▸adly ellipsoid, smooth,
▸–5×5–6.5, non-amyloid,
▸nophilic. Cystidia
▸sent. HYPHAL SYSTEM di-
▸trimitic.

3

▸hnoderma resinosum*.
▸abitat, distribution, flesh,
▸it body surface. FRUIT
▸DY 10–15, annual,
▸acket-like, narrowly –
▸oadly attached, flat –
▸nvex above,±concentri-
▸lly zoned, at first±velv-
▸y – finely granular, then
▸ooth and darker,
▸argin±rounded, often
▸ghtly lined. PORE SURFACE
▸ite-ochre. Tubes <0.1
▸ep, whitish buff. Pores
▸6/mm, rounded. SPORE
▸INT white. FLESH white-
▸uff, soft, fleshy, hard
▸hen dry. Usually in small,

overlapping groups. On
dead wood of broad-leaved
trees, especially beech.
Summer – autumn. Pre-
dominantly southern and
eastern. Rare. Inedible.
SPORES cylindrical, smooth,
2–2.5×5–6, non-amyloid.
Cystidia absent. HYPHAL
SYSTEM monomitic.

4

Piptoporus betulinus. Habitat, flesh, fruit body surface. FRUIT BODY 5–20,
annual, bracket-like,
often±fan-shaped, nar-
rowly attached, usually by
umbonate base, slightly
convex above, smooth,
often very finely cracked
when old, margin blunt-
inrolled. PORE SURFACE
white-cream. Tubes <0.1
deep, white-cream. Pores
3-4/mm, rounded –
angular. SPORE PRINT white.
FLESH white, soft, corky.
Solitary or in small, often
spaced groups. On dead
wood of birch causing soft
powdery rich red decay.
Summer – autumn. Wide-
spread. Extremely com-
mon. Inedible. SPORES
sausage-shaped, smooth,
1.5–2×5–6, non amyloid.
Cystidia absent. HYPHAL
SYSTEM dimitic.

5

Polyporus badius. Overall
form, cap features, spores.
CAP 5–20, at first convex,
then flattened – funnel-
shaped, often markedly
wavy, smooth – slightly
wrinkled, margin wavy.
STEM 2–8, sometimes
rudimentary, fairly
slender, at first±equal, at first
finely downy-velvety, then
wrinkled. PORE SURFACE at
first white-cream, then
buff. Tubes <0.3 deep,
white-cream, decurrent.
Pores 6–9/mm, rounded.
SPORE PRINT white. FLESH
white-cream, soft, corky.
In small tufted or trooping
groups. On dead wood of
broad-leaved trees, when
above ground or buried in
soil. Spring – autumn.
Widespread. Rare. Inedi-
ble. SPORES cylindrical –
elongated-ellipsoid,
smooth, 3–4×6–10, non-
amyloid. Cystidia absent.
HYPHAL SYSTEM dimitic.

6

Polyporus brumalis **Winter
Polypore.** Overall form,
pores, spores. CAP 2–8, at
first slightly convex, then
flattened, often slightly
umbilicate, finely velvety-
scaly, sometimes slightly
zoned, margin smooth or
slightly wavy. STEM 2–8,
fairly slender,±equal but
often slightly swollen at
base, at first finely downy-

velvety, then smooth. PORE
SURFACE white-cream, then
buff. Tubes 0.1–0.3 deep,
white-cream, decurrent.
Pores 2–3/mm, rounded.
SPORE PRINT white. FLESH
white-cream, elastic,
tough. Solitary or in small
tufted or trooping groups.
On dead wood of broad-
leaved trees, especially
when lying on soil.
Winter – spring. Wide-
spread. Very common.
Inedible. SPORES
cylindrical – sausage-
shaped, smooth, 2–2.5×6–
7, non-amyloid. Cystidia
absent. HYPHAL SYSTEM
dimitic.

7

Polyporus lentus. Overall
form, pores, spores, very
like a small *P. squamosus*
but scales and stem base
especially differ. CAP 2–10,
at first convex, then
flattened – slightly funnel-
shaped,±concentrically
covered with flattened,
finely tufted scales, margin
smooth or slightly wavy.
STEM 1–6, fairly slender,±
equal, rather hairy at base,
occasionally lateral. PORE
SURFACE white-cream.
Tubes <0.3 deep, white-
cream, deeply decurrent.
Pores <0.02×0.01, angu-
lar-elongated, smooth.
SPORE PRINT white. FLESH
white-cream, elastic,
tough. Solitary or in small
tufted or trooping groups.

On dead wood of broad-
leaved trees, especially
beech and oak. Spring –
summer. Widespread. Un-
common. Inedible. SPORES
cylindrical – elongated-
ellipsoid, smooth, 4–6×12–
16, non-amyloid. Cystidia
absent. HYPHAL SYSTEM
dimitic.

8

Polyporus squamosus.
Overall form, size, pores,
spores. CAP 10–60, semicircular – tongue-shaped, at
first slightly convex, then
flattened,±concentrically
covered with flattened,
scales with round ends,
margin smooth and often
slightly inrolled. STEM 2–10,
lateral – eccentric,
stout,±equal, dark and
smooth at base. PORE SUR-
FACE white-cream. Tubes
<0.7 deep, white-cream,
deeply decurrent. Pores
<0.02×0.01, irregularly
angular, eventually
toothed. SPORE PRINT white.
FLESH white-cream, leath-
ery, tough. Solitary or in
small overlapping groups.
On wood of broad-leaved
trees. Spring – summer.
Widespread. Very com-
mon. Inedible. SPORES
cylindrical – elongated-
ellipsoid, smooth, 4–6×12–
16, non-amyloid. Cystidia
absent. HYPHAL SYSTEM
dimitic.

181

POLYPORACEAE

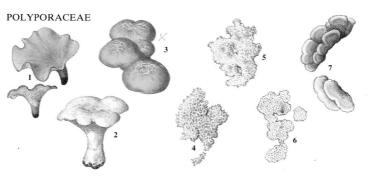

1
Polyporus varius. Cap surface features, stem base, pores, spores. CAP 2–8, circular – kidney-shaped, at first slightly convex, then flattened – depressed, smooth – slightly wrinkled towards wavy margin. STEM 1–5, central – lateral, fairly slender, ±equal, smooth, dark at base. PORE SURFACE white-cream. Tubes <0.3 deep, white-cream, deeply decurrent. Pores 4–5/mm, angular. SPORE PRINT white. FLESH white-cream, corky, tough. Solitary or in small±tufted groups. On wood of broad-leaved trees. All year. Widespread. Common. Inedible. SPORES cylindrical – sausage-shaped, smooth, 2–3.5×7–9, non-amyloid. Cystidia absent. HYPHAL SYSTEM dimitic.

2
Albatrellus ovinus. Overall form, colour, habitat, distribution. CAP 5–15, irregularly round – fan-shaped, at first convex, then flattened – slightly depressed, margin±wavy and often inrolled. STEM 2–4, fairly stout, tapering downwards, sometimes flattened in cross-section, smooth, dark at base. PORE SURFACE at first white-cream, bruising yellowish, brownish when older. Tubes <0.5 deep, white-cream, deeply decurrent. Pores 2–4/mm, rounded – angular. SPORE PRINT white. FLESH white-cream, fleshy. Solitary or in small±fused groups. On soil in coniferous woods, especially with spruces. Summer – autumn. Widespread, not Britain. Edible. SPORES broadly ellipsoid – spherical, smooth, 3–3.5×4–4.5, non-amyloid. Cystidia absent. HYPHAL SYSTEM monomitic.

3
Albatrellus confluens. Overall form, colour, habitat, distribution, often confused with *A. ovinus* but no flesh colour change. CAP 5–15, irregularly round – fan-shaped, at first convex, then flattened – slightly depressed, but whole structure often barely discernible because several fruit bodies usually fused together into±club-shaped mass, often warty, smooth – velvety. STEM (when distinct from cap) 3–8, stout, tapering downwards, sometimes flattened in cross-section, often completely covered with decurrent tubes and pores. PORE SURFACE white-cream. Tubes <1 deep, white-cream, very deeply decurrent. Pores 1–3/mm, angular-elongated. SPORE PRINT white. FLESH white – yellowish cream, fleshy. Usually in densely fused groups. On soil in coniferous woods, especially with spruce. Summer – autumn. Widespread, predominantly montane, not Britain. Inedible. SPORES broadly ellipsoid – spherical, smooth, 3–4×4–5, non-amyloid. Cystidia absent. HYPHAL SYSTEM monomitic.

4
Ceriporia reticulata. Overall size, tube depth, pore surface, microscopical features. FRUIT BODY irregular, usually <6–7, resupinate, loosely attached to substrate, annual, porous – ±net-like, margin very thin, paler. Tubes <0.05 deep, white-cream. Pores 2–4/mm, angular. SPORE PRINT white. FLESH whitish, soft, waxy, hard and brittle when dry. On dead wood of broad-leaved or more rarely coniferous trees, especially beneath fallen logs. Spring – autumn. Widespread. Uncommon. Inedible. SPORES cylindrical – sausage-shaped, smooth, 2.5–4×6–10, non-amyloid. Cystidia

absent. HYPHAL SYSTEM monomitic.

5
Ceriporia viridans. Microscopical features, tube colours, size, pore surface. FRUIT BODY irregular, resupinate, usually±effused, tightly attached to substrate, annual, porous, margin at first±porous, then sterile. Tubes 0.1–0.2 deep, white-cream, sometimes pink-violet spotted. Pores 3–5/mm, rounded – angular. SPORE PRINT white. FLESH whitish, soft, waxy, hard and brittle when dry. On dead wood of broad-leaved or more rarely coniferous trees, especially beneath fallen logs. Summer – autumn. Widespread. Uncommon. Inedible. SPORES cylindrical – sausage-shaped, smooth, 1.5–2.5×3–5, non-amyloid. Cystidia absent. HYPHAL SYSTEM monomitic.

6
Ceriporiopsis (=*Tyromyces*) *gilvescens*. Microscopical features, fruit body colour and colour change, pore size. FRUIT BODY irregular, resupinate, usually±effused, tightly attached to substrate, annual, porous, at first finely velvety, then smooth, often bruising brownish, margin at first±hairy, then porous and distinct. Tubes<0.5 deep, white-pinkish, bruising brownish. Pores 4–5/mm, rounded – angular or±wavy slit-like. SPORE PRINT white. FLESH whitish, soft, waxy, hard and brittle when dry. On dead wood of broad-leaved (or rarely coniferous?) trees, especially beech. Summer – autumn. Widespread. Uncommon. Inedible. SPORES±cylindrical – slightly sausage-shaped, smooth, 1.5–2×3.5–4.5, non-amyloid. Cystidia absent. HYPHAL SYSTEM monomitic.

7
Bjerkandera adusta. Colo[ur] contrast between flesh an[d] tubes, overall fruit body form, microscopical features. FRUIT BODY irregular resupinate and±effused, but usually at least partly bracket-like, <4, annual, flat and at first finely velvety-downy above, then smoother – warty, porou[s] below, margin at first pal[e] wavy. Tubes <0.2 deep, grey-black. Pores 4–6/mm rounded – angular. SPORE PRINT white. FLESH whitis[h] fibrous, leathery. Usually in±fused masses. On dea[d] wood of broad-leaved (or rarely coniferous) trees. A[ll] year. Widespread. Extremely common. Ined[i]ble. SPORES elongated-ellipsoid – ±cylindrical, smooth, 2.5–3×4–5, no[n]-amyloid. Cystidia absent. HYPHAL SYSTEM monomiti[c].

8
Hapalopilus nidulans. Overall form, chemical test, microscopical features. FRUIT BODY 2–10, annual, bracket-like, semicircular – kidney-shaped, broadly attached flat – slightly convex above, at first finely velvety, then smooth, barely zoned, margin rather sharp and often slightly wavy. PORE SURFAC[E] ochre – reddish brown, usually with marked pore[s] less margin. Tubes <1 deep, ochreous white. PORES 2–4/mm, angular. SPORE PRINT white. FLESH pale reddish brown, soft, spongy-fibrous, rather bri[t]tle. KOH on fruit body surface, deep violet. Solitary or in small,±overlapping groups. On dead wo[od] of broad-leaved (or rarely coniferous) trees. Summe[r] – autumn. Widespread. Uncommon. Inedible. SPORES elongated-ellipsoi[d] – cylindrical, smooth, 2–3[.5] ×3.5–5, non-amyloid. Cy[s]tidia absent. HYPHAL SYST[EM] monomitic.

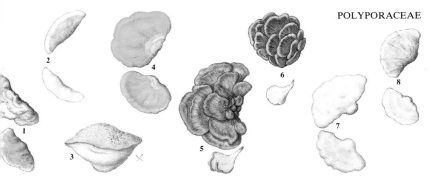

1

eletocutis amorphus.
olour contrast between
rface and flesh, microsco-
al features. FRUIT BODY
egular, resupinate,
used, loosely attached to
bstrate, annual, porous,
ten with bracket-like out-
owths, <5, at first velvety
ove, then±smooth,
rely zoned, margin paler,
nged. Tubes 0.05–0.1
ep, white, sometimes
th reddish orange flush.
res 3–4/mm, angular.
ORE PRINT white. FLESH
ite, soft above, gelati-
us below close to tubes.
n dead wood of conifer-
s trees. Summer –
tumn. Widespread.
ncommon. Inedible.
ORES sausage-shaped,
ooth, 1–1.5×3–4.5, non-
yloid. Cystidia absent.
PHAL SYSTEM dimitic.

2

keletocutis nivea
= Incrustoporia semi-
leata). Pore size, overall
rm, habitat, spores. FRUIT
st finely velvety-downy
d±effused, or bracket-
ke, <4, annual, porous, at
st finely velvety-downy
ove, then smooth but
ten pitted or warty,
rely zoned, margin
hite, finely hairy, distinct.
ubes <0.4 deep, white-
eam, bruising greenish
own. Pores 6–8/mm,
rely visible without lens,
unded – angular. FLESH
RINT white. FLESH white-
le brownish, corky,
ugh. On dead wood of
oad-leaved trees, espe-
ally ash. Summer –
tumn. Widespread. Very
mmon. Inedible. SPORES
usage-shaped, smooth,
5–1×3–4, often elusive,
n-amyloid. Cystidia
sent. HYPHAL SYSTEM
imitic.

3

ongipellis spumeus. Mic-
scopical features, flesh
ructure. FRUIT BODY 10–
), annual, bracket-like,
micircular, broadly

attached or narrowed
to±rooting base, convex
above, finely velvety-hairy,
not zoned, margin
rounded, often darker.
PORE SURFACE at first white,
then straw-coloured. Tubes
<1.5 deep, white – straw-
coloured. Pores 1–2/mm,
rounded. SPORE PRINT
white. FLESH white-cream,
soft above, denser and
fibrous below. Solitary. On
dead wood of broad-leaved
trees, especially in parks
and gardens. Summer –
autumn. Widespread, not
Britain. Inedible.
SPORES broadly ellipsoid –
subspherical, smooth, 4.5–
6.5×6–8.5, non-amyloid.
Cystidia absent. HYPHAL
SYSTEM monomitic.

4

Laetiporus sulphureus
Chicken of the Woods.
Overall colour, habitat.
FRUIT BODY 10–30, annual,
bracket-like, semicircular –
fan-shaped, broadly
attached,±flat – slightly
convex above, smooth, not
zoned, often slightly wavy.
PORE SURFACE vivid sulphur-
yellow, paler when dry,
then straw-coloured. Tubes
<0.4 deep, sulphur-yellow.
Pores 3–5/mm, rounded.
SPORE PRINT white. FLESH
cream – yellowish orange,
white when dry, soft and
juicy, crumbly and chalky
when dry. Usually in large,
overlapping groups. On
wood, usually on living
broad-leaved trees, espe-
cially oaks, also yew, causing dark reddish brown
cubical rot. Spring –
autumn. Widespread, pre-
dominantly southern.
Extremely common. Edi-
ble, good when young.
SPORES broadly ellipsoid –
subspherical, smooth, 3.5–
5×5–7, non-amyloid. Cystidia absent. HYPHAL SYSTEM
dimitic.

5

Meripilus giganteus **Giant
Polypore.** Size, habitat,
overall fruit body form,
microscopic features. FRUIT

BODY 5–20, (but collectively
50–80), annual, fan-like,
narrowly attached, often
with stem,±flat above,
smooth – finely scaly,±
wavy, radially grooved, often concentrically zoned,
margin wavy,±indented.
STEM rudimentary, stout or
absent. Widespread. Very com-
ish, bruising±black. Tubes
<0.8 deep, white-cream.
Pores 3–5/mm,±rounded.
SPORE PRINT white. SMELL
indefinite, pleasant. FLESH
white, soft, fibrous. Tufted
in large masses arising from
common base. On wood of
broad-leaved (or rarely
coniferous) trees, usually at
base of trunk on beech
causing serious brownish
rot. Summer – winter.
Widespread, predomi-
nantly southern. Very common. Inedible. SPORES
broadly ellipsoid –
subspherical, smooth, 4.5–
6×6–7, non-amyloid. Cystidia absent. HYPHAL SYSTEM
dimitic.

6

Grifola frondosa. Size,
habitat, overall fruit body
form, microscopic features.
FRUIT BODY 5–10, (but col-
lectivley 20–50), annual,
tongue-shaped, usually
depressed towards
stem,±ear-like, usually
radially wrinkled-lined,
margin wavy, often split.
STEM 2–5, stout, usually
flattened. PORE SURFACE
white-cream. Tubes <0.3
deep, white. Pores 2–3/
mm, angular – rounded.
SPORE PRINT white. SMELL
unpleasant, mice. FLESH
white, soft, fibrous. Tufted
in large masses arising from
common base. On wood of
broad-leaved trees, often at
base of trunk on beech,
oak, hornbeam or sweet
chestnut causing white
pocketed rot. Summer –
autumn. Widespread, pre-
dominantly southern.
Uncommon. Edible.
SPORES broadly ellipsoid,
smooth, 3.5–5×5–7, non-
amyloid. Cystidia absent.
HYPHAL SYSTEM monomitic.

7

Tyromyces albellus (=
chioneus). Colour, microscopic features. FRUIT BODY
4–10, annual, bracket-like,
semicircular – fan-shaped,
at first finely downy-velvety
but quickly smooth-warty,
gradually wrinkled. PORE
SURFACE white-cream,
rather shiny. Tubes <0.8
deep, white. Pores 3–4/
mm, angular – rounded.
SPORE PRINT white. FLESH
white, soft, hard when dry.
Solitary or in small groups.
On wood of broad-leaved
(or rarely coniferous) trees,
sometimes on sawn timber.
Summer – autumn. Wide-
spread. Uncommon. Inedi-
ble. SPORES cylindrical –
±sausage-shaped, smooth,
1.5–2×3.5–4, non-amyloid.
Cystidia absent. HYPHAL
SYSTEM dimitic.

8

Tyromyces caesius. Colour,
habitat, microscopic fea-
tures. FRUIT BODY 1–4,
annual, bracket-like, na-
rrowly attached, semicircular, sometimes±decurrent
onto substrate – resupin-
ate, convex above, at first
finely downy-velvety, then
smooth, bruising darker,
margin wavy, distinct,
rather sharp. PORE SURFACE
white – greyish blue, bruising darker. Tubes <0.8
deep, white – greyish blue.
Pores 4–5/mm, angular,
finely toothed. SPORE PRINT
white. FLESH greyish above,
white below, soft, fibrous,
hard when dry. Solitary or
in small overlapping or
fused groups. On dead
wood of coniferous (or
rarely broad-leaved) trees.
Summer – autumn. Wide-
spread. Very common.
Inedible. SPORES
cylindrical – ±sausage-
shaped, smooth, 0.5–1×4–
5, weakly amyloid. Cystidia
absent. HYPHAL SYSTEM
monomitic.

183

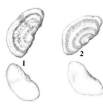

1
Tyromyces gloeocystidiatus (= *leucomallellus*). Colour, habitat, microscopic features. FRUIT BODY irregular, resupinate – shortly bracket-like, usually with projecting parts above resupinate portion, annual, at first finely fibrous-velvety, then±smooth, barely zoned, porous. Tubes <1 deep, white-cream, darkening reddish on drying. Pores 3–4/mm, angular, elongated on sloping or vertical substrates. SPORE PRINT white. FLESH white, soft, fibrous, hard and±brittle when dry. On dead wood of coniferous trees. Summer – autumn. Widespread. Uncommon. Inedible. SPORES sausage-shaped, smooth, 1–1.5 ×4.5–6, non-amyloid. Cystidia cylindrical – bluntly club-shaped, with granular contents, often elusive. HYPHAL SYSTEM monomitic.

2
Tyromyces kymatodes (= *balsameus*). Microscopic features, fruit body surface. FRUIT BODY 2–5, bracket-like – ±tongue-shaped, narrowly – broadly attached, annual,±flat above, at first very finely velvety, then smooth, broadly zoned, margin narrow, sharp. PORE SURFACE at first white, then cream – pale reddish brown. Tubes <0.4 deep, white-cream, brownish when dry. Pores 3–5/mm, angular, elongated where decurrent onto substrate. SPORE PRINT white. FLESH brownish, corky, tough. Solitary or in small, overlapping groups. On dead wood of coniferous trees. Summer – autumn. Widespread. Uncommon. Inedible. SPORES ellipsoid – ±cylindrical, smooth, 2–3×4–5.5, non-amyloid. Cystidia very broadly awl-shaped, rather wavy, smooth or incrusted at apex, often elusive. HYPHAL SYSTEM monomitic.

3
Tyromyces lacteus (including *T. tephroleucus*). Colour, overall fruit body form, microscopic features. FRUIT BODY 2–6, bracket-like, semicircular – elongated, sometimes almost knob-like, broadly attached, annual, convex – hemispherical above,±triangular in cross-section, at first finely downy, eventually smooth – radially fibrous, barely zoned. PORE SURFACE white-cream, darker when dry. Pores 3–5/mm, angular. SPORE PRINT white. FLESH white, soft and dense, hard and brittle when dry. On dead wood of broad-leaved or rarely coniferous trees, causing white (*tephroleucus*) or brown (*lacteus*) rot. Summer – autumn. Widespread. Common (*lacteus*); rare (*tephroleucus*). Inedible. SPORES sausage-shaped, smooth, 1–1.5×4–6, non-amyloid. Cystidia absent. HYPHAL SYSTEM monomitic.

4
Tyromyces mollis. Colour, colour change, overall fruit body form, microscopic features. FRUIT BODY 2–6, bracket-like, semicircular – elongated, sometimes almost knob-like, broadly attached, often decurrent – resupinate in part, annual, ±flat – convex above, often±triangular in cross-section, at first finely downy, eventually smooth, barely zoned. PORE SURFACE white, bruising red-violet. Tubes <0.8 deep, white, bruising reddish. Pores 3–4/mm,±rounded – elongated, slit-like. SPORE PRINT white. FLESH white – pinkish, often veined and zoned, soft, spongy, very hard when dry. Usually in small, fused groups. On dead wood of coniferous or rarely broad-leaved trees. Summer – autumn. Widespread. Rare. Inedible. SPORES sausage-shaped, smooth, 1.5–2×5–7.5, non-amyloid. Cystidia absent. HYPHAL SYSTEM monomitic.

5
Tyromyces stipticus. Fruit body surface, smell, colour, microscopic features. FRUIT BODY 3–8, bracket-like,±semicircular, broadly attached, annual,±flat above, often±triangular in cross-section, very finely downy-velvety – smooth or often slightly warty, margin sharp and distinct. PORE SURFACE at first white, then creamy-yellowish. Tubes <0.6 deep, white. Pores 3–4/mm, rounded – elongated, slit-like where pore surface sloping. SPORE PRINT white. SMELL strong, indefinite, unpleasant. FLESH white, fibrous, tough. Solitary or in small, fused groups. On dead wood of coniferous or rarely broad-leaved trees, less commonly on living trees. Summer – autumn. Widespread. Uncommon. Inedible. SPORES elongated – ellipsoid – ±cylindrical, smooth, 1.5–2×3.5–4.5, non-amyloid. Cystidia absent. HYPHAL SYSTEM monomitic.

Schizophyllum commune **Split-Gill.** Overall form, spore-bearing surface. CA 1–4, fan-shaped, irregula wavy, densely covered w. velvety down, margin irregularly lobed and wavy. STEM rudimentary. SPORE BEARING SURFACE gill-like whitish ochre, fairly crowded, 'gills' split lengthwise and rolled back, radiating from origin at base. SPORE PRINT white. FLESH at first brownish, later white, soft, tough. Usually in small,±tufted overlapping groups. On dead wood of broad-leave trees, often on sawn timber. All year. Widesprea predominantly southern. Rare, locally common. Inedible. SPORES elongate ellipsoid – cylindrical, smooth, 2.5–3×6–7, non-amyloid. Cystidia absent. HYPHAL SYSTEM monomiti

SCHIZOPHYLLACEAE
Fruit body at first cup-shaped, sometimes with stem-like base, often spreading and becoming more broadly attached to substrate in centre but retaining loose margin. Usually whitish or pale-coloured. Spore-bearing surface±smooth, loosely folded or so tightly folded as to simulate true gills. Spores broadly ellipsoid – cylindrical, slightly flattened or depressed on one side, smooth, non-amyloid. Flesh tough, soft when wet, often reviving from dried state. Spore print white. Hyphal system monomitic. Smell not usually distinctive. Usually on wood or other plant debris, more rarely animal tissues. Saprotrophic or biotrophic. Not edible, none poisonous, but pathogenic. Only one common genus and species.

CYPHELLACEAE (in a restricted sense). Fruit body cup-, saucer-or disc-shaped, or tubular, with obscure or rudimentary stem, often attached to substrate via a broadly effused subiculum. Usuall whitish or pale-coloured. Spore-bearing surface usually smooth or very slightly folded, lining the fruit body above (cup-like species) or within (tubular species). Spores variable i shape, smooth, non-amyloid. Flesh usually soft and fragile when fresh. Spore print white. Hyphal system monomitic. Outer or marginal hairs of fruit body often distinctive. Usually on wood or other plant debris. Saprotrophic. Not edible, none poisonous. A assorted group of uncertain taxonomic affinities, often confused with 'Discomycetes' and some species were once classified as such

...nningsomyces candida.
...verall form, size, colour,
...bitat, only a few related
...e species have similar
...ucture. FRUIT BODY tubu-
..., 0.02–0.04 diam×0.05–
...1 mm long, outer surface
...ughened – slightly
...ughened. SPORE BEARING
...RFACE lining tubes,
...ite, smooth. SPORE PRINT
...ite. FLESH white-cream,
...ft, fragile. Solitary or in
...nsely tufted or trooping
...oups. On underside of
...rk and wood of conifer-
...s or more rarely broad-
...ved trees. Spring –
...tumn. Widespread.
...ncommon. Inedible.
...ORES subspherical,
...ooth, 4–5×4.5–6, non-
...nyloid. Cystidia absent.
...PHAL SYSTEM monomitic.
...ooth, very finely bran-
...ed.

Cyphellopsis anomala.
Overall form, size, colour,
often confused with stem-
less 'Discomycetes' but
microscopic features very
different. FRUIT BODY 0.02–
0.05, shallowly cup- or
saucer-like on subiculum,
outer surface densely hairy,
margin paler, fringed hairy.
STEM absent. SPORE BEARING
SURFACE lining cup, cream-
ochre, smooth. SPORE PRINT
white. FLESH pale ochreous,
soft, fragile, hard when
dry. In large, densely tufted
groups. On dead wood of
broad-leaved or rarely coniferous trees. All year.
Widespread. Uncommon.
Inedible. SPORES ellipsoid –
±sausage-shaped, smooth,
3.5–4.5×8–9.5, non-
amyloid. Cystidia absent.
HYPHAL SYSTEM monomitic.
Outer hairs brown, thick-
walled, incrusted from half-
way, tip club-shaped, paler.

Lachnella alboviolascens.
Overall form, size, colour,
often confused with stem-
less 'Discomycetes' like
Dascyscyphus spp. but microscopic features very
different. FRUIT BODY 0.05–
0.15, irregularly and
shallowly saucer-like, outer
surface densely hairy, margin white, fringed hairy,
inrolled. STEM absent.
SPORE BEARING SURFACE
lining cup, grey-whitish,
smooth, often bearing
secondary fruit bodies.
SPORE PRINT white. FLESH
whitish, waxy, soft, fragile.
In densely tufted groups.
On dead wood of broad-
leaved trees and other plant
debris. Spring – autumn.
Widespread. Rare. Inedi-
ble. SPORES broadly and
irregularly ellipsoid, sometimes flattened on one side,
smooth, 10–11×12.5–15,
non-amyloid. Cystidia
absent. HYPHAL SYSTEM
monomitic. Outer hairs
white above, brownish
towards base, thick walled,
narrowly cylindrical,
incrusted, dextrinoid.

Sparassis crispa **Cauliflower Fungus.** Overall form, size,
colour, habitat, distinctive
but in parts of Europe the
related *S. laminosa* on
broad-leaved wood is com-
moner. FRUIT BODY 10–30,
hemispherical, many times
branched, branches
flattened, wavy, crowded,
±leaf-like, smooth, finely
branched and curly at tips.
STEM stout, often very short
and usually obscure. SPORE
BEARING SURFACE ochreous,
smooth. SPORE PRINT white-
cream. SMELL earthy-mush-
roomy, pleasant. FLESH
ochreous, tough, elastic.
Solitary. On soil at base of
coniferous trees on which it
causes a brown cubical rot.
Summer – autumn. Wide-
spread. Uncommon. Edi-
ble. SPORES broadly ellipsoid
– subspherical, smooth,
3.5–4.5×4.5–6, non-amy-
loid. Cystidia absent.
HYPHAL SYSTEM monomitic.

...alyptella capula. Overall
...rm, size, colour, often
...nfused with stalked 'Dis-
...mycetes' but microscopic
...atures very different.
...UIT BODY cup-like, 0.2–
...5, goblet or funnel-
...aped, outer surface
...ooth, margin wavy,
...ooth or slightly inde-
...ed. STEM <0.2, tapering
to cup. SPORE BEARING
...RFACE lining cup, white-
...eam, smooth. SPORE PRINT
...hite. FLESH white-cream,
...ft, fragile. Solitary or in
...fted or trooping groups.
...n dead and rotting wood
...r other plant debris in wet
...aces. Summer – autumn.
...idespread. Very com-
...on. Inedible. SPORES
...lipsoid – boat-shaped,
...ooth, 3.5–4.5×6–9, non-
...nyloid. Cystidia absent.
...YPHAL SYSTEM monomitic.

Flagelloscypha citrispora.
Overall form, size, colour,
often confused with stem-
less 'Discomycetes' like
Dascyscyphus spp. but
microscopic features very
different. FRUIT BODY 0.03–
0.1, irregularly and
shallowly cup- or saucer-
like, outer surface densely
hairy, margin white,
fringed hairy, almost
completely inrolled when
dry. STEM absent. SPORE
BEARING SURFACE lining
cup, grey-ochre, smooth.
SPORE PRINT white. FLESH
whitish, soft, fragile. In
densely tufted groups. On
dead wood of broad-leaved
or coniferous trees and
other plant debris. Summer
– autumn. Widespread.
Uncommon. Inedible.
SPORES pip- to boat-shaped,
smooth, 3.5–4.5×7–10,
non-amyloid. Cystidia absent. HYPHAL SYSTEM mono-
mitic. Marginal hairs white,
thick-walled, incrusted to
half-way, tip smooth, tapering, very slender.

SPARASSIDACEAE
Fruit body erect, with stem,
many branched to form a
mass of flattened
and±wavy lobes, fairly
brightly coloured yellowish
ochre. Spore bearing sur-
face beneath horizontally
orientated lobes, smooth.
Spores broadly ellipsoid,
smooth, non-amyloid.
Flesh whitish or pale, soft,
rather cartilaginous when
dry, tough. Spore print pale
cream. Hyphal system
monomitic. Smell often distinctive. On wood or other
plant debris. Saprotrophic
or biotrophic. Edible and
good. One common and
distinctive genus.

STEREACEAE
Fruit body always flattened
and usually±resupinate
and effused or effused –
reflexed, with or without
stem, more rarely±erect.
Variably coloured but
usually whitish or pale.
Spore-bearing surface
usually smooth or±ribbed.
Spores variably shaped,
smooth, amyloid or non-
amyloid. Flesh whitish or
pale, usually leathery,
woody or corky, sometimes
(especially smaller species)
soft and fibrous or gelatinous, usually with distinct
layers. Spore print white.
Hyphal system usually
dimitic, sometimes mono-
mitic, rarely trimitic. Smell
not usually distinctive. Usually on wood, sometimes
other plant debris, some-
times (some rarer, stem-
med species) terrestrial.
Saprotrophic or biotrophic.
Not edible, not poisonous.

185

Amylostereum chailletii.
Overall fruit body form,
habitat, colour, microscopic features. FRUIT BODY
irregular, resupinate,
effused or effuso-reflexed,
loosely attached to substrate, smooth – slightly
warty, sometimes with
small cap-like projections,
often with slight lilac flush,
paler and ±finely cracked
when dry, margin distinct
with darker border. SPORE
PRINT white. FLESH whitish
buff, soft, waxy, hard when
dry. On dead wood of coniferous trees. All year.
Widespread. Uncommon.
Inedible. SPORES
cylindrical – ±sausage-shaped, smooth, 2.5–
3×5.5–7, amyloid. Cystidia
brownish, thick-walled,
conical – awl-shaped,
incrusted from half-way.
HYPHAL SYSTEM dimitic.

Amylostereum laevigatum.
Overall fruit body form,
habitat, colour, microscopic features. FRUIT BODY
irregular, resupinate,
effused, crust or skin-like,
tightly attached to substrate, smooth, finely
cracked when dry, margin
distinct and sharp. SPORE
PRINT white. FLESH greyish
buff, soft, waxy, hard and
crusty-brittle when dry. On
living wood of yew or more
rarely dead wood and other
conifers. All year. Widespread. Uncommon. Inedible. SPORES cylindrical –
ellipsoid, smooth, 3–4×7–
9, amyloid. Cystidia brownish, thick-walled,
cylindrical – broadly awl-shaped, incrusted from
half-way. HYPHAL SYSTEM
monomitic.

Stereum gausapatum. Overall fruit body form, habitat,
colour, colour change, microscopic features. FRUIT
BODY irregular, effused –
reflexed, also resupinate,
especially when beneath
substrate, fused in groups
but individual fruit bodies
discernible, very finely
downy-velvety above, margin paler, sharp, markedly
wavy, smooth – finely
warty, grey – reddish
brown below and on surface of resupinate areas,
bleeding red when cut.
SPORE PRINT white. FLESH
reddish ochre, elastic,
tough, hard and brittle
when dry. On dead wood,
often when still attached to
oaks or more rarely other
broad-leaved trees. All
year. Widespread. Common. Inedible. SPORES
cylindrical – ellipsoid,
smooth, 3–4×6.5–9,
weakly amyloid. Cystidia-like structures thin-walled,
cylindrical, smooth with
red-brown contents.
HYPHAL SYSTEM dimitic.

Stereum hirsutum. Overall
fruit body form, although
very variable, habitat, colour, microscopic features.
FRUIT BODY 3–10, bracket-like, semicircular – fan-shaped, broadly attached,
usually decurrent onto substrate and often partly
resupinate,±flat above,
wavy, distinctly downy-hairy, markedly concentrically zoned, margin paler,
sharp, wavy. SPORE-BEARING
SURFACE smooth – finely
warty, yellow – brownish
orange, not bleeding when
cut. SPORE PRINT white.
FLESH ochreous, elastic,
tough. Usually in large or
very large, overlapping and

fused groups. On dead
wood of broad-leaved
trees. All year. Widespread. Extremely common. Inedible. SPORES
cylindrical – ellipsoid,
smooth, 2–3×5.5–6.5,
weakly amyloid. Cystidia-like structures thick-walled,
cylindrical, smooth.
HYPHAL SYSTEM dimitic.

Stereum rameale (=*ochraceoflavum*). Habit, habitat,
overall fruit body form,
colour, microscopic features. FRUIT BODY 0.5–2,±
bracket-like, semicircular
– fan-shaped, broadly attached,±flat above, slightly
wavy, very finely velvety-smooth, often coloured
green by algal growth,
barely and indefinitely
zoned, margin sharp, fringed, slightly wavy. SPORE-BEARING SURFACE smooth –
finely warty, greyish ochre,
not bleeding when cut.
SPORE PRINT white. FLESH
whitish ochre, elastic,
tough. Usually in fused linear groups. On dead wood
of broad-leaved trees, especially oak. All year. Widespread. Uncommon. Inedible. SPORES cylindrical –
ellipsoid, smooth, 2–3×7–
9, amyloid. Cystidia-like
structures thick-walled,
cylindrical, smooth.
HYPHAL SYSTEM dimitic.

Stereum rugosum. Habit,
colour change, microscopic
features. FRUIT BODY perennial, irregular, resupinate,
±effused, fairly loosely attached to substrate, especially when older, sometimes with projecting mar-

ginal zones, smooth-slightly warty, margin distinct,
paler, bleeding red when
cut. SPORE PRINT white.
FLESH whitish ochre, markedly layered when older,
elastic, tough, hard and
crusty when dry. On dead
wood of broad-leaved
trees, especially oak and
hazel. All year. Widespread. Extremely common. Inedible. SPORES
ellipsoid – ±boat-like,
smooth, 3.5–4.5×6.5–9,
amyloid. Cystidia-like
structures thick-walled,
cylindrical, smooth, often
with red-brown contents.
HYPHAL SYSTEM dimitic.

Stereum sanguinolentum.
Habit, habitat, colour
change, microscopic features. FRUIT BODY irregula,
resupinate,±effused and
loosely attached to substrate, smooth or warty-wrinkled, often with viole
flush, paler at wavy indented and distinctly bounde
margin, bleeding red whe
cut, often projecting to
become±bracket-like and
finely downy-hairy above
with concentric zoning.
SPORE PRINT white. FLESH
whitish ochre, layered,
elastic, tough, hard when
dry. On dead wood of con
iferous trees. All year.
Widespread. Very common. Inedible. SPORES
cylindrical – ellipsoid,
smooth, 2.5–3×8–9, amyloid. Cystidia-like structures thick-walled,
cylindrical – spindle-shaped, smooth, with red-brown contents. HYPHAL
SYSTEM dimitic.

Steccherinum fimbriatum.
Overall fruit body form,
habitat, microscopic features. FRUIT BODY irregula
resupinate,±effused,
loosely attached to substrate, markedly wrinkled,

h fringed warts or short
th, paler at margin
ere very distinctly
nged and with extensive
zomorph development.
RE PRINT white. FLESH
kish brown, tough, hard
en dry. On dead wood of
ad-leaved or more
ely coniferous trees. All
ar. Widespread. Uncom-
n. Inedible. SPORES
adly ellipsoid, smooth,
–3×4–5, non-amyloid.
stidia thick-walled,
indrical – club-shaped,
ooth, incrusted from
f-way. HYPHAL SYSTEM
nitic.

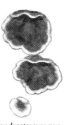

ondrostereum pur-
eum. Colour, fruit body
m, habitat, microscopic
tures. FRUIT BODY irregu-
, resupinate, ±effused,
sely attached to subs-
te, smooth – slightly
rty, wavy, slightly wrink-
l, paler at margin and
nged, usually with±
acket-like projections,
wny-hairy and barely
ned above. SPORE PRINT
ite. FLESH purplish
wn – whitish with dis-
ct dark line, tough, hard
en dry. On dead wood of
ad-leaved or more
ely coniferous trees, also
living broad-leaving
es, especially plums,
using silver leaf disease.
l year. Widespread. Very
nmon. Inedible. SPORES
indrical – ellipsoid,
ooth, 2.5–3.5×6.5–8,
-amyloid. Cystidia (1)
ndle-shaped, often with
rkedly narrowed apex,
etimes incrusted, (2)
b-shaped with markedly
ollen tips, smooth.
PHAL SYSTEM mononitic.

ELEPHORACEAE
uit body very variable,
used, effused-reflexed or
ct and divided into stem
d cap or variously bran-
ed and rather coral-like.
riably coloured, some-
es fairly bright. Spore-
aring surface variable,
ooth, warty, toothed,
ded, porous or gill-like.
ores ellipsoid – sub-
rical, often irregular in

outline, smooth – warty or
spiny, non-amyloid. Flesh
pale or fairly brightly
coloured, soft, fibrous,
leathery or fleshy. Spore
print usually brownish.
Hyphal system monomitic.
Smell sometimes dis-
tinctive. Usually terrestrial,
sometimes on wood or
other plant debris.
Mycorrhizal. Not edible,
not poisonous. There are
many species, especially of
Tomentella, that are
uncommon and very dif-
ficult to distinguish.

Tomentella fusca. Microscopic features, overall fruit
body form. FRUIT BODY
irregular, resupinate,
effused, loosely attached to
substrate, loosely hairy,
mealy-warty or almost
membranous, margin
usually slightly paler. SPORE
PRINT brown. FLESH reddish
brown – greyish brown,
fibrous, cottony. On dead
and rotting wood of broad-
leaved or coniferous trees.
Summer – autumn. Wide-
spread. Uncommon. Inedi-
ble. SPORES broadly ellipsoid – subspherical, spiny,
9–10×9.5–11 (including
spines). Cystidia absent.
HYPHAL SYSTEM monomitic.

Tomentella pannosa. Microscopic features, overall
fruit body form. FRUIT BODY
irregular, resupinate,
effused, loosely attached to
substrate, membranous,
almost smooth, margin
usually slightly paler. SPORE
PRINT pale brown. FLESH
reddish brown – greyish
brown, membranous. On
dead and rotting wood of
broad-leaved or coniferous
trees. Summer – autumn.
Widespread. Rare. Inedi-
ble. SPORES irregularly
pyramidal, narrowly spiny,
7–9 (including spines). Cystidia absent. HYPHAL SYSTEM
monomitic.

Caldesiella ferruginosa.
Microscopic features,
overall fruit body form and
surface. FRUIT BODY
irregular, resupinate,
effused, loosely attached to
substrate, finely downy-
membranous, partly
warty – distinctly toothed
with short conical teeth,
margin distinctly bounded,
often with rhizomorphs.
SPORE PRINT brown. FLESH
reddish brown, soft,
fibrous, cottony. On dead
and rotting wood of broad-
leaved or coniferous trees.
Autumn – spring. Wide-
spread. Rare. Inedible.
SPORES subspherical, spiny,
10–15 (including spines).
Cystidia absent. HYPHAL
SYSTEM monomitic.

Thelephora anthocephala.
Overall fruit body form,
microscopic features. FRUIT
BODY 3–6 (height), erect,
many branched, coral-like,
branches cylindrical and
narrowing upwards,
circular in cross-section,
fairly slender, pointed and
whitish at tips, smooth,
sometimes entire fruit body
flattened and rosette-like,
branching from base and
with white-fringed,
flattened lobes about 1–2
long. STEM rudimentary,
stout. SPORE PRINT brown.
SMELL indistinct. FLESH
dark brown, soft, elastic,
fibrous. Solitary or in small
groups. On soil, often with
mosses and other vegeta-
tion in broad-leaved and
coniferous woods. Sum-
mer – autumn. Wide-
spread. Uncommon. Ined-
ible. SPORES subspherical –
irregularly ellipsoid, spiny,
6–9×9–11 (including
spines). Cystidia absent.
HYPHAL SYSTEM monomitic.

Thelephora palmata.
Overall fruit body form,
smell, microscopic
features. FRUIT BODY 4–7
(height), erect, many
branched, coral-like,
branches cylindrical,
circular in cross-section,
fairly slender, markedly
flattened, fringed-toothed
and paler at tips, smooth.
STEM rudimentary, stout.
SPORE PRINT brown. SMELL
very strong, repulsive.
FLESH brown, corky, tough.
Solitary or in small±tufted
groups. On soil in
coniferous woods.
Summer – autumn.
Widespread. Rare.
Inedible. SPORES broadly
and irregularly ellipsoid –
subspherical, spiny, 8–
12×11–13 (including
spines). Cystidia absent.
HYPHAL SYSTEM monomitic.

Thelephora terrestris **Earth
Fan.** Overall fruit body
form, microscopic features.
FRUIT BODY 1–4 (height), ±
erect, branched into ros-
ette-like lobes, ±fused radially to form large irregular
patches, radially downy-
hairy, concentrically zoned
above, margin paler and
often with small flap-like
outgrowths, irregularly
warty-wrinkled beneath.
STEM rudimentary, stout.
SPORE PRINT brown. SMELL
fairly faint, earthy. FLESH
brown, fibrous, tough. In
small – large fused groups.
On soil, among leaf litter
or±covering plant debris in
coniferous woods or more
rarely broad-leaved woods
or other areas on acid sites.
Summer – autumn. Wide-
spread. Very common. In-
edible. SPORES broadly and
irregularly ellipsoid, irregularly warty-knobbly, 5–7×
8–9. Cystidia absent.
HYPHAL SYSTEM monomitic.

187

Thelephora terrestris var. *resupinata*. Overall fruit body form, habitat, microscopic features. FRUIT BODY irregular, resupinate, effused, tightly attached to substrate, membranous, smooth – warty, ±concentrically zoned, margin paler, distinct. SPORE PRINT brown. SMELL ? FLESH brown, fibrous, tough. On dead wood of coniferous trees and other plant debris. Summer – autumn. Widespread. Uncommon. Inedible. SPORES broadly and irregularly ellipsoid, irregularly warty-knobbly, 5–7× 8–9. Cystidia absent. HYPHAL SYSTEM monomitic.

Thelephora spiculosa. Overall fruit body form, surface features, microscopic features. FRUIT BODY 1–4 (height)±erect, branched into spiky lobes, ± fused radially to form large irregular patches, markedly downy-woolly, tips whitish, irregularly warty – wrinkled beneath. STEM rudimentary, stout. SPORE PRINT brown. SMELL? FLESH pale brown, fibrous, tough. In small – large fused groups. On soil, among leaf litter or±covering plant debris in woods. Autumn. Widespread. Rare. Inedible. SPORES broadly and irregularly ellipsoid, spiny, 6–7×7–12. Cystidia absent. HYPHAL SYSTEM monomitic.

Hydnellum concrescens. Overall fruit body form, colours, smell, microscopic features. CAP 2–7, rosette-like with depressed rather finely scaly centre, finely velvety, concentrically zoned, radially wrinkled-grooved, usually with irr-egular knob-like outgrowths. STEM 1–5, tapering downwards but±bulbous at base, rather stout, finely velvety. SPORE-BEARING SURFACE pink-reddish, coarsely spiny-toothed, decurrent. SPORE PRINT pale brown. SMELL mealy. FLESH markedly zoned, dark wine-red, bruising darker, corky, tough. In small – large, fused groups. On soil in woods, among leaf litter and other plant debris, often with mosses. Summer – autumn. Widespread. Rare. Inedible. SPORES irregularly subspherical, coarsely warty, 3.5–4.5× 4.5–6. Cystidia absent. HYPHAL SYSTEM monomitic.

Hydnellum ferrugineum Overall fruit body form, habitat, microscopic features. CAP 3–10, irregularly top-shaped – spherical, then flatter and funnel-shaped, at first smooth-velvety, then rougher, radially grooved and with blood-red droplets in wet weather, at first whitish, then red-brown, decurrent, spiny spore-bearing surface beneath. STEM 1–5, stout, solid. SPORE PRINT brown. SMELL faint, mealy. FLESH pale reddish brown, concentrically zoned, especially pine. Summer – autumn. Widespread. Rare. Inedible. SPORES subspherical, irregularly warty-knobbly, 5–6×3.5–5, non-amyloid. Basidia 20–30, slenderly club-shaped, 4-spored. Cystidia absent. HYPHAL SYSTEM monomitic.

Hydnellum aurantiacum. Overall fruit body form, colours, habitat, microscopic features. CAP 2–7, ros-ette-like – funnel-shaped with depressed centre, at first finely velvety, smooth, then faintly concentrically zoned, radially wrinkled-grooved, usually with irreg-ular knob-like outgrowths, markedly paler at margin.

STEM 2–5, tapering down-wards but±bulbous at base, rather stout, finely velvety. SPORE-BEARING SURFACE at first whitish, then orange-brown, coarsely spiny-toothed, decurrent. SPORE PRINT pale brown. SMELL strong, pleasant. FLESH sometimes faintly zoned, white – orange-brown, corky, tough. Solitary or in small – large, fused groups. On soil, among leaf litter and other plant debris, especially in coniferous woods. Summer – autumn. Widespread, predomi-nantly northern. Rare. Inedible. SPORES irregularly subspherical, coarsely warty, 4.5–5×5.5–6.5. Cystidia absent. HYPHAL SYSTEM monomitic.

Hydnellum caeruleum. Overall fruit body form, colours, smell, habitat, microscopic features. CAP 3 –7,±rosette-like, often slightly depressed, at first velvety then smooth, rad-ially wrinkled-grooved, margin paler, wavy, indented. STEM 2–5, tapering downwards and usually fused into substrate, rather stout, finely velvety. SPORE-BEARING SURFACE at first bluish brown, then greyish, then brown, coarsely spiny-toothed,±decurrent. SPORE PRINT pale brown. SMELL faint, mealy. FLESH grey-bluish black in cap, red-orange-brown with blue flush in stem, zoned, corky, tough. Solitary or in±tuft-ed or fused groups. On soil, among mosses, leaf litter and other plant debris, in coniferous or mixed woods. Summer. Widespread, pre-dominantly southern. Rare. Inedible. SPORES irregularly ellipsoid – subspherical, coarsely warty, 5–6×7–8. Cystidia absent. HYPHAL SYSTEM monomitic.

Hydnellum peckii (=*diabo-lum*). Overall fruit body form, colours, smell, habi-tat, microscopic features. CAP 3–8, depressed rosette-like – top-shaped, radial-grooved – pitted,±cover with erect, pointed scales darker on aging, bearing blood-red liquid drops, margin paler, wavy, inde nted, often darkly spotte from dry drops. STEM 1–5 tapering downwards and often±fused into substra rather stout, finely velve SPORE-BEARING SURFACE a first whitish, then red-brown, coarsely spiny-toothed, decurrent. SPOR PRINT pale brown. SMELL faint, unpleasant, sour. FLESH pinkish brown, da ker spotted, zoned, cork tough. Solitary or in±tu ed or fused groups. On s among mosses, leaf litter and other plant debris, e ecially in or near to coni ous woods. Summer – a umn. Northern. Uncom-mon. Inedible. SPORES irr ularly ellipsoid – subsph ical, coarsely warty, 4–4. 5–6. Cystidia absent. HYPHAL SYSTEM monomi

Hydnellum suaveolens. Overall fruit body form, colours, smell, habitat, microscopic features. CAF –10,±irregularly rosette-like, at first finely velvety then smooth – fibrous, wavy, warty – wrinkled, concentrically zoned, ofte with bluish flush, often irregular scaly outgrowth markedly paler and inde nted at margin. STEM 1.5-tapering downwards but often±bulbous at base, rather stout, finely velve SPORE-BEARING SURFACE a first bluish white, then brownish, coarsely spiny-toothed, decurrent. SPOR PRINT pale brown. SMELL pleasant, aniseed? FLESH bluish white, distinctly zoned, corky, tough. Usually in large, fused groups. On soil, among l litter and other plant debris, especially in or n to coniferous woods. Summer – autumn. Wide spread, mainly northern. Rare. Inedible. SPORES i gularly polygonal, coarse warty, 2–3.5×3.5–5. Cys dia absent. HYPHAL SYSTE monomitic.

ydnellum scrobiculatum
=velutinum var. scrobicu-
tum). Overall fruit body
rm, colours, smell, habi-
t, microscopic features.
AP 2–6, ±rosette-like, often
ghtly depressed, velvety
fibrous, radially grooved,
coarsely scaly in centre,
argin paler, bruising dark-
, wavy, indented. STEM 2–
tapering downwards and
ten ±fused into substrate,
ther stout, finely velvety.
ORE-BEARING SURFACE at
st whitish, then red-
own, coarsely spiny-
othed, ±decurrent. SPORE
INT pale brown. SMELL
int, mealy-spicy. FLESH
irk reddish brown, often
iler spotted, zoned,
orky, tough. Usually
±tufted or fused groups.
n soil, among mosses,
af litter and other plant
ebris, in coniferous or
oad-leaved woods, espe-
ally with oak. Summer –
itumn. Southern. Rare.
edible. SPORES irregularly
lipsoid – subspherical,
arsely warty, 4–4.5×5.5–
5. Cystidia absent.
PHAL SYSTEM monomitic.

XOBASIDIALES
ore-bearing surface one-
ded, smooth, sometimes
arely continuous. Fruit
ody rudimentary or
oscure, on or within host
ant tissues. Spores
ariously shaped, white,
nooth, non-amyloid, sep-
te or not. Conidia usually
resent with the basidio-
ores which bud them off
s a prelude to germina-
on. Basidia 2–8-spored.
iotrophic on or within tis-
ies of higher plants. One
mily **Exobasidiaceae**
ith about five genera, only
ie of which, *Exobasi-
ium*, is common and likely
be noticed. There are
veral species, many caus-
g similar symptoms on
milar host plants although
e microscopic features
e usually fairly distinct.

EXOBASIDIACEAE

Exobasidium vaccinii.
Overall form, habit, habitat. SYMPTOMS swollen,
often reddish gall-like
growths on leaves and
shoots, each ±covered with
discontinuous spore-
bearing surface in the form
of powdery whitish mould
growth. SPORE PRINT white.
On leaves and shoots of
plants in the family Eri-
caceae, especially *Vaccinium* species and cultivated
Rhododendron species in
the azalea groups. Spring –
autumn. Widespread.
Uncommon. SPORES irregu-
larly cylindrical, sometimes
bent, 1–6-septate, 2.5–
4.5×11–16, non-amyloid,
(also cylindrical conidia, 1–
1.5×5–9). Basidia 50–60,
elongated club-shaped,
wavy, 4–6-spored.

Exobasidium rhododendri.
Overall form, habit, habitat. SYMPTOMS swollen, gall-
like growths, at first yellowish, then pink-reddish, on
leaves, each ±covered with
discontinuous spore-
bearing surface in the form
of powdery whitish mould
growth. SPORE PRINT white.
On leaves and shoots of
Rhododendron species,
especially *R. hirsutum* and
R. ferrugineum and their
hybrids. Spring – autumn.
Widespread, not Britain.
SPORES irregularly cylindrical – ±sausage-shaped, 1-
septate at maturity, 1.5–
2×12–15, non-amyloid,
(also cylindrical conidia,
1.5–2×5–9). Basidia 40–50,
irregularly cylindrical, 4–6-
spored.

DACRYMYCETALES
Spore-bearing surface
exposed during develop-
ment, one- or two-sided,
smooth. Fruit body usually
gelatinous, occasionally
waxy or dry, very variable,
disc-, club-, coral- or cup-
shaped, ±spherical, cylindrical or with distinct cap
and stem. Spores variously
shaped, smooth, non-
amyloid, usually septate.
Spore print white or yel-
low. Conidia usually pre-
sent with the basidiospores
which bud them off as a
prelude to germination.
Basidia highly characteristic, non-septate and club-or
tuning-fork-shaped, 2-
spored. Saprotrophic on
wood. A remarkably
homogeneous group with a
unique basidium structure.
One Family **Dacrymyce-
taceae** and about nine
genera but only a few very
common species.

Dacrymyces stillatus.
Extremely variable but
microscopic features
usually reliable, similar and
related species are very
much rarer. FRUIT BODY
0.1–0.15, variable, com-
monly knob-like but also
sometimes cup- or saucer-
like with rudimentary stem-
like base, smooth (conidial
stage) – finely wrinkled
(basidiferous stage), often
rather shiny. SPORE PRINT
white. FLESH orange-white,
soft – firm, ±gelatinous,
translucent. Solitary or in
small – large trooping or
fused groups. On dead, rotting wood of broad-leaved
or coniferous trees, including structural timber. All
year (but overlooked when
dry). Widespread. Very
common. Inedible. SPORES
elongated ellipsoid –
cylindrical, often slightly
curved, smooth, 3-septate
at maturity, 4.5–6×13–16,
non-amyloid, (usually with
cylindrical conidia, 3–4×9–
12, in chains). Basidia 35–
40, tuning-fork-shaped.

DACRYMYCETACEAE

Calocera cornea. Overall
fruit body form, colour,
microscopic features. FRUIT
BODY 0.5–1.5 (height), ±
spine- or tooth-like, slightly wavy, occasionally forked near rather sharply pointed tip, smooth – finely
wrinkled. SPORE PRINT
white. FLESH yellowish,
firm, gelatinous. In small –
large groups, trooping or
tufted. On dead, rotting
wood of broad-leaved (or
rarely coniferous?) trees.
Summer – autumn. Wide-
spread. Very common.
Inedible. SPORES elongated-
ellipsoid – sausage-
shaped, smooth, 1-septate
at maturity, 3–4×7–10,
non-amyloid. Basidia at
first 25–30, tuning-fork-
shaped.

Calocera glossoides. Overall fruit body form, colour,
microscopic features. FRUIT
BODY 0.3–1.0 (height), ±
club-shaped, swollen upper
part finely and irregularly
wrinkled longitudinally,
smooth below. SPORE PRINT
white. FLESH yellowish,
firm, gelatinous. In small –
large groups, trooping or ±
tufted. On dead, rotting
wood of broad-leaved trees.
Summer – autumn. Wide-
spread. Uncommon. Inedi-
ble. SPORES elongated-ellipsoid – sausage-shaped,
smooth, 1–3-septate at
maturity, 3–4×12–14, non-
amyloid. Basidia at first 30–
40, ±cylindrical with
tuning-fork-shaped apex.

189

DACRYMYCETACEAE

Calocera viscosa. Overall fruit body form, colour, habitat, microscopic features. FRUIT BODY 3–8 (height), ±antler-shaped, cylindrical below, several times branched towards apex, often rather flattened and grooved below, smoother above, sticky-slimy when wet. SPORE PRINT white. FLESH yellowish golden, firm, gelatinous. In small – large groups, ±tufted. On dead, rotting wood of coniferous trees. Summer – autumn. Widespread. Very common. Inedible. SPORES elongated-ellipsoid – slightly sausage-shaped, smooth, 0–1-septate at maturity, 3–4.5×8–10, non-amyloid. Basidia at first 30–40, ±cylindrical with domed apex which later becomes tuning-fork-shaped.

Ditiola pezizaeformis. Overall fruit body form, habitat, microscopic features. FRUIT BODY 0.5–1.5, erumpent, cushion, top- or cup-shaped, usually ±flat and wrinkled in centre, margin even or slightly wavy. SPORE PRINT yellow. FLESH whitish yellow, soft, gelatinous. In small – large groups, trooping – ± tufted. On dead, rotting wood of broad-leaved (or rarely coniferous) trees, especially oak. Summer – autumn. Widespread. Uncommon. Inedible. SPORES elongated-ellipsoid – ±cylindrical, smooth, 7–15-septate at maturity, 8–10.5×18–25, non-amyloid, (often with subspherical conidia, 0.5–1). Basidia at first 50–80, ±cylindrical with domed – ±tuning-fork-shaped apex.

Guepiniopsis chrysocoma. Overall fruit body form, habitat, microscopic features. FRUIT BODY 0.05–0.15, at first cushion-shaped, then top-or cup-shaped, obscurely rooted in substrate, usually±flat and wrinkled in centre, margin even or slightly wavy. SPORE PRINT yellow? FLESH whitish yellow, soft, gelatinous. In small – large groups, trooping – ±tufted. On dead, rotting wood of coniferous trees. All year? Widespread. Rare. Inedible. SPORES elongated-ellipsoid – ±sausage-shaped, smooth, 3–7-septate (with some transverse) at maturity, 7.5–9×16–24, non-amyloid. Basidia at first 45–85, at first±cylindrical – club-shaped, but then – ± tuning-fork-shaped at apex, sharply narrowed at base.

TREMELLALES

Spore-bearing surface exposed during development, one-or two-sided, smooth. Fruit body gelatinous, waxy, dry, fleshy or corky, resupinate, cushion-like, club-shaped, coral-like or with distinct cap and stem. Spores variously shaped, smooth or more rarely spiny or warty, non-amyloid, non-septate. Spore print white. Conidia occasionally present with the basidiospores. Basidia highly characteristic, irregularly subspherical, pear-shaped, club-shaped, or more rarely spindle-shaped or in chains, divided by longitudinal or oblique septa into 2–4 sterigma-bearing cells. Saprotrophic on wood or other plant debris or more rarely biotrophic on other fungi. The unusual basidium structure is characteristic. Four families, but two are small, rare and obscure and twenty-seven of the thirty genera, described all those described here occur in the **Tremellaceae**.

TREMELLACEAE

Exidia plana (=*glandulosa*) **Witches' Butter**. Overall fruit body form, colour, microscopic features, often confused with *Bulgaria inquinans* but spore print and microscopic features very different. FRUIT BODY 2–5, at first irregularly cup-shaped or ear-like, gradually becoming more complexly distorted, folded and wrinkled, eventually brain-like, glandular, attached rather closely to substrate in centre, not at margin, smooth and shiny. SPORE PRINT white. FLESH black, soft, gelatinous. Solitary or in small – large fused groups. On dead wood of broad-leaved trees or on dead tissues and wounds on living trees. All year (but overlooked when dry). Widespread. Very common. Inedible. SPORES cylindrical – ±sausage-shaped, smooth, 4.5–5×12–14, non-amyloid. Basidia 16–18, pear-shaped, longitudinally septate, 4-spored.

Exidia thuretiana. Overall fruit body form, colour, microscopic features, often confused with *Myxarium nucleatum* q.v. FRUIT BODY 0.2–1 (individually, much larger en masse) at first irregularly knob- or cushion-like, gradually becoming more complexly distorted, folded and wrinkled, eventually brain-like, smooth and matt, rather like mother-of-pearl. SPORE PRINT white. FLESH white, tough, gelatinous. Solitary or in small – large fused groups. On dead wood of broad-leaved trees, especially beech. All year (but almost invisible when dry). Widespread. Uncommon. Inedible. SPORES cylindrical – ±sausage-shaped, smooth, 5–7×13–20, non-amyloid.

Basidia 15–24, subspherical – pear-shaped, longitudinally septate, 4-spored.

Tremella encephala. Habitat, overall fruit body form, microscopic features. FRUIT BODY 0.5–2, at first irregularly knob-or cushion-like, gradually becoming more complexly distorted, folded and wrinkled, eventually± brain-like, smooth, shiny – matt, sometimes tending to appear rather like mother-of-pearl. SPORE PRINT white. FLESH white, tough, gelatinous, with hard white core. Solitary or in small – large fused groups. On dead wood of coniferous trees, always with *Stereum sanguinolentum* which it parasitises. Spring – autumn (but almost invisible when dry). Widespread. Rare. Inedible. SPORES broadly ellipsoid – subspherical, smooth, 7.5–9×9–11, non-amyloid. Basidia 13–20, subspherical, longitudinally septate, 4-spored.

Tremella foliacea. Colour, overall fruit body form, microscopic features. FRUIT BODY 3–10, at first irregularly knob- or cushion-like, composed of closely matted leaf-like lobes arising from a common base, gradually becoming more complexly folded and wrinkled, smooth, shiny – matt. SPORE PRINT white. FLESH brown, soft, gelatinous. Solitary or in small,±trooping groups. On dead wood of broad-leaved or more rarely coniferous trees. All year (but almost invisible when dry). Widespread. Rare. Inedible. SPORES broadly ellipsoid – subspherical, smooth, 6–8×9–11, non-amyloid. Basidia 13–16, subspherical, longitudinally septate, 2–4-spored.

...mella lutescens. Colour, rall fruit body form, roscopic features, poss- a colour variant of *T. enterica* but appears ays to lack conidia. IT BODY 2–8, at first irre-arly knob-, cushion- or in-like, composed of sely matted irregular -like lobes arising from ommon base, gradually oming more complexly ded and wrinkled, ooth, shiny – matt. RE PRINT white. FLESH low, soft, gelatinous. itary or in small, ±troo-g groups. On dead wood road-leaved trees. All ır. Widespread. Rare. dible. SPORES broadly psoid, smooth, 7–10× -16, non-amyloid. Basi-20–25, broadly ellipsoid lub-shaped, longitudi-ly septate, 4-spored.

...emella mesenterica Yel-w Brain Fungus. Colour, erall fruit body form, croscopic features, very ilar to *T. lutescens* q.v. UT BODY 2–8, at first irre-arly knob-, cushion- or ain-like, composed of sely matted irregular f-like lobes arising from ommon base, gradually coming more complexly ded and wrinkled, ooth, shiny – matt. ORE PRINT white. FLESH llow, soft, gelatinous. litary or in small, ± ooping groups. On dead od of broad-leaved es, and especially gorse. ll year. Widespread. ommon. Inedible. SPORES oadly ellipsoid, smooth, -8×10–16, non-amyloid. lso subspherical conidia, 5–3.5×3–4.5). Basidia 20 25, broadly ellipsoid – ub-shaped, longitudinally ptate, 4-spored.

Myxarium nucleatum. Overall fruit body form, colour, microscopic fea-tures, often confused with *Exidia thuretiana*, even by experts, the lack of a basi-dium stalk in *Myxarium* being the only reliable character although its fruit body is usually softer and more watery. FRUIT BODY 0.2–1 (individually, much larger en masse), at first irregularly knob- or cushion-like, gradually becoming more complexly distorted, folded and wrinkled, sometimes even-tually almost brain-like, smooth and matt, rather like mother-of-pearl. SPORE PRINT white. FLESH white, watery, gelatinous around hard centre. Solitary or in small – large fused groups. On dead wood of broad-leaved trees, especially beech and ash. All year (but almost invisible when dry). Widespread. Uncom-mon. Inedible. SPORES cylindrical – ±sausage-shaped, smooth, 3.5–5×10 –14, non-amyloid. Basidia 11–16, subspherical – pear-shaped, longitudinally sep-tate, 4-spored.

Pseudohydnum gelatino-sum **Jelly Tongue.** Overall fruit body form, spore-bearing surface, microsco-pic features. FRUIT BODY 2–6, bracket- or tongue-like with stem-like base, vari-able in colour, white – greyish brown, smooth – coarsely granular above, smoother and wavy at mar-gin, densely spiny on spore-bearing surface beneath. SPORE PRINT white. FLESH whitish, soft, gelatinous. Usually in tufted or over-lapping groups. On dead and rotting wood of con-iferous trees. Summer – autumn. Widespread.

Common. Inedible. SPORES broadly ellipsoid – subspherical, smooth, 4.5–5.5×5–6, non-amyloid. Basidia 10–15, elongated-ellipsoid – pear-shaped, longitudinally septate, 4-spored.

Sebacina incrustans. Over-all fruit body form, habit, microscopic features. FRUIT BODY irregular, resupinate, effused, closely attached to substrate, smooth – densely wrinkled and almost brain-like, often with irregular conical out-growths, margin fibrous. SPORE PRINT white. FLESH whitish, waxy, tough. On twigs, other plant debris, grasses, herbaceous plant stems. Summer – autumn. Widespread. Uncommon. SPORES broadly ellipsoid, smooth, 9–10×14–18, non-amyloid. Basidia 17–22, elongated-ellipsoid, longi-tudinally septate, 4-spored.

AURICULARIALES

Spore-bearing surface exposed during develop-ment, one-or two-sided, smooth. Fruit body gelatin-ous, waxy, dry or fleshy, resupinate, cushion-like, club-shaped, coral-like or with distinct cap and stem (rarely±absent in some obscure biotrophic forms). Spores variously shaped, smooth, non-amyloid, usually non-septate. Spore print white. Conidia occa-sionally present with the basidiospores. Basidia highly characteristic,±cy-lindrical, curved or occas-ionally coiled, usually divided by 1–3 transverse septa into 2–4 sterigma-bearing cells. Saprotrophic or biotrophic on higher plants, cryptogams or other fungi. The unusual basidium structure is characteristic. One Family, the **Auricular-iaceae** but only two common species.

Auricularia mesenterica **Tripe Fungus.** Overall fruit body form, flesh, microsco-pic features. FRUIT BODY irregular, resupinate, loosely attached to subs-trate, also generally at least partly bracket-like, 2–4,± downy hairy, wrinkled – wavy, concentrically zoned above, reddish purple and with white bloom beneath. SPORE PRINT white. FLESH brownish, tough, gelatin-ous, elastic, hard and brittle when dry. On dead or more rarely living wood of broad-leaved trees. All year. Widespread. Common, rather rare northwards. In-edible. SPORES cylindrical – ±sausage-shaped, smooth, 6–7×15–17.5, non-amyloid. Basidia 50–70,±cylindrical, transversely septate, 2–4-spored.

Hirneola (=*Auricularia*) *auricula-judae* **Jew's Ear.** Fruit body form, habitat, flesh, microscopic features. FRUIT BODY 2–8,±ear-shap-ed, narrowly attached,± stem-less, finely velvety, smooth – wrinkled above, purplish brown, wrinkled – veined on spore-bearing surface beneath. SPORE PRINT white. FLESH brown-ish, tough, gelatinous, elas-tic, hard and brittle when dry. On dead or moribund wood of broad-l. trees, esp. elder. All year. Wide-spread. Extremely com-mon. Edible. SPORES cylindrical – ±sausage-shaped, smooth, 6–8×17–19, non-amyloid. Basidia 50–80,±cylindrical, trans-versely septate, 4-spored.

191

GASTEROMYCETES

Spores usually produced in a well-defined fruit body of extremely variable form, often, at least in European species, superficially spherical or cylindrical. Spore-bearing basidia enclosed, at least during the early part of their development, sometimes on a distinctly recognisable if convoluted spore-bearing surface, but often on scattered cells in spore-bearing tissue or gleba within the fruit body. Spores are characteristically never discharged forcibly from the basidium, but are released passively into a cavity in the fruit body. Sometimes a sterile thread-like capillitium remains after the gleba has been dispersed. Spores usually±spherical and brown, usually spiny, warty or with reticulated patterns, occasionally smooth. Basidia of little importance in identification and classification. Mostly saprotrophic and terrestrial, some subterranean, few on dead wood or dung, two aquatic, very few biotrophic, few mycorrhizal. Some edible, none? poisonous. Divided into nine or ten orders on the basis of presence or absence of distinct spore-bearing surface, development of basidia, fruit body structure and other features although most species can be assigned to Orders on the strength of overall fruit body form. Most Orders are represented in Europe and included here although many species are extremely rare and many groups are predominantly tropical. The Gasteromycetes are a very diverse group of fungi and the most important feature distinguishing them from other macroscopic Basidiomycetes is the lack of active spore discharge from the basidium. They include puff-balls, earth-balls, earth-stars, birds'-nest fungi and stinkhorns.

SCLERODERMATALES

Terrestrial, sometimes subterranean, fruit body± stem-less, usually spherical or star-like but sometimes simpler with many spore-containing bodies on a stroma. No distinct spore-bearing surface, the basidia being produced in groups scattered through spore-bearing tissue which becomes powdery at maturity. The basidia often mature sequentially in several generations, but not all the generations produce spores. Usually no capillitium.

Spores smooth, spiny, warty or net-patterned. Includes about five families of which three are important in Europe and included here: **Sclerodermataceae** (*Scleroderma* and *Pisolithus*), **Astraeaceae** (*Astraeus*) and **Sphaerobolaceae** (*Sphaerobolus*).

Scleroderma areolatum. Stem-like structure, spores, habitat, very similar to *S. verrucosum*. FRUIT BODY 2–4, subspherical – ±pear-shaped, peridium thin (<0.1), leathery, tough,± covered with smooth, dark scales, at maturity rupturing irregularly at apex, tapering below into short, thick, deeply rooting stem-like structure (1–2 long). GLEBA at first whitish, firm, then brownish black-and-white marbled, then deep purple-brown, powdery, no capillitium. Usually in small, trooping or±tufted groups. On bare soil or among moss or sparse vegetation in damp places. Summer – autumn. Widespread. Uncommon. Inedible. SPORES dark brown, spherical, spiny, 9–14 (excluding spines).

Scleroderma bovista. Spores, habitat. FRUIT BODY 2–6, subspherical – ±pear-shaped, peridium thin (<0.1), leathery, tough, smooth or±covered with smooth, reddish brown scales, at maturity rupturing irregularly at apex, tapering below into indefinite short, thick, rooting, stem-like structure (1–2 long) with matted mycelium. GLEBA at first whitish, firm, then brown and yellowish marbled, then deep brown-black, powdery, no capillitium. Solitary or in small, trooping or±tufted groups. On bare soil or among grass and other vegetation, often in woods, apparently always on

chalky sites. Summer – autumn. Widespread. Uncommon. Inedible. SPORES dark brown, spherical, ribbed in net-like pattern, 10–12.5 (excluding ribs).

Scleroderma citrinum **Common Earth-Ball.** Spores, mycelial threads, habitat. FRUIT BODY 3–12, subspherical, peridium thick (<0.5), leathery, tough,± covered with coarse, brown scales, at maturity rupturing irregularly at apex, attached to substrate below with coarse mycelial threads. GLEBA at first whitish with violet flush, firm, then brownish black-and-white marbled, then purplish black, powdery, no capillitium. Solitary or in small, trooping or±tufted groups. On bare soil or among mosses or other vegetation, especially in or close to woods, on sandy, acid sites. Summer – autumn. Widespread. Extremely common. Inedible. SPORES dark brown, spherical, with (usually incomplete) net-like pattern with spiny extensions, 9–13 (excluding ornamentation).

Scleroderma verrucosum. Stem-like structure, spores, habitat, very similar to *S. areolatum*. FRUIT BODY 2.5–7, subspherical, often flattened slightly above, peridium thin (<0.1), leathery, tough,±covered with small, smooth brownish scales, at maturity rupturing irregularly at apex, tapering below into thick, grooved, stem-like structure (< 5) with massed mycelial strands. GLEBA at first whitish, firm then brownish black-and-white marbled, then deep purple

brown, powdery, no capillitium. Usually in small, trooping or±tufted groups. On rich, bare soil or among grass or other vegetation in woods, fields, parklands. Summer – autumn. Widespread. Uncommon. Inedible. SPORES dark brown, spherical, spiny, 8–12 (excluding spines).

Pisolithus arhizus (= *tinctorius*). Overall form, stem-like structure, spores, habitat. FRUIT BODY 6–12, irregularly subspherical, peridium thin (<0.1), brittle, covered with flattened±coarsely hair-like surface, at maturity rupturing irregularly to reveal dark brown, pea-like peridioles, tapering below into thick, long, irregular, grooved, stem-like structure (<25), deeply rooting in substrate. GLEBA at first whitish, firm, then brownish black as peridioles form, powdery, no capillitium. Solitary or in small, trooping or±tufted groups. On light sandy soils or other well drained places, especially on coal or spoil heaps. Autumn. Widespread, predominantly southern. Rare, especially in Britain. Inedible. SPORES brown, spherical, spiny – warty, 7–9 (excluding spines), producing a yellow stain in wet weather.

Astraeus hygrometricus. Overall form, habitat, spores, often confused with *Geastrum* spp. but development differs and spores much larger. FRUIT BODY 1–4, subspherical, stem-less, outer peridium smooth-coarsely granular

tting when moist at
turity into 6–15, pointed
fish-like rays to reveal
re sac, closing again
en dry. SPORE SAC 1–3,
spherical, stem-less,
yish, inner peridium
y thin, papery, splitting
rregular tear at apex.
BA at first whitish, firm,
n brownish, powdery,
e greyish much bran-
d capillitium. Solitary or
mall, trooping groups.
light dry sandy soils or
d dunes, remaining
ied below surface until
turity. Autumn. Wide-
ead, predominantly
thern. Rare, especially
Britain. Inedible. SPORES
wn, spherical, spiny –
ty, 7–10 (excluding
1es).

aerobolus stellatus.
e, overall form. FRUIT
y 0.15–0.3, subspher-
, stem-less, outer
idium±smooth, split-
g at maturity into 5–9
v, fringe-like orange rays
reveal smooth, brownish
idiole which is then forc-
y ejected. GLEBA whitish,
n, no capillitium.
ually in large,±fused
ups. On sawdust, straw,
gs, dung and other plant
bris. Autumn. Wide-
ead. Common. Inedible.
RES white, ellipsoid,
ooth, 4–5.5×7.5–10.

LANOGASTRALES
restrial (or in one rare
ance, marine on drift-
od), and saprotrophic or
corrhizal, usually sub-
ranean at least until
turity, fruit body stem-
s or occasionally with
m-like structure, usually
gularly spherical. No
inct spore-bearing sur-
e, the basidia being pro-
ced in groups scattered
ough the spore-bearing
ue of the gleba which is
t and mucilaginous at
turity. The basidia often
ture sequentially in
eral generations, but not
the generations produce
res. No capillitium.
ores dark brown
erical – elongated-
psoid, smooth but with
rty or net-like mucilagi-
us outer coating. Two
nilies and about five

genera, all rare or obscure
and only one species in the
Melanogastraceae is at all
likely to be encountered. In
habit, the Melanogastrales
are the basidiomycete
equivalents of ascomycete
truffles.

Melanogaster broomeianus.
Overall fruit body form and
habitat; superficially similar
ascomycetes have very
different spores; related
basidiomycetes have larger
spores and different smell.
FRUIT BODY 1–4, irregularly
subspherical, very finely
velvety-smooth but with
irregular lumps and hol-
lows. GLEBA at first whitish,
firm, then brownish black,
with cavities, no capillitium. SMELL fruity. Solitary
or in small scattered
groups. Subterranean,
usually close to soil surface
under broad-leaved trees,
especially beech and pop-
lar. Summer – autumn.
Widespread. Rare. Inedi-
ble. SPORES dark brown,
elongated-ellipsoid,
smooth, sharply cut-off at
one end, 3.5–5×5–10.

TULOSTOMATALES
Terrestrial, saprotrophic,
not subterranean, fruit
body±spherical on a
definite stem. No distinct
spore-bearing surface, the
basidia being produced in
groups scattered through
the spore-bearing tissue of
the gleba which is powdery
at maturity. The basidia
often mature sequentially
in several generations, but
not all the generations produce spores. Capillitium
present, at least in the early
stages of development.
Spores dark brown or
white,±spherical, smooth,
spiny, warty or with net-
like pattern. Two rather
distinct families and about
eight genera of stalked
puff-balls, all rare or
obscure and only two spe-

cies in the **Tulostomataceae**
are at all likely to be
encountered.

Battarraea phalloides.
Overall form, splitting of
spore sac, stem features.
SPORE SAC 2.5–9, irregularly
subspherical, sometimes
flattened slightly above,
borne aloft on stem, peridium thin, smooth –
granular, splitting all round
at maturity and the whole
upper portion falling away
to expose the gleba. STEM
10–25, fairly slender,
±spindle-shaped, coarsely
shaggy with basal volva.
GLEBA at first whitish, firm,
then brown, powdery, cap-
illitium-like fibrous material
present. Solitary or in small
trooping groups. On dry
sandy soil, apparently associated with decaying
wood. Summer. Southern
England (type locality) and
throughout central Europe.
Rare. Inedible. SPORES
brown, spherical, finely
warty, 5–6.5.

Tulostoma brumale. Over-
all form, splitting of spore
sac, habitat; several related
and even rarer species are
occasionally reported,
especially in southern
Europe. SPORE SAC 1–
2,±spherical, sometimes
flattened slightly above,
borne aloft on stem, peridium thin, smooth –
granular, splitting at maturity by circular apical pore
with distinct brown halo.
STEM 2–5, fairly
slender,±spindle-shaped or
tapering upwards, warty –
fibrous with pronounced
basal volva. GLEBA at first
whitish, firm then brown,
powdery, capillitium
present,±covered with
crystalline material. Solit-

ary or in small trooping
groups. On dry sandy
chalky soil or sand dunes,
often with mosses.
Autumn. Widespread.
Rare. Inedible. SPORES yellowish brown, spherical,
finely warty, 3.5–5.

LYCOPERDALES
Terrestrial or rarely on
wood, saprotrophic, not
subterranean at maturity,
fruit body±spherical, occasionally very large, stem-
less. Distinct spore-bearing
surface present, the gleba
powdery at maturity and
the basidia maturing simultaneously. Capillitium present, usually as a central
tuft and a separate, periph-
eral part. Spores usually
dark brown,±spherical,
usually<10 diameter, spiny
or warty, rarely smooth or
net-patterned. Four fami-
lies, of which two are
obscure and exotic, while
the **Geastraceae** (earth-
stars) and the **Lycoperdaceae** (puff-balls) are important in Europe with several relatively common species. Of the genera included
here, Geastrum and Myrio-
stoma are in the Geastra-
ceae and the remaining five
in the Lycoperdaceae.

Geastrum coronatum.
Overall form, size, rays,
pore features, habitat,
spores. FRUIT BODY 2.5–10,
subspherical, stem-less,
outer peridium fibrous –
coarsely granular, brow-
nish, splitting at maturity
into 4–8, pointed starfish-
like rays to reveal spore
sac. SPORE SAC 1.5–5, subspherical, on short, stout
stem, greyish brown, inner
peridium±smooth, very
thin, papery, opening by
fairly ill-defined central
apical pore. GLEBA at first
pale, firm, then brownish,
powdery, capillitium
unbranched with marked
central tuft. Usually in
small, trooping or±tufted
groups. On soil in coniferous or broad-leaved woods.
Autumn. Widespread.
Rare. Inedible. SPORES dark
brown, spherical, markedly
warty, 3.5–4.5.

193

GEASTRACEAE

Geastrum vulgatum. Size, colour, ray form, overall form, halo. FRUIT BODY 4, subspherical, stem-less, outer peridium fibrous – coarsely scaly, at first creamy pink, then pinkish brown, very thick, fleshy, splitting at maturity into 6–9, pointed, starfish-like rays to reveal spore sac. SPORE SAC 2–3, subspherical, stem-less or on short stout stem, creamy ochre-brown, inner peridium smooth, very thin, papery, opening by fringed central apical pore without halo. GLEBA at first pale, firm, then brownish, powdery, capillitium unbranched with marked central tuft. Solitary or in small – large trooping or ± tufted groups. On soil in broad-leaved or coniferous woods. Summer – autumn. Widespread. Rare. Inedible. SPORES dark brown, subspherical, finely warty, 3.5×4–5.

Geastrum fornicatum. Arching rays, habitat, spores, like *G. quadrifidum* but habitat, pore and size differ. FRUIT BODY 5–9, subspherical, stem-less, outer peridium fibrous – coarsely granular, brownish, splitting at maturity into 4–8, pointed, arching rays to reveal spore sac and lift fruit-body off substrate, stilt-like. SPORE SAC 1.5–3.5, subspherical, on short, stout stem, greyish brown, inner peridium v. thin, papery, opening by central apical pore with everted fringe. GLEBA first pale, firm, then brownish, powdery, capillitium unbranched w. marked central tuft. Usually small, trooping or ± tufted troups. On rich soil in broad-l. woods. Summer – autumn. Widespread. Rare. Inedible. SPORES dark brown, spherical, spiny – warty, 3–3.5.

Geastrum quadrifidum. Arching rays, habitat, spores, like *G. fornicatum* but habitat, pore and size differ. FRUIT BODY 1.5–4, subspherical, stem-less, outer peridium fibrous – coarsely granular, brownish, splitting at maturity into 4–8 pointed, arching rays to reveal spore sac and lift the upper fruit-body from the lower part and off substrate, stilt-like. SPORE SAC 0.5–3, subspherical, on short, stout stem, greyish brown, inner peridium v. thin, papery, opening by central apical pore w. everted fringe, pale halo. GLEBA first pale, firm, then brownish, powdery, capillitium unbranched w. marked central tuft. Usually small, trooping or ± tufted groups. On soil in coniferous or less commonly broad-leaved woods, esp. on chalky sites. Summer – autumn. Widespread. Rare, esp. in Britain. Inedible. SPORES dark brown, subspherical, spiny – warty, 4.5–5×3.5–4.

Geastrum striatum. Size, ray form, habitat, pore features, like *G. nanum* but habitat esp. differs. FRUIT BODY 2–6, subspherical, stem-less, outer peridium fibrous – coarsely scaly, brownish, splitting at maturity into 5–8, pointed, starfish-like rays to reveal spore sac. SPORE SAC 1–4, subspherical, w. distinct collar-like basal groove, on short, stout stem, greyish brown, inner peridium smooth, v. thin, papery, opening by central apical pore on spout-like extension, usually with halo, c. 20 shallow, grooves. GLEBA first pale, firm, then brownish, powdery, capillitium unbranched w. marked central tuft. Usually trooping or ± tufted groups. On rich soil in broad-l., conif. or mixed woods. Summer – autumn. Widespread. Rare. Inedible. SPORES dark brown, subspherical, finely warty, 3.5–4×4–4.5.

Geastrum nanum. Size, ray form, habitat, pore features. FRUIT BODY 2–5, subspherical, stem-less, outer peridium fibrous-coarsely scaly, brownish, splitting at maturity into 5–8, pointed, starfish-like rays to reveal spore sac. SPORE SAC 1–4, subspherical, on very short, stout stem, greyish brown, inner peridium smooth, very thin, papery, opening by central apical pore on spout-like extension and halo with 15–20 deep grooves. GLEBA at first pale, firm, then brownish, powdery, capillitium unbranched with marked central tuft. Usually in trooping or ± tufted groups. On light sandy soil or sand-dunes. Summer – autumn. Widespread, predominantly coastal. Rare, locally common. Inedible. SPORES dark brown, subspherical, spiny – warty, 4–4.5×4.5–5.

Geastrum sessile (=*rufescens*). Colour, ray form, habitat, pore features. FRUIT BODY 2–5, subspherical, stem-less, outer peridium fibrous – coarsely scaly, cream-ochre, splitting at maturity into 5–8, pointed, starfish-like rays to reveal spore sac. SPORE SAC 1–4, spherical, stem-less, cream-ochre, inner peridium smooth, v. thin, papery, opening by ill-defined central apical pore. GLEBA first pale, firm, then brownish, powdery, capillitium unbranched w. marked central tuft. Usually in small-large, trooping groups. On rich soil with broad-l. or less commonly conif. trees. Summer – autumn. Widespread. Uncommon but the most frequent *Geastrum* in northern Europe. Inedible. SPORES dark brown, subspherical, very finely spiny, 2.5–3×3–3.5.

Geastrum triplex. Size, colour, ray form, overall form, habitat. FRUIT BODY 7–10, onion-shaped, stem-less, outer peridium smooth – scaly above, fibrous – coarsely scaly below, then creamy, then greyish brown, v. thick, fleshy, splitting at maturity into 4–8, pointed, starfish-like rays to reveal spore sac usually resting on thick, bowl-like base. SPORE SAC 2.5–4, subspherical, ± stem-less, creamy ochre-brown, inner peridium smooth, v. thin, papery, opening by central apical pore, usually with halo. GLEBA first pale, firm, then brownish, powdery, capillitium unbranched w. marked central tuft. Usually trooping or ± tufted groups. On rich soil in woods, parks, gardens, embankments, sand-dunes. Summer – autumn. Widespread. Uncommon. SPORES dark brown, spherical, warty, 3.5–4.5

Myriostoma coliforme. Overall fruit body form, pores, distribution. FRUIT BODY 2–6, subspherical, stem-less, outer peridium fibrous – coarsely scaly, ochreous brown, splitting at maturity into 5–12, pointed, slightly arching starfish-like rays to reveal spore sac. SPORE SAC 1.5–subspherical, with several short, rather slender stems, creamy ochre-brown, inner peridium very finely granular-scurfy, thin, papery, opening by several fringed pores without halos. GLEBA at first pale, firm, then brownish, powdery, capillitium unbranched with several tufts. Solitary or in small trooping groups. On light, sandy soil, field ledges, open grassy places in woods. Widespread, not Britain (extinct). Inedible. SPORES brown, spherical, finely net-patterned, 3–3.5.

194

·ista aestivalis. Fruit
y form, gleba, spores.
ıT BODY 1–3,
spherical – onion-bulb
ped, stem-less but
etimes with short stem-
base, outer peridium
prising minutely spiny
ıules, flaking off to
eal smooth, shiny brow-
papery inner peridium,
ning by small, fringed,
gular central apical
e. GLEBA at first white,
, then olive then
wn, powdery, with
ngy sterile base, capilli-
ı yellowish brown,
nched. Usually in
ll – large trooping
ups, becoming detached
en mature and blowing
und. On sandy soil,
ecially on chalky sites,
dunes. Summer –
ımn. Widespread.
e. Edible when young.
RES yellowish brown,
erical, very finely warty,
ked, 4–6.

·ista nigrescens. Fruit
ly form, capillitium,
·e, spores. FRUIT BODY
, subspherical, stem-less
attached to substrate
ı single mycelial strand,
ter peridium white,
ooth, flaking off to
eal smooth – wrinkled,
·k red-brown – black
ny papery inner peri-
m, opening by large,
·gular±apical fissure-
· pore. GLEBA at first
ite, firm, then olive then
·k purple-brown, pow-
·y, without sterile base,
pillitium brown, bran-
·d. Usually in small –
ge trooping groups,
·oming detached when
ture and blowing
·und. On soil, grassland,
·tures, golf-courses.
·nmer – autumn. Wide-
·ead, predominantly
·thern. Uncommon. Edi-
when young. SPORES
·wn, subspherical, finely
·rty, blunt-ended stalk,
·–5×5.5–6.

Bovista plumbea. Fruit
body form, capillitium,
pore, spores. FRUIT BODY
2–3, subspherical, stem-less
but attached to substrate
with slender mass of mycelial strands, outer peridium
white, smooth, flaking off
to reveal±smooth, dark
grey papery inner peri-
dium, opening by±circular
small apical pore. GLEBA at
first white, firm, then buff,
then olive-brown, pow-
dery, without sterile base,
capillitium brown, bran-
ched. Usually in small –
large trooping groups,
becoming detached when
mature and blowing
around. On soil, grassland,
pastures, golf-courses.
Summer – autumn. Wide-
spread. Common. Edible
when young. SPORES brown,
ellipsoid – subspherical,
very finely warty –
±smooth, taper-ended
stalk, 4.5–5.5×5–6.

Bovista pusilla. Fruit body
form, capillitium, pore,
habitat, spores. FRUIT BODY
1–2, subspherical, stem-less
but attached to substrate
with slender mass of mycelial strands, outer peridium
whitish, comprising
minute, flattened scales,
flaking off to reveal±
smooth, shiny, brown pap-
ery inner peridium, open-
ing by irregular small apical
pore. GLEBA at first white,
firm, then yellowish, then
olive-brown, powdery,
without sterile base, capillitium yellowish brown,
branched. Usually in small
– large trooping groups, becoming detached and blowing
around. On soil, grassland,
pastures, golf-courses,
especially on dry, acidic
sites. Summer – autumn.
Widespread. Rare. Edible
when young. SPORES brown,
ellipsoid – spherical, finely
warty, stalked, 3.5–4.

*Lycoperdon atropur-
pureum.* Fruit body surface
and base, colours, sterile
base, habitat, spores. FRUIT
BODY 2.5–6, subspherical –
pear-shaped, stem-less or
narrowed into stem-like
base with massed rhizo-
morphs adhering to subs-
trate, outer peridium
greyish-yellowish brown,
comprising long, slender
spines, often fused at tips
and which fall away to
reveal±smooth, shiny,
light brown-purplish inner
peridium, opening by
irregular small apical pore.
GLEBA at first white, firm,
then olive, then dark
purple-brown, powdery,
sterile base spongy, shallow, capillitium reddish
brown unbranched.
Usually in small – large
trooping groups. On soil in
woods. Summer – autumn.
Widespread. Uncommon.
Edible ? SPORES dark
purple-brown, spherical,
markedly warty,
sometimes±stalked, 5–7.

Lycoperdon echinatum.
Fruit body surface, gleba,
sterile base, habitat,
spores. FRUIT BODY 2.5–6,
subspherical – pear-
shaped, tapering below into
short, stout, stem-like base,
outer peridium white-
brown, comprising long,
dense, slender spines, fused
in threes or fours at tips to
form groups of pyramids
which fall away to reveal
net-patterned, brown pap-
ery inner peridium, open-
ing by small round apical
pore. GLEBA at first white,
firm, then light brown, then
dark brown, powdery, sterile base cottony, shallow,
capillitium brown unbran-
ched. Solitary or in small
trooping groups. On rich
soil in woods, especially
with beech on chalky sites.
Summer – autumn. Wide-
spread. Uncommon. Inedi-
ble. SPORES dark brown,
spherical, markedly warty,
4–5.

Lycoperdon foetidum.
Fruit body surface, gleba,
sterile base, habitat,
spores. FRUIT BODY 2–5,
subspherical, tapering
sharply below into very
short, stout, stem-like base,
outer peridium pale – dark
brown, comprising short,
dense spines,±fused in
groups at tips, at least when
young, and eventually falling away to reveal net-
patterned, brown papery
inner peridium, opening by
small round apical pore.
GLEBA at first white, firm,
then brown, powdery, sterile base spongy, large,
capillitium brown unbran-
ched. Usually in small –
large, trooping or±tufted
groups. On soil in woods,
especially on acid sites.
Summer – autumn. Wide-
spread. Very common.
Inedible. SPORES brown,
spherical, finely spiny –
warty, 4–5.

Lycoperdon lividum
(=*spadiceum*). Size, fruit
body surface, sterile base,
habitat, spores. FRUIT BODY
1.5–3, subspherical – pear-
shaped, tapering sharply
below into very short,
stout, stem-like base, outer
peridium ochre brown,
coarsely warty – granular,
rarely with few short spines
at first, gradually falling
away to reveal smooth,
faintly veined brown inner
peridium, opening by small
irregular apical pore. GLEBA
at first white, firm, then
brown, powdery, sterile
base spongy, fairly large,
capillitium brown unbran-
ched. Usually in small –
large, trooping or±tufted
groups. On soil in open,
grassy areas and on sand-
dunes. Summer – autumn.
Widespread. Uncommon,
locally common. Inedible.
SPORES brown, subspher-
ical, finely spiny – warty,
3.5–4×3.5–4.5.

LYCOPERDACEAE

Lycoperdon mammae-forme. Fruit body surface, sterile base, habitat, spores. FRUIT BODY 3–6, subspherical – pear-shaped with broad umbo tapering gradually below into stout, stem-like base, outer peridium at first white, coarsely woolly, then finely spiny with irregular woolly scales, ochre-brown, flaking off to reveal smooth, pinkish brown papery inner peridium, opening by small central apical pore. GLEBA at first white, firm, then yellowish brown, then dark brown, powdery, sterile base spongy, large, capillitium brown, unbranched. Solitary or in trooping or ± tufted groups. On soil in woods on chalk. Summer – autumn. Widespread, predominantly southern. Rare. Inedible ? SPORES brown, spherical, warty, 4.5–5.5.

Lycoperdon molle. Fruit body surface, sterile base, habitat, spores, very variable in overall form and colour. FRUIT BODY 2–4, variable, subspherical – pear-shaped – top-like, tapering rather sharply below into stout, stem-like base, outer peridium variable, comprising short, soft spines, some fused at the tips, falling away to reveal smooth, creamy brown papery, inner peridium, opening by small central apical pore. GLEBA at first white, firm, then olive-brown, then dark brown, powdery, sterile base spongy, large, capillitium brown unbranched. Usually in trooping or ± tufted groups. On soil in broad-leaved or coniferous woods. Summer – autumn. Widespread, predominantly southern. Uncommon. Inedible? SPORES brown, spherical, coarsely warty,

usually with detached sterigma debris, 4–5.

Lycoperdon pedicellatum. Fruit body form, habitat, spores. FRUIT BODY 2–5, subspherical – pear-shaped, tapering rather sharply below into markedly elongated stout, stem-like base, outer peridium ochreous brown, comprising short spines, some fused at the tips, and more granule-like towards stem-like base, falling away to reveal smooth, greyish brown papery inner peridium, opening by central rather fringed apical pore. GLEBA at first white, firm, then yellowish brown, then olive-brown, powdery, sterile base coarsely spongy, filling stem-like base, capillitium brown unbranched. Usually in trooping or ± tufted groups. On soil in damp usually acid places, moors, in mosses. Autumn. Northern. Rare, especially in Britain. Inedible? SPORES olive-brown, spherical, very finely warty, long-stalked, 3.5–4.5.

Lycoperdon perlatum. Fruit body form and surface, habitat, spores. FRUIT BODY 2–6, pear-shaped – club-shaped, tapering sharply below into markedly elongated stout, stem-like base, outer peridium at first white then ochreous brown, comprising short, conical warts, falling away to reveal net-patterned, ochreous papery inner peridium, opening by small central apical pore. GLEBA at first white, firm, then yellowish brown, then olive-brown, powdery, sterile base spongy, filling stem-like base, capillitium brown unbranched. Usually in small – large, trooping or ± tufted groups. On soil in broad-leaved, coniferous or mixed wood-

land. Summer – autumn. Widespread. Very common. Edible when young. SPORES olive-brown, spherical, finely warty, 3.5–4.

Lycoperdon pyriforme. Habitat, spores. FRUIT BODY 1.5–5, pear-shaped – club-shaped, tapering sharply below into markedly elongated stout, stem-like base with white rhizoids, outer peridium at first white then ochre, coarsely granular – warty or ± finely spiny, flaking off to reveal smooth, ochreous brown papery inner peridium, opening by small central apical pore. GLEBA at first white, firm, then yellowish brown, then olive-brown, powdery, sterile base spongy, filling stem-like base, capillitium brown unbranched. Usually in large tufted groups. On wood, stumps, logs or buried fragments in soil. Summer – autumn. Widespread. Very common. Edible when young. SPORES olive-brown, spherical, smooth, 3–4.5.

Lycoperdon umbrinum. Fruit body surface, habitat, gleba, spores. FRUIT BODY 3–6, subspherical – pear-shaped, ± constricted below into very short stem-like base, outer peridium ochreous, comprising short dark spines, some fused at the tips, falling away to reveal smooth, yellowish ochre, shiny, papery inner peridium, opening by small central apical pore. GLEBA at first white, firm, then yellowish, then yellowish brown, powdery, sterile base coarsely spongy, capillitium yellowish brown unbranched. Usually in trooping or ± tufted groups. On soil in leaf litter and other plant debris in conif.

woods. Summer – autumn. Predominantly montane. Rare. Edible ? SPORES yellowish brown, spherical, warty, short-stalked, without detached sterigma debris, 4.5–5.5.

Vascellum pratense. Fruit body surface, spore sac opening, habitat, spores. FRUIT BODY 2–5, subspherical – pear-shaped, often flattened above, tapering below into short stout stem-like base, outer peridium at first whitish, then ochreous, coarse, scurfy – finely spiny, falling away to reveal smooth, whitish ochre shiny, papery inner peridium, opening at first by small central apical pore but then entire upper part tearing away. GLEBA at first white, firm, then olive, then olive-brown, powdery, sterile base spongy, large, capillitium colourless, unbranched, sparse. Usually in trooping or ± tufted groups. On soil in grassy places, wood edges, fields, golf-courses, parks. Summer – autumn. Widespread. Common. Edible when young. SPORES olive brown, subspherical, finely warty, 3.5–4×3.5–4.5.

Langermannia gigantea **Giant Puff-Ball.** Size. FRUIT BODY 10–80, irregularly subspherical, tapering below into short stout stem-like base and attached loosely to substrate by mycelial strands, outer peridium whitish, smooth, leathery, flaking away to reveal smooth, whitish ochre shiny, papery inner peridium, splitting irregularly and disintegrating, especially when blown around by wind. GLEBA at first white, firm, then olive, then olive-brown, powdery, sterile base

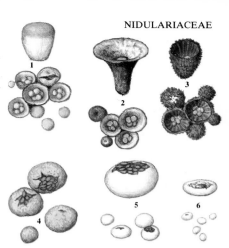

dimentary or absent,
pillitium brown unbran-
ed. Usually in trooping or
ufted groups. On soil in
assy places, wood edges,
lds, golf-courses, parks.
mmer – autumn. Wide-
ead. Uncommon, locally
mmon. Edible when
ung. SPORES olive-brown,
herical, very finely warty,
5–5.

outer peridium at first
white, then dark greyish
brown, at first comprising
fairly coarse granules and
warts, then coarsely net-
like, falling away to reveal
smooth, greyish papery
inner peridium, splitting
irregularly from apex and
disintegrating to leave a
goblet or cup. GLEBA at first
white, firm, then yellowish
brown, then olive-brown,
powdery, sterile base
spongy, large, capillitium
brown, branched. Usually
in small trooping or ± tufted
groups. On soil in dry
grassy places, wood edges,
heaths, fields. Summer –
autumn. Widespread.
Common. Edible when
young. SPORES olive-brown,
spherical, smooth, 4–5.

lvatia excipuliformis.
ores, overall fruit body
rm, similar to *C. utrifor-*
s but taller than wide at
aturity, when young simi-
 to *L. molle* q.v. FRUIT
DY 3–10, pear-shaped –
b-shaped, tapering
arply below into elon-
ted, stout stem-like base,
stle-shaped outer peri-
um at first white, then
hreous, comprising fairly
e spines and warts, fall-
g away to reveal smooth,
hre, papery inner peri-
um, splitting irregularly
m apex and disintegrat-
g. GLEBA at first white,
m, then yellowish brown,
en purple-brown, pow-
ry, sterile base spongy,
rly large, capillitium
own, branched. Usually
small – large, trooping
± tufted groups. On soil
grassy places, wood
ges, heaths, fields.
mmer – autumn. Wide-
read. Common. Edible
en young. SPORES olive-
own, spherical, warty,
ort stalked, sometimes
th detached sterigma
bris, 3.5–5.5.

lvatia utriformis. Spores,
erall fruit body form,
nilar to *C. excipuliformis*
t wider than tall at
aturity. FRUIT BODY 6–12,
bspherical – pear-
aped, tapering sharply
low into short, grooved-
inkled stem-like base,

NIDULARIALES

Terrestrial, on dung, wood
or other plant material,
saprotrophic, not subterranean at maturity, fruit body
at first ± spherical but then
opening to become ± bowl-
like, stem-less, usually <1
in diameter usually in large
groups. Distinct spore-
bearing surface present, the
gleba at maturity comprising hard, seed-like peri-
dioles, and the basidia
maturing simultaneously.
Spores white, smooth,
ellipsoid – subspherical,
often large. One Family,
Nidulariaceae with about
five genera, most with fairly
common European repres-
entatives although *Sphaero-*
bolus (p. 193), formerly
classified here, is now grouped in a different order
Sclerodermatales. The
group is known for obvious
reasons as the Bird's-Nest
Fungi.

1
Crucibulum laeve **Common
Bird's-Nest.** Overall fruit
body form, habitat, spores.
FRUIT BODY 0.4–0.8, sub-
spherical, stem-less, at first
covered with yellowish
ochre scurfy membrane
which ruptures to reveal up
to 15, lens-shaped, smooth,
creamy grey peridioles each
attached to a greyish lined
cup by a fine thread. In
large tufted groups. On
wood, twigs and other plant
debris. Autumn – winter.
Widespread. Common.
Inedible. SPORES white,
ellipsoid, smooth, 3.5–
5×7–10, non-amyloid.

2
Cyathus olla. Overall fruit
body form, habitat, spores,
similar to *C. striatus* but
cup lining differs. FRUIT
BODY 0.8–1.2, at first ± cylin-

drical or top-shaped, then
inverted bell-shaped, stem-
less, at first covered with
whitish scurfy membrane
which ruptures to reveal up
to 10, lens-shaped, smooth,
greyish brown peridioles
each attached to a greyish
silver lined cup by a fine
thread. In small – large
trooping or ± tufted groups.
On soil, twigs or other plant
debris, often in green-
ouses. Spring – winter.
Widespread. Common.
Inedible. SPORES white,
ellipsoid, smooth, 6–7×9–
11, non-amyloid.

3
Cyathus striatus. Overall
fruit body form, habitat,
spores, similar to *C. olla*
but cup lining differs. FRUIT
BODY 0.7–1.2, at first ± cylindrical or top-shaped, then
inverted bell-shaped, stem-
less, at first covered with
whitish scurfy membrane
which ruptures to reveal up
to 16, lens-shaped, smooth,
greyish peridioles each attached to a greyish silver
grooved lined and extern-
ally hairy cup by a fine
thread. In small – large
trooping or ± tufted groups.
On wood, twigs or other
plant debris. Spring – winter. Widespread. Uncom-
mon. Inedible. SPORES
white, ellipsoid, smooth, 7–
8.5×16–18, non-amyloid.

4
Nidularia farcta. Overall
fruit body form, habitat.
FRUIT BODY 0.3–1, subspherical, stem-less, at first
covered with thin yellowish
brown scurfy membrane
which ruptures to reveal
numerous lens-shaped,
smooth, ochre-brown peri-
dioles embedded in gelatinous material. In large ±
fused groups. On wet and

rotting wood or sawdust.
Summer – autumn. Wide-
spread. Rare. Inedible.
SPORES white, broadly ellipsoid, smooth, 4–7×6–10,
non-amyloid.

5
Mycocalia denudata. Overall fruit body form, peridioles, habitat. FRUIT BODY
0.2–1, subspherical, stem-
less, at first covered with
thin white scurfy mem-
brane which ruptures to
reveal several yellowish
brown lens-shaped,
smooth, peridioles embed-
ded in gelatinous material.
In small – large trooping
or ± fused groups. On rotting plant debris in wet
acidic places, especially
Juncus effusus remains,
also dung. All year. Widespread. Rare. Inedible.
SPORES white, broadly ellipsoid, smooth, 6–7×5–5.5,
non-amyloid.

6
Mycocalia minutissima.
Size, overall fruit body
form, peridiole, habitat.
FRUIT BODY 0.1–0.2, sub-
spherical, stem-less, at first
covered with thin white
scurfy membrane which
ruptures to reveal one yellowish brown lens-shaped,
smooth peridiole embed-
ded in gelatinous material.
In small – large trooping
or ± fused groups. On rotting plant debris in very wet
acidic places, especially
Juncus effusus remains. All
year. England, but prob-
ably widespread. Rare.
Inedible. SPORES white,
broadly ellipsoid, smooth,
3–3.5×4.5–5, non-amyloid.

197

PHALLALES
Terrestrial, on dung, wood or other plant material, saprotrophic, not usually subterranean at maturity, with distinct spore-bearing surface and the basidia maturing simultaneously. Fruit body structure complex, ±spherical (and known as an egg) with± smooth membranous outer peridium covering a gelatinous layer within which is a fleshy green-brown gleba. In some species, the peridium remains intact and the fruit body spherical but in others the gleba is borne on a spongy or honeycomb-like receptacle which elongates in various ways through the ruptured peridium to expose the gleba above the substrate. As this takes place, the gleba changes chemically to form a repulsively smelling slime. Spores brown, smooth, ellipsoid – cylindrical and fairly large in the groups that retain spherical fruit bodies, colourless, smooth, ±cylindrical and very small in those that elongate. Six families, with marked individual features, but three are exotic and contain very few, imperfectly studied species. Of the three European families, the **Hysterangiaceae** (represented here by *Hysterangium*) are subterranean and remain± spherical. They are sometimes placed in a separate Order Hysterangiales. The remaining families are the **Clathraceae** and the **Phallaceae.** In the former, the elongating receptacle is often brightly coloured and star-fish or cage-like with the gleba on the inside. There are about six European genera, including *Clathrus* and the introduced *Anthurus* and *Lysurus*. In the Phallaceae, the elongated receptacle forms a phallus-like organ with the gleba on the outside. European genera are *Phallus* and *Mutinus*, the stinkhorns. Despite their subsequent foul smell, some species are edible when young.

Hysterangium nephriticum. Habit, habitat, fruit body colour, spores, only likely

to be confused with *Melanogaster*, *Rhizopogon* or ascomycete truffles among subterranean species to be found at all commonly but spores very different. FRUIT BODY 1–2.5, subspherical, finely downy, ±surrounded by white mycelial growth, outer peridium white, thick, elastic. GLEBA at first pinkish, then pale bluish grey, mucilaginous. Usually in small scattered or±fused groups. Subterranean in woods. All year. Widespread. Rare. Inedible. SPORES olive-green, elongated ellipsoid, smooth, 4–6×13–18.

Phallus hadriani. Habit, habitat, fruit body colour, spores, only likely to be confused with *P. impudicus* but young fruit body colour and smell differ. FRUIT BODY 3–6, at first subspherical – pear-shaped, part buried, smooth – warty, at first white, then pinkish, elongating to 12–15, with±conical white honeycombed head covered with glebal mass, and stout, white, hollow, spongy stem-like portion. GLEBA at first pale then olive-green, firm, gelatinous, then darker olive and slimy as fruit body elongates. SMELL (when mature) faint, sweet, pleasant. Usually in small trooping groups. On light sandy soil and sand-dunes. Summer – autumn. Widespread, predominantly southern, coastal in the north. Rare. Edible when young? SPORES yellowish, ellipsoid, smooth, 1.5–2×3–4.

Phallus impudicus **Stinkhorn.** Habit, habitat, smell, fruit body colour, spores, only likely to be confused with *P. hadriani* but young fruit body colour and smell differ. FRUIT BODY 3–6, at first subspherical – pear-shaped, part buried, smooth – warty, whitish cream, rarely with any pronounced pink flush, elongating to 12–22, with±conical white honeycombed head covered with glebal mass, and stout, white, hollow, spongy stem-like portion. GLEBA at first pale then olive-green, firm, gelatinous, then darker olive and slimy as fruit body elongates. SMELL (when mature) repulsive, sewage, apparent for many metres. Solitary or in small trooping groups. On soil, woods, gardens. Summer – autumn. Widespread. Extremely common. Edible when young. SPORES yellowish brown, ellipsoid, smooth, 1.5–2×3.5–4.

Mutinus caninus **Dog Stinkhorn.** Habit, habitat, smell, fruit body colour, spores, only likely to be confused with *P. hadriani* but young fruit body colour and smell differ. FRUIT BODY 2, at first elongated-ellipsoid – subspherical, part buried, smooth, whitish cream, elongating to 10–12, with narrowly conical orange honeycombed head covered with glebal mass, and rather slender, white, hollow, spongy stem-like portion. GLEBA at first pale then olive-green, firm, gelatinous, then darker olive and slimy as fruit body elongates. SMELL (when mature) faint, sweet, unpleasant. Usually in small,±trooping groups. On soil, among leaf litter in broad or less commonly coniferous woods. Summer – autumn. Widespread. Very common, less so northwards. Inedible. SPORES yellowish, ellipsoid, smooth, 1–2×4–5.

Phallus impudicus

Clathrus archeri. Overall fruit body form and colour FRUIT BODY 2.5–4, at first elongated-ellipsoid – subspherical, part buried, smooth, whitish ochre, elongating to 4–7, with tentacle-like arching red arms, covered on net-like pitted upper surfaces with glebal mass. GLEBA at first pale then olive-green, firm, gelatinous, then darker olive and slimy as fruit body elongates. SMELL (when mature) repulsive, foetid. Usually in small, trooping groups. On soil broad-leaved or rarely coniferous grass in pastures, meadows. Summer. Southern extreme south only in England, probably introduced to Europe from Australia or New Zealand in c.191 with war supplies. Rare. Inedible. SPORES greenish yellow, elongated-ellipsoid, smooth, 2–2.5×5–6

Clathrus ruber. Overall fruit body form and colour FRUIT BODY 2–3, at first± subspherical, part buried, smooth, whitish, elongating to 7–10, with net- or cage-like arching red structure, covered on net-like pitted inner surfaces with glebal mass. GLEBA at first pale then olive-green, firm, gelatinous, then darker olive and slimy as fruit body elongates. SMELL (when mature) repulsive, foetid. Usually in small,±trooping groups. On soil in gardens, broad-leaved woods. Predominantly southern, recorded from England, Scotland and Ireland but probably introduced from southern Europe. Rare. Inedible. SPORES greenish yellow, cylindrical, smooth, 1.5–2×5–6.

198

...surus gardneri. Overall it body form, habitat. UT BODY 4–5, at first ± spherical, part buried, ooth, whitish, elongat- to 8–10, with 6, ± erect, dish brown tapering ns, with longitudinal ove and transverse rib- g, covered on inner oper) surfaces with glebal ss, and surmounting ut, white, spongy, hol- v, stem-like portion. EBA at first pale, firm, atinous, then brownish d slimy as fruit body ngates. Solitary or in all, ± trooping groups. soil among stable use. Southern England d Ireland, probably roduced with imported ain, the similar *L. crutus* occurs in Europe. re. Inedible. SPORES ownish, elongated- psoid – cylindrical, ooth, 2.5–3×1–1.5.

'MENOGASTRALES
rrestrial, subterranean, h distinct spore-bearing face and the basidia turing simultaneously. ten with higher plants, corrhizal. Fruit body icture complex, ± spher- with variable outer per- am and sometimes inner ridium covering a fleshy, tilaginous or powdery ba. Capillitium absent. ores white or coloured, ally warty or otherwise amented, spherical – psoid. Probably about e families but the Order s arguable limits. It is w generally treated as a oup of subterranean igi, obviously closely ated to other Gaster- aycetes but probably ated also to conventional ishrooms, toadstools and her Hymenomycetes. e superficial resembl- ce is negligible but this nclusion derives from tailed studies of fruit dy, spores and basidium rm and development. ere are many species, most are elusive and very re, and are represented re by one member of the ost frequently reported nily, the **Rhizopogoceae.**

Rhizopogon luteolus. Over- all fruit body form, habitat, rather similar to *M. broomeianus* but habitat differs, also similar to ascomycete truffles but spores very different. FRUIT BODY 1.5–5, irregularly subspherical, ± covered in brownish mycelial growth, peridium yellowish brown, thick, tough. GLEBA at first pale, then olive, firm. Usually in ± scattered groups, close to tree roots. Subterranean in light sandy soil in pine woods. Autumn. Widespread, pre- dominantly northern. Rare. Inedible. SPORES olive-brown, elongated- ellipsoid, smooth, 2.5– 3.5×5–8.5.

TELIOMYCETES
No well-defined fruit body but recognisable macroscop- ically by distinctive lesions or other symptoms on host plants. Basidiospores pro- duced on a basidium-like promycelium which arises on the germination of another type of spore called a teliospore. Teliospores are interpreted structurally as encysted forms of imma- ture basidia and in turn are produced either in a sorus embedded in (or sometimes scattered throughout) the host plant tissues, this development producing the distinctive lesions. Divided into two quite distinct and probably fairly unrelated Orders, the Ustilaginales (smut fungi), with many basidiospores on the pro- mycelium and the Uredi- nales (rust fungi) with only four in more typical basi- dium fashion. All are biot- rophic on higher plants and many cause very important crop diseases. The life cycles are often highly complex and may involve alternation from one host species to another. The basidiospores are elusive and of little value in identification or classification which is based instead on host species, (most of the fungal species are restricted to particular hosts or related groups of hosts), the structure and size of teliospores and in some groups, the structure and size of two other types of spore, urediniospores and aeciospores. Telio- spores are almost always dark-coloured, thick- walled, more than 1-celled, smooth. Urediniospores are single celled, usually paler-coloured, often brown or yellowish and spiny. Aeciospores are single celled, very pale- coloured and warty.

USTILAGINALES
Biotrophic on flowering plants, often producing serious diseases. Usually produce many basidios- pores on the promycelium. Urediniospores and aecios- pores absent, no alterna- tion of hosts. Teliospores produced in sori comprise single spores or spore balls, usually black but some- times brown or yellow en masse. Within individual species, especially small- spored types, the telios- pores are rather inconstant in size range, but usually subspherical in shape and either smooth or character- istically ornamented with warts, spines, net-patterns or other features. There is now good evidence from detailed microscopic structural studies for believing that the Ustilagi- nales are not only unrelated to the Uredinales but that they may be quite distinct from all other Basidiomy- cetes and diverged from them at an early stage in their evolutionary history. There are about 35 genera, traditionally divided between two families, the **Ustilaginaceae** and **Tilletiaceae** on the basis of the mode of germination of the teliospores. Of the genera represented here, *Urocystis*, *Ustilago* and *Entyloma* are placed in the former and *Tilletia* in the latter. Together, these genera include most of the 1,100 world species.

Urocystis anemones causes **Anemone Smut.** Host plants. SORI blister-like swellings beneath rupturing epidermis of leaves and stems. SPORE MASS black, powdery. On cultivated *Anemone* spp., wild *A. nemorosa, Pulsatilla vul-* *garis and Ranunculus repens*. Spring – autumn. Widespread. Common. SPORE BALLS 16–32, irregu- larly subspherical, compris- ing 1–3 spores partly sur- rounded by yellowish cells. SPORES black, elongated- ellipsoid – subspherical, angular, smooth, 12–26 (mostly 14–18).

Urocystis cepulae causes **Onion Smut.** Host plants. SORI ± circular or elongated, blister-like or swellings beneath rupturing epidermis of leaves. SPORE MASS dark brown, powdery. On cultivated onion, leek or wild crow garlic (*Allium*). Spring – autumn. Wide- spread. Uncommon. SPORE BALLS 14–22, ellipsoidal – spherical, comprising 1 spore surrounded by yel- lowish spherical – ellip- soidal cells. SPORES red- brown, ellipsoid – sub- spherical, smooth, 11–14.

Ustilago violacea causes **Carnation Anther Smut.** Habit, host plants. SORI ± filling anthers. SPORE MASS pinkish purple, pow- dery. On cultivated carna- tion, several *Silene* spp., *Lychnis flos-cuculi* and a few related plants in the family Caryophyllaceae. Spring – autumn (but all year on glasshouse carna- tions). Widespread. Com- mon. SPORE BALLS absent. SPORES pale violet, broadly ellipsoid – subspherical, finely net-patterned, 5–12.

199

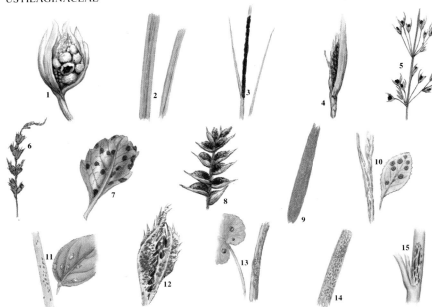

1
Ustilago maydis causes
Maize Smut. Habit, occurrence, host plants. SORI as bloated whitish-cream swellings on flowers, cobs and other above-ground parts. SPORE MASS dark brown, powdery. On maize and sweet corn. Summer – autumn. Widespread, but southern in Britain and only seen in very hot summers. Rare. SPORE BALLS absent. SPORES brown, broadly ellipsoid – subspherical, with warty coat, 8–18.

2
Ustilago longissima. Host plants. SORI elongated, blister-like swellings beneath rupturing epidermis of host plant leaves, gradually emptying to remain as narrow channels. SPORE MASS brown, powdery. On *Glyceria maxima* and *G. fluitans.* Summer – autumn. Widespread. Common. SPORE BALLS absent. SPORES yellow-brown, ± subspherical, very finely roughened (use oil immersion lens), 4–6.

3
Ustilago hypodytes causes
Grass Stem Smut. Host plants. SORI surrounding internodal regions on

stems, at first beneath leaf sheaths, sometimes spreading to affect entire stem and eventually dispersing to leave stem markedly pinched and withered. SPORE MASS dark brown, powdery. On Sand Couch (*Elymus farctus*), Sea Couch (*E. pungens*), related species and hybrids between them, Marram (*Ammophila arenaria*), California Brome (*Bromus carinatus*), Upright Brome (*B. erectus*), Lyme Grass (*Leymus arenarius*), Giant Fescue (*Festuca gigantea*) and Yellow Oat Grass (*Trisetum flavescens*). Summer – autumn. Widespread. Very common. SPORE BALLS absent. SPORES yellow-brown, ± subspherical, often rather irregular, smooth, 4–7.

4
Ustilago hordei causes
Covered Smut of Oats and Barley. Host plants, *U. avenae* also occurs on oats but has ± exposed sori. SORI ± filling the spikelets in place of the plant's ovaries and internal glume tissues and ± covered by plant tissue. SPORE MASS dark brown – purplish black, firm. On barley and oats. Summer – autumn. Widespread. Very common. SPORE BALLS absent. SPORES yellow-brown – greenish brown, paler on one

side, ± subspherical, smooth, 7–11.

5
Ustilago avenae causes
Loose Smut of Oats. Host plants, *U. hordei* also occurs on oats but has ± concealed sori. SORI ± filling the spikelets in place of the plant's ovaries and internal glume tissues, occasionally in leaves also. SPORE MASS dark greenish brown, at first firm then powdery. On oats and False Oat Grass (*Arrhenatherum elatius*). Summer – autumn. Widespread. Very common. SPORE BALLS absent. SPORES pale greenish brown, paler on one side, ± subspherical, very finely spiny – ± smooth, 4–8.

6
Ustilago nuda causes **Loose Smut** of Wheat and Barley. Host plants, *U. hordei* also occurs on barley but has concealed sori; *Tilletia caries* also occurs on wheat but is foul smelling with different spores. SORI ± filling the spikelets in place of the plant's ovaries. SPORE MASS dark greenish brown – blackish brown, at first firm then powdery, eventually dispersing to leave tissues bare. On wheat and barley. Summer. Widespread. Very common. SPORE BALLS absent. SPORES pale yellowish brown, paler on one

side, ± subspherical, very finely spiny, 5–9.

7
Entyloma calendulae f. *dahliae* causes **Dahlia Smut.** Host plant; superficially similar to fungal leaf spot diseases but spores quite different. SORI in form of ± circular spots (<1) on leaves, at first pale buff, then darker brown, often fusing together and surrounded by dead tissues. SPORE MASS inapparent. On dahlia (rarer related forms and species on other members of the Compositae and other plant families). Summer. Widespread. Uncommon. SPORE BALLS absent. SPORES very pale yellow, subspherical – polygonal, smooth, 9–14.

8
Tilletia caries causes **Wheat Bunt.** Host plant, *Ustilago nuda* also occurs on wheat but has no smell. SORI in the ovaries, partly concealed by glumes and causing grain to be filled with spores. SPORE MASS dark brown-black, powdery, foul smelling when crushed. On wheat and rye. Summer. Widespread, predominantly southern. Uncommon. SPORE BALLS absent. SPORES pale brown, subspherical, net-patterned, 14–20.

200

EDINALES
‣trophic on flowering
nts, conifers and Pterphytes, often producing
ious diseases commonly
‑ed rusts. Usually pro
‑e four basidiospores on
promycelium. Life
les sometimes very comx and sometimes with
‑ernation of host plants.

to five spore types, ureiospores (produced in
i called uredinia),
‑iospores (produced in
‑ia), teliospores (pro
‑ed in telia), basidios
‑res and pycniospores,
hough only the first three
‑ used in identification
‑d classification. Uredi
‑ospores usually pale
‑own or yellowish, singleled, with characteristic
‑res and spiny ornamenta
‑n. Aeciospores usually
‑y pale coloured, singleled, lacking pores, and
‑rty rather than spiny.
liospores usually dark
‑own or black, very vari
‑e in morphology,
lked or not, often with
‑o or more cells, smooth,
‑own or yellow en masse.
‑ere are about 100 genera
‑d 4,000 species, classified
‑ncipally on features of
‑ life cycle stage produc
‑g teliospores, but most
‑mmon species can be
‑ntified fairly accurately
the basis of host plant.
‑ccinia is very much the
‑gest genus and includes
‑out three-quarters of all
‑own species. Uredinales
‑e sometimes divided into
‑o families, the **Melampraceae** with stalkless
‑iospores and the **Pucci
‑aceae** with stalked telios
‑res but the classification
‑ these fungi is fraught
‑th problems and this sub
‑vision is not widely used.

9
‑ccinia striiformis causes
llow Rust of Cereals.
‑st plants, arrangement
uredinia. UREDINIA nar
‑wly oblong (0.05–0.1)
‑d grouped in lines on
‑her pale spots on upper
‑d lower leaf surfaces and
‑florescences, not usually
‑sing, powdery, lemon
‑llow. TELIA oblong, on
‑wer leaf surfaces or
‑ems, dark brown-black,
‑covered by leaf surface
‑sues. AECIA absent. On
‑neat, barley, rye and sev
‑al wild grasses, espec
‑ly cocksfoot. (*Dactylis
‑omerata*). Spring –
‑tumn. Widespread. Very
‑mmon. UREDINIOSPORES
‑ange-yellow, broadly
‑lipsoid – subspherical,
‑iny, 8–10 indistinct
‑attered germ pores, 12–
‑×25–30. TELIOSPORES

brown, 2-celled, club-
shaped, often with sharply
flattened apex, slightly constricted at septum, tapering
below to very short stalk,
smooth 9–24×30–70. Paraphyses brown, numerous,
curved.

10
Puccinia graminis causes
Black Rust of Cereals. Host
plants, microscopic features, UREDINA oblong
(0.2–0.3), scattered or in
lines, often fusing, on
upper and lower leaf surfaces, leaf sheaths and
stems, surrounded by ruptured host tissues, powdery, yellowish brown.
TELIA oblong (0.2–0.3), in
lines, on upper and lower
leaf surfaces, cushion-like,
black, soon exposed. AECIA
irregularly cylindrical with
erect, ragged margin, scattered or in small groups, on
lower leaf surfaces and
fruit, often on thickened
reddish-purple-bordered
spots. Uredinia on wheat,
also on oats, barley, rye
and many wild grass species. Aecia on *Berberis vulgaris*, *Mahonia aquifolium*
and *M. ×bealii*. Spring –
autumn. Widespread. Very
common on wheat, much
less so on other cereals and
grasses, very rare in Britain
on *Berberis* and *Mahonia*
(rust on *Mahonia* in Britain
is more likely to be caused
by *Cumminsiella*). UREDI
NIOSPORES at first yellowish
brown, then golden-brown,
broadly ellipsoid, spiny,
usually 4 equatorial germ
pores, 16–22×21–42.
TELIOSPORES brown, 2-
celled, elongated club-
shaped, usually rounded at
apex, very slightly constricted at septum, tapering
below to long stalk (<60),
smooth, 12–22×35–60.
AECIOSPORES white – pale
orange, subspherical,
smooth, 14–16.

11
Puccinia coronata causes
Crown Rust of Oats. Host
plants, microscopic features. UREDINIA oblong,
minute, scattered or in
lines, occasionally fusing,
on upper and lower leaf
surfaces, powdery, orange.
TELIA oblong, irregularly
scattered, on lower leaf surfaces or stems, black, at
first covered by leaf tissues
but soon exposed. AECIA
irregularly cylindrical with
white, erect, ragged margin, scattered or in small
rounded groups, on lower
or rarely upper leaf surfaces and leaf stalks, often
producing tissue distortion
on latter. Uredinia and

telia on oats and on several
wild grass species, especially *Lolium perenne*,
Alopecurus pratensis and
Arrhenatherum elatius.
Aecia on *Rhamnus catharicus* and *Frangula alnus*.
Spring – autumn. Widespread. Common. UREDI
NIOSPORES yellow, subspherical, finely spiny,
usually 3–4 scattered germ
pores, 10–35×14–39.
TELIOSPORES brown, 2-
celled, club-shaped, flat at
apex with 5–8 blunt, sometimes branched teeth,
barely constricted at septum, tapering below to
short, thick stalk, smooth,
14–20×30–60. AECIOSPORES
orange, subspherical, very
finely warty, 12–20×16–25.

12
Puccinia punctiformis.
Host plant, smell, microscopic features. UREDINIA ±
oblong, minute, scattered
over entire lower leaf surface, often fusing, powdery, yellowish buff, smell
pleasant. TELIA ± oblong,
minute, scattered over entire lower leaf surface, dark
brown. AECIA oblong, minute, scattered over entire
lower leaf surface, at first
reddish brown, then darker.
On *Cirsium arvense*. Spring
– winter. Widespread.
Very common. UREDINIO
SPORES pale brown, broadly
ellipsoid – subspherical,
spiny, usually 3 irregularly
placed germ pores, 21–28.
TELIOSPORES brown, 2-
celled, broadly ellipsoid,
rounded at apex and below,
barely constricted at septum, tapering below to
short, thin stalk, finely
warty, 17–25×26–42.

13
Puccinia calthicola. Host
plant, microscopic features.
UREDINIA oblong, minute,
scattered on lower and less
commonly upper leaf surfaces, surrounded by erect
host tissues, reddish brown.
TELIA oblong, irregularly
scattered, on lower or less
commonly upper leaf surfaces, brown, at first
covered by leaf tissues but
soon exposed. AECIA at first
hemispherical then cup-
shaped, with ± erect, ragged
yellow margin, scattered or
in small rounded –
elongated groups, on lower
leaf surfaces and leaf stalks.
On *Caltha palustris*.
Spring – autumn. Widespread. Common. UREDI
NIOSPORES reddish brown,
ellipsoid, spiny, usually 2–
3 ± equatorial germ pores,
20–25×22–30. TELIOSPORES
brown, 2-celled, elongated-
ellipsoid, rounded at apex
and below, barely con

stricted at septum, tapering
below to short, thick stalk,
very finely warty, 24–35×
35–60. AECIOSPORES yellow,
ellipsoid – subspherical,
very finely warty, 16–24×
20–28.

14
Puccinia recondita. Host
plants, microscopic features. UREDINIA oblong
(0.1–0.2), scattered on
upper and less commonly
lower leaf surfaces, rarely
fusing, reddish brown.
TELIA oblong, usually irregularly scattered, on lower
leaf surfaces or leaf
sheaths, black, fairly persistently covered by leaf tissues. AECIA cup-shaped or
occasionally cylindrical,
scattered in irregular
groups or in lines, on lower
leaf surfaces. Uredinia and
telia on many members of
family Gramineae. Aecia
on many members of families Boraginaceae, Crassulaceae and Ranunculaceae.
Spring – autumn. Widespread. Very common.
UREDINIOSPORES pale reddish brown – yellowish,
broadly ellipsoid –
subspherical, spiny, 4–8
scattered germ pores, 13–
24×16–34. TELIOSPORES
brown, 1–3-celled, elongated club-shaped,
rounded or flattened at
apex, slightly constricted at
septum, tapering below to
short, fairly thick stalk,
smooth, 13–24×36–65.
AECIOSPORES white,
ellipsoid – subspherical,
very finely warty, 13–
26×19–29.

15
Puccinia antirrhini causes
Antirrhinum Rust. Host
plants, microscopic features. UREDINIA circular,
scattered on lower and less
commonly upper leaf surfaces, surrounded by torn
host tissues, reddish brown.
TELIA circular, usually
minute, scattered or fusing,
on pale spots usually on
lower leaf surfaces, dark
brown-black, surrounded
by torn host tissues. AECIA
absent. On *Antirrhinum
glutinosum* and *A. majus*.
Spring – autumn. Widespread. Common. UREDI
NIOSPORES pale reddish
brown, broadly ellipsoid –
subspherical, finely spiny,
2–3 equatorial germ pores,
16–24×21–30. TELIOSPORES
reddish brown, 2-celled,
elongated ellipsoid, rounded or flattened at apex,
slightly constricted at septum, tapering below to long
(<30), rather slender stalk,
smooth, 17–26×36–54.

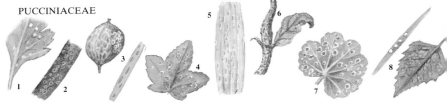

1

Puccinia horiana causes **Chrysanthemum White Rust.** Host plants, colour, microscopic features. URE-DINIA absent. TELIA ±circular, scattered on lower or more rarely upper leaf surfaces, yellowish – greyish white. AECIA absent. On *Chrysanthemum* species, especially cultivated types in glasshouses and nurseries. All year (in glasshouses). Widespread. Rare. TELIOSPORES pale yellow, 2-celled, elongated club-shaped, rather pointed at apex, slightly constricted at septum, tapering below to long (<45), rather slender stalk, smooth, 12–18×32–45.

2

Puccinia lagenophorae. Host plants, microscopic features. UREDINIA absent. TELIA oblong (0.1–0.2), usually associated with aecia, on stems, dark brown, fairly persistently covered by leaf tissues. AECIA cup-shaped, in large, conspicuous orange groups on upper and lower leaf surfaces, usually with swelling of host tissues. On *Senecio squalidus* and *S. vulgaris.* Spring – autumn. Widespread. Extremely common. TELIOSPORES dark brown, 1–2-celled, broadly ellipsoid – bluntly club-shaped, ±rounded at apex, slightly constricted at septum, tapering below to short, fairly thick stalk, 1–2 raised ridges, 12–18×20–41 (1-celled spores smaller than 2-celled). AECIOSPORES orange, subspherical, very finely warty, 10–16.

3

Puccinia caricina causes **Gooseberry Rust.** Host plants, microscopic features. UREDINIA oblong (<0.05), usually scattered on lower leaf surfaces, pale brown. TELIA oblong (<0.1), scattered or in lines, usually on lower leaf surfaces, brownish black. AECIA cup-shaped, with torn, recurved margin, in large, conspicuous groups on lower and occasionally upper leaf surfaces, also stems, leaf stalks and fruit, usually associated with

marked swelling of host tissues. Uredinia and telia on many *Carex* species. Aecia on cultivated and wild currants and gooseberries, also *Urtica* species, *Parnassia palustris* and *Pedicularis palustris.* Spring – autumn. Widespread. Extremely common. UREDINIOSPORES yellowish brown, subspherical, spiny, 2–3 equatorial pores, 20–38×17–30 (size range varies on different hosts). TELIOSPORES dark brown, 2-celled, club-shaped, rounded at apex, constricted at septum, tapering below to short, rather slender stalk, smooth, 14–23×35–66 (size range varies on different hosts). AECIOSPORES orange, polygonal, warty, 12–20×16-26.

4

Puccinia malvacearum causes **Hollyhock Rust.** Host plants, microscopic features. UREDINIA absent. TELIA oblong, scattered on conspicuous yellowish orange spots, on lower leaf surfaces, leaf stalks and stems, cushion-like, hard, reddish brown. AECIA absent. On cultivated hollyhocks, also *Malva, Sidalcea, Lavatera* species and related plants. Spring – autumn. Widespread. Extremely common. TELIOSPORES yellowish brown, 2-celled, elongated spindle-shaped, rather pointed at apex, barely constricted at septum, tapering below to rather slender stalk, smooth, 12–26×35–75.

5

Puccinia allii causes **Leek Rust.** Host plants, microscopic features. UREDINIA ± oblong, scattered on upper and lower leaf surfaces, on faint yellowish spots, fairly persistently covered by swollen host tissues, yellow – reddish yellow. TELIA ± oblong, usually scattered, on upper and lower leaf surfaces or stems, brownish black, persistently covered by host tissues. AECIA ±cylindrical, white, with torn margin, usually in rounded or elongated groups, on upper and lower leaf surfaces. On onions, leeks and other species of *Allium.* Spring – autumn. Wide-

spread, not aecia in Britain. Very common. UREDINIO-SPORES yellowish, broadly ellipsoid – subspherical, finely spiny, 5–10 scattered germ pores, 20–24×23–29. TELIOSPORES brown, 2-celled, ellipsoid, usually flattened at apex, slightly constricted at septum, tapering below to short, fairly slender stalk, smooth, 20–26×28–45. AECIOSPORES yellow, spherical, warty, 19–28.

6

Puccinia menthae causes **Mint Rust.** Host plants, microscopic features. URE-DINIA rounded, scattered on lower leaf surfaces, usually on slightly swollen brownish or yellowish spots, usually surrounded by swollen host tissues, sometimes fusing, reddish brown. TELIA rounded, scattered on lower leaf surfaces, usually on slightly swollen brownish or yellowish spots, usually surrounded by swollen host tissues, sometimes fusing, dark brown. AECIA irregularly cup-shaped, usually in groups of orange-purplish spots on lower leaf surfaces, leaf stalks and stems, margin barely torn. On *Mentha* species, *Origanum, Satureja* and related plants in family Labiatae. Spring – autumn. Widespread. Very common. UREDINIO-SPORES pale brown, ellipsoid, spiny, 3 equatorial germ pores, 14–19×17–28. TELIOSPORES dark brown, 2-celled, elongated-ellipsoid – subspherical, rounded at apex and below, barely constricted at septum, narrowing sharply to long, slender stalk, smooth, 19–23×26–35. AECIOSPORES pale yellow, ellipsoid, warty, 17–28×24–40.

7

Puccinia pelargonii-zonalis causes **Pelargonium Rust.** Host plant, microscopic features. UREDINIA ±rounded, scattered or grouped on lower leaf surfaces, often eventually in concentric circles, surrounded by torn host tissues, powdery, reddish brown. TELIA absent as distinct structures. AECIA absent. On zonal pelargoniums (*Pelargonium*

zonale) in cultivation. Spring – autumn. Widespread, predominantly western and southern, introduced from South Africa to Europe in 1962. Very common. UREDINIOS-PORES yellowish brown, broadly ellipsoid – subspherical, finely spiny, 2 equatorial germ pores, 19–22×21–29. TELIOSPORES mixed with urediniospores, sparse, pale brown, 2-celled, ellipsoid – club-shaped, ± rounded at both ends, slightly constricted at septum, narrowing to short, rather slender stalk, smooth, 16–24×36–50.

8

Melampsoridium betulinum. Host plants, microscopic features, other superficially similar rust fungi on larch differ microscopically and have different alternate hosts. AECIDIA hemispherical (0.01–0.05) scattered below lower leaf surface tissues and apparent from yellow spots, firm, eventually opening at apex. TELIA scattered below lower leaf surface, often extensive, at first orange then yellowish brown, firm. AECIA ±cup-shaped reddish orange – white, with irregularly torn margin, solitary or in lines on either or both sides of midrib on under surfaces of leaves. Uredinia and telia on *Betula pendula* and *B. pubescens* (on saplings). Aecia on *Larix decidua* and (rarely) *L. kaempferi.* Spring – autumn. Widespread. Very common. UREDINIOSPORES white, ellipsoid – ±club-shaped, sparsely spiny, 9–15×22–38. TELIOS-PORES white, 1-celled, prism-shaped, rounded at both ends, stalkless, smooth, 8–16×30–52. AECIOSPORES reddish yellow, broadly ellipsoid – subspherical, very finely warty except for smooth area on one side, 16–24×12–18.

9

Phragmidium violaceum. Host plants, microscopic features. UREDINIA minute, on conspicuous reddish, violet-bordered spots on lower leaf surfaces, orange yellow. TELIA scattered or sometimes fusing, ±circula

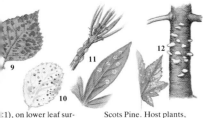

‹1), on lower leaf sur-
ces, powdery, black.
ᴄɪᴀ diffuse, on conspi-
ous reddish, violet-
rdered spots on lower
af surfaces and stems,
attered or fusing, orange-
llow. On blackberries,
ganberries and several
lated plants in the genus
ubus. All year. Wide-
read. Extremely com-
on. ᴜʀᴇᴅɪɴɪᴏsᴘᴏʀᴇs yel-
w, ellipsoid – subspheri-
l, markedly warty, 18–25
19–30. Paraphyses white,
club-shaped. ᴛᴇʟɪᴏsᴘᴏʀᴇs
ddish brown,1–5-celled,
long or cylindrical,
unded at both ends with
hall apical bump, barely
nstricted at septa, long
‹190) club-shaped stalk,
arty, 2–4 pores/cell, 30–
×65–100. ᴀᴇᴄɪᴏsᴘᴏʀᴇs
llow, elongated –
lipsoid, markedly warty –
iny, 17–24×19–30. Para-
hyses white, usually
ghtly curved.

10

aragmidium tuberculatum
uses **Rose Rust.** Host
ants, microscopic fea-
res, very similar to *P.
ucronatum* on same hosts
d often confused with it.
ʀᴇᴅɪɴɪᴀ minute, on lower
af surfaces, scattered or
groups, powdery, pale
llow. ᴛᴇʟɪᴀ very small,
attered or in groups, on
wer leaf surfaces, pow-
ry, black. ᴀᴇᴄɪᴀ rounded,
shion-like – pustular, on
igs, leaf stalks and leaf
ins, bright orange. On
ltivated and wild roses.
ring – autumn. Wide-
read. Extremely com-
on. ᴜʀᴇᴅɪɴɪᴏsᴘᴏʀᴇs yel-
w, ellipsoid – subspheri-
l, warty – spiny, 16–24×
–25. Paraphyses white, ±
ub-shaped, curved. ᴛᴇʟɪᴏ-
ᴏʀᴇs reddish brown, 4–6-
lled, elongated-
lipsoid – cylindrical,
unded at base, tapering
apex into blunt point,
ot constricted at septa,
ng (‹110) club-shaped
alk, warty, 2–3 pores/cell,
–36×55–110. ᴀᴇᴄɪᴏ-
ᴏʀᴇs yellow, elongated-
lipsoid – subspherical,
arkedly warty – spiny,
–24×20–30. Paraphyses
hite, club-shaped.

11

ronartium flaccidum
auses **Resin-Top Disease** of

Scots Pine. Host plants,
microscopic features.
ᴜʀᴇᴅɪɴɪᴀ±circular, pustu-
lar with circular pore,
minute, on lower leaf surfaces, scattered or in
groups, white. ᴛᴇʟɪᴀ very
small, scattered or in
groups, on lower leaf surfaces, usually arising within
uredia, emerging as waxy,
cylindrical curved or
straight spore mass,
yellow – reddish brown.
ᴀᴇᴄɪᴀ erumpent from bark,
forming elongated warty,
yellow-orange bladders
(0.2–0.3×0.2–0.7). Uredia
and telia on *Paeonia mas-
cula* and *Tropaeolum
majus*. Aecia on *Pinus sylvestris*. Spring – autumn.
Widespread, uredia and
telia only southern Eng-
land. Rare, locally common
in north on pine. ᴜʀᴇᴅɪ-
ɴɪᴏsᴘᴏʀᴇs white, broadly
ellipsoid – subspherical,
spiny, 14–20×18–30.
ᴛᴇʟɪᴏsᴘᴏʀᴇs yellow –
reddish brown,1-celled,
ellipsoid, in chains,
smooth, 10–16×20–60.
ᴀᴇᴄɪᴏsᴘᴏʀᴇs white, broadly
ellipsoid – subspherical or
polyhedral, markedly
warty, 16–23×24–31.

12

Cronartium ribicola causes
White Pine Blister Rust.
Host plants, microscopic
features. ᴜʀᴇᴅɪɴɪᴀ±circu-
lar, pustular with circular
pore, minute, on lower leaf
surfaces, in groups on pale
spots, yellow. ᴛᴇʟɪᴀ very
small, crowded, especially
on veins on lower leaf surfaces, arising within uredinia, emerging as cylindrical
spore mass, brownish yel-
low. ᴀᴇᴄɪᴀ erumpent from
bark, rounded – elongated
(0.1–0.3×0.2–0.6) minutely
warty. Uredia and telia on
Ribes nigrum and related
Ribes species. Aecia on
Pinus strobus and related
species. Spring – autumn.
Widespread, especially in
north. Rare, locally com-
mon in north. ᴜʀᴇᴅɪɴɪᴏs-
ᴘᴏʀᴇs orange, broadly ellipsoid, markedly spiny, 13–
18×21–25. ᴛᴇʟɪᴏsᴘᴏʀᴇs
white, 1-celled, ellipsoid –
cylindrical, in chains,
smooth, 10–21×30–70.
ᴀᴇᴄɪᴏsᴘᴏʀᴇs orange,
ellipsoid – subspherical or
polyhedral, markedly warty
except on small, smooth
area, 18–20×22–29.

13

Uromyces muscari causes
Bluebell Rust. Host plants,
microscopic features. ᴜʀᴇ-
ᴅɪɴɪᴀ absent. ᴛᴇʟɪᴀ
rounded – elongated
(‹0.05), usually in elon-
gated concentric groups,
fairly persistently covered
by host tissues, then splitting longitudinally, pow-
dery, dark brown. ᴀᴇᴄɪᴀ
absent. On bluebell
(*Hyacinthoides non-scripta*)
and related species of *Scilla*
and *Muscari*. Spring –
autumn. Widespread.
Common. ᴛᴇʟɪᴏsᴘᴏʀᴇs
brown, 1-celled, broadly
ellipsoid – subspherical,
elongated stalk, smooth,
14–22×18–32.

14

*Melampsorella caryophyl-
lacearum*. Host plants,
gross symptoms on *Abies*,
microscopic features. ᴜʀᴇ-
ᴅɪɴɪᴀ circular,±pustular
with small circular pore,
minute, grouped or scat-
tered below tissues of lower
or rarely upper leaf sur-
faces or leaf stalks, usually
associated with stomata,
orange-yellow. ᴛᴇʟɪᴀ
irregular, erumpent on
lower or rarely upper leaf
surfaces on white or pinkish
spots. ᴀᴇᴄɪᴀ hemispherical
– cylindrical, on lower leaf
surface, in two rows, one
each side of midrib, reddish
yellow, associated with
witches' broom develop-
ment. Uredia and telia on
Cerastium and *Stellaria* species. Aecia on *Abies* species. Spring – autumn.
Widespread. Rare. ᴜʀᴇᴅɪ-
ɴɪᴏsᴘᴏʀᴇs orange-yellow,
broadly ellipsoid, sparsely
spiny, 12–21×16–30.
ᴛᴇʟɪᴏsᴘᴏʀᴇs white, usually
1-celled, ellipsoid – subspherical, sometimes±ang-
ular, smooth, 12–25. ᴀᴇᴄɪᴏsᴘᴏʀᴇs orange-yellow,
ellipsoid – subspherical or
polyhedral, markedly
warty, 14–20×16–30.

15

Melampsora populnea.
Host plants, microscopic
features. ᴜʀᴇᴅɪɴɪᴀ±circu-
lar, minute, on lower leaf
surfaces, cushion-like,
powdery, yellowish orange.
ᴛᴇʟɪᴀ±circular, scattered
below surface tissues on
lower leaf surfaces, dark
brown. ᴀᴇᴄɪᴀ variable with

hosts, diffuse, erumpent
through young shoots, solitary, elongated (0.3×2),
reddish orange on *Pinus*,±
circular, bright orange,
clustered on pale yellow
spots on lower leaf surfaces
and stem on *Mercurialis*,
diffuse, minute, pale yellow, usually on yellowish
spots on lower leaf surfaces
of *Larix*. Uredia and telia
on *Populus alba* and *P. tre-
mula*. Aecia on *Pinus* and
Larix species and *Mercurialis perennis*. Spring – summer. Widespread. Com-
mon, rarer on *Pinus* and
Larix. ᴜʀᴇᴅɪɴɪᴏsᴘᴏʀᴇs orange, broadly ellipsoid –
subspherical, sparsely
spiny, 15–25×11–18. Para-
physes white,±club-shap-
ed. ᴛᴇʟɪᴏsᴘᴏʀᴇs pale brown,
usually 1-celled, prism-
shaped, rounded at both
ends, smooth, 7–12×22–60.
ᴀᴇᴄɪᴏsᴘᴏʀᴇs orange-yellow,
subspherical – angular,
finely warty, 11–17×13–24.

16

Tranzschelia discolor. Host
plants, microscopic fea-
tures. ᴜʀᴇᴅɪɴɪᴀ±circular,
on yellowish brown spots
on lower leaf surfaces,
cushion-like but soon
exposed, powdery, reddish
brown. ᴛᴇʟɪᴀ±circular, on
yellowish brown spots on
lower leaf surfaces,
cushion-like but soon
exposed, powdery, dark
brown. ᴀᴇᴄɪᴀ±flat with
broad, coarsely lobed margin, scattered over lower
leaf surface. Uredia and
telia on plums and related
Prunus species. Aecia on
Anemone coronaria and
related anemones. Spring –
autumn. Widespread.
Common on plums, rarer
on anemones. ᴜʀᴇᴅɪɴɪᴏs-
ᴘᴏʀᴇs pale – dark brown,
broadly ellipsoid, markedly
warty – spiny, 10–19×20–
40. Paraphyses yellowish
brown, with±thickened
heads. ᴛᴇʟɪᴏsᴘᴏʀᴇs pale
brown, 2-celled, ellipsoid,
deeply constricted at septum
and separating, upper cell
subspherical, densely warty,
lower cell elongated-
ellipsoid,±smooth, pale
brown, short, stout stem.
ᴀᴇᴄɪᴏsᴘᴏʀᴇs pale yellow-
brown, subspherical, finely
warty, 16–24.

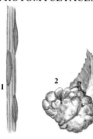

ASCOMYCOTINA

Usually mycelial, occasionally yeast-like, either with macroscopic well-defined fruit body or lacking a fruit body and with its function replaced by microscopic hyphae. Cell walls lack cellulose and contain chitin. Reproduce sexually by formation of ascospores borne internally in a modified hyphal structure rather resembling a cigar-tube and called an ascus, and usually discharged from it forcibly. Spores discharged either into outside air or first into a ±enclosed fruit body. Many form asexual spores, usually called conidia. Many on plant tissues, some terrestrial, some aquatic. Saprotrophic or biotrophic, a few causing important crop diseases. Divided primarily on the basis of the presence or absence of true fruit body, fruit body structure, ascus structure and other features into six Classes of which five are included here, the sixth being a group of obscure external parasites of arthropods. Modern taxonomy tends to diminish the significance of the Class divisions within the Ascomycotina and concentrate at the Order level, although Classes are retained here as they correspond with fairly readily recognisable types of fruit body form. The Ascomycotina is the largest group of fungi with well over 15,000 species.

HEMIASCOMYCETES

Differ from all other Classes in the absence of a distinct fruit body, the asci being formed singly from non-aggregated mycelium. There are two Orders, Endomycetales and Taphrinales. The former are saprotrophic and include about 20 genera in 4 families among which are several microscopic non-mycelial yeasts, including *Saccharomyces* and *Schizosaccharomyces* species, the brew-

ers' and bakers' yeasts. The Taphrinales comprise two families, **Protomycetaceae** with two genera and the monogeneric **Taphrinales**. The Taphrinales are all biotrophic on higher plants and include the four species described here.

1

Protomyces macrosporus. Host plants, symptoms, asci. SYMPTOMS slight swelling or galling of host tissues. FRUIT BODY absent. In leaves and stems of plants in family Umbelliferae, especially *Aegopodium podagraria* and *Anthriscus sylvestris.* Spring – autumn. Widespread. Common. ASCI subspherical, thin-walled, many-spored, 50–70. ASCOSPORES colourless, broadly ellipsoid, smooth, 3×4.5. CHLAMYDOSPORES subspherical, thick-walled, smooth, 50–70.

2

Taphrina deformans causes **Peach Leaf Curl Disease.** Host plants, symptoms. SYMPTOMS puckering and reddening of leaves, followed by white surface bloom and eventually shrivelling. FRUIT BODY absent. In leaves and inconspicuously on shoots of *Prunus amygdalus* and *P. persica.* Spring – autumn. Widespread. Very common. ASCI club-shaped – cylindrical, stalked, usually 8-spored, 7–15×20–50. ASCOSPORES colourless, subspherical, ±clustered, smooth, sometimes budding within ascus, 3–7.

3

Taphrina populina causes **Poplar Leaf Blister Disease.** Host plants, symptoms. SYMPTOMS localised golden-yellow puckering of leaves. FRUIT BODY absent. In leaves and inconspicuously on shoots of *Populus* species, especially *P. nigra.* Spring – autumn. Widespread. Common. ASCI club-shaped – cylindrical,

sometimes stalked, many-spored, 18–22×70–90. ASCOSPORES colourless, subspherical, smooth, inapparent because immediately budding within ascus to give many bud-spores, each 1×2.

4

Taphrina betulina causes **Birch Witches' Broom.** Host plants, symptoms. SYMPTOMS witches' brooms on branches. FRUIT BODY absent. In abnormally small and pale leaves on witches' brooms on *Betula* species. All year. Widespread. Extremely common. ASCI cylindrical, 8-spored, 10–26×23–73. ASCOSPORES colourless, broadly ellipsoid, ±clustered, smooth, budding within in ascus, 2–5.5×3.5–6.5.

'PLECTOMYCETES'

Fruit body sometimes rudimentary but usually comprising loosely aggregated hyphae or most commonly±spherical cleistothecia, often rather sparse and usually very small. Each fruit body with one or several broadly ellipsoid, subspherical or club-shaped unitunicate asci, containing two or several non-septate ascospores. A loose grouping of several orders, almost certainly not closely related. The Eurotiales and Gymnoascales are two related and large Orders of about six or seven families that include many important biotrophs causing diseases of plants and animals. None is included here although *Onygena* is an

interesting and fairly common genus on hair, feathers, shed horns and antle while the common and important deuteromycet genera *Penicillium* and *Aspergillus* (p. 223) are the asexual phases of some c the Eurotiales. The Elaphomycetales, compri ing the single monogene family **Elaphomycetace** are subterranean forms, producing large fruit bod and sometimes grouped with the truffles in the Tuberaceae (p. 219). The commonest species is included here. The Erysiphales are all obligate biotrophs and cause pow dery mildew diseases of a enormous range of flowe ing plants. The Order co prises one family, the **Er** **siphaceae** with seven genera, all represented ir Europe and with many v common and important species. The genera are identified principally by details of the cleistotheci appendages but as fruit bodies are often absent a the conidia-bearing myce lium very uniform, it is often only possible to hazard a broad guess at species from the nature c the host plants. Representatives of three of the commonest genera are included.

Elaphomyces granulatus. Habitat, fruit body form, microscopic features, ofte confused with truffles or subterranean basidiomycetes but microscopic features very different. FRUIT BODY 2–4, cleistothecial, broadly ellipsoid – subspherical, irregularly warty, with very thick, 2-layered wall, very commonly parasitised by *Cor dyceps ophioglossoides.* SPORE MASS purplish black powdery, entirely enclose Usually in small, scattere groups. Subterranean, short distance below soil surface of coniferous, or rarely broad-leaved woo especially with pines. All year. Widespread. Uncom mon. Inedible. ASCI subspherical – pear-shaped, thin-walled, usually 6-spored, quickly breaking down, 35–45×3 60. ASCOSPORES colourless brownish black, spherica irregularly warty, 24–32.

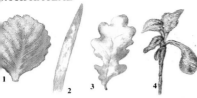

1
Erysiphe cichoracearum causes **Powdery Mildew Diseases.** Overall colony appearance, host plants, *E. polygoni* on similar hosts has 3–8-spored asci, several other species are also common, especially *E. graminis* on cereals and wild grasses. SYMPTOMS, irregular powdery white coating to leaves, stems and other above-ground parts of hosts. FRUIT BODY <0.01, cleistothecial,±spherical, black,±net-patterned, with spreading, pale brownish branches fusing into mycelium, scattered over general mycelial growth, each usually with 2–12 asci, rather sparse. On leaves, stems and other above-ground parts of many different herbaceous plants, typically on cultivated cucurbits. Spring – autumn. Widespread. Extremely common. ASCI broadly ellipsoid, usually short-stalked, 2-spored, 30–45×45–75. ASCOSPORES colourless, subspherical, smooth, 10–15×20–25. CONIDIA of *Oidium* species usually abundant on mycelium, colourless, ellipsoid, in chains, size very variable, depending on host plants.

2
Erysiphe polygoni causes **Powdery Mildew Diseases.** Overall colony appearance, host plants, *E. cichoracearum* on similar hosts has 2-spored asci, several other species are also common, especially *E. graminis* on cereals and wild grasses. SYMPTOMS irregular powdery white coating to leaves, stems and other above-ground parts of hosts. FRUIT BODY <0.01, cleistothecial,±spherical, black,±net-patterned, with spreading, pale brownish branches fusing into mycelium, scattered over general mycelial growth, each usually with 2–12 asci, rather sparse. On leaves, stems and other above-ground parts of many different herbaceous plants, rather typically on members of family Umbelliferae. Spring – autumn. Widespread. Extremely common. ASCI broadly

ellipsoid, usually short-stalked, 3–8-spored, 30–45×45–75. ASCOSPORES colourless, subspherical, smooth, 10–15×20–25. CONIDIA of *Oidium* species usually abundant on mycelium, colourless, ellipsoid, in chains, size very variable, depending on host plants.

3
Microsphaera alphitoides causes **Oak Powdery Mildew Disease.** Overall colony appearance, fruit body appendages, appendage species of *Microsphaera* on other hosts are much rarer. SYMPTOMS irregular powdery white coating to leaves and young shoots of host plant, especially on lammas shoots. FRUIT BODY <0.02, cleistothecial,±spherical, black,±net-patterned, with <20 spreading, pale brownish forked branches fusing into mycelium, scattered over general mycelial growth, each with several asci, rather sparse. On oaks and less commonly beech or sweet chestnut. Spring – autumn. Widespread, but largely confined to oak in Britain. Extremely common, although rarely found with fruit bodies. ASCI broadly ellipsoid, short-stalked, 4–8-spored, 30–40×40–60. ASCOSPORES colourless, subspherical, smooth, 5–15×18–24. CONIDIA of *Oidium* species usually abundant on mycelium, colourless, ellipsoid, in chains, 15–20×25–30.

4
Podosphaera leucotricha causes **Apple and Pear Powdery Mildew Disease.** Colony appearance, fruit body appendages, other *Podosphaera* with appendages occur mostly on *Crataegus*, other rosaceous trees and *Vaccinium*. SYMPTOMS irregular powdery white coating to leaves, shoots and flowers. FRUIT BODY <0.01, cleistothecial,±spherical, dark brown-black,±net-patterned, with 2–8 erect, apical, sometimes forked appendages, scattered over general mycelial growth, each with one ascus, rather sparse. On *Malus* and *Pyrus* species. Spring – autumn. Widespread.

Extremely common. ASCI subspherical, 8-spored, 45–50×50–70. ASCOSPORES colourless, subspherical, smooth, 12–14×22–26.

'PYRENOMYCETES'
Fruit body comprising enclosed±spherical or flask-shaped perithecia, with a pore or ostiole through which spores are liberated, dispersed singly over substrate or±aggregated together on a common tissue called a stroma. Each fruit body with broadly ellipsoid, subspherical or club-shaped unituncate inoperculate asci with apical pore or slit and containing 2–8 ascospores. The Class is now usually divided into about nine Orders on the basis of a range of microscopic structural and developmental features. Seven of the Orders are represented here, but relatively few of the numerous species are included as most are small and easily overlooked in the field. The following list indicates the approximate numbers of European members of each Order, and the representative genera included: Clavicipitales – *Claviceps*, *Cordyceps* and *Epichloë*, 2 families, about 13 genera; Hypocreales – *Nectria*, 3 families, about 29 genera; Ophiostomatales – *Ceratocystis*, one family, 3 genera; Diatrypales – *Diatrype*, one family, about 6 genera; Diaporthales – *Cryptosphaeria* and *Diaporthe*, 5 families, about 50 genera; Sphaeriales – *Hypoxylon*, *Ustulina*, *Daldinia* and *Xylaria*, 4 families, over 80 genera; Sordariales – *Sordaria*, 5 families and over 40 genera.

Claviceps purpurea causes **Ergot Disease** of rye and many grass species. Sclerotial form and habit, host plants, may represent more than one species. FRUIT BODY 0.1–0.4, as club-shaped – subspherical stromatal head, cream-purple, dotted with dark openings of perithecial ostioles, with

CONIDIA of *Oidium* species usually abundant on mycelium, colourless, ellipsoid, in chains, 12–15×28–30.

cylindrical, slender, pale purple, smooth stem, 0.5–1.5, arising singly or in small groups from fallen sclerotia. SCLEROTIA varying greatly in size with host species, elongated cylindrical, often curved, grooved longitudinally, very hard, dark brownblack, arising from beneath ovary of host flower and emerging to take its place. On inflorescences of many genera in the family Gramineae. Spring – autumn (sclerotia), spring (fruit bodies). Widespread. Common (especially as sclerotial form). Deadly poisonous. PERITHECIA immersed in stroma with protruding ostioles. ASCI elongated-cylindrical, thick-walled with apical pore but blued with Melzer's reagent, 8-spored, c. 5×150. ASCOSPORES colourless, extremely elongated, hair-like, lying side by side, smooth, septate after discharge, 1×100. CONIDIA of *Sphacelia segetum*, in sticky yellowish fluid on flowers, usually found detached from mycelium, colourless, ellipsoid, smooth, 2.5–4×3–7.5.

Cordyceps militaris. Habit, host; excavate carefully to identify host. FRUIT BODY 0.3–1, elongated spindle-shaped – cylindrical stromatal head, v. finely warty, tapering down to cylindrical, slender, wavy, smooth stem, 1–3. Usually solitary. On pupae and larvae of lepidopterous insects, usually shallowly buried in soil. PERITHECIA completely immersed in stroma. Summer – autumn. Widespread. Uncommon. ASCI elongated cylindrical, fragile, thick-walled at apex, not blued with Melzer's reagent, 8-spored, 3–6×250–300. ASCOSPORES colourless, v. elongated, hair-like, lying side by side, smooth, septate after discharge, 1–2× 250–300, soon breaking into many barrel-shaped part-spores, 1–1.5×3.5–6. CONIDIA of *Cephalosporium* sp.

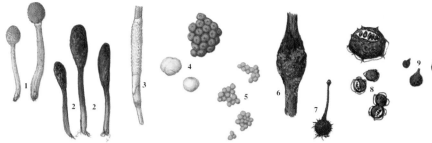

1

Cordyceps gracilis. Habit, host, care needed to excavate soil carefully to obtain host for identification. FRUIT BODY 0.4–0.5, as elongated-ellipsoid stromatal head, smooth, finely dotted, tapering rather sharply downwards to cylindrical, rather stout, straight, smooth stem. 1–3. PERITHECIA completely immersed in stroma. Usually solitary. On pupae and larvae of lepidopterous insects, usually when shallowly buried in soil. Summer – autumn. Widespread. Uncommon. ASCI elongated cylindrical, fragile, thick-walled at apex, not blued with Melzer's reagent, 8-spored, 3–6×250–300. ASCOSPORES colourless, extremely elongated, hair-like, lying side by side, smooth, septate after discharge, 1–2×250–300, but soon breaking into many cylindrical part-spores, 1–1.5×3.5–6. CONIDIA of *Cephalosporium* sp. (?), sparse, scarce, indistinct.

2

Cordyceps ophioglossoides. Habit, host, care needed to excavate soil carefully to obtain host for identification. FRUIT BODY 0.5–1, as elongated-ellipsoid – cylindrical stromatal head, at first yellow, then darker, smooth, finely dotted, tapering rather sharply downwards to cylindrical, rather stout, straight, smooth stem, 3–7. PERITHECIA completely immersed in stroma. Solitary or in small groups. On fruit bodies of buried *Elaphomyces* species. Summer – autumn. Widespread. Uncommon. ASCI elongated-cylindrical, fragile, thick-walled at apex, not blued with Melzer's reagent, 8-spored, 4–8×225–250. ASCOSPORES colourless, extremely elon-gated, hair-like, lying side by side, smooth, septate after discharge, 1–2×190–225 but soon breaking into many cylindrical part-spores, 2×2.5–5. CONIDIA of *Verticillium* sp.

3

Epichloë typhina causes **Choke Disease.** Habit, host plants. FRUIT BODY as cylindrical stroma, at first white, smooth, then golden-yellow, rather rough, sheathing stems of host plants. PERITHECIA 0.025, subspherical, completely immersed in stroma. On stems of several grass species, especially *Dactylis glomerata.* Summer. Widespread. Very common. ASCI elongated cylindrical, thick-walled at apex, not blued with Melzer's reagent, 8-spored, 6–8×80–100. ASCOSPORES colourless, extremely elongated, hair-like, lying side by side, smooth, septate after dis-charge, 1.5–2×80–90. CONIDIA of *Sphacelia typhina.*

4

Nectria cinnabarina causes **Coral-Spot Disease.** Overall fruit body form, presence of conidial pustules especially characteristic. FRUIT BODY 0.1–0.4, erumpent, cushion-like dark red stroma, bearing dense masses of perithecia (see also CONIDIA). PERITHECIA 0.03–0.04, subspherical – flask-shaped, dark red, rough, with apical, shortly beaked ostiole. In dense groups on dead and dying twigs and branches of broad-leaved or very rarely coniferous trees. All year. Wide-spread. Extremely common, especially in asexual state. ASCI club-shaped – cylindrical, 8-spored, 9–12 ×70–90. ASCOSPORES col-ourless, ellipsoid – cylin-drical, 1-septate, ± biseriate, smooth, 4–9 × 12–25, CONIDIA of *Tuberculina vulgaris* abundant, in pink cushion-like pustules, similarly sized to fruit body.

5

Nectria coccinea. Overall fruit body form, host plants, microscopic fea-tures. FRUIT BODY some-times present as an inde-finite stroma bearing small groups of perithecia but often absent and perithecia arise singly. PERITHECIA 0.02–0.03, subspherical – pear-shaped, bright red, smooth, with distinct dar-ker papilla. In dense groups on dead and dying twigs and branches of broad-leaved trees, especially beech and maples. All year. Widespread. Very common. ASCI elongated cylindrical, 8-spored, 7–10×60–100. ASCOSPORES colourless – pale brown, ellipsoid, 1-septate, uniseri-ate, finely rough, 5–6×12–15. CONIDIA of *Cylindrocar-pon candidum.*

6

Nectria galligena causes **Apple and Pear Canker Dis-ease.** Symptoms on host plants, microscopic fea-tures. FRUIT BODY compris-ing aggregated groups of perithecia on indefinite stroma. PERITHECIA 0.02–0.03, broadly ellipsoid – subspherical, bright red, smooth – finely rough, with indistinct papilla. In fairly dense groups on canker lesions of branches and trunks of broad-leaved trees, especially apples and pears. All year. Wide-spread. Extremely com-mon. ASCI elongated-ellipsoid – cylindrical, 8-spored, 12–15×80–110. ASCOSPORES colourless, ellipsoid, 1-septate, unseriate, ±smooth, 6–9×14–22. CONIDIA of *Cylin-drocarpon heteronemum.*

7

Ceratocystis ulmi causes **Dutch Elm Disease.** Symp-toms on host plants, mic-roscopic features. FRUIT BODY absent, perithecia arising individually. PERITHECIA <0.01, flask-shaped, dark brown-black, smooth, with greatly elon-gated beak (<0.03). In small – large groups on wood, below dead bark an in tunnels produced by bark beetles on elms, associated with wilting and dying back of branches. A year. Widespread. Extremely common (but fruit bodies rare). ASCI irre-gularly subspherical, 8-spored, elusive, soon breaking down to become loose in a jelly-like matrix, 18–22. ASCOSPORES colour-less, elongated-ellipsoid – cylindrical – sausage-shaped, non-septate, irregular, ±smooth, 1–1.5×4.5–6. CONIDIA of *Graphium* (=*Pesotum*) *ulmi* abundant, ellipsoid, a tips of coremial stalks, col-ourless, on same substrate as perithecia, 1–3×2–5.

8

Diatrype disciformis. Host plants, overall fruit body form. FRUIT BODY <0.3,± circular, cushion-like stro-ma with flat top, at first pale with dark dots, then darke with white flesh. PERITHECI <0.02–0.04, elongated-ell ipsoid, embedded in strom with ostioles protruding slightly, dark brown-black and contrasting with white flesh. Scattered in small – large groups, sometimes fusing to form extensive crust. On dead branches and twigs of beech or rare other broad-leaved trees. All year. Widespread. Extremely common. ASCI elongated club-shaped, with long tapering stalk, apical ring not blued with Melzer's reagent, 8-spore 2–5×30–40. ASCOSPORES colourless – very pale brown, sausage-shaped, non-septate, irregular, smooth, 1.5–2×5–8. CON-IDIA of *Libertella disciformis.*

9

Cryptosphaeria eunomia. Host plant, overall fruit body form. FRUIT BODY irregular, effused stroma,

206

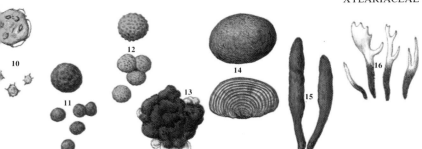

rely within bark, upper face inevident and sealed only by slightly protruding black ostioles, ...er surface forming ...yish patch on inner bark face revealed when ...led back. PERITHECIA ...05, spherical, embed-... in stroma with ostioles ...truding slightly, dark ...y-black. On dead bran-...s and twigs of ash. All ...r. Widespread. ...remely common. ASCI ...ngated-club-shaped, ...h long tapering stalk, ...cal ring not blued with ...lzer's reagent, 8-spored, 2×120–140. ASCOSPORES ...lowish brown, sausage-...ped, non-septate, ± ...stered, smooth, 2–3×13 ... CONIDIA of *Cytospor-millepunctata*.

10

...aporthe eres. Overall ...t body form, many ...sely related species, ...st fairly host-specific. ...JT BODY irregular, ... used stroma, within ...k, but upper surface ...using evident dark discol-...ration of bark surface, ...ecially around small ...nples through which ...ups of dark ostioles ...erge, both upper and ...ver surfaces apparent as ...k lines when bark cut ...rtically through stroma. ...RITHECIA <0.08, spher-...l, embedded in stroma in ...all groups with ostioles ...otruding slightly, black. ... dead branches, twigs of ...ad-l. trees. All year. ...idespread. ...mmon. ASCI elongated ...ıb-shaped, apical ring not ...ued with Melzer's reag-...t, 8-spored, 6–8×50–60. ...OSPORES colourless, ...ongated-spindle-shaped, ...septate, biseriate, ...ooth, 2.5–4×9.5–14. ...NIDIA of *Phomopsis* sp.

11

...poxylon fuscum. Overall ...t body form, several ...sely related similar

species, some fairly host-specific. FRUIT BODY variable, usually cushion-like stroma, <0.4 on bark or more rarely effused, crust-like stroma on wood, pur-plish brown – purplish grey, smooth, with ostiolar pores. PERITHECIA <0.05, subspherical – flask-shaped, fully embedded in stroma, greyish black. On dead branches and twigs of hazel and alder. All year. Widespread. Extremely common. ASCI cylindrical, apical ring blued with Mel-zer's reagent, 8-spored, 6–8×130–150. ASCOSPORES dark brown, ellipsoid, flattened on one side, non-septate, uniseriate, smooth, with distinct fur-row on one side, 5–7×12–15. CONIDIA of *Nodulisporium* sp.

12

Hypoxylon fragiforme. Overall fruit body form, host, several closely related and similar species, some fairly host-specific. FRUIT BODY <1, hemispherical stroma, at first pink, then darker and eventually black, markedly warty. PERITHECIA <0.05, ±flask-shaped, fully embedded in stroma, black. On dead and dying branches and twigs of beech. All year. Wide-spread. Extremely com-mon. ASCI cylindrical, apical ring blued with Mel-zer's reagent, 8-spored, 6–8×130–150. ASCOSPORES dark brown, ±spindle-shaped, flattened on one side, non-septate, uniseri-ate, smooth, with distinct furrow on one side, 5–7×11–15. CONIDIA of *Nodulisporium* sp.

13

Ustulina deusta. Overall fruit body form, host, micro-scopical features. FRUIT BODY <10, irregularly cushion-like or crusty stroma, often effused, very brittle, loosely attached to substrate, at first greyish white, then black with whit-

ish flesh. PERITHECIA <0.1×0.15, spherical, almost fully embedded in stroma, black. On rotten stumps and roots of beech. All year. Widespread. Extremely common. ASCI cylindrical, apical ring blued with Melzer's rea-gent, 12–15×300 –325. ASCOSPORES black, spindle-shaped, flattened on one side, non-septate, uniseriate, smooth, with distinct furrow on one side, 7–10×28–34. CONIDIA ?

14

Daldinia concentrica **Cramp Balls, King Alfred's Cake.** Overall fruit body form and size, hosts. FRUIT BODY 1–5, hemispherical stroma, usually incurved at base, at first reddish brown but soon black, hard, rather brittle, shiny, smooth, with minute ostio-lar pores, flesh dark pur-plish black, concentrically zoned, fibrous. PERITHECIA <0.05, subspherical, fully embedded in stroma in single layer below surface, black. On dead and dying branches of broad-leaved trees, especially on ash, but also quite commonly on alder, birch and gorse, sometimes markedly smal-ler on latter two, the form on burnt gorse now consi-dered a distinct species, *D. vernicosa*. All year. Wide-spread. Extremely com-mon. ASCI cylindrical, apical ring blued with Mel-zer's reagent, 10–12×200–210. ASCOSPORES black, ellipsoid – spindle-shaped, flattened on one side, non-septate, uniseriate, smooth, distinct furrow on one side, 6–9×12–17. CONIDIA of *Nodulisporium* sp.

15

Xylaria longipes. Overall fruit body form, hosts, similar to *X. polymorpha* but smaller with smaller spores. FRUIT BODY 0.7–1, cylindrical – club-shaped, often rather bent stromatal

head, coarsely warty and roughened, cracked in net-pattern, flesh white, taper-ing below to cylindrical, rather stout, brownish black stem, 2–5, ±equal or tapering upwards, smooth above, rather velvety below. PERITHECIA <0.05, subspherical, fully embed-ded in stroma in closely packed single layer below surface, black. On dead and dying branches of broad-leaved trees, espe-cially *Acer* species lying on the ground. All year. Wide-spread. Common. ASCI cylindrical, apical ring blued with Melzer's rea-gent, 8-spored, 6–8×125–140. ASCOSPORES dark brown, ellipsoid – kidney-shaped, flattened on one side, non-septate, uniseri-ate, smooth, with distinct furrow on one side, 5–7×12–16. CONIDIA ?

16

Xylaria hypoxylon **Candle Snuff Fungus, Stag's Horn.** Overall fruit body form habitat. FRUIT BODY 3–5 (height), cylindrical – antler-shaped stroma, usually flattened in cross-section, at first whitish towards apex, then black-tipped, black and velvety below. PERITHECIA <0.05, subspherical, fully embed-ded in stroma in closely packed single layer below surface towards apex of fruit body, black. On dead wood of broad-leaved or more rarely coniferous trees. All year. Wide-spread. Extremely com-mon. ASCI cylindrical, apical ring blued with Mel-zer's reagent, 8-spored, 6–8×100–150. ASCOSPORES black, ±kidney-shaped, non-septate, uniseriate, smooth, with distinct fur-row on one side, 5–6×11–14. CONIDIA towards apex of fruit body, forming white covering.

Xylaria polymorpha **Dead Man's Fingers.** Overall fruit body form, hosts, similar to *X. longipes* but much stouter with larger spores. FRUIT BODY 3–8×1–2.5, irregularly club-shaped stromatal head, coarsely warty and roughened, rather finely wrinkled and cracked around ostiolar pores, flesh white, tapering rather sharply below to indistinct, short, cylindrical, slender, brownish black stem, ±equal or tapering upwards, smooth above, rather velvety below. PERITHECIA <0.08, subspherical, fully embedded in stroma in closely packed single layer below surface, black. On dead stumps of broadleaved trees, especially beech, usually at or close to soil level. All year. Widespread. Common. ASCI cylindrical, apical pore blued with Melzer's reagent, 8-spored, 8–10×150–210. ASCOSPORES dark brownblack, ±lemon-shaped, flattened on one side, non-septate, uniseriate, smooth, with distinct furrow on one side, 5–9×20–32. CONIDIA ? covering young stroma with indefinite whitish bloom.

Xylaria carpophila. Overall fruit body form, habitat, similar to *X. carpophila* but habitat differs. FRUIT BODY 2–5 (height), often cylindrical but also sometimes antler-shaped stroma, usually flattened in cross section, at first whitish towards apex, then blacktipped, black and velvety below. PERITHECIA <0.05, subspherical, fully embedded in stroma in closely packed single layer below surface towards apex of fruit body, black. On fallen beech mast. All year. Widespread. Very common. ASCI cylindrical,

apical ring blued with Melzer's reagent, 8-spored, 6–8×100–150. ASCOSPORES black, ±kidney-shaped, non-septate, uniseriate, smooth, with distinct furrow on one side, 5–6×11–14. CONIDIA towards apex of fruit body, forming white bloom.

Sordaria fimicola. Overall fruit body form, size, habitat. FRUIT BODY <0.04, perithecial, pear-shaped, smooth, usually with anchoring hyphae below, black. Scattered on dung with base±embedded. All year. Widespread. Common. ASCI cylindrical, apical ring not blued with Melzer's reagent, 8-spored, 15–20×175–200. ASCOSPORES black, ellipsoid, nonseptate, uniseriate, smooth, germ pore, 10–13×19–25. CONIDIA ?

'DISCOMYCETES'
Fruit body usually comprising±open, cup-, bowl- or saucer-shaped apothecia, from which spores are liberated directly into the open air. Sometimes with a stem of varying importance and in some species a complex folded or otherwise contorted apothecial head surmounts a tall stem to give a superficially toadstool-like form. In one family the apothecia are grouped together, enclosed and the entire fruit body is subterranean with spore dispersal dependent on rodents (p. 219). Each fruit body usually has many ellipsoid – club-shaped unituncate operculate or inoperculate asci containing eight ascospores and also contains sterile paraphyses of characteristic form. The Class is now usually divided into four Orders, principally on the basis of microscopic details of apothecium structure although in many species these correlate fairly well with gross fruit body form. Representatives of all Orders are included here.

RHYTISMATALES
A small Order of probably unrelated species that have apothecia immersed in and

structurally united with the tissues of the host plant. Leaf inhabiting biotrophic species sometimes cause serious defoliation of affected plants, called needle casts when on conifers. Three families and about 26 genera, all the species described here in the family **Rhytismataceae.**

Rhytisma acerinum causes **Tar Spot Disease** of maples. Symptoms on host plant. FRUIT BODY <2, ±circular, flattened disc-like stroma, black, rather shiny, like a blob of bitumen on upper leaf surface. APOTHECIA ellipsoid, greyish brown, embedded in stroma and exposed by elongated cracks in its surface. On living and fallen leaves of sycamore or more rarely other *Acer* species. All year, apothecia in Spring. Widespread. Very common. ASCI club-shaped, conical at apex, 8-spored, 8–10×125–130. ASCOSPORES colourless, hair-like, thickened at one end, nonseptate, lying side by side, smooth, 1.5–2.5×60–80. PARAPHYSES hair-like, sometimes forked, curved at tips, septate. CONIDIA of *Melasmia acerina.*

Lophodermium pinastri causes **Needle Cast Disease** of pines. Symptoms on host plant, several very similar species occur on the same and related hosts. FRUIT BODY 0.05–0.1, apothecial, ellipsoid, erumpent through small black blisters on upper and lower needle surfaces, disc grey and surrounded by black line, transverse black lines also on

needles close to lesions. On living needles of pines. All year. Widespread. Common. ASCI cylindrical, 8-spored, 9–12×110–155. ASCOSPORES colourless, hair-like, non-septate, sometimes spirally coiled smooth, 1.5–2.5×70–150 PARAPHYSES hair-like, sometimes swollen at tips septate. CONIDIA in pycni of *Leptostroma* sp. in sim lar position to apothecia, colourless, rod-like, 0.5×4.5–6.

Cyclaneusma minus (=*Naemacyclus minor*). Habitat, size, microscopi features, superficially similar fungi occur in similar habitats. FRUIT BODY 0.05×0.1–0.15, apothecial, ellipsoid, erur pent through single longit dinal slit in upper and low needle surfaces which cur back, disc whitish, margi indistinct. On fallen needles of pines, especially *Pinus sylvestris.* All year. Widespread. Common. ASCI cylindrical – clubshaped, not blued with Melzer's reagent, 8-spore 12–14×110–120. ASCOSPORES colourless, hair-like 1–2-septate, rather curve smooth, 2–3×75–85. PARAPHYSES hair-like, swollen tips, sometimes forked, septate. CONIDIA ?

HELOTIALES
A huge group of about 11 families of which the six largest are represented here, and well over 200 genera of predominantly small species. Most are saprotrophic but a few are important biotrophs and a few cause serious canker diseases on trees. The fru body is typically a cup-or saucer-shaped apotheciur and is almost invariably superficial on the substrat stemless or with short – long stem, dark or light coloured, sometimes char acteristically hairy on the outer surface. Asci club-shaped cylindrical – club-shaped, inoperculate. Ascospores typically colourless and non-septate although not invariably so.

·GLOSSACEAE
t body relatively large,
-shaped, long-
med, terrestrial, com-
ly known as Earth
gues. Eight genera, dis-
ished mainly by colour
consistency of fruit
y, presence or absence
·tae and ascospore col-

hoglossum hirsutum.
rall fruit body form,
rficially similar basi-
aycetes are very diffe-
microscopically. FRUIT
× 3–8 (height), apothe-
cylindrical – spindle-
·ed with club-shaped
d, black, velvety, taper-
·harply below to
ened, furrowed and
·ved stem. Usually in
l, trooping groups. On
especially among
agnum on wet, acid
. Summer – autumn.
espread. Uncommon.
cylindrical – club-
·ed, apical pore blued
Melzer's reagent, 8-
·ed, 20–25×150–220.
·SPORES brown,
·gated-cylindrical, 15-
ate when mature, lying
by side, smooth, 6–
00–150. PARAPHYSES
·like, curved, brown at
·k, slightly swollen at
SETAE numerous,
k, thick-walled, stiff,
·ted, projecting, CON-
?

Microglossum viride. Overall fruit body form, colour,
superficially similar basidiomycetes are very different microscopically. FRUIT
BODY 2.5–5, (height),
apothecial, ±irregularly
club-shaped, smooth and
furrowed above, tapering
sharply below to furrowed,
twisted, shiny stem, green.
Usually in small, tufted
groups. On soil in broad-
leaved woods, especially
among mosses and attached
to plant debris. Summer –
autumn. Widespread.
Rare. ASCI cylindrical –
club-shaped apical pore
blued with Melzer's rea-
gent, 8-spored, 8–10×125–
150. ASCOSPORES colourless,
elongated-cylindrical –
spindle-shaped, 3-septate
when mature, irregularly
biseriate, smooth, 5–6×15–
20. PARAPHYSES hair-like,
branched, slightly swollen
at tips. CONIDIA ?

Mitrula paludosa. Overall
fruit body form, colour,
superficially similar basidiomycetes are very different microscopically. FRUIT
BODY 1–4, (height), apothecial, ellipsoid – club-
shaped, smooth, often furrowed at base, tapering
sharply below to smooth,
white stem. Usually in
small, tufted – trooping
groups. On dead leaves or
other plant debris in ditches
and other wet places often
among *Sphagnum*. Spring –
autumn. Widespread.
Rare. ASCI cylindrical –
club-shaped, apical pore
slightly blued with Melzer's
reagent, 8-spored, 8–

9×100–150. ASCOSPORES
colourless, elongated-
cylindrical, non-septate,
biseriate, smooth, 2.5–
3×10–15. PARAPHYSES hair-
like, branched, septate.
CONIDIA ?

ORBILIACEAE
A small family of only two
genera and about 22 species
with small,±stemless
apothecia, usually on wood
or bark and mostly pale in
colour, waxy, translucent
appearance, very small asci
not blued with Melzer's
reagent and small, non-
septate ascospores. Dif-
ficult to examine because
asci and paraphyses are
coherent in a waxy layer
but swollen paraphysis tips
are characteristic.

Orbilia auricolor. Overall
fruit body form, texture
and ascus and ascospore
sizes are characteristic of
this and releated fungi.
FRUIT BODY 0.05–0.15,
apothecial, irregularly
saucer-shaped, disc flat or
slightly convex, waxy, margin indistinct, with short
white anchoring hyphae on
outer surface, stemless.
Usually in small – large
trooping groups. On bark
and wood of broad-leaved
trees. Spring – autumn.
Widespread. Common.
ASCI cylindrical – club-
shaped, not blued with
Melzer's reagent, 8-spored,
4–4.5×25–30. ASCOSPORES
colourless, rod-shaped,
non-septate, biseriate,
smooth, 1–1.5×5–11. PARA-
PHYSES hair-like, swollen at
tips. CONIDIA ?

DERMATEACEAE
About 46 genera of species
united in having small, predominantly soft, fleshy
apothecia but very variable
otherwise. Usually on bark,
wood or dead herbaceous
stems.

Pezicula livida. Overall
fruit body form, microscopic features, typical of
many small related species
in this type of habitat. FRUIT
BODY 0.05–0.15, apothecial,
at first top-shaped, then ±
cushion-like or saucer
-shaped, disc convex,
floury, margin indistinct, ±
stemless, erumpent from
obscure stroma in substrate.
Usually in small – large
groups. On twigs, bran-
ches and sometimes cones
of coniferous trees. Aut-
umn – spring. Widespread.
Very common. ASCI club-
shaped, very obvious pore
markedly blued with Mel-
zer's reagent, 4–8-spored,
15–20×90–120. ASCOSPORES
colourless, ellipsoid –
spindle-shaped, 3-several-
septate, uni-biseriate,
smooth, 6–7×22–24. PARA-
PHYSES hair-like, swollen at
tips. CONIDIA of *Myxospor-
ium abietinum.*

DERMATEACEAE

Tapesia fusca. Overall fruit body form, microscopic features; one of the commonest of many small species with fruit body arising on wood from a mycelial mat. FRUIT BODY 0.05–0.2, apothecial, at first pitcher-shaped, then saucer-shaped, slightly convex, rather shiny, margin paler, stemless, on dark brown, felty mycelial mat-like stroma effused over substrate. Usually in small – large rather scattered groups. On dead wood and bark, especially of broad-leaved trees. All year. Widespread. Very common. ASCI club-shaped, pore blued with Melzer's reagent, 8-spored, 5–7×45–50. ASCOSPORES colourless, ellipsoid – spindle-shaped, non-septate, biseriate, smooth, 2–2.5×8–11. PARAPHYSES hair-like, branched, septate. CONIDIA of *Cystodendron* sp.

Trochila ilicina. Overall fruit body form, habitat. FRUIT BODY 0.03–0.05, apothecial, circular – irregular, fully embedded in host tissue, exposed when circular patch of tissue tears away, lid-like, disc greyish olive, flat, margin indistinct. Usually in large groups, ±covering upper sides of fallen holly leaves. Winter – spring. Widespread. Very common. ASCI club-shaped, pore blued with Melzer's reagent, 8-spored, 8–10×70–80. ASCOSPORES colourless, ellipsoid, non-septate, biseriate, smooth, 3.5–4.5×9–12. PARAPHYSES hair-like – elongated-club-shaped. CONIDIA ?

Mollisia cinerea. Overall fruit body form, habit, colour, although many similar species occur on herbaceous stems and wood. FRUIT BODY 0.05–0.2, apothecial, at first ±saucer-shaped, then flattened and often markedly wavy and irregular, disc pale grey, wavy, smooth, margin paler, outer surface ± smooth and often with brownish anchoring hyphae, stemless. Usually in large groups closely compressed together and adding to distortion. On dead, rotting wood. All year. Widespread. Very common. ASCI cylindrical – club-shaped, pore blued with Melzer's reagent, 8-spored, 5–6×50–70. ASCOSPORES colourless, elongated-ellipsoid – slightly sausage-shaped, non-septate, biseriate, smooth, 2–2.5×7–9. PARAPHYSES cylindrical, blunt-ended. CONIDIA ?

Mollisia ligni. Overall fruit body form, habitat, colour, microscopic features. FRUIT BODY 0.05–0.1, apothecial, cup-to saucer-shaped, disc dark grey, concave, margin paler, outer surface finely downy, black-brown, stemless, dries characteristically in triangular shape. Usually in large groups, trooping – ±tufted. On dead, barkless wood of broad-leaved trees, also woody debris and fallen beech-mast. All year. Widespread. Very common. ASCI cylindrical – club-shaped, pore blued with Melzer's reagent, 8-spored, 5–6×45–70. ASCOSPORES colourless, elongated-ellipsoid – cylindrical, non-septate, biseriate, smooth, 2– 2.5×6–12. PARAPHYSES cylindrical, forked, slightly swollen at tips. CONIDIA ?

Calloria neglecta
(=*Callorina fusarioides*). Habitat, overall fruit body form, colour, microscopic features. FRUIT BODY 0.05– 0.1, apothecial, ±saucer-shaped, erumpent, disc orange, soft, margin barely distinct, outer surface rather rough, very soft-fleshed, stemless. Usually in large trooping groups. On dead stems of *Urtica dioica*. Spring. Widespread. Very common. ASCI cylindrical – club-shaped, pore not blued with Melzer's reagent, 8-spored, 7– 10×70–95. ASCOSPORES colourless, elongated-ellipsoid – cylindrical, 1-septate, biseriate, smooth, 3–4×9–15. PARAPHYSES hair-like, forked, slightly swollen at tips. CONIDIA abundant in pycnidia of *Cylindrocolla urticae*, similar to apothecia in colour and size.

HYALOSCYPHACEAE
A large and important family of about 40 genera, usually with very small, pale-coloured, soft-fleshed apothecia, short-stemmed or stemless, ±densely covered with characteristic hairs and superficial on the substrate. Asci medium-large, club-shaped, usually bluing with Melzer's reagent. Ascospores±elongated, 0-several-septate. Conidia producing forms usually obscure. Most saprotrophic.

Dasyscyphus apalus. Overall fruit body form, colour, hairs and other microscopic features. FRUIT BODY 0.02– 0.05, apothecial, cup-to saucer-shaped, disc white drying slightly pinkish orange, margin and outer surface white with dense white hairs, short-stemmed. Usually in small

HYALOSCYPHAC

trooping groups. On de stems and leaves of *Jun* All year. Widespread. common. ASCI cylindric club-shaped, pore blue with Melzer's reagent, spored, 6–7.5×60–75. ASCOSPORES colourless, needle-like, 1–7-septat lying side by side, smoo 1.5×35–45. PARAPHYSE narrowly lance-shaped longer than asci. HAIRS ourless, thin-walled, se tate, very finely incrust CONIDIA ?

Dasyscyphus brevipilu. Overall fruit body form hairs, very similar to *D* *niveus* and *D. virgineu* paraphyses differ. FRUI BODY 0.05–0.1, apothec cup-shaped, disc cream margin and outer surfa white with dense white hairs, short-stemmed. large trooping groups. dead and rotting wood year. Widespread. Ver common. ASCI cylindric club-shaped, pore blue with Melzer's reagent, spored, 3.5–4.5×45–55 ASCOSPORES colourless, spindle-shaped, non-se ate, uniseriate, smooth 1.5–2.5×6–10. PARAPH narrowly lance-shaped slightly longer than asc HAIRS colourless, thin-w ed, septate, very finely crusted. CONIDIA ?

Dasyscyphus niveus. Ov all fruit body form, hair very similar to *D. virgin* but paraphyses differ. Fr BODY 0.05–0.2, apothec cup-shaped, disc at first white, then yellowish, smooth, margin and out surface white with dense white hairs, short-stem med. In large trooping tufted groups. On dead rotting wood, especially oak. Winter – spring. Widespread. Very common. ASCI cylindrical – club-shaped, pore blued with Melzer's reagent, 8 spored, 4.5–5×50–55. ASCOSPORES colourless, spindle-shaped – ±club

ped, non-septate, irre-
arly biseriate, smooth,
-2×6–10. PARAPHYSES
-like, barely longer
n asci. HAIRS colourless,
k-walled, septate, very
ly incrusted, elongated
l smooth at tips and
netimes exuding liquid.
NIDIA ?

syscyphus mollissimus.
erall fruit body form,
our, habitat, hairs, mic-
copic features. FRUIT
oy 0.05–0.2, apothecial,
o-shaped, disc whitish,
rgin and outer surface
h long golden-yellow
rs, short-stemmed. In
all – large tufted –
oping groups. On dead
ms of herbaceous plants,
pecially in family Umbel-
erae. Spring – summer.
despread. Very com-
n. ASCI cylindrical –
b-shaped, pore blued
h Melzer's reagent, 8-
ored, 5–6×50–55. ASCOS-
RES colourless, ±spindle-
aped, non-septate, biseri-
e, smooth, 1.5–2×10–15.
RAPHYSES lance-shaped,
ich longer than asci.
IRS yellowish, thin-
lled, septate, coarsely
d sparsely incrusted.
NIDIA ?

syscyphus nudipes.
erall fruit body form,
lour, habitat, hairs, micscopic features. FRUIT
DY 0.05–0.15, apothecial,
p-shaped, disc white-
eam, margin and outer
rface white with dense
nite hairs, short-stem-
ed. In large – very large ±
ooping groups. On dead
ems of Filipendula ulm-
ia and possibly other
ants. Spring-summer.
idespread. Very com-
on. ASCI cylindrical –
ub-shaped, pore blued
th Melzer's reagent, 8-

spored, 5–6×50–55. ASCOS-
PORES colourless, narrowly
spindle-shaped, non-
septate, biseriate, smooth,
1.5–2×10–12. PARAPHYSES
lance-shaped, much longer
than asci. HAIRS colourless,
thin-walled, septate, finely
incrusted, often with a few
large crystals at the tops.
CONIDIA ?

Dasyscyphus sulfureus.
Overall fruit body form,
colour, habitat, hairs, microscopic features. FRUIT
BODY 0.05–0.2, apothecial,
cup-shaped, disc greyish
white, smooth, margin and
outer surface with long
golden-yellow hairs, stem-
less. In small – large,
trooping groups. On dead
stems of herbaceous plants,
especially Urtica dioica and
members of family Umbel-
liferae. Summer – autumn.
Widespread. Very com-
mon. ASCI cylindrical –
club-shaped, pore blued
with Melzer's reagent, 8-
spored, 8–10×90–100.
ASCOSPORES colourless,
elongated cylindrical, often
slightly curved, obscurely
septate at maturity, biseriate, smooth, 2×25–35.
PARAPHYSES very narrowly
lance-shaped, longer than
asci. HAIRS yellowish, thin-
walled, septate, sparsely
incrusted, contents some-
times purple in KOH. CON-
IDIA ?

Dasyscyphus virgineus.
Overall fruit body form,
colour, habitat, hairs, microscopic features. FRUIT
BODY 0.05–0.1, apothecial,
cup-shaped, disc cream,
margin and outer surface
white with dense white
hairs, rather long-stemmed.
In small – large trooping

groups. On Rubus stems,
fallen beech mast and also
on other plant debris.
Spring-summer. Wide-
spread. Very common.
ASCI cylindrical – club-
shaped, pore blued with
Melzer's reagent, 8-spored,
5–6×50–55. ASCOSPORES
colourless, spindle-
shaped – club-shaped, non-
septate, uniseriate,
smooth, 1.5–2.5×6–10.
PARAPHYSES broadly lance-
shaped, much longer than
asci. HAIRS colourless, thin-
walled, septate, tips slightly
swollen, finely incrusted.
CONIDIA ?

Lachnellula occidentalis
(=hahniana). Overall fruit
body form, colour, habitat,
hairs, microscopic features.
FRUIT BODY 0.1–0.4, apothecial, erumpent, at first
cushion-shaped, then cup- to
saucer-shaped, disc orange,
concave – flat, margin and
outer surface white with
dense white hairs, very
short-stemmed. Usually in
small trooping groups. On
dead twigs of Larix species.
Spring – autumn. Wide-
spread. Very common. ASCI
cylindrical – club-shaped,
pore blued with Melzer's
reagent, 8-spored, 10–
12×150–155. ASCOSPORES
colourless, elongated-
ellipsoid, non-septate, uniseriate, smooth, 5–6×13–20.
PARAPHYSES (1) hair-like,
wavy, ±equal to asci, (2)
hair-like but swollen
between septa, like string
of sausages, ±equal to asci.
HAIRS colourless, thin-
walled, septate, finely
incrusted. CONIDIA ?

Lachnellula willkommii
causes Larch Canker Dis-
ease. Overall fruit body
form, colour, habitat, hairs,

microscopic features. FRUIT
BODY 0.2–0.4, apothecial,
erumpent, at first cushion-
like, then cup- to saucer-
shaped, disc pale orange-
yellowish, concave – flat,
margin and outer surface
white with dense white
hairs, very short-stemmed.
Usually in very small trooping groups. On bark of
Larix species, always associated with canker lesions.
Spring – autumn. Wide-
spread. Uncommon. ASCI
cylindrical – club-shaped,
pore blued with Melzer's
reagent, 8-spored, 10–
13×140–160. ASCOSPORES
colourless, elongated-
ellipsoid, non-septate, uniseriate, smooth, 7–9×17–25.
PARAPHYSES hair-like,
slightly longer than asci.
HAIRS colourless, thin-
walled, septate, very finely
swollen at tips, finely
incrusted. CONIDIA ?.

Lachnellula subtilissima.
Overall fruit body form,
colour, habitat, hairs, microscopic features. FRUIT
BODY 0.1–0.5, apothecial,
erumpent, at first cushion-
like, then cup- to saucer-
shaped, disc orange,
concave – flat, margin and
outer surface white with
dense white hairs, very
short-stemmed. Usually in
small – large trooping
groups. On dead twigs of
Pinus species. Autumn –
spring. Widespread. Com-
mon. ASCI cylindrical –
club-shaped, pore blued
with Melzer's reagent, 8-
spored, 4–5×45–50. ASCOS-
PORES colourless,
elongated-ellipsoid, non-
septate, irregularly biseriate, smooth, 2–2.5×6–11.
PARAPHYSES hair-like,
slightly longer than asci,
septate, sometimes bran-
ched at base. HAIRS colourless, rather thick-walled,
septate, sometimes very
finely swollen at tips, finely
incrusted. CONIDIA ?

211

Hyaloscypha hyalina.
Overall fruit body form and size, colour, habitat, microscopic features. FRUIT BODY 0.02–0.05, apothecial, cup-shaped, disc white, translucent, margin and outer surface white with variable white hairs arising from bulbous bases, ±stemless. Usually in large trooping groups. On dead wood of broad-leaved trees, especially oak. All year. Widespread. Extremely common. ASCI cylindrical – club-shaped, pore obscurely blued with Melzer's reagent, 8-spored, 5–6×30–35. ASCOSPORES colourless, ellipsoid, non-septate, biseriate, smooth, 2–3×6–10. PARAPHYSES hair-like, not longer than asci, sparsely septate, sometimes branched. HAIRS colourless, thin-walled, septate at base, pointed at tips, smooth. CONIDIA ?

Arachnopeziza eriobasis.
Overall fruit body form, microscopic features. FRUIT BODY 0.05–0.1, apothecial, cup-shaped, disc cream, margin and outer surface white with dense, white hairs, stemless, on individual mat of white hyphae. Usually in large trooping groups. On dead wood, dead herbaceous stems and dead oak leaves in damp places. Autumn. Widespread. Uncommon. ASCI cylindrical – club-shaped, pore blued with Melzer's reagent, 8-spored, 5–6×40–50. ASCOSPORES colourless, ellipsoid, 1-septate, biseriate, smooth, 1.5–2×6–10. PARAPHYSES hair-like, barely longer than asci, septate, branched. HAIRS colourless, thin-walled, wavy, septate, ±smooth. CONIDIA ?

SCLEROTINIACEAE

About 20 genera, closely related to Helotiaceae (p. 213) but generally biotrophic, some causing important plant diseases either in apothecial or conidial states, and having apothecia generally soft, long-stemmed and arising from sclerotia. Asci usually large and broadly club-shaped.

Sclerotinia sclerotiorum.
Habit, habitat, microscopic features. FRUIT BODY 0.3–1, apothecial, cup-shaped, disc yellowish brown, smooth, concave, margin indistinct or slightly darker, on slender, cylindrical, slightly wavy, yellowish brown stem, very finely downy. Solitary or in small groups. From black, cushion-like sclerotium close to or on rotting stems of many herbaceous plants, usually in damp conditions near soil level. Spring – summer. Widespread. Uncommon. ASCI cylindrical – club-shaped, pore blued with Melzer's reagent, 8-spored, 8–10×120–130. ASCOSPORES colourless, ellipsoid, non-septate, uniseriate, smooth, 4–6.5×9–13. PARAPHYSES cylindrical, shorter than asci, septate, slightly swollen at tip. CONIDIA of *Sclerotium* species.

Monilinia johnsonii
(=*fructigena*). Habit, habitat, microscopic features, several related species on other fallen fruits. FRUIT BODY 0.3–0.8, apothecial, cup- to saucer-shaped, disc pale brown, smooth, concave, margin indistinct or slightly darker, on slender,

cylindrical, slightly wavy, yellowish brown stem, very finely downy. Usually solitary. From fallen mummified fruit of hawthorn and other *Crataegus* species on or partly buried in soil. Spring. Widespread. Uncommon. ASCI cylindrical – club-shaped, pore blued with Melzer's reagent, 8-spored, 9–10×150–170. ASCOSPORES colourless, ±ellipsoid, non-septate, uniseriate, smooth, 5–6×10.5–14. PARAPHYSES cylindrical, shorter than asci, septate, slightly swollen at tip. CONIDIA colourless, subspherical, in chains, on brown sweet-smelling blotches on *Crataegus* leaves, 11×13. CONIDIA of *Monilia* sp.

Ciboria amentacea. Habit, habitat, microscopic features, several related species on other fallen catkins. FRUIT BODY 0.3–1, apothecial, cup-shaped, disc pale brown, smooth, concave, margin and outer surface slightly floury, on slender, cylindrical, slightly wavy, pale brown stem, very finely floury-downy. Usually solitary. On fallen catkins of alder, hazel and willow. Winter – spring. Widespread. Common. ASCI cylindrical – club-shaped, pore blued with Melzer's reagent, 8-spored, 6–9×100–135. ASCOSPORES colourless, ±ellipsoid, non-septate, uniseriate, smooth, 4.5–6×7.5–10.5. PARAPHYSES cylindrical, slightly longer than asci, non-septate, slightly swollen at tip. CONIDIA ?

Rutstroemia echinophila. Habit, habitat, microscopic features, several related species on similar substrates. FRUIT BODY 0.2–0.7, apothecial, cup-shaped, disc reddish brown, smooth, flat – convex, margin darker and finely

toothed, on slender, cylindrical, short pale brown stem. Solitary or in small groups. On inner surface fallen husks of sweet chestnut. Autumn. Widespread. Common. ASCI cylindrical club-shaped, pore blued with Melzer's reagent, 8-spored, 10–13×110–120. ASCOSPORES colourless, sausage-shaped, 3-septate when mature, uniseriate irregularly biseriate, smooth, 4.5–6×16–20. PARAPHYSES cylindrical, brownish contents, slightly longer than asci, non-septate, slightly swollen at tip. CONIDIA of *Myriconium* species.

Poculum firmum
(=*Rutstroemia firma*). Habit, habitat, microscopic features. FRUIT BODY 0.5–1, apothecial, cup-shaped, disc reddish brown, smooth, flat – convex, margin darker and sometimes upturned, on slender, cylindrical, short pale brown stem, on blackened surfaces. Solitary or in small groups. On rotten twigs and branches of oak. Autumn. Widespread. Common. ASCI cylindrical club-shaped, pore blued with Melzer's reagent, 8-spored, 9–12×125–150. ASCOSPORES colourless, elongated-ellipsoid, 3–5-septate when mature, uniseriate, smooth, 4–6.5×14–19. PARAPHYSES cylindrical barely longer than asci, non-septate, slightly swollen at tip. CONIDIA ?

HELOTIACEAE

A huge family of over 60 genera, characterised by microscopic features of apothecium structure but with some more obvious features also. Although many superficially resemble the Hyaloscyphaceae in many respects, they differ in their smooth, not hairy, outer surface. Many have distinct stems and most have predominantly light-coloured apothecia.

...tia lubrica **Jelly Babies**. ...rall fruit body form and ...ur, habit, habitat, mic-...opic features, rather ...lar to *Geoglossum* and ...tives (p. 209). FRUIT ...y apothecial with dis-...t CAP 1–1.5, convex – ...onate, smooth, rather ...y-sticky, margin irregu-...y lobed, overhanging. ...4 3–6, ±equal, rather ...t, round – flattened in ...s-section, sometimes ...oved and pitted, finely ...ular. Usually in ...ll±tufted groups. On ... among mosses or plant ...ris, in wet places, espe-...y in woods under ...cken. Summer – ...umn. Widespread. ...ommon. ASCI ...ndrical – club-shaped, ...e not blued with Mel-...s reagent, 8-spored, 8–...130–150. ASCOSPORES ...urless, spindle-shaped, ...n slightly curved, 5–7-...ate when mature, unis-...te, smooth, 5–6×20–25. ...APHYSES hair-like, ...ely longer than asci, ...ate, slightly swollen at ...branched, smooth. ...IDIA ?

...brophila violacea. ...rall fruit body form and ...ur, habitat. FRUIT BODY ...0.4, apothecial, at first ...nion-shaped, then con-...with flattened upper ...ace which curls back at ...gin, smooth, soft, ±gel-...ous, tapering below to ...rt stem, stout, tapering ...wards. Solitary or ...e usually in small, ...ping groups. On ...aying leaves in wet, ...shy places. Autumn. ...lespread. Uncommon. ...t cylindrical – club-...ped, pore blued with ...zer's reagent, 8-spored,

7–8×60–80. ASCOSPORES colourless, ellipsoid, non-septate, uniseriate, smooth, 3–4×6–11. PARAPHYSES cylindrical, barely longer than asci, non-septate, slightly swollen at tip, smooth. CONIDIA ?

Neobulgaria pura. Overall fruit body from, habitat, rather similar to some basidiomycete jelly fungi (p. 189) but microscopic features very different. FRUIT BODY 1–2, apothecial, cushion-shaped – top-shaped, but often contorted through being in tight groups, disc whitish with pale violet-pinkish tints, at first slightly concave, then flat, smooth, elastic-gelatinous, margin indistinct. In densely packed tufts, collectively ±brain-like. On fallen branches and trunks, especially of beech. Autumn. Widespread. Uncommon. ASCI cylindrical – club-shaped, pore±blued with Melzer's reagent, 8-spored, 8×70–95. ASCOSPORES colourless, ellipsoid, non-septate, uniseriate, smooth, 3–4×6–9. PARAPHYSES cylindrical – hair-like, barely longer than asci, non-septate, slightly swollen towards tip, smooth. CONIDIA ?

Ascocoryne sarcoides. Overall fruit body form and colour, texture, *A. cylichnium* on same substrates is superficially similar but has larger spores. FRUIT BODY 0.5–1, apothecial, at first spherical, then top-like or cup-shaped, disc reddish purple, concave – flat, usually rather wavy, margin usually darker, outer sur-

face smooth – finely granular. Usually densely tufted. On fallen branches and trunks, especially of beech. Autumn – winter. Widespread. Very common. ASCI cylindrical – club-shaped, pore blued with Melzer's reagent, 8-spored, 8–10×120–160. ASCOSPORES colourless, ellipsoid, 1–3-septate when mature, uni-biseriate, smooth, 3–5×10–19. PARAPHYSES cylindrical, barely longer than asci, sparsely septate, sometimes slightly swollen towards tip, branched, smooth. CONIDIA of *Coryne dubia* in similarly coloured pycnidia in same habitat.

Bulgaria inquinans **Black Bulgar**. Overall fruit body form and colour, texture, often confused with *Exidia plana* (p. 190) but microscopic features very different. FRUIT BODY 1–4, apothecial, at first top-like, then cup-shaped, disc black, ±concave, smooth, shiny when wet, margin rather sharp, outer surface dark brown, finely granular, ±stemless. Solitary or ±densely tufted. On fallen branches and trunks of broad-leaved trees, especially of oak, and often on newly cut branches. Autumn – winter. Widespread. Common. ASCI cylindrical – club-shaped, pore blued with Melzer's reagent, 8-spored, 8–9×100–175. ASCOSPORES (1) upper 4 in ascus dark brown, kidney-shaped, non-septate, uniseriate, smooth, 6–7×11–14, (2) lower 4, colourless, kidney-shaped, non-septate, uniseriate, smooth, 2–4×5–7. PARAPHYSES hair-like, barely longer than asci, non-septate, slightly swollen, darker and branched towards tips, smooth. CONIDIA ?

Bisporella citrina. Overall fruit body form and colour, several similarly coloured small 'Discomycetes' also occur in similar habitats. FRUIT BODY 0.1–0.3, apothecial, ±saucer-shaped, disc orange-yellow, ±concave, smooth, margin often darker, outer surface paler, smooth, ±stemless. In large, trooping – ±tufted groups. On old wood and bark of broad-leaved trees, especially elm. All year. Widespread. Very common. ASCI cylindrical – club-shaped, pore barely blued with Melzer's reagent, 8-spored, 8–9×100–135. ASCOSPORES colourless, ellipsoid, usually 1-septate when mature, irregularly biseriate-uniseriate, smooth, 3–5×9–14. PARAPHYSES hair-like, barely longer than asci, non-septate, markedly swollen towards tips, smooth. CONIDIA ?

Bisporella sulfurina. Habitat, overall fruit body form and colour. FRUIT BODY 0.05–0.15, apothecial, ±irregularly saucer-shaped, disc sulphur-yellow, flat, smooth, margin slightly projecting paler, outer surface also paler, finely downy, ±stemless. Usually in small, trooping – ±tufted groups. On old wood, always with old fruit bodies of 'Pyrenomycetes'. All year. Widespread. Very common. ASCI cylindrical – club-shaped, pore not blued with Melzer's reagent, 8-spored, 4×60–90. ASCOSPORES colourless, ellipsoid – spindle-shaped, 1-septate, biseriate, smooth, 2×9–10. PARAPHYSES cylindrical, barely longer than asci, non septate, containing many yellow droplets, smooth. CONIDIA ?

213

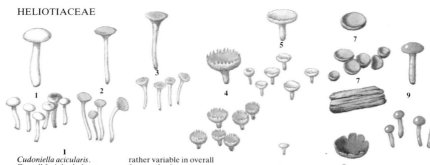

1
Cudoniella acicularis.
Overall fruit body form, colour, habitat, microscopic features. FRUIT BODY 0.1–0.4, apothecial, at first top-like, then with cushion-like cap, disc at first whitish, then greyish brown, convex, smooth, margin ± turned back, tapering below to slender, cylindrical, similarly coloured stem (0.2–1). Usually in large trooping groups. On old rotting wood of broad-leaved trees, especially on old, hard stumps of oak. Autumn – winter. Widespread. Very common. ASCI cylindrical – club-shaped, pore not blued with Melzer's reagent, 8-spored, 10–13×110–120. ASCOSPORES colourless, irregularly spindle-shaped, 1–3-septate when mature, biseriate, smooth, 4–5×15–22. PARAPHYSES hair-like, barely longer than asci, septate, gradually thickening towards apex, smooth. CONIDIA ?

2
Hymenoscyphus fructigenus. Fruit body form, overall fruit body form, microscopic features. FRUIT BODY 0.1–0.3, apothecial, cup- to saucer-shaped, disc cream-yellow, flat, margin often incurved, tapering sharply below to slender, ± equal, cylindrical, cream stem (<0.5). In small, ± trooping groups. On fallen acorns, beech mast and other nuts. Summer – autumn. Widespread. Very common. ASCI cylindrical – club-shaped, pore blued with Melzer's reagent, 8×150–200. ASCOSPORES colourless, irregularly spindle-shaped, 0–1-septate, biseriate, smooth, 3–4×13–21. PARAPHYSES cylindrical, barely longer than asci, septate, sometimes branched, smooth. CONIDIA ?

3
Hymenoscyphus scutula. Habitat, overall fruit body form, microscopic features,

rather variable in overall form and colour. FRUIT BODY 0.1–0.4, apothecial, cup- to saucer-shaped, disc cream-yellow, drying darker, flat, margin often sharp and paler, outer surface whitish and ± finely fibrous, tapering sharply below to slender, ± equal, cylindrical, white stem (<0.7). In small ± trooping groups. On dead stems of herbaceous plants, especially in family Compositae. Summer – autumn. Widespread. Very common. ASCI cylindrical – club-shaped, pore blued with Melzer's reagent, 8-spored, 8–11×100–120. ASCOSPORES colourless, cylindrical – club-shaped, appearing slightly hooked at apex and pointed below, usually with colourless bristle at one or both ends, 0–1-septate, biseriate, smooth, 3.5–5×18–27. PARAPHYSES cylindrical, not longer than asci, septate, not swollen at tips, smooth. CONIDIA ?

4
Crocicreas coronatum (= *Cyathicula coronata*). Fruit body form, habitat, microscopic features. FRUIT BODY 0.1–0.3, apothecial, cup- to saucer-shaped, disc white-cream, concave, smooth, margin with long, narrow, distant, pointed teeth, smooth, outer surface yellowish, smooth, tapering sharply below to slender, ± equal, cylindrical, yellowish stem (<0.5). In small, ± trooping groups. On dead stems of herbaceous plants, also less commonly on wood. Summer – autumn. Widespread. Common. ASCI cylindrical – club-shaped, pore not blued with Melzer's reagent, 8-spored, 8–9×80–110. ASCOSPORES colourless, cylindrical – spindle-shaped, non-septate, biseriate, smooth, 3–4.5×15–20. PARAPHYSES hair-like, barely longer than asci, septate, not swollen at tips, smooth. CONIDIA?

5
Crocicreas cyathoideum (= *Cyathicula cyathoidea*). Fruit body form, habitat, microscopic features. FRUIT BODY 0.05–0.2, apothecial, cup- to saucer-shaped, goblet-shaped when young, disc whitish cream, concave, smooth, margin ± inrolled, barely toothed, outer surface whitish cream, smooth, tapering sharply below to slender, ± equal cylindrical, whitish-cream stem (<0.15). In small, ± trooping groups. On dead stems of herbaceous plants. Spring. Widespread. Extremely common. ASCI cylindrical – club-shaped, pore blued with Melzer's reagent, 8-spored, 4–5×40–50. ASCOSPORES colourless, spindle-shaped, non-septate, biseriate, smooth, 1.5–2.5×6–12. PARAPHYSES hair-like, barely longer than asci, septate, not swollen at tips, smooth. CONIDIA ?

6
Crocicreas (= *Pezizella*) *amenti.* Habitat, microscopic features. FRUIT BODY 0.03–0.05, apothecial, cup- to saucer-shaped, disc greyish white, at first concave, then flat, smooth, margin indistinct, outer surface white, very finely downy, tapering sharply below to slender, ± equal, cylindrical, short whitish stem. In small, ± trooping or tufted groups. On fallen female willow catkins. Winter – spring. Widespread. Common. ASCI cylindrical, pore blued with Melzer's reagent, 8-spored, 5–6×50–55. ASCOSPORES colourless, elongated-pear-shaped and curved or comma-like, non-septate, uniseriate – irregularly biseriate, smooth, 3–4×6–12.

PARAPHYSES cylindrical, rather longer than asci, non-septate, barely sw towards tips, smooth. ꟾDIA ?

7
Chlorociboria (= *Chlor splenium*) *aeruginascens*. Colour, habitat, microscopic features, effects wood are seen more co monly than fruit bodies FRUIT BODY 0.2–0.5, ap ecial, cup- to saucer-sha disc blue-green, somet yellowish-spotted, ± fla smooth, margin often rather sharp, outer sur blue-green, very finely downy, tapering sharp below to slender, ± equ cylindrical, short blue-green stem. In small, ± trooping or tufted grou On old rotting wood of broad-leaved trees, esp ially oak, wood stained blue green. Autumn. V spread. Uncommon, although wood staining common. ASCI cylindri club-shaped, pore blue with Melzer's reagent, spored, 5×60–70. ASCO PORES colourless, spind shaped, non-septate, b ate, smooth, 1.5–2×6– PARAPHYSES cylindrical longer than asci, septat branched, barely swolle towards tips, smooth. ꟾDIA of *Dothiorina tulas*

8
Encoelia furfuracea. Ha tat, microscopic feature FRUIT BODY 0.05–0.15, apothecial, erumpent, ± shaped, disc reddish brown, black when dry deeply concave, smooth margin incurved, often gularly split, outer surf paler and coarsely mea stemless. In small – lar ± tufted groups. On dea

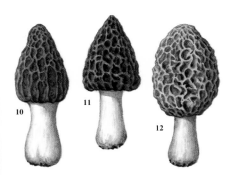

ll standing stems of hazel
nd occasionally on dead
der. Winter – spring.
idespread. Uncommon.
sci club-shaped, pore
ued with Melzer's
agent, 8-spored, 6–7×90
20. ASCOSPORES colour-
ss, cylindrical with roun-
d ends – ±sausage-
aped, non-septate, biseri-
e, smooth, 2–2.5×6–11.
RAPHYSES cylindrical –
ub-shaped, longer than
ci, non-septate, swollen
wards tips, smooth. CON-
IA ?

9

brissea truncorum. Habi-
t, overall fruit body form
d colour, microscopic
atures. FRUIT BODY apoth-
ial, divided into CAP 0.3–
5, disc yellow-orange,
nvex, margin curved
wnwards, STEM<1.5
ual, slender, cylindrical,
ite, downy-velvety with
ackish hairs. In small,
ooping groups. On twigs
d other woody debris in
ry wet places, or sub-
erged. Spring. Wide-
read. Uncommon. ASCI
lindrical, pore liued with
elzer's reagent, 8-spored,
9×200–300. ASCOSPORES
lourless, hair-like, multi-
ptate when mature, lying
le by side, smooth, 1.5×
0–200. PARAPHYSES hair-
ke, shorter than asci, sep-
te, branched and swollen
wards tips, smooth.
NIDIA ?

EZIZALES

ruit body usually large,
own, red or yellowish,
pically cup-shaped but
metimes long-stemmed
ith saddle-like or hon-
ycombed head. Asci
ually large and opercu-
te, opening by a hinged
d, ascospores large,
herical – ellipsoid, non-
ptate, smooth or charac-
ristically ornamented
ith warts or ridges. Most
rrestrial and saprot-
phic. Some edible and
uch sought after. A large
rder divided into twelve
milies, of which eight are
cluded here, on the basis
f overall fruit body form
d ascus and ascospore
atures.

MORCHELLACEAE

ruit body usually divided
to distinct cap and stem,
scospores smooth but with
aracteristic granules at
ach end. Includes the
orels, Morchella, with
everal barely distinguish-
ble species of uncertain
mits.

10

Morchella elata. Habitat,
overall fruit body form,
very similar to some specimens of M. conica but
sharply conical with±paral-
lel longitudinal ribs and
head tapers more gradually
into stem. (It is now generally thought that all eight or
more European Morchella
species are probably vari-
ants of only one or two.
Microscopically all are virtually identical and macroscopically almost all very
variable.) FRUIT BODY 5–15
(Height), apothecial, upper
half – two-thirds forming±
conical head, ridged and
pitted, honeycomb-like,
yellowish brown, ridges
dark grey-black, tapering
gradually below with nar-
row groove to white-
creamy stem, equal, often
rather furrowed, coarsely
granular, brittle. Solitary
or in small, trooping groups.
On soil in coniferous woods.
Spring. Predominantly northern. Rare. Edible. ASCI
cylindrical, 8-spored, 20×
250–300. ASCOSPORES col-
ourless, broadly ellipsoid,
non-septate, uniseriate,
smooth with small granules
at both ends, 11–15×18–25.
PARAPHYSES cylindrical,
septate, branched, slightly
swollen towards tips,
smooth. CONIDIA of Const-
antinella sp.

11

Morchella esculenta Com-
mon Morel. Habitat, over-
all fruit body form, see M.
elata. FRUIT BODY 5–20,
(height), apothecial, upper
half – two-thirds forming
irregularly subspherical
head, ridged and pitted,
honeycomb-like, at first
greyish then yellowish
brown, ridges generally
darker, tapering rather
sharply below to white-
cream stem, equal, taper-
ing upwards or±irregularly
bulbous, often rather furrowed, finely granular, brit-

tle. Usually solitary. On
soil with broad-leaved trees
or in grassland, path sides
and other grassy places.
Spring. Widespread. Rare.
Edible. ASCI cylindrical, 8-
spored, 20×250–330.
ASCOSPORES colourless,
broadly ellipsoid, non-
septate, uniseriate, smooth
with small granules at both
ends, 11–14×16–23. PARA-
PHYSES cylindrical, septate,
branched, slightly swollen
towards tips, smooth. CON-
IDIA of Constantinella sp.

12

Morchella conica. Overall
fruit body form, habitat,
see M. elata. FRUIT BODY
5–15, (height), apothecial,
upper half – two-thirds
forming irregularly conical
head, ridged and pitted,
honeycomb-like, at first
greyish then olive-brown,
ridges generally darker,
tapering rather sharply
below to white-creamy
stem, equal, tapering
upwards or±irregularly
bulbous, often rather
wrinkled-furrowed, finely
granular, brittle. Solitary or
in small, trooping groups.
On soil with broad-leaved
or coniferous trees. Spring.
Widespread. Rare. Edible.
ASCI cylindrical, 8-spored,
20–25×300–350. ASCOS-
PORES colourless, broadly
ellipsoid, non-septate, uniseriate, smooth with small
granules at both ends, 11–
14×18–24. PARAPHYSES
cylindrical, septate, branched, slightly swollen
towards tips, smooth. CON-
IDIA ?

13

Mitrophora semilibera.
Overall fruit body form,
differs from Morchella species in cap quite free from
stem, larger forms are
usually called Mitrophora
gigas. FRUIT BODY apothe-
cial, divided into, CAP 2.5–
5.0,±conical, ridged and
pitted, honeycomb-like

above, yellowish brown,
ridges darker, STEM 10–20,
cylindrical or tapering
slightly upwards, white-
cream, rather irregular,
wavy, finely grooved,
granular. Solitary or in
small, trooping groups. On
soil in wet places, woods,
near rivers, damp
meadows. Spring. Wide-
spread. Uncommon. Edi-
ble. ASCI cylindrical, 8-
spored, 18–25×300–450.
ASCOSPORES colourless,
broadly ellipsoid, non-
septate, uniseriate, smooth
but often with small gra-
nules at both ends, 14–
18×22–30. PARAPHYSES
cylindrical, septate, branched, swollen towards tips,
smooth. CONIDIA ?.

14

Verpa conica. Overall fruit
body form, attachment of
cap to stem, rather variable
and may be several forms
of one or few species, those
with more cylindrical head,
fitting close to stalk usually
called V. digitaliformis
FRUIT BODY apothecial,
divided into, CAP 1.5–
4,±bell-shaped, pendu-
lous, irregularly wrinkled-
furrowed above,±smooth,
ochre below, STEM 3–12,
cylindrical, white-cream,
slightly irregular, finely
granular in darker concentric bands. Solitary or in
small, trooping groups. On
soil in wet places, among
grass, path sides, hedgerows, often with hawthorn.
Spring. Widespread. Rare
but locally common in
some years. Edible. ASCI
cylindrical, 8-spored, 18–
23×350–350. ASCOSPORES
colourless, broadly ellipsoid, non-septate, unisei-
ate, smooth but often with
small granules at both ends,
12–14×20–24. PARAPHYSES
cylindrical, septate, branched, swollen towards tips,
smooth. CONIDIA ?

MORCHELLACEAE

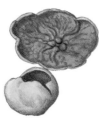

Disciotis venosa. Overall fruit body form, rather similar to some *Peziza* species but smell and microscopic features distinct. FRUIT BODY 5–15, apothecial, irregularly dish-shaped, disc markedly veined – wrinkled, brittle pale – brown, margin distinct, paler, wavy, often slightly inrolled, outer surface smooth or finely granular – wrinkled, outer surface smooth or finely granular – wrinkled towards base, tapering into short stout stem, often ± buried. SMELL chlorine. Solitary or in small – large, trooping or tufted groups. On soil in damp shady places, often with mosses. Spring. Widespread. Uncommon. Edible. ASCI cylindrical, 8-spored, 18–23×300–350. ASCOSPORES colourless, broadly ellipsoid, non-septate, uniseriate, smooth but often with small granules at both ends, 12–15×19–25. PARAPHYSES cylindrical, septate, branched, swollen and with darker contents towards tips, smooth. CONIDIA ?

Gyromitra esculenta **False Morel**. Overall fruit body form, microscopic features, a larger form with warty spores is usually called *G. gigas* but seems to be extinct in Britain. FRUIT BODY 5–15, apothecial, very irregularly subspherical head, lobed and convoluted, brain-like, yellowish – reddish brown, stem often barely visible beneath head, 1–4, ± equal, very stout, white, deeply furrowed-grooved, finely granular. Solitary or in small

trooping – tufted groups. On soil with coniferous trees on acid, usually sandy sites. Spring. Widespread, predominantly northern. Uncommon. Poisonous. ASCI cylindrical, 8-spored, 16–20×325–350. ASCOSPORES colourless, broadly ellipsoid, non-septate, uniseriate, smooth, 9–12×18–22. PARAPHYSES cylindrical, septate, branched, slightly swollen towards tips, smooth. CONIDIA ?

HELVELLACEAE

Some species are superficially similar to the Morchellaceae, having stalked fruit bodies with variously contorted caps, but the ascospores have no granules and in some genera are roughened. There are six genera but some are arguably not separable.

Helvella crispa. Overall fruit body form, microscopic features, colour, there are several other, rather similar much rarer *Helvella* species, while another similar but more robust fungus in northern pine woods is *Gyromitra infula.* FRUIT BODY apothecial, divided into, CAP 3–6, 2–3-lobed, saddle-like, white-ochre, smooth – wrinkled, wavy, margin not fused with stem, STEM 6–12, stout, tapering upwards, smooth, white-creamy, deeply grooved-furrowed. Solitary or in small trooping – tufted groups. On soil in broad-leaved or mixed woods. Summer – autumn. Widespread. Common. Inedible. ASCI cylindrical, 8-spored, 14–18×250–300. ASCOSPORES colourless, broadly ellipsoid, non-septate, uniseriate, smooth, 10–13×18–20. PARAPHYSES cylindrical, septate, branched, slightly swollen towards tips, smooth. CONIDIA ?

HELVELLACEAE

Helvella lacunosa. Overall fruit body form, colour, microscopic features. FRUIT BODY apothecial, divided into, CAP 3–5, 2-several-lobed, irregularly convoluted and crumpled, greyish black, smooth – wrinkled, wavy, margin fused with stem, STEM 3–10, stout, tapering upwards, smooth, white-creamy, deeply grooved-furrowed, hollow chambered within. Solitary or in small trooping – tufted groups. On soil in broad-leaved, coniferous or mixed woods, often on burnt ground. Autumn. Widespread. Uncommon. Inedible. ASCI cylindrical, 8-spored, 14–16×250–350. ASCOSPORES colourless, broadly ellipsoid, non-septate, uniseriate, smooth, 11–13×19–22. PARAPHYSES cylindrical – club-shaped, septate, slightly swollen towards tips, smooth. CONIDIA ?

Helvella (= *Leptopodia*) *stevensii.* Overall fruit body form, colour, microscopic features, very similar to *H. ephippium* but colour differs. FRUIT BODY apothecial, divided into, CAP 2–4, ± cup-shaped, convoluted, wavy, greyish brown, smooth, margin often inrolled, not fused with stem, underside greyish brown, coarsely velvety, STEM 4–5, rather slender, ± equal, often slightly flattened, finely downy. Solitary or in small trooping – tufted groups. On soil in broad-leaved woods. Autumn. Widespread. Rare. Inedible. ASCI cylindrical, 8-spored, 14–18×225–280. ASCOSPORES colourless, broadly

ellipsoid, non-septate, uniseriate, smooth, 12–13× 19. PARAPHYSES cylindric septate, club-shaped towards tips, smooth. CONIDIA ?

Helvella (= *Leptopodia*) *elastica.* Overall fruit body form, colour, microscopic features, rather similar to *H. stevensii* but colour usually differs and cap underside different. FRUIT BODY apothecial, divided into, CAP 2–4, irregularly saddle-like, convoluted, wavy, yellowish brown, smooth, margin barely inrolled, not fused with stem, underside ochre, smooth, STEM 7–10, rather slender, ± equal, often rather wavy, smooth or finely downy at apex. Usually in small trooping groups. On soil in woods. Summer – autumn. Widespread. Common. Inedible ASCI cylindrical, 8-spored 15–20×300–330. ASCOSPORES colourless, broadly ellipsoid, non-septate, uniseriate, smooth, 11–13×19–22. PARAPHYSES cylindrical septate, club-shaped towards tips, smooth. CONIDIA ?

Helvella (= *Leptopodia*) *ephippium.* Overall fruit body form, colour, microscopic features, very similar to *H. stevensii* but colour usually differs. FRUIT BODY apothecial, divided into, CAP 2–4, irregularly saddle-like, convoluted, wavy, greyish brown – yellowish smooth, margin often inrolled

, not tused with stem, derside greyish brown, rsely velvety, STEM 4–5, her slender, ±equal, en slightly flattened, ely downy. Solitary or in all trooping – tufted ups. On soil in broad-ved woods. Autumn. despread. Uncommon. dible. ASCI cylindrical, pored, 14–18×225–280. OSPORES colourless, adly ellipsoid, non-sep-e, uniseriate, smooth, 11 ×19–21. PARAPHYSES indrical, septate, club-ped towards tips, ooth. CONIDIA ?

lvella (=Macroscyphus) cropus. Overall fruit dy form, surface fea-es, *H. villosa* and *H. uliformis* are very simi-but with broader ooth spores and only one ge oil drop. FRUIT BODY thecial, divided into, • 1.5–4,±persistently -shaped, sometimes htly wavy, greyish wn, smooth, margin en slightly inrolled, derside paler greyish wn, densely felty-hairy, M 2–5, fairly slender, ering upwards, cylin-cal, felty-hairy. Solitary n small trooping groups. soil in broad-leaved or commonly coniferous ods. Summer – autumn. despread. Uncommon. dible. ASCI cylindrical, pored, 15–20×250–350. OSPORES colourless, adly ellipsoid – spindle-ped, non-septate, unis-ate, very finely warty – mooth, 1–3 oil drops, -12×20–30. PARAPHYSES indrical, non-septate, b-shaped towards tips, ooth. CONIDIA ?

Helvella (=*Paxina*) *acetabulum*. Overall fruit body form, season, *H. costifera* is a similar but rare autumn species. FRUIT BODY 2–8, apothecial, cup- to bowl-shaped, often becoming rather wavy, disc greyish-reddish brown, concave, smooth, underside pale, granular, becoming ribbed below and tapering into short, stout, whitish, markedly ribbed and grooved stem. Solitary or in small trooping groups. On soil in broad-leaved or coniferous woods or on sandy soils on heaths. Spring. Widespread. Uncommon. Inedible. ASCI cylindrical, 8-spored, 15–20×200–400. ASCOSPORES colourless, broadly ellipsoid, non-septate, uniseriate, smooth, 12–14×18–22. PARAPHYSES cylindrical, septate, branched, becoming club-shaped towards tips, smooth. CONIDIA ?

Rhizina undulata. Habitat, fruit body form, microscopic features. FRUIT BODY 2–10, (but sometimes fusing into large irregular masses), apothecial, flat – ±cushion-shaped, irregularly wavy, disc dark brown – black, wavy, smooth, margin whitish, underside ochreous, with branched root-like growths, stemless. In small – large, usually fused groups. On plant debris on old fire sites in coniferous woods, causing Group Dying disease of conifers. Summer – autumn. Widespread. Uncommon. Inedible. ASCI cylindrical, 8-spored, 15–20×300–400. ASCOSPORES colourless, spindle-shaped, non-septate, ±uniseriate, finely warty with marked appendage at each end, 8–11×22–40 (excluding appendages). PARAPHYSES cylindrical, septate, becoming club-shaped towards tips, smooth but with brownnish incrustation at tip. CONIDIA ?

PEZIZACEAE

11 mostly terrestrial genera with cup-shaped or flattened apothecia, stemless or very short-stemmed, usually >1, typically brown or black and rarely with red or orange colours, outer surface smooth, asci and ascospores variable. Includes most of the common large brown cup fungi.

Plicaria leiocarpa. Habitat, overall fruit body form and colour, microscopic features, *P. anthracina* in the same habitat is similar but with markedly spiny spores. FRUIT BODY 3–6, apothecial, at first cup-shaped, then irregularly flattened, disc dark brown – black, concave – convex, margin and underside finely granular, exuding yellow juice when cut. In trooping-fused groups. On soil on old fire sites, especially on sandy heaths. Autumn – spring. Widespread. Uncommon. Inedible. ASCI cylindrical, not blued with Melzer's reagent, 8-spored, 8–10×180–200. ASCOSPORES colourless – pale brown, spherical, uniseriate, smooth, 8–9. PARAPHYSES cylindrical, septate, becoming club-shaped towards tips, smooth. CONIDIA ?

Peziza badia. Overall fruit body form, colour, microscopic features. FRUIT BODY 3–8, apothecial, irregularly cup-shaped, disc dark reddish brown, concave, outer surface reddish brown, granular-mealy, stemless. Usually in small, trooping – fused groups. On soil in woods, often on light, sandy sites, often at pathsides. Autumn. Widespread. Very common. Inedible. ASCI cylindrical, blued at tip with Melzer's reagent, 8-spored, 12–15×300–330. ASCOSPORES colourless, ellipsoid, non-septate, uniseriate, with irregular ridges – general net patterning, 9–12×17–20. PARAPHYSES cylindrical, septate, barely swollen at tips. CONIDIA ?

Peziza cerea. Habitat, overall fruit body form, colour, microscopic features. FRUIT BODY 3–5, apothecial, irregularly cup-shaped, disc pale ochre – yellowish brown, concave, outer surface white, finely granular, stemless. Usually in small, trooping – fused groups. On woody plant debris, old sacking, often on soil and mortar between bricks or stones in cellars. All year. Widespread. Common. Inedible. ASCI cylindrical, blued at tip with Melzer's reagent, 8-spored, 12–16× 300–350. ASCOSPORES colourless, ellipsoid, non-septate, uniseriate, smooth, 8 –10×14–17. PARAPHYSES cylindrical, septate, barely swollen at tips. CONIDIA of *Oedocephalum* sp.

Peziza echinospora. Habitat, overall fruit body form, colour, microscopic features. FRUIT BODY 3–8, apothecial, cup-shaped, disc dark brown, concave, outer surface pale brown – whitish, markedly granular, stemless. Solitary or in small groups. On charcoal or on soil on old fire sites. Summer – autumn. Widespread. Common. Inedible. ASCI cylindrical, blued at tip with Melzer's reagent, 8-spored, 12–14×250–300. ASCOSPORES colourless, elongated-ellipsoid, non-septate, uniseriate, finely warty, 7–9.5×14–18. PARAPHYSES cylindrical, septate, barely swollen at tips. CONIDIA of *Oedocephalum elegans*.

217

Peziza micropus. Habitat, overall fruit body form, colour, microscopic features, sometimes confused with *P. varia* but flesh not layered. FRUIT BODY 2–5, apothecial, very irregularly cup- to saucer-shaped, disc ochreous – pale fawn, concave, margin markedly split and toothed, outer surface pale brown – whitish, finely granular-mealy, short-stemmed. Solitary or in small±fused groups. On bark of fallen logs, especially on elms and increasingly common in Britain following elm disease. Summer – autumn. Widespread. Common. Inedible. ASCI cylindrical, blued at tip with Melzer's reagent, 8-spored, 12–14×230–250. ASCOSPORES colourless, ellipsoid, non-septate, uniseriate, smooth, 9–11×15–19. PARAPHYSES cylindrical, branched, septate, barely swollen at tips. CONIDIA of *Oedocephalum*.

Peziza repanda. Habitat, overall fruit body form, colour, microscopic features, sometimes confused with *P. varia* but colour and paraphyses differ. FRUIT BODY 3–12, apothecial, cup-shaped, becoming markedly irregular on aging, disc ochreous brown, concave – ±flattened, margin often±split and toothed, outer surface whitish buff, finely granular-mealy, stemless. Solitary or in small±tufted groups. On soil among leaves or other plant debris in woods, also in large form on sawdust. Spring – summer. Widespread. Common. Inedible. ASCI cylindrical, blued at tip with Melzer's reagent, 8-spored, 11–13×250–300. ASCOSPORES colourless, ellipsoid, non-septate, uniseriate, smooth, 9–10×15–16. PARAPHYSES cylindrical, barely swollen at tips. CONIDIA of *Oedocephalum*.

Peziza varia. Overall fruit body form, colour, flesh, microscopic features, similar to several other *Peziza* species but combination of colour, flesh layers and paraphyses is diagnostic. FRUIT BODY 2–5, apothecial, cup-shaped, becoming slightly irregular on aging, disc greyish brown, concave, outer surface whitish buff, finely granular-mealy, stemless, flesh markedly layered when cut. Usually in small trooping – tufted groups. On rotten wood and in soil associated with rotting wood. Spring – autumn. Widespread. Common. Inedible. ASCI cylindrical, blued at tip with Melzer's reagent, 8-spored, 12–14×250–280. ASCOSPORES colourless, ellipsoid, non-septate, uniseriate, smooth, 9–11×14–16. PARAPHYSES cylindrical, septate, markedly constricted at septa to give chain-like appearance, not swollen at tips. CONIDIA ?

Otidea alutacea. Overall fruit body form, colour, microscopic features, oft confused with other *Otia* species (about seven in B tain) which can only reli ably be distinguised by c our differences when fre FRUIT BODY 3–6×2–4, apothecial,±irregularly cup-shaped, often elon gated to one side, split o opposite side, disc greyis buff, smooth, deeply con cave, outer surface pale buff, finely granular-mealy,±stemless. FLESH yellowish. Solitary or in small trooping – tufted groups. On soil in woods Autumn. Widespread. Uncommon. Inedible. AS cylindrical, not blued at with Melzer's reagent, 8-spored, 10–15×250–300. ASCOSPORES colourless, ellipsoid, non-septate, u eriate, smooth, 6–7×12– PARAPHYSES narrowly cy drical, branched, septate markedly curved at tips. CONIDIA ?

Peziza praetervisa. Habitat, overall fruit body form, colour, microscopic features, sometimes confused with *P. violacea* in same habitat which has smooth spores and paraphyses curved at the tips. FRUIT BODY 1–4, apothecial, at first cup-shaped, then irregularly± flattened, disc violet – brownish violet, concave – ±flattened, outer surface pale violet, finely granular-mealy, stemless. Solitary or in small±tufted groups. On soil or on burnt wood on old fire sites. Summer – autumn. Widespread. Uncommon. Inedible. ASCI cylindrical, blued at tip with Melzer's reagent, 8-spored, 8–10×220–250. ASCOSPORES colourless, ellipsoid, non-septate, uniseriate, finely warty, 6–8× 11–13. PARAPHYSES±club-shaped, branched, septate, swollen at tips. CONIDIA of *Oedocephalum*.

Peziza succosa. Overall fruit body form, colour, juice, microscopic features. FRUIT BODY 2–5, apothecial, cup-shaped, becoming slightly irregular on aging, disc greyish – olive-brown, concave, outer surface paler, greyish, often yellowish towards margin, finely granular-mealy, stemless, exuding yellow juice when cut. Solitary or in small trooping – tufted groups. On soil in woods. Summer. Widespread. Common. Inedible. ASCI cylindrical, blued at tip with Melzer's reagent, 8-spored, 15–18×330–350. ASCOSPORES colourless, ellipsoid, non-septate, uniseriate, coarsely warty – ribbed, 9–12×17–22. PARA-PHYSES cylindrical, sometimes branched, septate, barely swollen at tips. CONIDIA ?

Peziza vesiculosa. Habitat, overall fruit body form, microscopic features. FRUIT BODY 4–8, apothecial, persistently cup- to bowl-shaped, disc yellowish brown, concave but often wrinkled, margin usually markedly incurved, outer surface pale buff, coarsely granular, stemless. Usually in small trooping – tufted groups. On manure or compost heaps, well manured soil. Spring – autumn. Widespread. Common. Inedible. ASCI cylindrical, blued at top wtih Melzer's reagent, 8-spored, 18–25× 320–380. ASCOSPORES colourless, ellipsoid, non-septate, uniseriate, smooth, 11–14×20–24. PARAPHYSES cylindrical, septate, slightly constricted at septa, slightly swollen at tips. CONIDIA of *Oedocephalum pallidum*

Otidea cochleata. Overall fruit body form, colour, microscopic features, see *O. alutacea* FRUIT BODY 3– apothecial,±irregularly cup-shaped, often elon gated to one side and spli on opposite side, disc da brown, smooth, deeply concave, margin usually persistently folded, oute surface pale buff, finely granular-mealy,±stemles FLESH pale brown. Solita or in small trooping – tufted groups. On soil in woods. Autumn. Wide spread. Rare. Inedible. ASCI cylindrical, not blue at tip with Melzer's rea gent, 8-spored, 11–14×1 –225. ASCOSPORES colour less, ellipsoid, non-septa uniseriate, smooth, 9–11 16–18. PARAPHYSES narro ly cylindrical, branched, septate, markedly curved at tips. CONIDIA ?

tidea onotica **Hare's Ear**.
verall fruit body form,
olour, microscopic fea-
.res, see *O. alutacea*.
UIT BODY 4–6 (×<10 tall),
othecial, at first ±irregu-
rly cup-shaped, elong-
ed to one side and split on
pposite side, then hare's-
r-shaped, disc ochreous
ith pink flush, smooth,
eeply concave, margin us-
lly persistently inrolled,
iter surface ochre, finely
anular-mealy, tapering
elow to short, stout white
em. FLESH white. Solitary
· in small trooping –
fted groups. On soil in
oods. Summer. Wide-
oread. Uncommon. Inedi-
e. ASCI cylindrical, not
ued at tip wtih Melzer's
eagent, 8-spored, 8–
)×225–250. ASCOSPORES
olourless, broadly ellip-
oid, non-septate, uniseri-
e, smooth, 5–6×12–13.
ARAPHYSES narrowly cylin-
rical, branched, septate,
arkedly curved at tips.
ONIDIA ?

arzetta catinus. Overall
uit body form, colour,
abit, microscopic features.
UIT BODY 2–5, apothecial,
ip-shaped, disc pale
chreous-cream, smooth,
oncave, margin becoming
nely toothed, outer sur-
ice pale ochreous-cream,
nely downy, either partly
ink into substrate or with
distinct very short stem.
olitary or in small troop-
g groups. On soil in
oods, especially with
eech, also gardens, path-
des. Summer – autumn.
/idespread. Uncommon.
iedible. ASCI cylindrical,
ot blued at tip with Mel-
er's reagent, 8-spored, 16–
)×280–350. ASCOSPORES

---

colourless, ellipsoid, non-
septate, uniseriate,
smooth, 11–13×20–24.
PARAPHYSES narrowly cylindrical, branched, septate,
slightly swollen and/or
lobed at tips. CONIDIA ?

TUBERACEAE
and TERFEZIACEAE
About 5 genera with fruit
bodies wholly or partially
subterranean, asci
inoperculate, only recog-
nisably related to other
members of Pezizales
through careful study of
fruit body structure which
is believed to represent
apothecia that have
become enclosed within
a ±solid mass of tissue.

Tuber aestivum **Summer
Truffle**. Habitat, overall
fruit body form, surface
features, microscopic features. FRUIT BODY 3–9, irregularly subspherical, dark
brown-black, densely
covered with 5–6 sided
pyramidal warts. FLESH at
first whitish, then
yellowish – grey-brown
and marbled with white
veins. SMELL strong, sweet,
pleasant. Solitary or in
small groups. Subterranean
in broad-leaved woods on
chalky soils, especially with
beech. Summer – autumn.
Widespread. Rare. Edible,
good. ASCI subspherical,
not blued with Melzer's
reagent, 2–5-spored, 50–
70×60–90. ASCOSPORES at
first colourless, then yellowish brown, broadly
ellipsoid – subspherical,
non-septate, irregularly
arranged, ornamented with
network of ridges, 17–35×
25–50 (larger spores in asci
with fewer spores). PARA-
PHYSES absent. CONIDIA ?

TUBERACEAE

Tuber melanosporum **Peri-
ord Truffle**. Habitat, overall fruit body form, surface
features, microscopic features. FRUIT BODY 3–6, irregularly subspherical, dark
brown-black, densely
covered with 6-sided pyramidal warts. FLESH blackish
violet with white veins
which darken when cut.
SMELL strong, sweet, pleasant. Solitary or in small
groups. Subterranean in
broad-leaved woods on
chalky soils especially with
oak. Winter. Southern, not
Britain. Edible, widely considered the best edible fungus. ASCI subspherical, not
blued with Melzer's rea-
gent, 2–5-spored, 50–
70×60–90. ASCOSPORES at
first colourless, then yellowish brown, broadly
ellipsoid – subspherical,
non-septate, irregularly
arranged, spiny, 22–35×29
–55 (larger spores in asci
with fewer spores). PARA-
PHYSES absent. CONIDIA ?

Tuber magnatum **White
Truffle, Piedmont Truffle**.
Habitat, overall fruit body
form, surface features, microscopic features. FRUIT
BODY 3–12, irregularly subspherical, yellowish buff,
rather coarsely granular.
FLESH greyish white, often
with pink flush and marbled
with white veins. SMELL
strong, onion. Solitary or
in small groups. Subterranean in broad-leaved
woods on chalky soils especially with oak. Autumn –
winter. Southern, not Britain. Edible. ASCI subspherical, not blued with Mel-
zer's reagent, 2–5-spored,
50–70×60–90. ASCOSPORES
at first colourless, then yel-

TERFEZIACEAE

lowish brown, broadly
ellipsoid – subspherical,
non-septate, irregular
arranged, spiny, 22–35×29
–55 (larger spores in asci
with fewer spores). PARA-
PHYSES absent. CONIDIA ?

*Choiromyces meandrifor-
mis*. Habitat, overall fruit
body form, surface fea-
tures, microscopic features.
FRUIT BODY 3–12, irregularly
subspherical, yellowish
buff,±smooth. FLESH at
first white, then yellowish
and streaked with yellowish
lines. SMELL ? Solitary or in
small groups. On soil surface or partly buried in
broad-leaved woods. Sum-
mer – autumn. Wide-
spread. Rare. Inedible.
ASCI club-shaped, not blued
with Melzer's reagent, 8-
spored, 50–70×150–180.
ASCOSPORES yellow, spher-
ical, non-septate, irregularly arrange, irregularly
ornamented with long
curved spines (<4), 16–21.
PARAPHYSES absent. CONIDIA
?

ASCOBOLACEAE

Mainly dung-inhabiting fungi with 9 genera of small or minute stemless apothecia and markedly broad operculate asci with biseriate ascospores (most operculate asci are uniseriate) adapted to long range dispersal from dung.

Ascobolus brassicae. Habitat, size, microscopic features. FRUIT BODY 0.05–0.1, apothecial, saucer-shaped, disc at first whitish, smooth, then purplish and warty, flat, margin finely toothed, outer surface whitish, stemless. Solitary or in small trooping groups. On dung, especially of rodents, also rotting stems of *Brassica* species. All year. Widespread. Common. Inedible. ASCI cylindrical, blued with Melzer's reagent, 8-spored, 18–22×110–116. ASCOSPORES at first colourless, then yellowish brown, spherical, non-septate, biseriate, dotted with small, pale purple warts, 12.5–14. PARAPHYSES ±hair-like, wavy, non-septate, branched and slightly swollen at tips. CONIDIA ?

SARCOSOMATACEAE

6 small genera of fungi with rather tough, small, hairy-downy apothecia growing on wood, asci markedly elongated cylindrical, not blued with Melzer's reagent. There are few temperate species but the sole common one is highly distinctive and beautiful.

Sarcoscypha coccinea **Scarlet Elf Cup.** Colour, size, habitat. FRUIT BODY 1–5, apothecial, cup-shaped, disc scarlet, smooth, concave, margin usually inrolled slightly, outer surface whitish ochre, usually tapering sharply below into whitish ochre, usually rather short stem. Solitary or more usually in small trooping – tufted groups. On damp, rotting and fallen twigs of broad-leaved trees. Winter. Widespread. Uncommon. Edible. ASCI cylindrical, not blued with Melzer's reagent, 14–16×400–450. ASCOSPORES colourless, elongated-ellipsoid, non-septate, uniseriate, smooth, with massed oil droplets at each end, 12–14×24–32. PARAPHYSES narrowly cylindrical – ±hair-like, septate, branched, not swollen at tips, wtih red granular contents. CONIDIA of *Molliardomyces coccinea.*

HUMARIACEAE

The largest family in the Order, with about forty genera. Apothecia usually flattened, small, sometimes brightly coloured, stemless and sparsely hairy on outer surface, with characteristic hair structure. Asci not blued with Melzer's reagent.

Iodophanus carneus. Size, habitat, chemical test, microscopic features. FRUIT BODY 0.05–0.15, apothecial, cushion-like, disc salmon-pink, slightly roughened, convex, rapidly turning blue with Melzer's reagent, margin irregular, outer surface salmon-pink, ±hairy, stemless. In small – large, trooping – tufted groups. On dung, rotting plant debris, wet cloth. All year. Widespread. Very common. Inedible. ASCI broadly club-shaped, blued with Melzer's reagent, 8-spored, 25–30×190–225. ASCOSPORES colourless, ellipsoid, non-septate, biseriate, finely warty, 10–12×18–22. PARAPHYSES narrowly cylindrical – ±hair-like, septate, sometimes branched, slightly swollen at tips. CONIDIA of *Oedocephalum* species.

Pyronema domesticum Habitat, overall fruit body form, colour, differs from *P. omphalodes* in spore size. FRUIT BODY 0.05–0.1 (but almost invariably fused into large irregularly lumpy masses), apothecial, cushion-like, disc orange – salmon-pink, ±smooth, convex, margin indistinct, outer surface salmon-pink, ±smooth but covered and surrounded with white hyphal growth, stemless. In large fused groups. On soil on fire sites, wet plaster or sterilised soil in glasshouses. All year. Widespread. Common. Inedible. ASCI cylindrical, not blued with Melzer's reagent, 8-spored, 13–15×150–200. ASCOSPORES colourless, ellipsoid, non-septate, uniseriate, smooth, 9.5–12×15–18. PARAPHYSES narrowly cylindrical, septate, barely swollen at tips. CONIDIA ?

Pyronema omphalodes. Habitat, overall fruit body form, colour, differs from *P. domesticum* in spore size. FRUIT BODY 0.05–0.1 (but almost invariably fused into large irregularly lumpy masses), apothecia cushion-like, disc orange – salmon-pink, ±smooth, convex, margin indistinct outer surface salmon-pink, ±smooth but covered and surrounded with white hyphal growth, stemless. large fused groups. On soil on fire sites or sterilised soil in glasshouses. All year. Widespread. Common. Inedible. ASCI cylindrical, not blued with Melzer's reagent, 8-spored, 13–15×150–200. ASCOSPORES colourless, ellilipsoid, non septate, uniseriate, smooth, 6.5–8.5×11–15. PARAPHYSES narrowly cylindrical, septate, barely swollen at tips. CONIDIA of *Oedocephalum glomerulosum*

Humaria hemisphaerica. Overall fruit body form, colour, habitat, microscopic features. FRUIT BODY 1–3, apothecial, cup-shaped, disc greyish white, smooth, concave, margin and outer surface brown, densely covered with dark brown, pointed hairs, stemless. In small – large, trooping – tufted groups. On wet soil or very rotten fallen wood in damp, shady places. Summer – autumn. Widespread. Common. Inedible. ASCI cylindrical, not blued with Melzer's reagent, 8-spored, 18–20×250–350. ASCOSPORES colourless, broadly ellipsoid, non-septate, uniseriate, coarsely warty, 10–12×20–24. PARAPHYSES narrowly cylindrical, septate, markedly club-shaped at tips. HAIRS dark brown, awl-shaped, septate, smooth, <500. CONIDIA ?

ellina scutellata **Eye-
Fungus**. Overall fruit
y form, colour, habitat,
roscopic features, there
several related and very
ilar *Scutellinia* species in
lar habitats. FRUIT BODY
-1, apothecial, saucer-
ped, disc scarlet,
ooth, concave – flat,
rgin and outer surface
wnish orange, densely
ered with dark brown-
ck, pointed hairs, stem-
. In small – large,
ɔping – tufted groups.
very rotten fallen wood.
mmer – autumn. Wide-
ead. Common. Inedible.
ı cylindrical, not blued
h Melzer's reagent, 8-
red, 18–25×250–300.
ɔospores colourless,
adly ellipsoid, non-
tate, uniseriate, finely
ghened, with many
nular particles, 10–
×18–19. PARAPHYSES
ndrical, septate,
rkedly club-shaped at
s. HAIRS dark brown,
-shaped, septate,
ɔoth,<2000. CONIDIA ?

Neotiella rutilans. Habitat,
colour, microscopic fea-
tures, there are a few
related and rather similar
Neotiella species associated
with different moss species.
FRUIT BODY 1–1.5, apothe-
cial, saucer-shaped, disc
orange–yellow, smooth,
concave, outer surface
whitish, densely covered
with masses of downy white
hairs, stemless or with short
stem±buried in substrate.
Solitary or in small
trooping – tufted groups.
On soil in light, sandy
places among *Polytrichum*.
Autumn – winter. Wide-
spread. Uncommon. Inedi-
ble. ASCI cylindrical, not
blued with Melzer's rea-
gent, 8-spored, 15–20×250
–300. ASCOSPORES colour-
less, ellipsoid, non-septate,
uniseriate, net-patterned,
13–15×22–25. PARAPHYSES
cylindrical, septate, slightly swollen at tips. HAIRS colourless, narrowly conical,
rounded tips, wavy, sept-
ate, smooth,<200. CONIDIA
?

Anthracobia macrocystis.
Habitat, colour, microscopic features; *A. melaloma* is
almost identical and probably commoner. FRUIT BODY
0.2–0.3, apothecial,±sau-
cer-shaped, disc dull reddish orange, smooth, con-
cave – flat, margin rather
densely covered with short,
very pale brown, tufted
hairs, outer surface pale
orange,±smooth, stemless.
Solitary or in small trooping – tufted groups. On soil,
old fire sites. Summer –
autumn. Widespread. Un-
common. Inedible. ASCI
cylindrical, not blued with
Melzer's reagent, 8-spored,
12–15×160–200. ASCO-
SPORES colourless, ellipsoid,
non-septate, uniseriate,
smooth, 7–8×16–18. PARA-
PHYSES cylindrical, septate,
±club-shaped at tips. HAIRS
±colourless, club-shaped,
septate, smooth,<65.
CONIDIA ?

Geopyxis carbonaria. Habitat, overall fruit body form.
FRUIT BODY 0.5–1.5, apothecial, cup-shaped, disc reddish brown, smooth, con-
cave, margin with fine
white teeth, outer surface
reddish brown, finely
granular-scaly, short stemmed. Solitary or in small
trooping – tufted groups.
On burnt ground and on
charcoal and burnt wood.
Autumn. Widespread.
Rare. Inedible. ASCI
cylindrical – narrowly club-
shaped, not blued with
Melzer's reagent, 8-spored,
9–10×180–200. ASCOSPORES
colourless, narrowly ellipsoid, non-septate, uniseriate, smooth, 6–8×13–16.
PARAPHYSES narrowly
cylindrical – ±hair-like,
septate,±slightly club-
shaped at tips. CONIDIA of
Hansfordia species.

ilymenia fimicola.
ɔitat, colour, microsco-
features, there are
eral related and very
ilar *Cheilymenia* species
ımilar habitats. FRUIT
y 0.2–0.5, apothecial,
cer-shaped, disc orange,
ooth, flat, margin and
er surface pale orange,
rsely covered with pale
dish brown, pointed
rs, stemless. Solitary or
nall trooping – tufted
ups. On cow dung or
commonly other types
lung. All year. Wide-
ead. Common. Inedible.
ı cylindrical, not blued
h Melzer's reagent, 8-
red, 12–16×170–200.
ɔospores colourless,
psoid, non-septate, unis-
ıte, smooth, 9–13×16–
. PARAPHYSES cylindrical,
tate, slightly swollen at
. HAIRS brown, narrowly
-shaped, septate,
ɔoth,<500. CONIDIA ?

Melastiza chateri. Habitat,
colour, microscopic fea-
tures. FRUIT BODY 0.5–1.5,
apothecial, cup- to saucer-
shaped, disc dull reddish
orange, smooth, concave –
flat or wavy, margin with
dark brown hairs of short,
downy hairs, outer surface
pale orange±smooth,
stemless. Solitary or in
small trooping – tufted
groups. On damp sandy soil
in open places. All year.
Widespread. Uncommon.
Inedible. ASCI cylindrical,
not blued with Melzer's
reagent, 8-spored, 12–15×
275–300. ASCOSPORES col-
ourless, ellipsoid, non-septate, uniseriate, coarsely
net-patterned, 9–11×17–
19. PARAPHYSES cylindrical,
septate, slightly swollen at
tips. HAIRS brownish, cylindrical with rounded tips,
wavy, septate, smooth,
<200. CONIDIA ?

Aleuria aurantia. Colour,
overall fruit body form.
FRUIT BODY 2–10,
apothecial,±irregularly
saucer-shaped, disc orange,
smooth, wavy, outer sur-
face whitish, very finely
downy, smooth, stemless.
Usually in small, trooping
groups. On soil in woods,
at path or road sides, also
among short grass on
lawns. Autumn. Wide-
spread. Very common.
Edible. ASCI cylindrical, not
blued with Melzer's rea-
gent, 8-spored, 10–13×185
–220. ASCOSPORES colour-
less, ellipsoid, non-septate,
uniseriate, coarsely net-
patterned, 9–11×17–24.
PARAPHYSES cylindrical,
septate,±club-shaped at
tips. CONIDIA ?

Coprobia granulata. Habitat, colour, overall fruit
body form, microscopic
features. FRUIT BODY 0.1–
0.2, apothecial, saucer-
shaped, disc yellowish
orange, smooth,±concave
– flat, margin and outer
surface paler, coarsely
granular, stemless. Usually
in small tufted groups. On
cow dung. All year. Wide-
spread. Extremely com-
mon. Inedible. ASCI cylindrical, not blued with Melzer's reagent, 8-spored, 10–
15×170–190. ASCOSPORES
colourless, ellipsoid, non-
septate, uniseriate,
smooth, 7–8×15–18. PARA-
PHYSES club-shaped, sep-
tate, markedly swollen at
tips. CONIDIA ?

221

Octospora humosa. Habitat, colour, overall fruit body form, microscopic features, several other *Octospora* species occur with mosses, each fungus usually with particular moss species or groups of species. FRUIT BODY 0.5–1, apothecial, saucer-shaped, disc orange, smooth, flat – convex, margin irregularly and finely toothed, outer surface paler, finely granular-scaly, stemless. Often solitary but also in small groups. On sandy soil with *Polytrichum*. Summer – winter. Widespread. Uncommon. Inedible. ASCI cylindrical, not blued with Melzer's reagent, 8-spored, 18–20×220–250. ASCOSPORES colourless, cylindrical – ellipsoid, non-septate, uniseriate, smooth, 11 –13×19–23. PARAPHYSES cylindrical, septate, slightly swollen and markedly hooked at tips. CONIDIA ?

commonest species of a very large genus that occurs typically on dead herbaceous stems. FRUIT BODY 0.03–0.04, pseudothecial, subspherical – conical, black, smooth, shiny, apical pore prominent, at first subepidermal, then erumpent. In large or very large scattered groups. On dead stems of *Urtica dioica*. Winter – spring. Widespread. Extremely common. Inedible. ASCI cylindrical – club-shaped, bitunicate, not blued with Melzer's reagent, 8-spored, 10–11×140–170. ASCO-SPORES yellowish, elongated spindle-shaped, often slightly curved, 6–10-septate, slightly constricted at septa, biseriate, smooth, 5–6×36–50. PARAPHYSES hair-like, septate, branched, not swollen at tips. CONIDIA of *Phoma acuta* in superficially similar fruit bodies in same habitat.

Platychora ulmi. Habitat, overall fruit body form, microscopic features. FRUIT BODY 0.01–0.02, pseudothecial, embedded collectively in stroma, 0.2–0.3, cushion-shaped, black, at first smooth, then finely roughened, dull, apical pores obscure, at first subepidermal, then erumpent. Stromata in small scattered groups. On fallen elm leaves. Winter – spring. Widespread. Extremely common. Inedible. ASCI cylindrical, obscurely bitunicate, not blued with Melzer's reagent, 8-spored, 7–8×58–60. ASCOSPORES at first colourless, then greenish, broadly ellipsoid – club-shaped, 1-septate, with septum markedly displaced towards one end, not constricted at septum, irregularly uniseriate, smooth, 4–4.5×10–12. PARAPHYSES absent. CONIDIA of *Piggotia ulmi* occur on living leaves.

larly uniseriate, smooth 8×12–15. PARAPHYSES absent. CONIDIA of *Spilo caea pomi*.

Hormotheca (= *Stigmate robertiani*. Habitat, over fruit body form, microsc pic features. FRUIT BODY 0.01–0.015, pseudotheci hemispherical with surrounding rim of dark, radiating hyphae, black, smooth, apical pore obscure, superficial. On small scattered spots. O leaves of *Geranium robe tianum*. Spring – autumn Widespread. Extremely common. Inedible. ASCI broadly cylindrical – ellipsoid, bitunicate, not blued with Melzer's reagent, 8-spored, 12–14×4 45. ASCOSPORES pale oliv green, ±club-shaped, 1-septate, with septum markedly towards one e slightly constricted at se tum, irregularly biseriate smooth, 4–5×10–14. PAR PHYSES absent ? CONIDIA

An assortment of fungi, grouped together on the basis of their bitunicate asci but not obviously closely related. It is a huge group, with one Order Dothideales but nearly forty families and several hundred genera. Few are commonly or readily collected or identified. The fruit bodies are neither strictly apothecial nor perithecial but may simulate either and in some cases are called pseudothecia.

Leptosphaeria acuta. Size, habitat, colour, overall fruit body form, microscopic features, probably the

Melanomma pulvis-pyrius. Size, habitat, colour, overall fruit body form, microscopic features. FRUIT BODY 0.03–0.05, pseudothecial, subspherical – conical, black, smooth – rough, shiny – dull, apical pore obscure. In large or very large scattered or more usually fused groups. On dead bark and wood of broad-leaved trees. Winter – spring. Widespread. Extremely common. Inedible. ASCI cylindrical, bitunicate, not blued with Melzer's reagent, 8-spored, 8–9×105–115. ASCOSPORES pale olive brown, ellipsoid – spindle-shaped, 3-septate, slightly constricted at septa, irregularly uniseriate, smooth, 4–6×12–20. PARAPHYSES hair-like, septate, not swollen at tips. CONIDIA of *Apos-phaeria agminalis*.

Venturia inaequalis causes **Apple and Pear Scab Disease.** Host plants, symptoms on host plants, microscopic features. SYMPTOMS dark greenish black spots on leaves and scab-like, crusty lesions on fruit. FRUIT BODY 0.01–0.03, pseudothecial, spherical, black, apical pore small, immersed in host tissue. On leaves, fruit, twigs, and other parts of broad-leaved trees, especially apple, associated with scab symptoms. All year. Widespread. Extremely common. ASCI cylindrical, bitunicate, not blued with Melzer's reagent, 8-spored, 7–12×60–70. ASCOSPORES olive-brown, irregularly elongated-ellipsoid, 1-septate, with septum towards one end, not constricted at septum, irregu-

Mycosphaerella fragariae Host plants, symptoms, microscopic features. SYMPTOMS ±circular, greyish – dark brown, brownish-purple-border spots on upper leaf surfaces. FRUIT BODY 0.01–0.018, pseudothecial, subspherical – ±conical black, smooth, apical po small, erumpent. On lea spots. On *Fragaria* speci Spring – autumn. Widespread. Very common. Inedible. ASCI cylindrical bitunicate, not blued wi Melzer's reagent, 8-spor 9.5–13×50–70. ASCOSPOR colourless, spindle-shape 1-septate, barely constricted at septum, irreg larly biseriate, smooth, 2 3×11–14.5. PARAPHYSES ?absent. CONIDIA of *Ram laria brunnea*.

EUTEROMYCOTINA

huge and extremely ried group of fungi having no sexual reproduction, t reproducing asexually conidia (see p. 230). most none can be identified with the naked eye d relatively few without reful artificial culture der closely controlled nditions. There are two ain divisions into the elomycetes, which bear eir conidia within closed structures, generay called pycnidia, or on issed hyphae called acerli, and the Hyphomytes which have no such dies and bear the conidia variously formed hyphal odifications called conophores. The few species cluded here are those ost likely to be seen by e field mycologist and clude examples of pycnial and acervulus-forming elomycetes and of phomycetes with colours and with dark coloured phae, known respectely as **Moniliaceae** and **matiaceae**.

Botrytis cinerea. Overall colony appearance and symptoms, conidiophores are characteristic of the genus *Botrytis* of which this is the commonest species. SYMPTOMS greyish, powdery mould growth over substrate, sometimes with small, very variable black sclerotia. FRUIT BODY absent. Ubiquitous on a wide range of organic substrates, associated with rotting, die-back, spotting and other pathological symptoms. All year. Widespread. Extremely common. CONIDIA colourless, ellipsoid, non-septate, smooth, 4–11×6–18. CONIDIOPHORES colourless, <2500, branched to form umbel-like heads. ASCOSPORES of *Botryotinia fuckeliana* (Helotiales, Sclerotiniaceae).

Cladosporium cladosporioides. Symptoms, other *Cladosporium* species and related dark-spored deuteromycetes occur in similar situations and are the usual causes of ubiquitous 'black mould'. SYMPTOMS spot-like or more irregular black – dark green dense velvety mould growth over substrate. FRUIT BODY absent. Ubiquitous on an enormous range of substrates, especially organic material but also on damp plaster and similar situations. All year. Widespread. Extremely common. CONIDIA olive-brown, ellipsoid – lemon-shaped, 0-several-septate, smooth – finely warty, in long branched chains, 2–5×3–11. CONIDIOPHORES olive-brown, <350, smooth – finely warty, unbranched. ASCOSPORES ?

Phoma hedericola. Symptoms, habitat, microscopic features, related and similar species of this large genus cause similar symptoms on many other plants. SYMPTOMS large,±rounded – irregular whitish brown leaf spots with broad brown margin. PYCNIDIA <0.1,± spherical, but sometimes rather flattened, black, beaked pore emerging through epidermis of upper leaf surface. On living ivy leaves. All year. Widespread. Extremely common. CONIDIA colourless, elongated-ellipsoid, aseptate, smooth, 2.5–3.5×4–6.5. CONIDIOPHORES colourless, very short-obscure, unbranched. ASCOSPORES ?

Aspergillus niger. Overall mptoms, microscopic features. SYMPTOMS sometimes definite, blackish mould owth, but often obscurely lourless. FRUIT BODY sent. On soil and a wide nge of organic substrates, metimes biotrophic on ants, animals and man. ll year. Widespread. xtremely common. CONIA black,±spherical, nonptate, warty – spiny, 4–5. NIDIOPHORES colourless, ownish at apex, <3000, branched, bearing conia on±spherical heads.

Penicillium expansum. Overall colony appearance, conidiophores are typical of the many *Penicillium* species. SYMPTOMS bluish green, dense, velvety mould growth over substrate. FRUIT BODY absent. Ubiquitous on a wide range of organic substrates and soil, especially frequent on fruit and the commonest blue mould on apples. All year. Widespread. Extremely common. CONIDIA greenish blue, ellipsoid – cylindrical, non-septate, smooth, in long, tangled chains, 2.5–3.5×4–5. CONIDIOPHORES colourless, <400, smooth – slightly warty, branched to form close clusters of heads like groups of fingers. ASCOSPORES ?

Graphium (=*Pesotum*) *ulmi* causes **Dutch Elm Disease.** Host plant, microscopic features. FRUIT BODY absent. In small – large groups on wood, below dead bark and in tunnels produced by bark beetles on elms. All year. Widespread. Extremely common. CONIDIA colourless, ellipsoid, non-septate, smooth, 1–3×2–5. CONIDIOPHORES colourless, unbranched, smooth, aggregated into synnemata, <2000. ASCOSPORES of *Ceratocystis ulmi* on same substrate (p. 206).

Septoria apiicola causes **Celery Leaf Spot Disease.** Host plants, symptoms. SYMPTOMS±circular or slightly angular pale brown and±depressed spots on upper and lower leaf surfaces, leaf stalks, seeds and seedling roots. PYCNIDIA <0.02, subspherical, becoming slightly flattened, brown-black, very slightly beaked pore emerging through epidermis. On living plants of celery and other *Apium* species. All year. Widespread. Very common. CONIDIA colourless,±hair-like, 1–5-septate, smooth, 2–2.5×22–56. CONIDIOPHORES colourless, short, unbranched. ASCOSPORES ?

MONILIACEAE

Diplodina acerina. Host plants, microscopic features. CONIDIOMATA <0.1, irregular, convoluted, locular, dark brown, on bark, at first subepidermal, then erumpent. On bark of *Acer* species. All year. Widespread. Common. CONIDIA very pale pinkish-colourless, elongated spindle-shaped, 1-septate, smooth, 3–3.5×13.5–15.5. CONIDIOPHORES <25, colourless, branched, smooth. ASCOSPORES of *Cryptodiaporthe hystrix* (Diaporthales, Valsaceae).

Libertella betulina. Habitat, spore tendrils (in wet weather), microscopic features, related and similar species occur on other woody hosts. ACERVULI <0.1, ±circular, at first pinkish, then yellow, on bark, at first subepidermal but eventually erumpent. On dead bark of *Betula* species. Autumn – spring. Widespread. Common. CONIDIA yellow, emerging in long, twisting toothpaste-like golden tendrils, elongated spindle-shaped – ± sausage-shaped, aseptate, smooth, 0.75–1×13–16. CONIDIOPHORES colourless, short, unbranched. ASCOSPORES of *Diatrype stigma* (Diatrypales, Diatrypaceae) rare on same host.

Marssonina salicicola causes **Willow Anthracnose Disease.** Habitat, symptoms, microscopic features. SYMPTOMS small, ashen or pale brown lesions on stems, small, scattered – fused red-brown spots on upper leaf surfaces. ACERVULI <0.1,±circular, whitish, on leaf and twig spots, at first subepidermal but eventually erumpent. On *Salix* species, especially weeping willow associated with dying back of twigs. Spring – autumn. Widespread. Extremely common. CONIDIA colourless, club-shaped – pear-shaped, 1-septate, with septum markedly displaced towards one end, barely constricted at septum, smooth, 5–8×15–18. CONIDIOPHORES colourless, short, unbranched. ASCOSPORES of *Drepanopeziza sphaeriodes* (Helotiales, Dematiaceae), rare on same host.

MYCELIA STERILIA

Sclerotium cepivorum causes **Onion White Rot Disease.** Host plants, symptoms. SYMPTOMS whitish mould around bulb and roots of host, within which are SCLEROTIA, 0.2–0.5,± spherical, black, smooth – pitted. On *Allium* species, especially onions, shallots, leeks, associated with bulb and root rotting and plant decline. All year. Widespread. Common. CONIDIA absent. ASCOSPORES absent.

MYCELIA STERILIA

A residual group of mycelial fungi that produce no known spores at all, sexual or asexual and which can only be identified by microscopic examination of vegetative structures or, as in the example included here, by some effects on a host plant.

ZYGOMYCOTINA

Mycelial, predominantly microscopic but often rendered conspicuous by mould-like gross colony growth, or when biotrophic species cause distortion or other symptoms on hosts. Cell walls predominantly contain chitin. Reproduce by sexually-produced zygospores and also by asexual spores produced within enclosed balloon-like bodies. Either terrestrial and saprotrophic (or more rarely biotrophic on plants or animals), or obligately biotrophic on arthropods. Divided on the basis of habit and morphology into two Classes, Trichomycetes (not included here) and Zygomycetes.

ZYGOMYCETES

Mycelial, predominantly microscopic but often rendered conspicuous by mould-like gross colony

MUCORACEAE

growth (on food or dung for instance) or when biotrophic species cause distortion or other symptoms on hosts. Reproduce by sexually-produced zygospores and also by asexual spores produced within enclosed balloon-like bodies. Terrestrial and saprotrophic (or more rarely biotrophic on plants, other fungi or animals). Divided largely on the basis of the type, formation and structure of asexual spores into three or four Orders. The commonest is the Mucorales with about fourteen families, of which the **Mucoraceae** (often called the pin moulds) and the dung-inhabiting **Pilobolaceae** are those most likely to be seen. Members of the Order Entomophthorales (which has one family, the **Entomophthoraceae**), are also commonly found parasitising insects. The examples of these three families included here are: Mucoraceae (*Mucor*, *Rhizopus*), Pilobolaceae (*Pilobolus*) and Entomophthoraceae (*Entomophthora*).

Mucor mucedo **Pin Mould.** Gross colony appearance, there are many *Mucor* species only identifiable with certainty in artificial culture, several related genera have different and characteristic sporangiophore form. SYMPTOMS ±circular patches of indefinite whitish mould growth bearing masses of minute FRUIT BODIES (sporangia) 0.01–0.02, spherical, at first yellowish, then grey, then black on long stems (sporangiophores), 1–10. On organic matter of many kinds, sometimes on dung or soil, especially common on old, damp bread, as mycelium-bearing aplanospores and rarely zygospores. All year. Widespread. Extremely common. APLANOSPORES colourless, ellipsoid, smooth, 3–6×6–12. ZYGOSPORES irregularly subspherical, black, spiny – warty, rarely observed other than in artificial culture, 90–250.

ropus nigrans. Gross
ny appearance, several
ed genera have diffe-
and characteristic
angiophore form.
·TOMS irregular patches
hitish mould growth
ing masses of minute
r BODIES (sporangia)
–0.35, spherical, grey
black, on long hyphal
s (sporangiophores)
–0.4, arising in groups
re arching stolon-like
hae touch the substrate.
organic matter of many
s, sometimes on dung
oil, as mycelium-
ing aplanospores and
ospores. All year.
espread. Extremely
mon. APLANOSPORES
urless, irregularly
pherical – ellipsoid,
oth, 6–17. ZYGOSPORES
ularly subspherical,
k, spiny – warty, rarely
rved other than in arti-
l culture, 160–220.

bolus kleinii. Gross col-
appearance and subs-
. SYMPTOMS irregular
hes of indefinite whit-
mould growth bearing
ses of minute FRUIT
ES (sporangia) 0.05×
hour-glass shaped, col-
ess below, grey then
k above, on long, rela-
y stout hyphal stems
rangiophores) 0.05–
On fresh dung, preced-
ascomycetes and basi-
ycetes, as mycelium-
ing aplanospores and
ly zygospores. All year.
espread. Extremely
mon. APLANOSPORES
urless, ellipsoid, 6–
12–20. ZYGOSPORES ?

Entomophthora muscae.
Substrate and gross colony
appearance; there are
many species of *Entomophthora* and related genera,
distinguishable with great
difficulty, partly by host
species and partly by microscopic features. SYMP-
TOMS indefinite, whitish
mould growth on corpses of
host insects, usually as concentric bands emerging
between body segments
and bearing masses of microscopic conidia with no
macroscopically visible
fruit body. On moribund
and dead house-flies and
other flies, most often seen
as a halo of discharged conidia around a corpse att-
ached to a window pane.
Many other species occur
on other types of insect. All
year. Widespread. Extre-
mely common. CONIDIA col-
ourless, subspherical –
pear-shaped, smooth, 22–
26×33–36. ZYGOSPORES ?

MASTIGOMYCOTINA
Mycelial, pseudo-mycelial
or non-mycelial, entirely
microscopic and only ren-
dered conspicuous when
biotrophic species cause
gross distortion or other
symptoms on hosts. Cell
walls predominantly con-
tain cellulose, chitin or
chitin-like chemicals.
Reproduce by various types
of sexually-produced spore
and also by motile post-
eriorly or anteriorly uni- or
biflagellate zoospores. Terrestrial or aquatic in fresh
or salt walter. Saprotrophic
or biotrophic on many
types of plant, animal or
other fungi. Divided on the
basis of zoospore type and
cell wall structure into four
Classes, Oomycetes,
Hyphochytriomycetes (not
included here), Chytri-
diomycetes and Plasmo-
diophoromycetes.

OOMYCETES
Mycelial, most groups
entirely microscopic but en
masse mycelium may be
visible as mould-like
growth, especially in Pero-

nosporales. Cell walls contain cellulose. Reproduc-
tion by formation of resting
oospores and also by anteriorly or laterally biflagellate
asexual zoospores or con-
idia in fresh or salt water. Saprotrophic or biotrophic on
or in higher plants, algae or
other fungi. Divided pri-
marily on the basis of
several microscopic structural and developmental features into five Orders and
thirteen families; the six
representative species
described here are in the
three families of the Order
Peronosporales, which
include the Downy Mildew
fungi and related species,
the only groups likely to be
visible to the field observer.

PERONOSPORALES
Mostly terrestrial, living
saprotrophically entirely
within the soil, or biot-
rophic on higher plants,
many causing important
crop diseases and rendered
visible by gross effects on
hosts or by massed mould-
like growth of mycelium. In
many biotrophic species,
separated spatially from
free water in the soil, the
zoospores never mature
and the spore-producing
structure itself functions as
an entire asexual spore.
Divided into three families,
with representatives chosen
as follows: **Peronospor-
aceae** (*Peronospora, Plasmopara, Bremia*): obligate
biotrophs with branched,
tree-like spore-bearing
hyphae, commonly called
Downy Mildews;
Pythiaceae (*Phytophthora,
Pythium*): non-obligate
biotrophs or saprotrophs;
Albuginaceae (*Albugo*),
obligate biotrophs with
unbranched spore-bearing
hyphae, commonly called
White Blisters. Most can be
identified with a fair degree
of certainty from the host
plants to which they are
usually fairly specific.

Peronospora parasitica
causes **Crucifer Downy Mildew Disease.** Host plant,
gross symptoms, microsco-

pic features. SYMPTOMS yellowish specks on upper surface of cotyledons and
leaves of seedlings with off-
white patches of mould
beneath when damp. Sev-
erely affected seedlings
may ultimately die. On
mature plants, brown-
yellow angular patches on
upper leaf surfaces with
white mould beneath when
damp. Affected organs
often distorted. In soil, as
oospores and mycelium;
also on roots and above
ground parts of plants of
the family Cruciferae. All
year. Widespread. Very
common. CONIDIA colour-
less, broadly ellipsoid –
subspherical, smooth, 24–
27×12–22. ZOOSPORES
absent. OOSPORES yellow-
brown, spherical, smooth
26–45.

Plasmopara viticola causes
**Grapevine Downy Mildew
Disease.** Host plant, gross
symptoms, microscopic features. SYMPTOMS pale yel-
lowish green patches on
upper surfaces of leaves
with off-white patches of
mould beneath when
damp. Affected areas later
turn brownish and affected
organs, flowers and fruit
may shrivel. In soil as oospores from fallen leaves
and as mycelium; also as
mycelium and conidia on
living leaves of grapevines
and other vines. Spring –
autumn. Widespread, pre-
dominantly southern.
Rare. CONIDIA colourless,
broadly ellipsoid, smooth,
17–25×10–16. ZOOSPORES
irregularly ellipsoid,
biflagellate, 4–5×6–8. OOS-
PORES brown, spherical,
smooth 28–40.

Bremia lactucae causes **Lettuce Downy Mildew Disease.** Host plant, gross symptoms, microscopic features. SYMPTOMS pale yellowish green patches on upper surfaces of leaves with off-white patches of mould beneath when damp. Affected areas later turn brownish and affected plants become debilitated. In soil as oospores from old leaves and as conidia on living lettuce plants and other members of the family Compositae. All year. Widespread. Common. CONIDIA colourless, broadly ellipsoid, smooth, 11–28×12–31. ZOOSPORES absent. OOSPORES brown, spherical, wrinkled 20–31.

Phytophthora infestans causes **Potato Blight Disease.** Host plant, gross symptoms, microscopic features. SYMPTOMS dark brown-black leaf blotches with white patches of mould beneath when damp; affected areas later coalesce and leaves and also tubers undergo rapid soft rot. In old diseased tubers as mycelium and oospores; also as mycelium, conidia and/or oospores on above ground parts of potato and tomato plants. All year (on tubers); spring – autumn (on plants). Widespread. Very common. CONIDIA colourless, smooth, 21–38×12–23. ZOOSPORES irregularly pear-shaped, biflagellate, often abundant, 7–8×10–12. OOSPORES brown, spherical, smooth 24–46.

Pythium ultimum causes **Damping-Off** and other **Stem and Root Rot Diseases.** Gross symptoms, microscopic features, there are many *Pythium* species with wide host ranges and most can be identified with certainty only in artificial culture. SYMPTOMS dark brown-black lesions on roots and stem bases, sometimes with greyish white mould growth; affected organs or plants decline rapidly. In soil as oospores which germinate to form either hyphae or zoospores; also as mycelium, oospores and conidia on and within many types of plant. All year. Widespread. Very common. CONIDIA colourless, subspherical, smooth, often around 20–25 but very variable. ZOOSPORES irregularly pear-shaped, biflagellate, often around 15–20×6–9 but very variable. OOSPORES colourless, spherical, smooth 15–18.

Albugo candida causes **Crucifer White Blister Disease.** Host plants, gross symptoms, microscopic features. SYMPTOMS white lesions, at first smooth, then powdery, on leaves and other above ground parts which look as if splashed with white paint; affected organs usually distorted. In soil as oospores (which germinate to form mycelium) and conidia (which germinate to form zoospores) and on above ground parts of plants of the family Cruciferae as mycelium, oospores and conidia. All year. Widespread. Common. CONIDIA colourless, spherical, smooth, 12–18. ZOOSPORES

?, irregularly pear-shaped, biflagellate. OOSPORES brown, subspherical, warty, 30–55.

CHYTRIDIOMYCETES
Non-mycelial, pseudo-mycelial or mycelial, sometimes with rhizoidal threads providing anchorage to substrate, sometimes inter-or intracellular, entirely microscopic. The presence of a few biotrophic species is rendered conspicuous by galls or other distortions on affected higher plants. Cell walls lack cellulose. Reproduction in various and often complex ways by formation of posteriorly uniflagellate asexual zoospores, usually also with resting spores or other sexually formed bodies. Terrestrial or aquatic in fresh or salt water. Saprotrophic or biotrophic on or in higher plants, algae, other fungi, insects and lower animals such as rotifers. Divided mainly on the basis of the degree of differentiation into true mycelium into four Orders and twelve Families, many elusive and obscure; the representative species described here is in the Order Chytridiales, family **Chytridiaceae**.

Synchytrium endobioticum causes **Potato Wart Disease.** Host plant, gross symptoms, microscopic features. GALLS <10, usually dark brown, irregularly knobbly, cauliflower-like, sometimes green, leafy. In soil as resting sporangia, and in tubers or rarely above ground parts of potatoes and related plants in the family Solanaceae as resting sporangia or thallus, especially on wet sites in cool areas. Spring – autumn. Widespread, predominantly northern. Rare. THALLUS non-mycelial, intracellular with 1–9 sporangia. RESTING SPORANGIA subspherical, minutely ridged, 35–80, dark brown, ZOOSPORES subspherical, 1.5–2, posteriorly uniflagellate, fairly elusive.

PLASMODIOPHORO-MYCETES
Non-mycelial, plasmod pseudo-amoeboid, enti microscopic, inter-and intra-cellular in algae, Oomycetes or higher plants. The presence of higher plant-attacking s cies is rendered conspi cuous by the spore-containing galls that usu form on affected organs Cell walls lack cellulose contain chitin. Reprodu by cleavage of plasmodi into few or numerous anteriorly biflagellate zo pores and/or separated clustered resting spores Terrestrial or aquatic in fresh or salt water. All o gately biotrophic, some causing serious crop dis eases. One Order Plasm diophorales with one fa **Plasmodiophoraceae.**

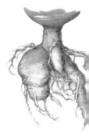

Plasmodiophora brassic causes **Clubroot Disease.** Host plants, gross symptoms, microscopic featur GALLS <20, irregularly brownish, usually fairly smooth, finger-like or cl shaped, decomposing through bacterial action when mature to produce foul-smelling mass. In so especially on wet, acid si or rarely in water as rest spores; also as resting spores, plasmodia and zoospore-forming bodies roots or rarely above-ground organs of plants family Cruciferae, especially cultivated species o *Brassica*. All year. Wide spread. Common. PLASM DIA uni-or multinucleate filling host cells. RESTING SPORES spherical, minute spiny (use oil immersion lens), 2.5–3.5,± colourle individually separated when mature. ZOOSPORES 2.5–3.5, irregular, anteri orly biflagellate, elusive.

SPORES

THE NATURE AND FUNCTION OF SPORES

Like all other living things, fungi must reproduce themselves and have a method of dispersing progeny from parent. It is by means of structures called spores that they achieve both of these objectives. Unlike seeds, which fulfil a similar role in flowering plants, spores occur in a wide range of types, formed in different ways, adapted to different circumstances and actually serving several quite varied functions. Also unlike seeds, they are made up of at the most only a few cells (most in fact are unicellular), and are therefore always microscopic in size. They have also evolved quite differently. If a parallel is to be drawn, at least in regard to function, it is more accurately between some types of spore and pollen-grains.

Spores are not unique to fungi and are universally produced among what are often described as 'lower' organisms, especially 'lower' plants or Cryptogams like Bryophytes (mosses and liverworts), Pteridophytes (ferns, horsetails and their allies) and Algae. Students of bacteria and protozoans also find themselves engaged for much of their time in the study of spores. To understand the nature, biology and functions of the fungal spore is to understand a great deal about the fungi in general, and in almost all fungal groups features of the spores are a major basis for classification and identification (p. 36). So the microscopic and elusive nature of spores was, historically, a major hindrance to the advancement of mycological study.

It was not until 1588 that an Italian, della Porta, first recorded the fact that spores had been seen, and not until the following century, and the inven-

tion and development of the microscope, that botanists began to appreciate spores for what they are. By the early part of the eighteenth century, della Porta's compatriot Micheli was observing spores in every type of fungus that he examined, and he made the highly significant observation that they could themselves be shown to develop into new fungi. Nonetheless, these perceptive observers referred to the objects as seeds and although the German, Hedwig, coined the word 'spora' in 1788, it was left to the Frenchman, Richard, twenty years later to set down a conviction that the spore and the seed were different. He wrote 'Spores differ from grains, not only in their mode of formation, but also and especially in the lack of an embryo'.

If the spore, then, lacks an embryo, what *does* it contain, and what is this mode of formation that even Hedwig realised was different from that of seeds? As explained, the typical fungal spore comprises but one cell, essentially similar to the cells that make up other organisms, and controlled by a central body called a nucleus. Its structure can best be envisaged as a tiny drop of a watery substance called cytoplasm with the nucleus and other minute organs (or organelles) inside, and the whole contained in a bag called the spore wall.

Diagram of a spore

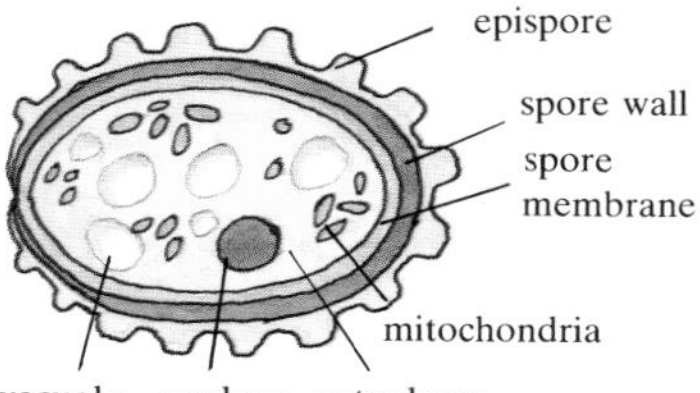

epispore
spore wall
spore membrane
mitochondria
vacuole   nucleus   cytoplasm

This spore wall is important for it is the spore's interface or region of contact with the outside world. The permeability of the wall to moisture, oxygen, carbon dioxide and other substances determines many important features of spore biology, such as susceptibility to drying out or bursting. To improve their general robustness, therefore, many types of spore have their walls impregnated by such substances as melanin, the black pigment that occurs widely among living organisms and in varying chemical forms is responsible for the dark colour of human hair and skin. Spore walls of different fungal groups also contain relatively different amounts of other chemicals, especially of cellulose, chitin (a tough material that is a major component of insects' external skeletons) and other carbohydrates, proteins and oils.

The way that spores form, and the manner in which they fit into the overall life cycle of fungi, is discussed on p. 294; but it is important first to appreciate that there is a great range of different types of spore, and that some are peculiar to certain groups of fungi while others occur widely. These different spore types are borne and dispersed in different ways and have a range of devices which enable them to overcome the problems they face in the environment at large. But the most important and fundamental division among spore types is into asexually produced and sexually produced forms.

Sexual and Asexual Spores
For most people, the word reproduction and the phenomenon of reproduction have sexual connotations. This is not surprising. People, and most of the types of animal that they meet in everyday life, reproduce when two individuals of opposite sex come together, mate, and thus fertilise an ovum with sperm. Even those who have routine dealings with the plant kingdom tend to think of reproduction in terms of flowers, bees, pollination, fruits and seeds. The gardener is frequently confronted with other multiplication systems in the shape of runners, offsets, rhizomes and bulbs, but such asexual methods involve quite separate and distinct structures and are barely considered as reproductive processes at all. They are certainly not thought of in the same context as flowers or seeds.

In coming to grips with fungal reproduction, however, it is soon apparent that the boundary between asexual and sexual reproductive systems is much more blurred, for both produce spores. Indeed, in many fungal species, not only do both sexual and asexual systems occur, but more than one type of spore may be produced in each. At its most extreme in some of the rust fungi, five different types of body occur; and all are given the name spore! But, even in such a biologically complex group, one type of spore is given the greatest significance in classification and taxonomy, and that is the one produced as a direct result of sexual reproduction. It is from this that most of the major fungal groupings take their names. It is appropriate therefore to consider each in turn.

Plasmodiophoromycetes and Chytridiomycetes
Of all the fungal groups described in this book, the Plasmodiophoromycetes and Chytridiomycetes are not only generally considered the least advanced, but they are also the most obscure and unfamiliar. Most people will happily pass their lives without

Microscopic views of the five different spore bodies in a rust fungus

basidiospore   aeciospores   teliospore   urediniospore   spermatium

seeing a Plasmodiophoromycete, but many gardeners and farmers will unfortunately encounter the practical manifestations of at least some aspects of the structure of their spores. For the most important member of this group is *Plasmodiophora brassicae* (p. 226), the cause of clubroot disease of cabbages and related plants. It is with dread that a vegetable grower discovers the presence of clubroot in his soil and it is the sexually produced spores of *Plasmodiophora* that stimulate his chagrin. For these spores, which are called resting spores and produced in the roots of diseased plants, are especially well endowed with the ability to survive through periods of adversity – their walls are thickened to resist the vagaries of the soil environment and the very name 'resting spore' is indicative of a body designed to lie dormant for long periods. Resting spores are single-celled, usually more or less spherical, commonly smaller than most other fungal spores (about 3 μm in diameter), and are produced either separately as in *Plasmodiophora brassicae* or aggregated into sporeballs containing varying numbers of individual spores, as in its close relative *Polymyxa graminis*.

Although it is itself among the most durable of the many types of fungal spore, a resting spore, when it germinates, gives rise to another type of spore that is one of the most fragile. This spore is a type of asexual spore, for no fertilisation takes place before its emergence, and it is called a zoospore. Alone among all the types of fungal spore, it is capable of free movement. It requires the presence of water to exploit this apparent ecological advantage; the Plasmodiophoromycetes, Chytridiomycetes and related minor groups of zoospore-producing fungi occur therefore only in the water of rivers, pools or the sea, or in soil where films of water around soil crumbs provide an acceptable environment. It is precisely because these zoospores require a moist environment through which to move, that improvement of garden drainage is so often advised to prevent clubroot

disease. It is particularly sad that so few mycologists, let alone field naturalists, ever see a zoospore, for these minute bodies, which provide the fungus with the means of dispersal from a sedentary resting spore, have an endearing nature as they busy themselves in swimming to and fro in search of the root of a suitable host plant. This swimming movement is achieved by means of a thin, whip-like organelle called a flagellum, often many times longer than the spore body itself and possessing an extraordinary complex internal structure, although so slender as to be barely visible under even the best of microscopes. The zoospores of the Plasmodiophoromycetes have two flagella, those of the Chytridiomycetes one but with vestiges of a second ancestral flagellum (see p. 12). Some fungi belonging to these groups also produce zoospores at other stages in the life cycle but they are morphologically almost identical to those that emerge from resting spores.

A resting spore ball

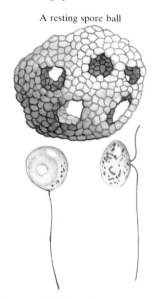

Zoospore of a Plasmodiophoromycete with two flagella (right), and of a Chytridiomycete with one flagellum (left)

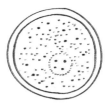

Oospore

Oomycetes (water moulds)

The sexually produced spore of the Oomycetes is called an oospore and is, like the resting spore, a thick-walled body adapted for long term survival. Some Oomycetes – such as the plant pathogenic genera *Phytophthora* (p. 226) (of which one species causes potato blight) and *Pythium* (p. 226) (a cause of seedling damping-off) – commonly produce water-requiring zoospores too; indeed, the Oomycetes collectively are often known as the water-moulds. Nonetheless, their zoospores never arise directly from oospores but are formed at a different stage in the life cycle; and their two flagella of unequal length betray their unrelatedness to the Plasmodiophoromycetes (see p. 12). Some Oomycete genera, like *Bremia* (p. 226), do not normally form zoospores; others, like *Peronospora* (p. 225), have totally lost the ability to produce them. *Bremia* and *Peronospora,* like *Phytophthora* and *Pythium,* are plant pathogens but tend to be restricted to the foliage rather than the soil and the roots, and they cause the symptoms called downy mildew. Hence, they live in a drier environment, less suitable for the movement and survival of zoospores. A vestigial form of zoospore-producing structure *does* occur in these non-zoosporic forms, but it acts itself as a type of spore, germinates directly to form a mycelium and, by analogy with asexually produced non-motile spores in general, is sometimes called a conidium.

Zygomycetes

The spores produced as a result of sexual reproduction in the Zygomycetes, typified by those of *Mucor* (p. 224) and of *Rhizopus* (p. 225), are thick-walled and warty bodies called zygospores; once again, structures that have evolved as a means of survival through adverse conditions. Their characteristic dark colour is due to the presence of melanins deposited in the wall. None of the Zygomycetes forms zoospores: like all the remaining groups of fungi to be described, they produce asexual spores, usually called conidia, that are non-motile and thus do not need water to swim in, but do of course need it for other reasons. In addition to conidia, however, the Zygomycetes also produce spores in varying numbers within enclosed, balloon-like bodies. It is these stalked spore-bearing structures that give the familiar minutely spiky appearance to the colonial growth of those forms like *Mucor* (p. 224) that are often to be found growing on stale bread and similar habitats and are known popularly as pin-moulds. This type of asexual spore is known as an aplanospore; a word derived from the Greek meaning 'not wandering' which emphasises its lack of motility.

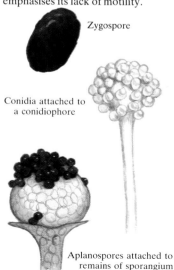

Zygospore

Conidia attached to a conidiophore

Aplanospores attached to remains of sporangium

Basidiomycetes

When mushroom and toadstool enthusiasts talk simply of 'spores' they are usually referring to the spores discharged from toadstool caps to produce the spore prints they find so valuable in identification, and which they so carefully measure under the microscope in order to separate one species from another. These are basidiospores, the sexually produced spores of the basidiomycetes, the large group to which mushrooms and toadstools, among many other types of fungi, belong. Basidiospores range widely both in size and shape (front endpaper) – although relatively few are spherical – and in the gross appearance of the fruit bodies in which they are produced; most of the illustrations in this book are of the variations in basidiomycete fruit body form. But while the precise point in the life cycle at which fertilisation occurs, and basidiospores form, varies throughout the group, there are certain features common to all basidiospores. They are always produced in a manner that exposes them to the outside air, in marked contrast to the spores of the ascomycetes (p. 235), the other large group of macro-fungi. They are almost always unicellular, although in a few groups, like the family Dacrymycetaceae (p. 189), they have internally dividing crosswalls or septa. The spore wall is usually relatively thin compared with that of other types of sexually produced spore and is often smooth, although in some groups, most notably the family Russulaceae (p. 94), the surface of the spore wall is complexly spiny or folded and reveals the characteristic surface features when viewed through a microscope that assume great importance in species identification (endpapers). Because of, or perhaps dictated by, their thin, fragile walls, basidiospores differ from many other types of sexually produced spore in that they are generally ill-equipped to survive for long periods through adverse conditions. Basidiospore colour is an important feature for the identification of basidiomycetes, but it is now con-

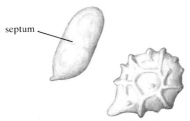

Dacrymycete spore with a septum

septum

Spore of a fungus in the family Russulaceae

sidered less important in classification (p. 37). But in the familiar mushrooms and toadstools of the Agaricales it is the colour of the spores deposited en masse in a spore print, rather than the colour shown by individual spores under the microscope, that is of greatest value. The pigment that gives rise to the colour may be present in the cytoplasm and/or the spore wall and it is an increase in the amount of pigmentation in the wall that brings about the change in the gross colour of the spore-bearing gills of many mushrooms and toadstools as they mature.

Stages in the colour-change of the maturing gills of a mushroom

Whatever the gross form of the body that contains them, all basidiospores are formed on modified hyphae called basidia which vary somewhat in appearance and structure (and are themselves sometimes valuable in identification) but all bear the spores at the tips of peg-like extensions called sterigmata (singular, sterigma). Most basidiomycetes normally produce four sterigmata and four basidiospores on each basidium. But *Agaricus bisporus* (p. 145) consistently produces only two; in the genus *Mycena* (p. 80), some species have two or one-spored basidia, (the spores tending to be larger than in four-spored basidia); and some *Sistotrema* species in the Hydnaceae (p. 173) have eight.

A range of other spore types is produced by the basidiomycetes. Oidia (singular oidium) will be mentioned only in passing, for they are unlikely to be encountered among the Agaricales unless the fungi are being artificially cultured in a laboratory, although their possible role in the transfer of genetic information will be referred to later (p. 295). Conventional asexual conidia are found rarely among the Agaricales, Aphyllophorales and other large fruit-bodied basidiomycetes, although they are formed by the parasitic agarics *Nyctalis* and *Asterophora* and some of the aquatic conidia-forming deuteromycetes (p. 223) are now known to be the asexual phases of basidiomycetes.

Different types of basidiospores

But it is among the smuts (Ustilaginales, p. 199) and especially the rusts (Uredinales, p. 201) that the diversity of basidiomycete spores reaches its zenith, and asexually produced spores attain tremendous importance.

Rusts and smuts are all plant pathogens and are so-called because of the rust-brown or sooty-black pustules that they produce on affected plants. These characteristically coloured pustules are reproductive structures within which asexual spores are produced. In the smuts their appearance is derived from masses of spores called teliospores. Their normally dark colouration results from the presence of large deposits of melanins in the spore wall, although in a few species brown or even yellow teliospores are formed. Nonetheless, the teliospores even of brown-spored species appear almost black en masse. The external appearance of mature smut teliospores may be more or less smooth as in *Ustilago hordei* (p. 200) or, more commonly, roughened with reticulations or with spines as in *Ustilago avenae* (p. 200) – a useful aid to identification, incidentally, as these two similar species both occur on the cultivated oat. Most teliospores are approximately spherical and unicellular, but in some species they cling together in loose groups; and in the genus *Urocystis* (p. 199), among others, a spore ball is formed comprising one or more central fertile cells or spores, surrounded by a small group of thinner-walled and sterile cells. Such varied arrangements of teliospores are important classificatory and identifying features. Teliospores range in size from about 3 μm to 20 or even 30 μm in diameter and are variable even within species; this variation tends to be less (and hence spore size more useful for identification and classification) in the smaller-spored forms. Spore balls of course may be very much larger than the dimensions quoted. It is following the germination of teliospores that basidiospores form.

Teliospores are also produced by rusts, and they too contain melanins

and are typically dark brown or black, though sometimes paler coloured. The rust teliospore is more commonly smooth-surfaced, though it may be minutely spiny; in *Puccinia smyrnii* the walls are deeply sculptured, and *Puccinia coronata*, crown rust (p. 201) is so named from the crown-like spines or teeth at one end of the teliospore. Rust teliospores are about the same size as those of smuts. Individually they are usually more or less spherical; and they may be produced singly (*Uromyces,* p. 203), or clustered into two (*Puccinia,* p. 201), three (*Triphragmium*), four (*Pucciniastrum*) or many-spored groups (*Phragmidium,* p. 203). It is a custom, moreover, and one which will be followed in this book, that the entire group, be it one-, two- or more-spored is referred to as 'the teliospore', the individual spores being called 'cells'. Thus, the species of the genus *Puccinia* are said to produce two-celled teliospores and the entire body in this important genus, as in some others, is characteristically stalked.

While it is the gross appearance of the teliospores that gives the smut fungi their popular name, it is a different type of asexual spore, produced by many species among the Uredinales, that makes the rusts 'rusty'. This spore is called a urediniospore. It is a single-celled, short-stalked, typically brown-coloured body (although appearing more or less colourless under the microscope) with a spiny or warty surface. Urediniospores are sometimes produced in chains, are usually more or less spherical in shape and commonly around 20 μm in diameter. Their walls usually contain pores that are fairly well seen under a good microscope and which, in their number and arrangement, have important taxonomic significance.

Yet a third type of asexual spore is found among some of the species of rust fungi. This is the aeciospore. Aeciospores are single-celled, usually yellow or orange spores, irregularly polygonal in shape as a result of their being crowded in the fruit body,

A smooth teliospore of a smut fungus

A rough teliospore of a smut fungus

A ball of smut teliospores

Teliospore of crown rust

Teliospore of a *Puccinia* species

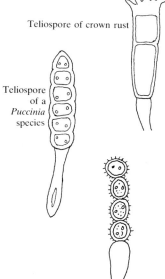

Urediniospores in a chain

233

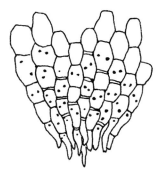

A group of aeciospores

called an aecium or cluster-cup, in which they are formed. They have a characteristically warty surface and are produced in chains, although dispersed as individuals. The occurrence of aeciospores in the life cycle is significant ecologically, for in some species of rust fungi, they are produced on different host plants from the urediniospores and teliospores (p. 297). Aeciospores are also normally associated with the final type of rust spore, the spermatium (plural spermatia). Although extremely important in the rust life cycle, (p. 297) spermatia will not be found frequently in the routine examination of rust specimens under the microscope. They are very small, often more or less oblong, thin walled cells that are the male gametes whose role is to fertilise the female cells.

Although all rusts are known or believed to produce spermatia, teliospores and basidia, there is considerable diversity in the numbers of additional spore types produced, even within a single genus; *Puccinia striiformis* (p. 201) for example, produces only urediniospores and *Puccinia lagenophorae* (p. 202) only aeciospores, while *Puccinia coronata* (p. 201) produces both and *Puccinia epilobii* neither. Rusts like *Puccinia coronata* that do produce all five types of spore are called macrocyclic; those that produce less than five, microcyclic and a shorthand system of notation using Roman numerals is used to denote the types of spores produced by individual species. Thus, the production of spermatia, aeciospores, urediniospores, teliospores and basidiospores is indicated respectively by the numerals 0, I, II, III and IV.

Ascomycetes
Hence to the spores produced by what is, numerically, the largest group of fungi, the ascomycetes. The group is sometimes known as the cup fungi from the cup- or bowl-shaped form of the fruit body displayed by some of the larger and more conspicuous members, although in reality this form is confined to relatively few species. The sexual spore of the ascomycetes is the ascospore; the asexual spore, the conidium, although the

Some species of rust fungi alternate from one host plant species to another, producing different types of spore on each.

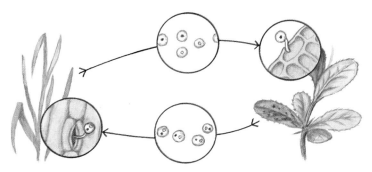

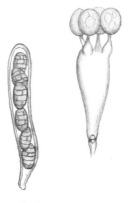

An ascus (left) contrasted with a basidium

quite astonishing array are also undeniably beautiful under the microscope, and the form and variety of the ascospore in particular is a major reason why many mycologists find this a most compulsive group to study and collect.

Some details of ascus structure as they relate to spore discharge (p. 241) and fruit body development (p. 242) are given elsewhere; but it should continually be remembered that the enclosed nature of the ascus is fundamentally different from the exposed basidium of the basidiomycetes. Within the ascus, which can best be likened to a microscopic cigar tube, the ascospores are confined while they mature and, although varying in important structural details (p. 42), the overall form of ascus tubes throughout the group is similar. If there is anything approaching constancy among the ascomycetes, it is in the number of spores contained within each ascus, for by far the majority produce eight. A few species have less; rather more species have more.

latter appears in a number of different guises: while some ascomycetes appear to have no conidia at all, others produce more than one type. Structurally, ascospores are more variable than any other type of fungal spore – at least of sexual spore – and no particular form can be said to be typical. They range in shape from uniformly or irregularly spherical, through egg, lemon and sausage shapes to extremely elongated, needle-like bodies, any of which may be variously curved in one or more planes. They range in size from the tiny spheres only 2 μm in diameter formed by *Sarea resinae* to the giant thread-like spores, over 180 μm long but only 2.5 μm wide produced by *Lophium mytilinum.* They may have walls either thin or variously thickened, smooth or with various folds, spines or other appendages on the surface; they may be colourless or variously pigmented especially in black, browns, or yellows. They may be single-celled or several-celled and, when several-celled, divided by internal cross walls or septa in a bewildering variety of ways. Some ascospores have a single nucleus, others have several, and to all of this variation may be added the variations in structure of the tube-like body or ascus in which they are confined and of the fruit body within which they are borne. The members of this whole,

Deuteromycetes

Consideration of the asexual spores of the ascomycetes inevitably means consideration of those of the deuteromycetes (p. 223) too, for they, by definition, lack any sexual spores and rely solely on conidia for reproduction and dispersal. Indeed, as explained earlier, most deuteromycetes *are* ascomycetes, merely being species that were discovered, described and named before their sexually-reproducing phases were recognised. Conidia show even greater variation in form than do ascospores, and considerably greater variation still in the structures on or within which they are borne (p. 298). If conidia do have any major structural features in common, these are their relatively thin spore walls, which do not confer great ability to overcome adverse conditions (conidia are not, in general, resting spores) and their smooth surfaces. Even here, there are exceptions in that some have thickening and surface ornamentation. In size,

conidia have a phenomenal range from tiny spores barely 1 μm in diameter, to such giants as those of the aquatic *Anguillospora* species that can be over 200 μm long and visible to the naked eye. In shape they spread across a bewildering and quite beautiful spectrum of diversity that includes spheres, needle- and sausage-shapes, three-dimensional stars (which are very common among aquatic forms) and even the most fantastically coiled springs. Such variation is presumably an adaptation to different dispersal systems (p. 244), as is the significant division into dry-spored and sticky-spored forms. In hue conidia range widely from colourless through reds, pinks and greens to blacks. (The division of the Hyphomycetes into the dark-spored forms like *Cladosporium* (p. 223) and the pale-spored forms like *Penicillium* (p. 223) is an important distinction for taxonomic and identification purposes.) Conidia-forming fungi also span a range from the many species like *Aspergillus* (p. 223) with single celled spores, to the many-celled forms with numerous and varied internal cross walls or septa.

Hyphomycetes and Coelomycetes

The major division of the deuteromycetes is into the Hyphomycetes which bear their conidia directly and fairly exposed on the mycelium, and the Coelomycetes which give some protection to the conidia by forming them within more or less enclosed structures. Within either category the individual conidia on their spore-bearing hyphae may be carried singly, in pairs, trios or in larger groups, in chains (which may themselves be branched) or in more irregular clusters.

Before progressing to an examination of the way that spores perform their functions, one important point must be emphasised. Reference has been made already to the fact that while some sexually formed spores are tough, thick-walled bodies, equipped for long term survival, others are inherently much more fragile. Moreover, whereas an agaric

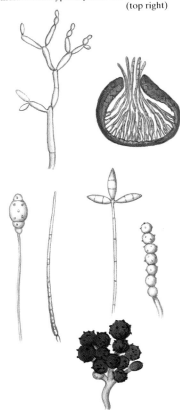

The varied form and arrangement of the conidia in the Hyphomycetes and Coelomycetes (top right)

such as *Amanita muscaria* (p. 55) or a bracket fungus like *Piptoporus betulinus* (p. 181), in common with most other large basidiomycetes, relies on its basidiospores for dispersal from one place to another, the basidiospores of the rusts (p. 201) and smuts (p. 199) take second place in this respect to their asexually formed spores. Similarly, while ascospores are the means of dispersal of most ascomycetes, other members of the group rely as much on their conidia. There is, indeed, no wholly consistent pattern in the ecological roles of the various types of spore that have been described.

Spore discharge

For a fungus to produce its spores, by whatever means, is one thing. To discharge them effectively from the spore-bearing structure is quite another. To ensure, moreover, that they are transported in a viable condition to a suitable site for growth, are equipped to survive trials and tribulations en route and, at the end of it all, provided with conditions conducive to germination, represents a challenging list of requirements. Few spore pilgrims setting out on their journey have any chance to arrive safely at the promised land and small wonder, therefore, that most fungal spores are produced in such prodigious quantity. A single plant root, parasitised by *Plasmodiophora brassicae* (p. 226) may be host to ten thousand million resting spores; a cap of *Agaricus campestris* (p. 147) can discharge as many basidiospores over the course of a week; and the bursting of the massive fruit body of *Langermannia gigantea* (p. 196) may almost instantly launch over seven million million basidiospores into the world.

But it is perhaps in the mechanisms of spore discharge that myco-engineering displays its most fantastic achievements. Sadly, they are achievements properly revealed only to the fortunate few who have peered for long hours through ingeniously arranged microscope systems. Although time-lapse photomicrography has brought some of the excitement of micro-ballistics to the armchair observer, nothing can compare with the tension of watching and waiting, for hour after hour, in the certain knowledge that the awaited split-second discharge of the spores is at least as likely to occur at the moment of the observer's blink as at any other.

But, it must be admitted, not all spore discharge is dramatic or entertaining. Few will gain great satisfaction or uncontrollable excitement from watching the decomposition of lettuce leaves that accompanies the discharge of the oospores of *Bremia lactucae* (p. 226) or from watching the gradual decay of a *Rhizopus* colony to leave behind its zygospores (p. 224). Perhaps the term release is a better one than discharge to describe such passive liberation of spores. Passive spore release may or may not, moreover, be followed by active dispersal. But where dispersal is subsequently important, it is essential that any discharge mechanism has a facility for placing the spore in the path of the dispersing agency. As has been implied already, passive spore release involves principally the disintegration and/or decay of the structure by which the spore adheres to the parent fungus. With most fungi, this is some form of mycelial structure, ranging from the simple, single hypha attached to the Zygomycete spore to the very much more complex tissues of the Gasteromycete puff-balls that shrivel away to release their basidiospores into the hollow sphere that is the puff-ball itself. Thereafter, a further passive phase (or, at least, passive in that the fungus itself plays no part in it), may result in the loose spores being given a lift a little further down the road towards freedom. Thus, once liberated from its parental mycelium, the *Bremia* oospore is released into the soil by the decay of the surrounding host plant tissues,

Time-lapse sequence showing spore formation and relase in *Rhizopus*

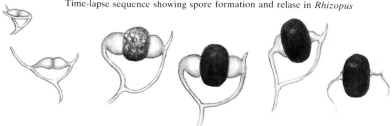

Spore discharge in a *Geastrum* species

whereas the loose basidiospores of *Lycoperdon* (p. 195) and *Geastrum* (p. 193) are puffed from their spherical prisons through a pore as rain, dripping from leaves, falls on the springy outer walls of their fruit bodies. Thereafter, dispersal takes over from discharge and other agencies have parts to play in the process.

Straddling the boundary between active and passive discharge mechanisms are those processes in which an external force wrenches the spores from their parent, without there necessarily being much disintegration of the physical attachment. The same force may or may not then play a further part in their more widespread dispersal. Wind is the commonest provider of such force and the conidia of the powdery mildews (p. 205) and of many of the downy mildews (p. 225), the teliospores of the loose smuts like *Ustilago nuda* (p. 200) and the urediniospores of rusts (p. 201) are readily blown from their birthplaces by mere breezes. Indeed, it is this very simple method of spore release that is the prelude to the very rapid and serious spread among crops that is displayed by so many disease-causing mildews, smuts and rusts. Water, in the form of rain drops, may similarly tear spores from

their anchorage. It is the main release method for the conidia of many deuteromycete moulds (p. 223), and has one of its most celebrated roles among the basidiomycetes with the bird's-nest fungi of the Order Nidulariales (p. 197). Here, the rain drops fall into the tiny nest-like fruit bodies and force out the 'eggs', or peridioles, which contain the basidiospores. Nonetheless, the bird's-nest fungus does not take an entirely passive role in the experience, for it possesses a spring-like cord that, when wet, swells in explosive fashion and catapults the peridioles a metre or more from the 'nest'.

Animals play their part too in spore release; just as spores are small, so it tends to be small animals that help them on their way. Insects are especially important, and no-one studies fungi for very long before becoming familiar with the role of flies in the release of basidiospores from the phallus-like fruit body of the stinkhorn *Phallus impudicus* (p. 198). The spores are embedded in a sugary slime endowed with an excremental aroma which, though repellent to humans, is attractive to flies. The slime and spores are eaten by the flies, and the spores are thus removed, both adhering to the flies' bodies and also surviving within their alimentary

Spore discharge in a Bird's-nest Fungus

tracts. The related Gasteromycete *Aseroë rubra* has a further apparent adaptation to insect attraction in being shaped like a crude flower with red petal-like rays to the fruit body. Would that the fossil record permitted comparison between the evolutionary histories of Gasteromycetes, flowers and flies! Many and ingenious are the adaptations of fungi to facilitate the removal of their spores by insects, but few more so than that of the smut *Ustilago violacea* (p. 199) which infects many plants of the carnation family Caryophyllaceae and causes the stamens to develop abnormally, so that at maturity they contain telio-spores instead of pollen grains. Moths still find the flowers attractive but collect spores instead of pollen – a remarkable instance of a parasite not only taking over the tissues of its host, but usurping the function of its repro-ductive messenger into the bargain.

Although the soil is replete with fungal life and with mycelium of fungi representative of all the major groups, relatively few types of larger fungi produce their fruit bodies below ground. Among the most important are the truffles, such as *Tuber* (p. 219) and its allies among the ascomycetes, and *Hydnangium* and *Hymenogaster* in the basidiomycetes. With their ascospores or basidiospores encased in fairly robust subterranean bodies, they would appear to be presented with a problem, both in discharge and in dispersal. The difficulty is neatly circumvented by the appeal of the fruit bodies to rodents which are attracted by their smell, uproot and eat them whole, and thus take the spores into their alimentary system, from which they subsequently emerge unscathed.

Several mechanisms seem to have evolved quite independently to dis-charge spores from the parent fungus without the intervention of any out-side body. In some instances (often known as the heavy artillery systems) such as the discharge of entire spore-bearing bodies of the Zygomycete, *Pilobolus* (p. 225) or the peridiole of the Gasteromycete, *Sphaerobolus* (p. 193), the force of discharge is so great and carries the spores so far

(over 2 metres vertically and 4 metres horizontally in the latter example) that no further dispersal may be needed. In most cases, however, the purpose of the discharge process is merely to enable the spores to be projected clear of the launching site to where the dispersing agency can take over. Even so, discharge of the spores over a few centimetres distance may be needed, and it is appropriate to start with one of the most widespread, intriguing but imperfectly understood processes, that of basidiospores from the caps of the Agaricales that gives rise to spore prints (p. 35). (The same system occurs also among the gelatinous basidiomycetes (Auricu-lariales, Dacrymycetales and Tremellales), the pore-bearing members of the Aphyllophorales, the rusts (Uredinales) and a few other groups.)

As long ago as 1845, it was noticed that the four basidiospores on a basidium were discharged forcibly, and in succession at intervals of a few seconds, to a distance of about 0.2 mm. How this is achieved is still imperfectly understood, but certain facts are clear. Each basidiospore is attached asymmetrically to its sterigma and the patient observer will see under his microscope that, just before the spore flies away, a tiny balloon appears at the point of attach-ment, increases to a certain size, and then seems to fly off with the spore. It appears that the balloon is a membrane-bound drop of liquid; but its role in discharge is enigmatic, for a few species such as the rust *Cronar-tium ribicola* (p. 203) appear to manage very well without it. Theories to explain the process have ranged from surface tension effects to some form of explosive discharge, and from

Discharge of a basidiospore from its sterigma

239

SPORE-BEARING SURFACES

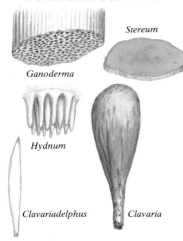

Stereum

Ganoderma

Hydnum

Clavariadelphus

Clavaria

a version of jet propulsion to opposing electrostatic charges on spore and sterigma. None is convincing.

Because forcibly discharged basidiospores can only be propelled over very short distances, almost all fruit body surfaces bearing them are arranged vertically with the basidia projecting horizontally from them in order to make use of the effect of gravity on the spores once they have parted company; there is simply not enough force available to propel them upwards into the air. This explains the vertical gills or tubes of the typical mushroom or toadstool fruit body in which the distance between adjacent gills or across the diameter of the tubes is greater than the range over which the spores are projected. The extremely refined mechanics of fruit body construction are revealed when it is appreciated that in a thick perennial bracket of the type produced by *Ganoderma* (p. 177), the tubes may ultimately be around 5 cm long but only 0.1 or 0.2 mm in diameter. Yet the spores are propelled with such accuracy into the centre of these tubes and fall vertically down them with such precision that very few become trapped on the sides but rain down in a continuous stream at the rate of several millions a

minute for 24 hours a day and over six months of the year. Less dependent on precise constructional dimensions are the more or less smooth, downward-facing spore-bearing surfaces such as those seen in *Stereum* (p. 186) and its allies, the downward facing pegs of *Hydnum* (p. 173) with basidia over the surface, the vertical branches of *Clavaria* (p. 162) and the slender clubs of *Clavariadelphus* (p. 163).

Usually, the basidiomycetes of familiar mushroom and toadstool type discharge their spores fairly uniformly from the entire spore-bearing surface, and this is associated with the uniform maturation of the spores that can be seen in those species whose spores change colour with age. The gills of a typical *Agaricus* (p. 145) for example, begin white, then turn pink and finally dark brown and do so uniformly over the surface. An exception is the genus *Panaeolus* (p. 156) which develops spotted gills, while in the genus *Coprinus* (p. 151) there is a progressive maturation of spores from the gill edge, upwards towards the gill base and outwards towards the edge of the cap, and this is revealed by the pattern of colour change from white to black, and by the gill tissue of *Coprinus* undergoing auto-digestion after spore discharge to form a black liquid (the feature that gave these fungi the name ink-caps). Because the spores are only being discharged at or close to the gill edge, therefore, they

Time-lapse of colour-change in Agaricus (above) and *Coprinus* gills

have only a very short distance to fall before reaching the freedom of the air; thus special arrangements to exploit the pull of gravity (see geotropism, p. 257) are not necessary for *Coprinus* gills.

Unlike the basidiomycetes, the ascomycetes produce their spores within enclosed, tubular bodies and in order for ascospores to be liberated therefore, some mechanism is needed for rupture of this body, the ascus, and propulsion of the spores outwards. There are several versions of this process, all more clearly understood than is basidiospore discharge. In most ascomycetes the rupture is an explosive phenomenon that follows an increase in pressure within the ascus following water uptake. Apparently a chemical change of the sugars present within the mature ascus results in water moving through the ascus wall. Rather like the safety-valve on a pressure-cooker, the ascus ruptures at its weakest point, the tip, either by throwing off a small cap, or flinging back a hinged lid, or merely breaking open a pore. The species of ascomycetes with caps or lids on their asci are known as operculate while the types having a pore are called inoperculate. (The difference is an important one in the classification and identification of the group.)

Once the ascus is ruptured, the ascospores are ejected forcibly, either in rapid succession as in *Cordyceps militaris* (p. 205) and *Trichoglossum hirsutum* (p. 209), or more or less simultaneously as in *Sordaria fimicola* (p. 208) where the spores may actually stick together to some extent. The distance over which discharge is effective

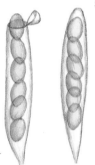

Operculate (left) and inoperculate asci of ascomycetes

varies greatly, but it is invariably further than that for basidiospores. Around 1 or 2 cm is perhaps the commonest range, but the special problems associated with many of the dung-inhabiting species (p. 277) – which must ensure that their spores land, not on another part of the dung, but where they are likely to be eaten by herbivores – mean that much greater distances must be achieved. *Podospora fimicola* for instance, can propel its spores for at least 30 cm; and it has been calculated that the ascospores of *Sordaria* leave the ascus at a speed of around 1000 cm/sec, or about 36 km/hr. Many ascomycetes have more or less symmetrically-shaped spores, but others tend to be more ovoid and these are almost invariably ejected with the large end first. There is some evidence that the latter form more efficient projectiles, and it is certainly true that most species with ovoid spores tend to shoot over a longer range. Given this fairly constant method of liberating ascospores from the ascus, there is a wide range

Podospora fimicola in its natural environment, showing its firing range

of variations in the shape of the ascomycete fruit body, and in the way in which the spores are liberated.

Many 'Discomycetes' such as *Aleuria aurantia* (p. 221) have a dish- or even plate-like fruit body, or apothecium, with an almost flat spore-bearing surface. Others show varying degrees of reflexion that reach their most extreme in such stalked species as *Helvella elastica* (p. 216). In such forms the ascospores will be thrown clear of the parent fungus, but what of the many types like *Peziza* (p. 217) which have the fruit body shape that gave the 'Discomycetes' their popular name of cup-fungi, or the contorted, almost brain-like surface of *Morchella* (p. 215) or *Gyromitra* (p. 216)? What prevents ascospores being thrown wastefully against the opposite spore-bearing surface? The answer lies in the ingenious phenomenon of positive phototropism, growth towards the light (popularly imagined to be associated solely with the photosynthetic nutrition of green plants). The ascus possesses photosensitive chemicals that cause its tip, or even a large proportion of its total length, to curve towards the light and hence ensure that the spores are ejected away from the spore-bearing surface and into the open air. In a few stalked species, the entire fruit body grows towards the light.

Sitting very quietly on the ground at a woodland edge among a group of mature ascomycete fruit bodies, the inexperienced mycologist may be surprised to hear as well as seen. The simultaneous explosive discharge of many thousands of ascospores is called 'puffing' and can give a clearly audible 'pop'. It is a phenomenon that seems to occur when a sudden shaft of bright sunlight or a rush of dry air strikes them. The biological significance of this phenomenon is not known, but one plausible explanation is that, as the spores are thrown higher than occurs with single ascus discharge (because the air above the fruit body is disturbed by the mass exodus), they can be thrust clear of the almost still layer of air that exists close to the ground.

SPORE-BEARING SURFACES

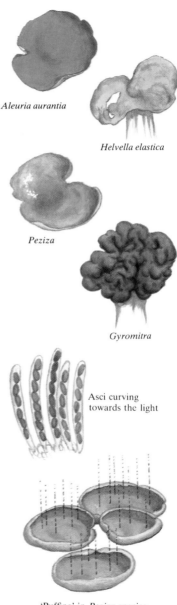

Aleuria aurantia

Helvella elastica

Peziza

Gyromitra

Asci curving towards the light

'Puffing' in *Peziza* species

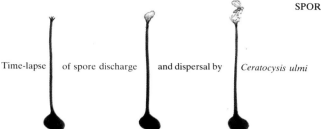

Time-lapse | of spore discharge | and dispersal by | *Ceratocysis ulmi*

Unlike the exposed spore-bearing surface of the 'Discomycete' apothecium, the more enclosed structures called perithecia produced by the 'Pyrenomycetes' offer the ascospores the prospect of a less straightforward journey to the exterior, for, on the face of it, they will be discharged merely into the interior of the fruit body. There is, nonetheless, an escape-route in the form of a small opening at the top but it is small indeed and as a quick way out seems to leave a great deal to be desired. Indeed, in many species, like *Ceratocystis ulmi* (p. 206), the Dutch elm disease fungus, the actual orifice is situated at the apex of a long neck. There are several ways in which the ascospores find their way through this opening. In *Chaetomium* species, for example, there is no explosive discharge at all and the asci break down inside the perithecium to be squeezed through the opening in a toothpaste-like tendril of spores and mucilage, very like the tendrils of asexual conidia released from the fruit bodies of some deuteromycetes. In others, like the long-necked species of *Ceratocystis* (p. 206), the spores and mucilage are squeezed little beyond the opening itself where they are held by a small rosette of radiating hyphae pending their removal by wind or insects.

Nonetheless, many 'Pyrenomycete' species do display the more conventional explosive ascospore discharge which occurs as, one by one, the individual asci elongate and grow up the neck until the tip protrudes into the exterior. After the spores have been liberated, the empty ascus retracts into the fruit body and eventually gelatinises, another then elonga-

ting in its place. Clearly, this confers both advantages and disadvantages compared with the 'Discomycete' system. Puffing and the simultaneous release of many asci into turbulent air is impossible; but, conversely, the little-by-little approach is likely to ensure that at least some spores are discharged when conditions are favourable for their dispersal. Moreover, some long-necked 'Pyrenomycetes' have managed to speed up the explosive discharge by having the empty ascus expelled by the next one in line, rather than waiting for it to retract.

Asci elongating, protruding, retracting and gelatinising in a normal (left) and a long-necked 'Pyrenomycete'

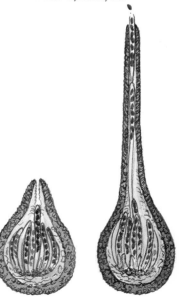

Outside the ascomycetes, explosive discharge as a result of the bursting of a cell under pressure is rare; but two notable examples occur among the Zygomycetes. The dung-inhabiting mould *Pilobolus* (p. 225) is faced with the same problem as *Podospora* in its need to throw the spores clear of the dung and onto the surrounding vegetation. It has evolved a quite phenomenal artillery piece, out of all proportion to its size, in order to achieve this objective. The spore-containing body has a liquid-filled bulb-like structure at its base which ultimately bursts along a line of weakness and hurls the entire body vertically as much as 2 metres and horizontally even further to adhere firmly to plants nearby. A similar but less dramatic version of this system occurs in the spore discharge of the insect parasite *Entomophthora muscae* (p. 225) and the results of the process are often seen when flies, killed by the fungal infection, adhere to a window pane and are surrounded by the dusty white halo of discharged conidia.

There are other explosive methods of spore discharge, apart from the bursting of cells. In one widespread system pressure builds up in irregularly shaped cells; but, instead of bursting, the cells release the tension by rounding off suddenly. The discharge of rust aeciospores for a distance of several millimetres employs this system, which reaches its peak in the Gasteromycete *Sphaerobolus*

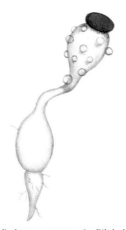

Spore discharge apparatus in *Pilobolus*

(p. 193) where a mass of cells under pressure suddenly rounds off and throws a spore cluster over 4 metres. Among some of the dark-spored deuteromycetes, conidial discharge arises as a result of a process comparable with that found quite widely among ferns, an explosive rupture following the build-up of water tension through evaporation. Some species in the Peronosporales (p. 225) rely on a sudden change from high to low humidity to sever spore-bearing hyphae from the parent fungus.

Spore dispersal

By one way or another, therefore, spores are released, discharged, propelled or otherwise launched into independent existence. As suggested already, for some species this process may itself provide adequate separation from the parent or colony for successful growth and nutrition. But for most some further dispersal is needed, and here a comparison with the seeds, fruits and pollen-grains of higher plants is valid, for many of the same living and non-living dispersal agencies are employed. But the same environmental stresses and strains will be exerted upon the microscopic fungal spore as on the much more robust seed.

The small size and very light weight of the spores means that wind in particular can play a highly significant role in the dispersal process. Indeed,

Sphaerobolus cells rounding off and exploding

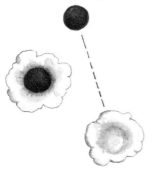

wind is far and away the most important spore-carrying agency; and the study of the physical behaviour of spores borne along in the atmosphere has spawned the science of aerobiology. This blends physics, mathematics, meteorology and topography, with a smattering of oceanography, geography and other disciplines and, of course, spore biology. Its tool is the spore-trap, a device that in its commonest form, draws in air at a uniform rate and passes it over a sticky surface to which spores adhere and can later be counted and, in most cases, identified under a microscope. By placing sampling traps at different localities and at different heights in the air (including mounting them on aircraft), it is possible to derive a picture of spore dispersal patterns in both time and space.

Borne by the wind, fungal spores are carried both vertically and horizontally, their concentration in the air decreasing the further they travel from the parent fungus. While it is clearly impossible to keep track for very long of the basidiospores from an individual fruit body, the urediniospores of cereal-infecting rusts, produced in quite prodigious quantity on diseased crops, are carried along in vast numbers, called spore-clouds. Vertically they may be borne aloft on thermals, and the urediniospores of *Puccinia graminis* (p. 201), for instance, have been recovered from heights of over 5,000 metres. Horizontally, distances of hundreds or even thousands of kilometres are well documented; and the annual arrival of the cereal rusts *Puccinia graminis* and *Puccinia recondita* (p. 201) in the wheat belt of the northern United States and Canada (where they cannot survive the cold winters) is the result of

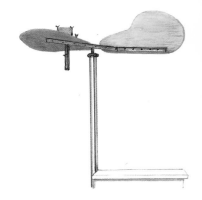

A spore trap

urediniospores being carried north from Mexico and the southern states. There is no reason to suppose that the spores of other fungi, numerically too small to be followed, are transported over any smaller distances; but transport is not necessarily synonymous with survival.

Important as such inter-continental dispersal of fungus spores is, both for the fungi themselves in colonising new territory and for the farmer whose crops fall prey to pathogens from foreign parts, the more parochial daily and seasonal changes in the types of spores present close to the ground reveal more about the timing of spore release. A sample of the spores present in the air close to the ground in temperate regions on a warm dry summer's day is likely to be composed predominantly of conidia of the ubiquitous deuteromycete mould *Cladosporium* (p. 223) together with asexual spores of rusts, smuts and others that depend on dry air for their release. In wet weather, ascospores predominate, their release relying on the absorption of moisture

A field affected by cereal rust

by the ascus. Ascospores are also common in the air at night, when they are joined most notably by the basidiospores of the Agaricales. The concentrations of spores found in the air fairly close to the ground can be prodigious and forty or fifty thousand per cubic metre is not at all uncommon. Some air-borne fungal spores can bring about allergic reactions when breathed in, and they may, on occasions, be at least as important as pollen grains in inducing the symptoms of hay fever.

The importance of rain in spore release has already been mentioned; it can also play a part in short-range dispersal, a phenomenon particularly obvious when soil containing spores of plant-pathogenic fungi is splashed by rain onto low-hanging vegetation, where infection occurs and the fungi thus become evident. But the dispersal of fungal spores in water is generally limited to aquatic species, not only those producing water-requiring zoospores, but also the many types of 'Hyphomycete' (p. 223) that live in or near water and whose remarkably branched conidia can be recovered from foam. Many of the latter species are known, tantalisingly, only from their spores which have never been germinated in the laboratory, and whose parental forms, therefore, have not yet been seen.

As with seeds, the dispersal of fungal spores by animals takes many forms, and almost all groups of the animal kingdom from nematodes to mammals have representatives that been implicated with one spore dispersal process or another. Mammals are important in the dispersal of dung fungi like *Pilobolus* (p. 225) and *Podospora*. Eaten with vegetation, the spores survive intact during their journey through the mammal's gastric enzymes; indeed, in some instances, such a journey is necessary to stimulate germination. Many other species of fungi must benefit from the adherence of their spores to the hair or fur of mammals. Man himself is probably not particularly important in the routine of spore dispersal of fungi; but when he *is* involved, his dispersal of species to completely new territories (resulting from his habit of almost unlimited movement throughout the world) can have immense ecological implications. The artificial introduction of Dutch elm disease to Britain is a particularly dramatic example of this.

Birds might be thought important in spore dispersal, for they move rapidly over long distances, but there is evidence for their role in only a few instances. One of the most notable, and at the same time enigmatic, is that of the ascomycete *Endothia parasitica,* the cause of a serious canker disease of sweet chestnuts (*Castanea* spp.) It is known that starlings, woodpeckers and tree creepers can carry spores of *Endothia,* and the latter two especially might be thought ideally equipped to introduce the fungus into healthy trees. Nonetheless, it appears

Rain falls on healthy fruit (left), and splashes spores of plant-pathogenic fungi up from the ground, causing disease.

Apple with scab

that only conidia and not ascospores are normally carried (examination of one woodpecker was said to reveal half a million conidia, although the report did not give details of how they were counted!) and it is a puzzle why migrating birds have never succeeded in introducing the fungus to Britain, for it is widespread in continental Europe.

The role and importance of insects in spore dispersal is well documented; the flies that detach the basidiospores from *Phallus impudicus* (p. 198) and the moths that collect the teliospores of *Ustilago violacea* (p. 199) are equally important in dispersing them. Probably the most dramatic result of insect dispersal of fungus spores in recent years has been the carrying by bark beetles (*Scolytus* spp) of the conidia and ascospores of *Ceratocystis ulmi* (p. 206), the cause of Dutch elm disease. The fungus produces its spores within the moist, sheltered environment provided by the bark-tunnels made by the beetles. As the young adult beetles emerge from their pupae in the bark, they feed on the fungal growth and so emerge with spores inside, and sticking to the outsides of, their bodies. They are thus ideally equipped to introduce the fungus into healthy trees. Indeed, the beetle-*Ceratocystis* association illustrates well two important features of insect dispersal: the spores are sticky to facilitate adhesion to the insects' bodies, and the feeding habits of the insects

practically guarantee that the spores are delivered to a site favourable for growth. Thus, just as the random dispersal of pollen by wind necessitates more copious pollen production than the precise insect–mediated delivery system, so wind-dispersed fungi generally produce far more spores than do insect-dispersed species.

Reference has been made to the smaller concentration of fungal spores in the air the greater the distance from their parental source. Why is there not always a corresponding gradient in new fungal colonies or individuals? In some instances, there is: perhaps the most familiar over a short range is displayed by the apple scab pathogen, *Venturia inaequalis* (p. 222). Diseased apples very commonly show one large scab lesion surrounded by many smaller ones, decreasing in density the further they are from the centre.

On a grosser scale, however, this

Dutch Elm Disease is caused by the fungus *Ceratocystis ulmi* carried by bark beetles.

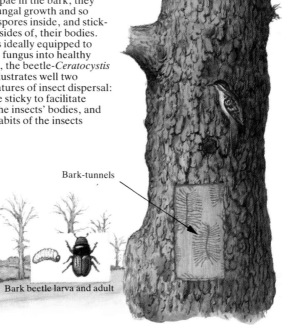

Bark-tunnels

Bark beetle larva and adult

trend is much less frequently apparent and there are several reasons for this. First, many spores may be eaten or die en route. Second, many may land in a viable state but fail to germinate because the conditions are unsuitable.

Third, some may germinate, but like many plant seedlings the resultant fungi never develop because the nutrient required for further growth is unavailable, or because they are unable to compete with other organisms (or for other reasons). Spores are usually tougher than hyphae, but even those with the added protection of particular chemicals in their walls are still fragile. Their environmental enemies are extremes of temperature or humidity and harmful radiation. As may be expected, resting spores, teliospores, and others intended specifically to survive adversity, are the most tolerant of environmental extremes. In turn, ascospores are generally more tolerant of adverse conditions than are basidiospores or conidia, while zoospores are probably the most delicate of all. Nonetheless, at the extremes, there are conidia of some heat-loving deuteromycetes (see p. 255) that can tolerate temperatures in excess of 60°C; and spores of most fungi can survive after being deep-frozen experimentally for long periods of time, although they are not equally tolerant of the spasmodic temperature changes that occur during natural freezing and thawing.

It is when spores are undergoing dispersal from one ecological niche to another that they are likely to experience intolerable conditions, and how long they are exposed to them can be critical. For example, being borne aloft in a thermal into dry air on a hot summer's day may expose spores to a temperature in excess of 50°C for a few hours, as well as threatening them with complete drying out. If they are borne high enough, they could also be exposed to large and potentially lethal doses of ultra-violet radiation. A swift return to earth in a thunderstorm may pre-empt any damage, whereas being carried along for days or even weeks under such conditions may be lethal.

Spore perennation

Even spores that do not participate in any type of hazardous dispersal process, but stay precisely where they were formed, will still face adversity in the shape of the environmental conditions that change with the seasons. In a temperate climate, the ranges of temperature and humidity in spring and summer can be very large indeed. In winter, many of the fungi that feed on or are otherwise dependent on plant life will be faced with the additional problem that the plants themselves have died down, died out or embarked on some survival process of their own. It is principally to provide for this short-term seasonal survival that most types of so-called resting structure have evolved among fungi. And although specialised vegetative structures play a major role in survival and over-wintering in some fungi, spores are the most important perennating bodies.

The resting spore, oospore and certain other spore types have already been mentioned as having this perennating function, but perhaps the most conspicuous example is displayed by some of the rust fungi. *Phragmidium tuberculatum* (p. 203) is familiar to gardeners as the cause of the rust disease of roses. During the summer, rose leaves are often peppered with the powdery yellow pustules within which urediniospores form; indeed urediniospores, which provide the means for the rapid dissemination of the fungus during the host plant's growing season, are often called summer spores. They are unable, however, to survive over winter and so, as autumn approaches, the yellow pustules are seen increasingly to be interspersed with black ones within which the much more resistant teliospores or winter spores form.

Spore longevity has been studied in detail under laboratory conditions, but it is often very difficult to equate experimental findings with the natural situation. Nonetheless, there is clear evidence that resting spores of *Plasmodiophora brassicae* (p. 226) can survive in a viable condition in

Phragmidium tuberculatum on rose leaves in summer (left) and autumn

soil for over twenty years, and spore balls of *Synchytrium endobioticum* (p. 226) for over thirty, whereas basidiospores of *Phaeolus schweinitzii* (p. 175) only manage about six months, and conidia of *Phytophthora infestans* (p. 226) barely last thirty days. On average, spores of most species can probably survive under their normal, natural conditions for about two years.

As well as the constraints of the physical environment, spores provide rich pickings for many other organisms that, like bacteria, bring about their disintegration piecemeal, like some amoebae that suck out their insides or, like mites, many insects and nematodes, devour them entire. Larger creatures such as snails, slugs and rodents that feed on ascomycete and basidiomycete fruit bodies also consume large numbers of spores and, although a few fungal species have responded to this challenge by developing resistance to the animals' digestive enzymes and have thus found a ready means of dispersal, most are not so blessed.

Microscopic view of bacteria surrounding a fungal spore

Spore germination

Assuming that a spore has, despite the odds, achieved a safe landing, it must successfully complete one more vital, complicated and somewhat fraught process before it can achieve its biological objective of perpetuating the species. It must germinate. And it is in germination and its associated processes that functional analogies between spores and seeds become most valid. Just as some seeds are capable of germination as soon as they ripen on the parent plant, whereas others enter a resting or dormant condition, so some spores are capable of germinating immediately (and in many instances when they are still attached to the parent), while others require a period of weeks or months before they may

Dung inhabiting fungus on a cow-pat

do so. Although the nature of the factors conferring dormancy on spores is imperfectly understood, it is known that some are internal biochemical features inherited from their parent fungus, whereas others are external, such as the presence or absence in the environment of certain chemicals or even of other microorganisms.

The conditions needed to break the dormancy and/or induce germination are more clearly known. High temperatures are needed in many cases, especially for ascospores. In the dung-inhabiting fungi, for instance, it is clear how this requirement may have evolved. Their spores seem unable to germinate until they have passed through the high temperatures inside the body of the animal that has

Rhizina undulata on a bonfire site

ingested them. Yet what logical explanation can there be for the requirement of some soil-inhabiting species like *Rhizina undulata* (p. 217) to experience the heat of a fire before they burst into life? Such fungi are quite common on areas where bonfires have been lit (p. 290) and it can only be assumed that, in pre-history, when the only cause of fires was lightning or volcanic eruptions, these species were rather rarer than they are today.

Many different chemical compounds have been suggested as stimulants of germination, but although a good deal of laboratory evidence for their roles has been forthcoming, there is not much information about their importance naturally. Some plant-pathogenic fungi undeniably seem to be stimulated to germinate in the presence of exudates from their host plants; conversely, some plant exudates operate as germination inhibitors and are indeed part of the plant's defence mechanism against fungal infection (p. 262). The spores of some mycorrhizal fungi (p. 267) seem to be stimulated to germinate by exudates from the roots of their mycorrhizal partners; *Russula adusta* (p. 101) basidiospores, for instance, are stimulated by pine roots, but it is unclear how widespread or specific are such interactions.

Spore germination in almost all fungi starts with the emergence from the spore of a hypha known as the germ tube. But this will be not only the beginning but also the end of fungal growth unless environmental conditions are appropriate and nutrient supplies available for the continued development of the fungal colony.

HYPHAE

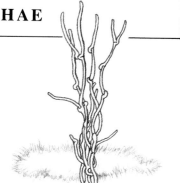

Aside from the very obvious structures like mushrooms, toadstools and other large fruit bodies, the word fungus will most readily conjure up visions of a 'mould', a growth on damp things in damp places. And the adjective used most commonly to describe such mould is 'fluffy'; the simile used most frequently is to cotton wool. Both fluffiness and similarity to cotton wool are due to the appearance of the basic structural unit common to almost all fungi, the hypha (plural hyphae). Yet it is this essentially thread-like body that, in varying degrees of aggregation and modification, gives rise to the enormous range of size and shape among the fungi at large. It is a range that extends from the miniature colonies of a tiny aquatic Oomycete, elusively buried within the root tissues of some water plant, unseen and unknown to all except the most patient and dedicated microscopist, to the puff-balls of *Langermannia gigantea* (p. 196), over a metre in diameter, or to the uncharted kilometres of growth in the soil that can sprout forth fruit bodies over 100 metres apart.

The fungal hypha has no close parallels among other living organisms (although its similarities and possible relationship to the algal filament are discussed on p. 12). It differs in several respects from what is usually defined as a cell, the basic unit of structure and growth of plants, animals and most other living things. And although superficially uniform in most respects, there are important variations between different fungal groups in the details of their hyphal

Enlargement of a cottonwool-like mould to show long, branching hyphae

structure. While some of these differences are chemical, elusive and esoteric, others are valuable in identification.

A hypha is a thin-walled transparent tube filled or lined with a layer of watery liquid cytoplasm. It is commonly around 5 μm in diameter, but in length is theoretically infinite. Hyphae are typically branched in many and often complex ways; a collective mass of hyphal filaments, some of which may be joined together through the fusion of their branches, is called a mycelium. This ability of

Microscopic view of a single hypha

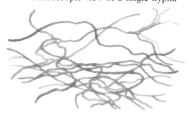

The long hyphae of some fungus species can deliver fruit bodies some distance apart.

Coprinus comatus can uplift tarmac

hyphae to fuse, not only with other hyphae that grew from the same spore, but sometimes with hyphae originating from other spores too, raises an interesting and curious question; how can one define an individual fungus? It is a straightforward matter to point to one dog, one lizard or one oak tree and know that this is a discrete and distinct organism. Even such colonial animals as sponges are fairly readily divisible into their separate, individual units. But although a mycologist may refer to *a* fruit body, *a* toadstool or *a* bracket, he will do so in the knowledge that it is only a small component of what is routinely called a fungal colony, parts of which may have had quite distinct parental or ancestral beginnings.

There is also the allied concept of virtually indefinite longevity among fungi. Although parts of a colony may die away, other parts physically connected to them will continue to grow and develop; and in the continued presence of nutrients and other requirements, they will theoretically do so forever.

The hypha may be sub-divided by internal cross walls or septa, and the presence or absence of these septa is characteristic of certain groups. The Oomycetes and Zygomycetes usually have aseptate hyphae (although septa may be present to divide a spore-bearing structure from the rest of the mycelium), while those of the basidiomycetes, ascomycetes and deuteromycetes are normally septate. The appearance of the septa varies and, at advanced levels of study, this variation is employed in classification and identification.

It has already been said that hyphae differ from cells. Apart from their greatly elongated form, one feature above all strikes at the heart of that most people learn about cells in school biology classes. Whereas a cell by most definitions contains only one nucleus, hyphae contain many nuclei which may vary genetically. (Such elongated, multinucleate structures are known as coenocytes.)

In addition to nuclei, hyphae contain within their cytoplasm most of the other minute structures normally to be found in cells, although they lack the chloroplasts characteristic of green plants. The boundary wall of the hypha has some very special features of structural importance, also significant in classification. It is the composition of the wall, in combination with the turgor pressure of the cytoplasm, that gives hyphae great structural strength combined with plasticity; and any who doubt this strength should observe the uplifting of tarmac by the fruit bodies of such basidiomycetes as *Coprinus comatus* (p. 151). Although hyphal walls, like the spore walls referred to earlier, have a complex chemistry (including proteins, fats and other substances), the nature of the large carbohydrate component is of the greatest significance. Fungi can be divided broadly into the major divisions of the Oomycetes and few minor groups that (like algae and higher plants) contain cellulose in the hyphal wall, and the remainder that contain some other carbohydrate, most commonly chitin, a substance found widely among the animal kingdom. The nature of these differences has been used to make deductions about the evolution and relationships of fungi (p. 12).

Mycelia

Higher plants possess clearly defined tissues called meristems where new growth takes place and new cells form; but fungal mycelia do not normally have any clearly differentiated growth regions, each hypha elongating by growth at its tip in an area immediately behind the apex where the wall is more plastic. Given a uniform nutritional environment in which to develop, fungi typically produce circular colonies as they spread out radially from a germinating spore or hyphal fragment. This is a familiar pattern, and will be seen in the colonies of *Penicillium* (p. 223) on rotting fruit, or of *Mucor* (p. 224) on damp bread, in the growth of such pathogens as *Septoria* (p. 223) producing spots on the leaf of a host plant, and in many toadstools in occurring in ring patterns (p. 274) as the fruit bodies emerge above ground close to the edge of the subterranean mycelium. That the colonies in a three-dimensional medium are actually spherical is best seen if a fragment of diseased plant tissue or a morsel of mouldy cheese is submerged in water when a globular mass of hyphae will sprout forth. The speed of growth of hyphae varies between species and with environmental conditions and nutrient availability, but at its maximum is probably about 6 mm per hour.

The extent to which the term tissue can be applied to fungal growth is arguable. By definition, a tissue is a collection of cells of the same type, associated together to serve some common and collective function. Even if it is accepted that fungi do not have cells, however, it can be argued that they have aggregates of hyphae that perform some unified function and within which there may even be some 'division of labour', different regions fulfilling some specific purpose to the common good. The nomenclatural problem is dodged by referring to the aggregates as pseudo-tissues: pseudo-parenchyma, for example, is so named by analogy with the relatively unspecialised higher plant tissue, parenchyma.

In hyphal aggregates, individual hyphae associate physically close together, and may undergo certain changes. Specific pigments may form, deposits and incrustations may arise on or within the walls to provide greater structural stability, and the wall itself may change chemically. The most familiar examples of hyphal aggregates are those in reproductive structures, especially the large fruit bodies of ascomycetes and basidiomycetes in which the different textures, shapes and colours even within the various parts of a single body are testimony to the hyphal changes just described. Superficially so solid in appearance, the true nature of such structures can readily be seen if a small portion of a toadstool is teased apart and examined under a microscope, or even with a hand lens, whereupon the filamentous, hyphal nature will be apparent.

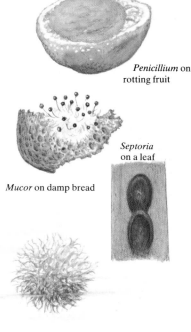

Penicillium on rotting fruit

Septoria on a leaf

Mucor on damp bread

A globular mass of hyphae proceeding from mouldy cheese submerged in water

Less familiar types of mycelial aggregate are the structures known as strands, rhizomorphs and sclerotia – less familiar, at least, to all except the gardener who has detected the killer honey fungus, *Armillaria mellea* (p. 71) spreading with rhizomorphs through the soil of his shrubbery. Often likened to black boot-laces, these structures display some of the highest levels of organisation found among fungal bodies, for within them are regions very similar to real apical growing points, real cells and real conducting tissues. Many an inexperienced microscopist, confronted with a section of rhizomorph in his practical examination, has interpreted it as a higher plant organ. The rhizomorphs of *Armillaria* found beneath tree bark are more flattened, and may be half a centimetre in diameter and contain several thousand individual hyphae.

Less complex is the looser aggregation of hyphae in a mycelial strand. It is to be hoped that few mycologists, at least in their own homes, will ever see one of its best known manifestations in the almost cobweb-like growth of *Serpula lacrimans,* the dry rot fungus (p. 170). Both strands and rhizomorphs provide a means for a fungus to cross a region of unfavourable environmental conditions and reach a new food source; *Armillaria* rhizomorphs across soil in search of tree roots, and *Serpula* strands across a brick wall in search of structural timbers, for instance.

The third major type of non-reproductive hyphal aggregate serves the purpose of enabling a fungus not to cross unfavourable spaces but to sit out unfavourable times: the sclerotium, like the various types of resting spore, is a survival or perennating body. Like many spores too, it contains accumulations of melanins, so that most sclerotia are black. They are frequently produced by plant-pathogenic fungi to enable them to survive over winter in the absence of their host plants and most are only about one millimetre in diameter. Notable exceptions include the ergots of *Claviceps purpurea* (p. 205), and

Microscopic view of an *Armillaria* rhizomorph

Dry rot

Sclerotium of an over-wintering plant-pathogenic fungus

related species, so important in former times as fungal toxins of flour (p. 302), often several centimetres long. (Even these, however, cannot rival *Polyporus mylittae,* an Australian basidiomycete with sclerotia that attain the size of footballs and are sometimes known as native bread, or the only slightly smaller *Polyporus tuberaster.*)

The sheath of fungal mycelium that envelops the roots and rootlets of many trees to form a symbiotic mycorrhizal association (p. 267) is an aggregate of sorts, but this will be described in more detail in respect of its role in fungal nutrition, as will the specialised feeding hyphae which are

used by certain plant pathogenic fungi to tap the nutrient resources of their host's cells (p. 262).

There is also, however, one aberrant but extremely familiar type of fungal structure. The fungal species often called baker's or brewer's yeast is an ascomycete, *Saccharomyces cerevisiae*, yet it is an ascomycete with no mycelium, and produces instead a mass of more or less rounded 'cells' that multiply by vegetative budding – each cell increases in volume and then buds off a new cell. There are many other yeast species too, and in artificial culture some can be induced to form ascospores. And although the natural origin of the yeast-like growth habit is unknown, it can be adopted by a wide range of fungi under certain environmental conditions.

Hyphal and mycelial growth

Like all other living things, fungi grow in response to the relative abundance in their environment of the nutrients they particularly need. They also grow, through the medium of their hyphae, in response to certain other well defined environmental influences – temperature, moisture, concentrations of oxygen and other gases, pH (acidity or alkalinity) and other chemical or physical factors. Some of these have been mentioned in relation to spore survival and germination; hyphae are generally more sensitive than spores to changes or extremes of environment and, even within the range of different hyphal activities, there are variations in their

A compost-heap cut away to show growth of *Volvariella speciosa*

response to temperature. But because, ultimately, fungal growth depends on biochemical processes essentially similar to those occurring in other organisms, their optimum growth takes place in a similar temperature range – mostly between about 15°C and 30°C, with a maximum tolerable temperature below 45°C and a minimum above 0°C. Nonetheless, as in other groups of organisms, some species have adapted to the extremes, and there are predominantly tropical and predominantly polar fungi as there are such higher plants. Interestingly, plant pathogenic fungi do not always inhabit the whole geographical distributions of their hosts, not always being able to tolerate the same temperature ranges.

Very few large basidiomycete species produce annual fruit bodies in the dead of winter; perhaps the most notable, *Flammulina velutipes* (p. 88) is actually accorded the name winter fungus, while another, *Polyporus brumalis* (p. 181) is called the winter polypore. The predominantly autumnal appearance of most agarics is at least partly a temperature-mediated phenomenon, and all mushroom collectors look forward to the harvest that occurs if autumn rains moisten a soil warmed through a long hot summer. Precisely which feature of fungal growth responds most to this critical temperature requirement is less perfectly understood.

It is probably from hot- and cold-tolerant that hot- and cold-requiring species have evolved. The most dramatic examples of heat-requiring (or thermophilic) fungi are not as might be supposed the inhabitants of far-off volcanic springs. Rather, they are, like *Talaromyces emersonii* and *Humicola lanuginosa,* the fungi of the compost-heap and the dung-hill. These two species have maximum and minimum growth temperatures of 60°C and 30°C respectively, perhaps no surprise to anyone who has seen fit to plunge their arm into a compost-heap in the height of summer. Cold-requiring fungi seem to have been reported much less frequently than

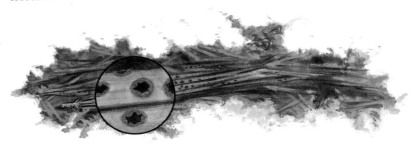

Phacidium infestans on pine-needles in snow

thermophiles, possibly because extreme cold occurs less frequently than extreme heat in regions where mycologists flourish! Nonetheless, there is now evidence for fairly common species of *Mucor* (p. 224) and *Rhizopus* (p. 225), among others, being able to grow on deep-frozen foodstuffs at −10°C; and *Phacidium infestans,* a fungus infecting pine needles, has been recorded as displaying mycelial growth in Swedish forests in temperatures as low as −21°C. But as with spores, so with mycelium: survival at the extremes is not necessarily synonymous with growth, although few would minimise the achievement of those fungi of the Arctic Tundra that can tolerate temperatures ranging between 0°C and −60°C for much of the year, simply to be able to grow for a single month in the brief northern summer.

On a much more parochial level, it may well be temperature gradients that are partly responsible for the distribution of fungi within a woodland, within the layers of leaf litter on the ground or even within different parts of the bark of a tree. Microecological studies still have a long way to go to elucidate all of these imponderables.

Just as there are global and local gradients in temperature, so there are gradients in the other environmental variables that affect hyphal growth. Moisture is highly significant for all fungi, for various reasons. Most importantly, it is in aqueous solution that nutrients are digested and absorbed, while the moisture content of the surroundings influences the availability of oxygen and of carbon dioxide. And, above all, the cytoplasm of the hyphae themselves is composed largely of water contained tenuously within a highly permeable outer wall. Dryness therefore presents one of the most stern of the adversities that hyphae must survive. Only when modified to form sclerotia, and all but overwhelmed with deposits of melanins, can they be considered really robust enough to tolerate a prolonged drought. In some instances, the varying dependence of different fungal species on different moisture levels is clear to see. Aquatic fungi, like aquatic plants, have obvious adaptations to an environment bathed permanently in water, while marine species and the micro-fungi that grow in pickling brines for instance have the additional facility to cope with surroundings of a high osmotic concentration. These and some of the many instances of moisture gradients influencing the ecological distribution of terrestrial fungi will be discussed on page 272.

Light was mentioned on p. 242 as having an influence on the growth of spore-bearing structures. This is an unexpected phenomenon, for fungi do not at first sight seem to have a light requirement at all, lacking as they do the photosynthesis pigment, chlorophyll. Moreover, the fact that there are immeasurably more kilometres of mycelium growing below ground and in the dark than ever there are in the light is testimony to this. But there are instances, already alluded to, when growth of spore-bearing hyphae in or towards light has the incidental advantage of placing

the spores in the open air and thus in a position more effective for dispersal. And while most fungi actually produce spore-bearing structures in light or dark conditions with equal facility, some do so more efficiently if light and dark alternate (a day-night phenomenon) evidenced in the concentric rings of conidia-bearing tufts of *Monilia fructigena* on rotting apples. A few fungi, including some *Coprinus* species (p. 151) among the Agaricales, have an unexplained absolute requirement for light before their toadstools form. All these effects are achieved through the presence in the hyphae of light-sensitive chemicals. There is sometimes, by contrast, a belief that the *absence* of light is necessary for some types of fungal growth – underground caverns and cellars are commonly associated in many people's minds with edible mushroom culture. In fact, it is not the absence of light that is necessary for mushroom growth; rather such dark habitats usually have the uniform temperatures that are valuable for good cropping. (Cellars, nonetheless, are often damp; and this can result in decay of the fruit bodies through their being attacked by other fungi having a higher moisture requirement).

Mention should also be made of the quite curious phenomenon of autoluminescence displayed by some species: they glow in the dark. Although such glowing is commoner in tropical fungi, *Armillaria mellea,* species of *Mycena, Omphalotus, Pleurotus* and the ascomycete *Xylaria polymorpha* frequently light up temperate woodlands (relatively speaking). Wood permeated by mycelia of certain species may also sometimes glow; with others, like *Mycena* and *Pleurotus,* only the fruit bodies display the phenomenon. Among some tropical peoples, luminescent fungi are used as bodily adornment by young girls to attract their lovers at night, although even the most avowed mycophile must wonder at the nature of bodies in need of such embellishment. The purpose of luminescence in fungi is

Tufts of *Monilia fructigena* on a rotting apple

unknown; it has been suggested that it attracts the insects that aid spore dispersal. The chemical origin of the glowing in at least some species, is similar to that occurring in glow-worms, in which a phosphate-containing substance called, appropriately enough, luciferin is involved.

Geotropism, growth in response to the influence of gravity, although much less marked among fungi than among higher plants is evidenced by the remarkably refined orientation displayed by gills, pores and other spore-bearing surfaces in many basidiomycetes as an aid to the efficient dispersal of basidiospores.

The hyphae of different species seem to vary widely in their tolerance of, or requirement for, particular levels of acidity or alkalinity: most fungi, at least when cultured artificially, grow best in slightly acidic conditions. But variations in the pH of the environment within which most fungi grow are so intimately associated with such factors as the relative availabilities of nutrients and toxic chemicals that it would be misleading to say that the occurrence of a particular species like *Boletus satanas* (p. 51) only in chalky soils is because its hyphae grow better solely because of the alkaline conditions. Some fungi certainly can tolerate a fairly wide range of pH levels; but among the micro-fungi that grow on and contaminate foodstuffs, none seems to be able to flourish on the most alkaline of foods, egg albumen (pH 9.4), although a few species can grow in lemon and lime juices at pH levels around 2.2

NUTRITION

The absence of photosynthesis

Fungi may be variously coloured by the different pigments in their hyphae; but they are hardly ever green. The few species like *Hygrocybe psittacina* (p. 92) that sometimes have greenish fruit bodies, and even the genus called *Chlorophyllum* that has a green spore print, do not contain chlorophyll. No fungus therefore (apart from species associated with algae in lichens) is capable of photosynthesis (the manufacture of food substances in the presence of light from carbon dioxide and water by means of chlorophyll) that is characteristic of virtually all green plants. Photosynthetic nutrition is so called as it relies on light as an energy source, but it is also one of the more general types of nutrition called autotrophic; the organisms that use it are independent of outside sources of organic matter for their own organic requirements. (Autotrophic nutrition is also displayed by a few types of bacteria that use inorganic raw materials, and some which use chemical rather than light-mediated energy sources; the sulphur bacteria, for example, use the oxidation of hydrogen sulphide.) But fungi, in common with all animals and most bacteria, have heterotrophic nutrition: their nutritional requirements must be met by organic materials from the environment. To a greater or lesser degree, therefore, they are dependent on other organisms, either living or dead.

Holozoic or absorptive nutrition?

Heterotrophic organisms do not all acquire their nutrients in the same way. The system employed by animals is called holozoic; in everyday terms, this means eating; and in various forms it can be recognised in all types of animal, from mammals to *Hydra*. Even amoebae envelop organic particles and take them bodily into their own tissues. By widely accepted definition, fungi do not eat. Their means of obtaining nutrients is absorptive – enzymic digestion takes place initially outside the fungal hyphae, the digested or partially digested products then being absorbed. The only group of organisms described in this book that appear, at least partially, to eat are the Plasmodiophoromycetes (p. 226), and this feature has been used in assigning the group to the taxonomic boundary between fungi and whatever may have been their ancestors (p. 10).

Having stated that fungi derive their nutrients from other organisms, either living or dead, it must be admitted that this is a simplistic view of some complex biological inter-relationships. In practice, fungi may obtain their nutrients from dead organisms, living organisms, the non-living products of living organisms or the non-living parts of living organisms. The organisms concerned may be lower or higher green plants, animals of all kinds, or other fungi. And those fungi that depend on other living organisms adopt one of two feeding systems; either they ensure that the host remains alive while parasitised or, alternatively, that it dies as a result of the infection.

Even so, the boundaries between these categories are often blurred. Until recently, most books on fungi used the terms saprophyte (having the Greek roots *sapros,* rotten, and *phyton,* a plant) or parasite (which actually has its roots in the Greek for 'beside the corn', but which is fairly widely understood) to embrace them all. Three terms are now generally preferred; they are not, of course, confined exclusively to fungi. A saprotroph is an organism that uses only dead organic matter as a nutrient source. A biotroph uses only living cells as nutrient sources. A necrotroph invades the living tissues of an organism, kills it, and then uses its dead tissues. The three terms are not

mutually exclusive: a fungus like *Botrytis cinerea* (p. 223) may live biotrophically on the leaves of a tomato plant, necrotrophically on leaf cells that die subsequently, and saprotrophically on the remains of tomato plants killed by frost and thrown onto the compost-heap. Nor are matters simplified by the need for the mycologist to decide when living tissue ceases to be alive! For present purposes, the distinction into saprotrophic and biotrophic modes of nutrition is adequate enough.

It is useful, however, to qualify the two terms with the expressions obligate and non-obligate. An obligate biotroph is restricted entirely to living organic matter as a nutrient source and can exist apart from its host organism only in a dormant state. Conversely, an obligate saprotroph is restricted entirely to dead matter. Non-obligate biotrophs or saprotrophs can exist with greater or lesser facility on living or dead material. Even so, the boundary between obligate and non-obligate biotrophs is less clearly marked than once it was, for while such fungi as the rusts (p. 201) certainly occur naturally only on living plants, they are now known to be amenable to artificial culture in the laboratory. And finally it should be noted that a biotroph may not necessarily be a pathogen, a cause of disease, although normally it is.

otrytis cinerea living (top to bottom) biotrophically as host spot' on tomato, necrotrophically on the dead tip f a broad bean pod and saprotrophically on decaying vede

Extra-cellular digestion

Before considering the ways in which biotrophic fungi invade and feed on their host's tissues and how they are different from the ways saprotrophic fungi feed on dead matter, it is appropriate to examine the ends that both strive to achieve. What are the essential nutrients that all fungi seek?

Fungi, like all organisms, are made up largely of organic substances and, by widely accepted definition, an organic substance contains carbon. Thus a source of the element carbon is, quite literally, vital; but the ways in which carbon is combined with other elements within other organisms are many, and not all fungi have the necessary enzymes to tap them all. Most biotrophs, certainly most obligate biotrophs, can use relatively few sources of carbon compared with saprotrophs; and they have to be simple, like amino acids and various sugars. Nonetheless, among the fungi at large there are species able to degrade, to a greater or lesser extent, all of the carbon compounds that occur in other organisms, including chitin, pectin, starch and, most importantly, cellulose and lignin. The differing abilities of fungi to utilise these nutrient sources is relevant to the ecological successions of fungi that occur in the breakdown of plant and other organic material. Some fungi can use oils and fats as carbon sources; and species exist capable even of degrading petroleum-based substances, and have caused havoc in aircraft fuel-tanks. While most synthetic organic compounds are fairly resistant to attack by fungi, some plastics like polyurethane can now be degraded by certain species, presumably through the arising of mutant forms with novel enzyme systems.

For their other chemical requirements, fungi use an enormous range of substances. Most can obtain nitrogen not only from inorganic sources like ammonia and nitrate and nitrite salts, but also from such organic substances as proteins. Some require a source of vitamins, others manufacture their own. And, like green

plants, they need a wide range of other mineral elements in varying amounts.

Biotrophy

All plants, animals and fungi are to some extent in competition with each other and with other organisms for their continued existence on the planet. The paradoxical expression 'balance of nature', the dynamic but apparently more or less stable state within which framework all life on earth does manage to survive, represents the outcome of struggles. There are relatively few instances of equitable symbiotic partnerships in the natural world at large; of mutual existence to the lasting common good. And so it is in the relationship between biotrophic fungi and their hosts: plants and animals do not usually take kindly to having fungi feeding on them, and take measures to prevent it.

Some fungi grow and feed on external surfaces of the host organism, with hyphae sometimes penetrating only slightly below that surface. Others can only grow on organs, tissues or cells that are buried inside the organism. In every instance of fungal biotrophy some defence mechanism of the host must first be breached. There are three main ways in which this occurs. First, the bio-trophic fungus may enter through natural openings that provide access to its required food source. Perhaps the commonest examples among plant-biotrophic species are those fungi that enter through the stomatal pores on leaf surfaces: the germ tube hypha of the rust *Puccinia graminis* (p. 201), for instance, emerging from a spore on a cereal leaf, seeks out the stomatal opening and there develops a special form of hypha that is able to penetrate below the leaf surface. The means by which such directed growth occurs is not fully understood and fungi vary in their ability to seek out entry-points. Some germ tubes are clearly directed by a stimulus, presumably chemical, whereas others seem to succeed through force of numbers: if enough spores germinate

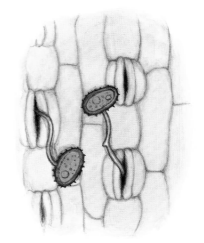

The invasion of cereal leaf stomata by the germ-tubes of a rust fungus

on each leaf, there is a good chance that at least some germ tubes will come into contact with stomata. Among animal-biotrophic species, one of the most notorious to use natural openings is the deuteromycete yeast fungus, *Candida albicans,* the cause of, *inter alia,* thrush in the throat and other body passages of man, other mammals and birds; it commonly gains entry through the mouth when the body inhales air-borne spores.

A second method is for a fungus to invade or colonise a wound, be it incidental or accidental. An incidental wound, such as the scar remaining after a leaf has fallen from a deciduous plant, differs from a natural opening in its transient nature. The leaf scar permits access to the conducting and other tissues of

Fungal spore landing on a leaf-scar of a deciduous tree

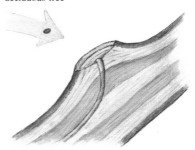

the plant stem for only a short time before it heals. To make use of it demands some measure of opportunism on the part of the invading fungus, and the same is of course true with the accidental wounds that also arise from time to time on all organisms. Some of the commonest and certainly best known invasive fungi are those that cause cankers (p. 264); among these the ascomycete *Nectria galligena* (p. 206) is familiar as the cause of apple canker. In this instance, the generally damp climatic conditions at the time of autumn leaf-fall are also those under which asco-spores are most effectively released (p. 241); biotrophic ascomycetes rarely make use of wounds in their hosts occurring in hot, dry conditions.

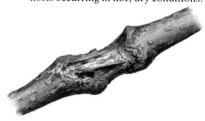

Apple canker

Accidental wounds on both plants and animals occur unpredictably. Fungi that would make best use of the opportunities they afford must have spores available more or less permanently. Thus it is that, among the fungi having markedly seasonal spore production and release such as the Agaricales, there are relatively few wound-invading biotrophs. The really effective ones, like many deutero-

A wood-decaying fungus invading a wound on a log

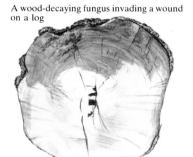

Fusarium mycelium in a potato tuber

mycetes and the 'polypores' among the larger basidiomycetes, generally produce and liberate their spores over periods of many months. The practices of agriculture and horticulture tend to produce many more accidental wounds on plants than occur naturally; hence wounds as points of invasion are more significant in, say, a managed plantation than in a natural forest. Many wood-decaying basidiomycete species commonly invade the wounds caused by the ripping away of bark and wood from standing trees when nearby trees are felled. Such fungi are markedly less common in natural forests, where they are are largely dependent upon natural accidental wounds like those that occur when branches are torn off in gales. (In passing, it should be mentioned that many of these fungi fall into the indeterminate area between biotroph and saprotroph, for while they do grow only on living trees, and render them physically unstable, they actually attack the exposed and *dead* heartwood, not the living tissues towards the periphery of the trunk or branch.) The increasing trend towards mechanical harvesting and handling of crops has also increased the incidence of wounds on plants and plant products. Many cooks will have noticed one consequence of the mechanical sorting and grading of potatoes in the increased incidence of the coloured mycelium of species of the deuteromycete fungus *Fusarium* in small pockets of decay within the flesh, for this species too can only attack the tissues through wounds and bruises (such as those caused by mechanical graders).

Finally, some biotrophic fungi are equipped to penetrate quite intact outer surfaces. Although many such examples are known, the relative importances of chemical (and presumably, enzymic) digestion of the surface and purely mechanical disruption are not well understood. The

Puccinia graminis on barberry leaf

same *Puccinia graminis* (p. 201) whose germ tubes from uredinio-spores enter wheat leaves through stomata, for instance, employs a direct-entry approach through the leaf cuticle when the basidiospore germ tubes seek to invade the barberry plant, its alternate host. Direct entry of biotrophic fungi into insect hosts often entails the breaching of considerable thicknesses of chitin and it is certain that this must first be degraded by fungal enzymes.

Zone-lines in section of wood attacked by fungus

Even when their outer defences have been breached, plants and animals rarely give up the fight against invading fungi, but bring more complex defences into play. Careful examination of the wood of a tree, sawn through at the point of some external wound, reveals zones of different colours and textures that reflect various attempts by the tree to use chemical secretions to poison the advancing fungus or to produce impervious substances to limit its

further spread physically. Such a section of wood is also a micro-ecological battle-ground between successions of invading organisms, all seeking the nutrients that the tree has to offer. Among animal biotrophs, there is no better example of an organism marshalling its defences than those employed against the deuteromycete *Microsporum audouinii,* the cause of a ringworm-like infection of the scalp in children. The problem normally disappears at puberty when there are changes in the types of fatty acids secreted by the scalp, those in mature individuals having fungicidal properties.

Entry by a fungus into a plant or animal does not of itself constitute biotrophy. Many types of fungi are quite capable of penetrating the tissue of particular species within which they then die out, evidently incapable of tapping the nutrient resources. On the other hand, a biotrophic species inside the *correct* host, and able to combat the host's continued defences, undergoes further development in a variety of ways. Sometimes the growth of the biotroph is fairly obvious to the external observer. The visible growth of a typical powdery mildew fungus such as *Podosphaera leucotricha* (p. 205) on apple trees gives a fair indication of its lateral

Podosphaera leucotricha on apple leaf

spread within the plant. Immediately below the visible surface mycelium will be hyphae growing between the outer cells of the leaf, and there will be penetrations by specialised feeding hyphae called haustoria into the still

Puccinia menthae on mint plant

living cells themselves, but little more. The same limited development is true of many rust fungi like *Puccinia pelargonii-zonalis* (p. 202) on pelargonium leaves. But within fungal groups, or even individual genera, there are differences; and other rusts, like *Puccinia menthae* (p. 202) for example, have a mycelium that permeates virtually the entire body of the host. Such a situation is called a systemic infection and is the reason why mint plants attacked by *P. menthae* will each year produce new shoots already diseased; pelargoniums must be invaded anew and are thus more readily protected by fungicidal sprays. Systemic infections are extremely rare among non-obligate biotrophs: widespread permeation of the tissues requires very special fungal feeding adaptations if the host is not to die quickly, rendering the invasion pointless. As most biotrophic fungi are non-obligate, the farmer and gardener have a better than even chance at controlling them with surface acting sprays; systemic fungicidal chemicals go further, and track down the fungus, no matter where in the host it hides. Systemic colonisation of an annual host's tissues may take place coincident with the growth of the host itself, and some of the smut fungi demonstrate this. Teliospores of *Tilletia caries* (p. 200) are carried on the seed of the wheat plant and germinate as the seed germinates, to infect the young seedling. A mycelium then grows within the plant's tissues to arrive eventually in the ovaries, where sporulation occurs,

and another generation of contaminated seeds is formed.

Fruit bodies on the surface of an infected host give little indication of the internal extent of mycelium, and there are no better examples of this than among the Agaricales and Aphyllophorales that attack trees. The appearance of brackets of polypores like *Rigidiporus ulmarius* (p. 180) or of agarics like *Pleurotus ostreatus* (p. 112) on branches and tree trunks almost invariably indicates a very extensive fungal development inside, with consequent decay of the timber and structural instability of the tree or branch. Indeed, to the tree owner, the appearance of fruit bodies on the main trunk of a tree at some distance from the ground is ominous. If they are recognised as of a species that infects through roots not stem wounds, the evidence is damning, for

Brackets of a polypore on a tree-trunk

it is proof that the fungus has already colonised an extensive area of tissue.

Among animal biotrophs, superficial and more or less systemic infections also occur and are variously called cutaneous, sub-cutaneous or deep-seated. Ringworm is a well-known example of the former and coccidiodomycosis, a serious disease of the lungs, skin, bone, central nervous system and subcutaneous tissues, caused by the fungus *Coccidioides immitis,* embraces both of the latter.

263

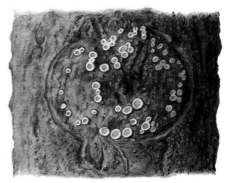

The development of an oval lesion caused by an ascomycete leads ultimately to the death of the distal part of the branch it is on.

Many fungi can be readily categorised as root-, leaf-, stem- or flower-infecting in that they invade through and remain in one part only of a plant. Quite commonly, moreover, fungi penetrate below the surface of the host, and are then restricted to particular tissues or regions within which they proliferate. Canker-causing fungi, many of which, like *Lachnellula willkommii* (p. 211) and *Nectria galligena* (p. 206) are ascomycetes, penetrate the bark as far as the cambium. There they grow slowly and radially outwards, killing slightly more of the cambium each year so that an ever-enlarging circular or oval lesion arises on the stem or branch, and no new bark forms. Ultimately, if fungal growth and cambial death extend right round the circumference of the branch, the distal part beyond the lesion dies. The so-called wilt fungi, many of which are deutero-mycetes but which also include important ascomycetes like *Cerato-cystis ulmi* (p. 206), grow primarily in the vascular conducting tissues; eventually, by mycelial growth and toxin production, they bring about blockages, water-starvation of the upper parts of the plant, and hence the characteristic wilt symptoms.

Perhaps the most extraordinary examples of the restriction of fungi to particular regions of their hosts' tissues are certain insect-infecting species of an obscure group of asco-mycetes called the Laboulbeniales. Among them are species that are limited to the right or left sides of some types of insect; in a few cases they infect in different positions on males and females. In at least one instance, this has been attributed to the particular way in which spores are passed from one individual insect to the other during mating.

Saprotrophy

Superficially, the saprotrophic mode of life seems much less complex than the biotrophic, for no such functional and structural adaptations as haus-toria are necessary to keep the host alive. The host offers no defence mechanisms to contend with: ability to penetrate dead tissue depends solely on enzymic ability to degrade tissue surfaces and cell walls. Other organisms, especially bacteria, may even enable saprotrophic fungi to penetrate tissues by breaking down the surface barriers for them. The arguments regarding the relative

Typical dark streaking in the stem of a plant affected by a wilt fungus

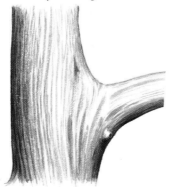

evolutionary advancement of the two conditions of biotrophy and saprotrophy have already been discussed (p. 13), but with the exceptions of rusts, smuts, powdery and downy mildews, Plasmodiophoromycetes and a few other groupings of exclusively obligate biotrophs, every major division of the fungi includes both biotrophic and saprotrophic species. Nonetheless, there are restrictions in the range of hosts for saprotrophic just as there are for biotrophic types. Every field mycologist of any experience knows that he will find certain fungi growing only on the debris of particular higher plants, just as he will find others on almost any decaying vegetation that he cares to examine. Whether the diets of biotrophs and saprotrophs are restricted or catholic depends on their abilities to exploit narrow or wide ranges of organic carbon sources (see p. 259).

While a biotroph has a continuing supply of nutrients as long as its host plant or animal remains alive and itself grows, a saprotroph in theory has no such assurance, for it is dependent on a finite body of tissue. The practical significance of this varies greatly from species to species. One colony of a particular saprotrophic fungus, grown from a single spore, restricted in its nutritional capabilities to the dead leaves of one species of host plant and growing on one isolated leaf, will very soon need to move on, by means of its spores or sclerotia, as that leaf becomes drained of nutrient. Growing on one leaf among countless others on a woodland floor, however, the same individual has the prospect ahead of it of growing from leaf to leaf and of continuing in vegetative growth without ever needing to resort to dispersal or survival structures. Similarly, the nutrient resources provided by the fallen trunk of an oak tree offer a long-term nutrient resource to the newly emerging germ tube of a wood-decaying saprotroph.

Nonetheless, one very important feature of fungal biology must always be borne in mind when considering such situations. The notion of the individual fungal organism is a hard one to define, for not only may colonies arising from different spores fuse and thus become integrated structurally, but the whole has potentially almost infinite growth capacity. Fungal growth and nutrition, quite unlike that of other organisms, adopts almost Parkinsonian precepts in that the 'individual' can expand to make use of the available nutrients. A fallen oak tree or the leaf litter on a woodland floor may present an embarras de richesses for an individual beetle larva or a single epiphytic fern plant; but for a fungal germ tube, initially only a few μm long, the potential to attain many kilometres in length will bring any nutrient source down to size.

A fallen oak log fully colonised by wood-decaying fungi

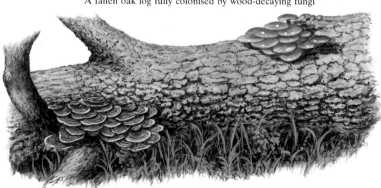

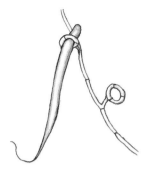

Arthrobotrys (left) and *Dactylaria* trapping nematodes

Predation

Much of what has been said so far about fungal nutrition and, indeed, about the fungi as a whole, indicates that they are structurally and behaviourally diverse, possessed of some surprisingly ingenious mechanisms and devices, but ultimately fairly staid. It may come as a surprise to learn that there are also some actively predatory species. They occur among several taxonomic groups, most notably the Zygomycetes, the Oomycetes and the deuteromycetes and attack amoebae, protozoans and nematodes (eelworms). Most exciting are those like the deuteromycete *Arthrobotrys*, which produces a sticky web-like mycelium that ensnares passing nematodes as a cobweb does a fly, and *Dactylaria* which forms ring-like hyphae in which unsuspecting nematodes are lassoed and ultimately garrotted. Feeding hyphae then grow into the bodies of the unfortunate creatures to complete the exercise.

Symbiosis

Symbiosis has been mentioned as a much more widespread state than is generally appreciated, and it is among the fungi that it displays some of its most important and dramatic manifestations. A popular and convenient definition of symbiosis is the living together of unlike or unrelated organisms', and this may take several forms.

In the first form of symbiosis there is no physical or organisational union. Ecological plant communities and the pollination of flowers by insects are two common instances; an outstanding mycological example is the culturing of some fungal species by beetles. That the tunnels of some species of wood-boring beetle have a white lining on which the beetle larvae feed has been known for over 150 years. The substance was given the fanciful name ambrosia and it is a name that has stuck, for when the white substance was discovered to be fungal mycelium, the fungi became known for evermore as ambrosia fungi. The association between beetle and fungus is highly developed, especially in the females of some species in the bark beetle family Scolytidae. These insects have small cavities in the exoskeleton within which mycelium grows and thus they introduce this mycelium into each new tunnel as it is bored. Somewhat similar fungal growths are found in termite tunnels; but it is now generally believed that these are mycelia of the agaric *Termitomyces*, which is tolerated but not actually used by the insects as food.

By contrast, in the second type of symbiosis, there is a physical or organisational union between the organisms and this may be on a 'social' level, as when epiphytic orchids or ferns grow on the bark of

trees. Or it may be on a nutritive level; biotrophy has been described as an antagonistic form of nutritive symbiosis but it is to the reciprocal form that the term is more familiarly applied. Here, two unlike organisms live and feed in intimate association and to mutual advantage. The terms commensalism and mutualism are sometimes used for this state, which to many people has come to represent symbiosis *in toto*. In its two most important manifestations, mycorrhiza and lichens, one of the partners is a fungus.

Mycorrhizas are symbiotic associations familiar to everyone who has ever collected or observed mushrooms and toadstools. The occurrence of many (perhaps most) agarics in particular types of woodland, beneath particular types of tree, or consistently in company with certain types of plant, is not mere chance; nor is it the result of two species requiring a similar ecological niche. It is because of the intimate mycorrhizal association which means that, under certain circumstances, the one partner cannot exist (or can do so inadequately) without the other. A mycorrhiza involves fungal hyphae and the roots of higher plants, (and also, to some extent, of some Pteridophytes and the rhizoids of Bryophytes too), and it may take the form of an ectomycorrhiza or an endomycorrhiza. It is with ectomycorrhizas that most field mycologists will be familar for these are the associations between fungi and the roots of forest trees like birch, beech, oak, larch and pine, in which the fungal mycelium forms an outer sheath around the fine rootlets. This can readily be seen if such rootlets are examined closely. Penetration of fungal hyphae into the root is limited and occurs only between the cells of the cortex. Ectomycorrhizas have been estimated to occur in about 3% of plant species, mostly in forest trees.

The importance of mycorrhizas to the plants whose roots they envelop is enigmatic: although it has long been known that they have a role in the uptake of nutrients by the roots from

Ectomycorrhiza on a tree rootlet

the soil, it has been demonstrated experimentally that sometimes plants can grow perfectly well without them. It now seems that it is on soils naturally deficient in nutrients that mycorrhizal presence is especially important, and this finding has had its greatest practical benefit in forestry. It is now standard practice in some parts of the world artificially to inoculate tree seedlings with mycorrhizal fungus when planting them into previously unafforested areas. Precisely how the mycorrhizal mycelium assists its host plant, and vice versa, is still imperfectly understood. It seems that the fungus obtains much of its necessary supply of carbon from the roots (and thus imposes a considerable drain on the plant); but in return it acts as an intermediary in the uptake of such nutrients as nitrogen, phosphate and potash from the soil. The mycorrhizal fungus seems better able to achieve this uptake, especially from poor soils, than does the plant acting on its own.

The fungal partners of ectomycorrhizas are not always identifiable unless they can be induced to produce some form of fruit body, but in as far as it is known, most appear to be basidiomycetes and most to be in

267

the order Agaricales. (Although a few basidiomycetes outside the typical mushrooms and toadstools (*Scleroderma*, for example, and also a few ascomycetes like *Gyromitra* may form ectomycorrhizas with roots, they are very much in the minority.) The very familiar occurrence of particular species of *Boletus* and its allies, and of *Amanita* and *Tricholoma* especially with certain types of tree, is the consequence of the mycorrhizal partnership of their mycelia with the roots, and indicates the high degree of specificity in the association. The larch bolete *Suillus grevillei*, for instance, is invariably associated with larch trees; the fly agaric *Amanita muscaria* almost always occurs under birch trees, because its mycelium seems to be an obligate mycorrhizal partner of birch roots, and very rarely of any other type of tree. With a little experience, knowledge of such associations becomes second nature to the mushroom and toadstool collector, and means that many of the species likely to be found in a particular type of woodland can be predicted quite accurately. Trees and woodlands have been used for these examples; but it could be that many of the other characteristic fungal floras of other habitats have a basis in mycorrhizal partnerships between their mycelia and the roots of the indigenous herbaceous plants. And it may be that the reasons some plants fail to establish satisfactorily on some sites is because the soils there lack the necessary mycorrhizal fungus.

The fungi that form endo-mycorrhizas span a much wider taxonomic spectrum, covering not only basidiomycetes and ascomycetes, but deuteromycetes and 'lower' fungi

Suillus grevillei under a larch

Amanita muscaria under a birch

too. Moreover, endomycorrhizas are of much more widespread occurrence than ectomycorrhizas. They are especially important in the orchid and heather plant families, but representatives have been found in many other families (the Cruciferae is the notable large exception), as well as in some ferns and fern allies, mosses and liverworts. They are usually invisible externally, because the fungal hyphae develop only within and between the root cells (although having direct connection with the mycelium in the soil). Indeed, in many instances, it has been impossible to assign such fungi to particular genera, and it is only features of hyphal structure (like the characteristics of the septa referred to on p. 252) that enables them to be placed even in broad taxonomic groupings. Although different in structure and in taxonomy, the endomycorrhizas of the heather family appear to fulfil a similar function to the ectomycorrhizas of other plants. Those occurring with the orchids are rather different, however.

The orchids comprise probably the largest family of flowering plants in the world, with over 20,000 species. All develop endomycorrhizas, virtually 'from birth'. Orchid seeds are among the smallest to be found among flowering plants and have almost no food reserves. On germination, however, the young seedling root becomes infected with fungal mycelium from the soil which, by still disputed means, provides the young seedling with a supply of nutrients. Thus the young orchid, lacking leaves or other green tissue and hence

unable to photosynthesise, lives saprotrophically on organic matter in the soil or bark on which it grows, aided in doing so by the fungal mycelium. Some orchid species live permanently in this manner, constantly and wholly dependent for nutrient on their fungal partners. But among the majority that produce green photosynthesising tissues the role of the fungus seems to decline as they mature.

The roles of host and fungus in respect of carbon supply, therefore, in orchid endomycorrhizas on the one hand and in tree ectomycorrhizas on the other, are opposite. In the former, the fungus supplies carbon to the host plant; in the latter, the host plant supplies it to the fungus.

Although the fungal species associated with orchids are quite capable of independent existence, there is one very widespread and important group of endomycorrhizal fungi in which dependence on the host has apparently reached an obligate state. Within the roots of many flowering plants, conifers (apart from the pine family), ferns and liverworts occurs the mycelium of a type of fungus that from microscopic struc-

Some orchids, like the Common Twayblade (left), only have fungal mycorrhiza when young, whereas others like the saprophytic Bird's-nest Orchid have a fungal partner throughout their lives.

ture appears to belong with the Zygomycetes. It has proved exceedingly difficult to induce these fungi to grow in artificial culture and to be identified and studied with precision. Most are given the generic name *Endogone*, and they are now the subjects of great interest for their presence appears indispensable to the successful growing of a very wide range of important crop plants, including cereals, citrus fruit, tea and rubber.

But obligate symbiosis surely reaches its zenith with the lichens, for here two organisms, a fungus and an algae, associate together, not only to mutual advantage, but also to form a uniquely distinct organism. It grows, and in some instances reproduces, quite separately and is given a distinct scientific name. The algae concerned belong either to the Green algae (Chlorophyceae), the Blue-Green algae (Cyanophyceae) or rarely to the Yellow-Green algae (Xanthophyceae), while the fungal partner is almost invariably an ascomycete. Most commonly it is a member of the Order Lecanorales, although some belonging to other ascomycete groups, and a very few members of the basidiomycetes and deuteromycetes, may also form lichens. The overall form of the lichen is determined largely by the fungal component, algal cells being enmeshed by the fungal hyphae; and fungal reproductive apothecia are clearly visible on many species. Typically, lichens reproduce and are dispersed in the form of the fungal ascospores. If these germinate in close proximity to an appropriate algal colony, a new lichen forms. Some lichen species also reproduce by forming small packages of hyphae and algal cells which are blown or otherwise dispersed from the parent colony. Other reproductive devices are also used in some groups.

The relationship between the two partners in a lichen varies, although it always seems to work to the advantage of the fungus; indeed, there are some grounds for considering the fungal partner to be parasitic upon the alga. The fungus may derive carbohydrates and/or nitrates from the alga, but there is little evidence for any return benefit in kind, other than the protection of the alga from dessication, heat and cold. Some lichens are extremely tolerant of extremes of environmental conditions, and many play an important role in the early stages of soil formation. Some are also highly sensitive to atmospheric pollution and have been used as indicators of the relative purity of the air in different localities.

A selection of lichens, with close-up views of algal cells, hyphae and apothecia, and the parts involved in reproduction and dispersal

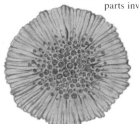

Calloplaca thallincola

Cladonia digitata

A dispersal package of algal cells (coloured) enmeshed with fungal hyphae

Physcia sp.

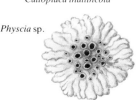

Cladonia rangiformis

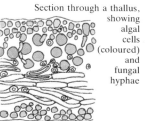

Section through a thallus, showing algal cells (coloured) and fungal hyphae

ENVIRONMENTS AND SUBSTRATES FOR FUNGI

A fungus will grow only where its particular food requirements are available. While the basic food requirements of all fungi are the same – as outlined on p. 259, they all need a supply of carbon, nitrogen and other chemicals – the source material varies enormously. The collector soon learns, for instance, that while most puff-balls grow on soil, one species, *Lycoperdon pyriforme* (p. 196), occurs on dead tree branches or other woody material. And while the jew's ear fungus, *Hirneola auricula-judae* (p. 191), can grow on several types of tree, it is almost always found on elder (*Sambucus nigra*). Such associations primarily represent a specialisation to exploit some particular chemical, or combination of chemicals, that the individual type of nutrient source supplies. Such material, upon which fungi grow and feed, is called a substrate and it is the availability of preferred substrates, together with the other environmental variables like temperature, humidity and pH, that determine the ecological niche occupied by any particular species at any particular time. This factor of time is important, for the substrates upon which fungi grow are dynamic ones in which the biological components are constantly changing as they alter the habitat and render it more favourable to the succeeding group of species. Such sequences are what the ecologist calls successions.

Micro-environments like the soil, leaf litter, wood and others differ significantly from macro-environments like woodland, bog and grassland with which higher plant and animal ecologists will be familiar. In the latter cases, each succeeding group of plants and animals dies and adds its own remains to the habitat, providing nutrient for longer-lived and physically larger plants and animals; ultimately, such a habitat reaches a climax where although indi-

Jew's-ear fungus on elder

Some species of puff-ball grow on the ground; others grow on trees.

viduals live and die, to be replaced by other individuals, the overall species composition remains fairly constant. Over much of western Europe, that climax community is the deciduous or, in the north, the coniferous forest. In the soil and other micro-environments, on the other hand, the sequence tends to be one of increasing depletion of the habitat: once a region of soil or an individual tree trunk has been rendered bereft of organic matter, the end result is not a climactic but a sterile community. While the higher plant ecologist can observe and sample his chosen habitat at different times and can count and

measure the numbers of species present, the mycologist who would study the sequences of fungi passing through a particular substrate, such as a given volume of soil over a period of time, faces daunting problems. Even with a microscope, he cannot actually see very much *in situ*, for the substrate itself, to use a particularly apt phrase, gets in the way. To extract microscopic fungal bodies from soil and other substrates is physically very difficult; to count them is well nigh impossible. The student of microecology is reduced, therefore, to biological extraction methods: he must induce fungi to grow in artificial nutrient culture from fragments of carefully selected material, painstakingly incubate them, and hope that they will produce recognisable fruit bodies from which they may be identified. Even then his sample, which will inevitably have excluded all those obligate biotrophs that cannot be reared in artificial culture and all those dormant or resting structures unwilling to germinate and grow, will represent only a very crude picture of the fungi present in those few crumbs of substrate at that particular moment. Imagine trying to describe the appearance of a wood to an uninitiated listener when the evidence available comprises a collection of plants in a greenhouse, some flowering and some not, grown from seeds obtained by scraping blindfold along the floor of a woodland that had in turn been chosen by sticking a pin into a map of the world; this may suggest some idea of the difficulty of presenting a realistic picture of the microecology of soil fungi. The soil indeed presents very special problems and it is appropriate to consider this substrate first.

Soil

The soil is the most important environment for fungi. Many, perhaps most, spend at least part of their life in or on it; and countless more are dependent less directly upon it for it is from the soil that their host plants grow. Most mushroom and toadstool collectors spend the greater proportion of their time in the field with their eyes directly firmly downwards for from the soil emanate perhaps as many as 80% of the macrofungi that they seek. To understand even a little of the physics, chemistry and biology of soil is to explain much of what they observe above ground and to give greater satisfaction, purpose and success to their collecting activities. The nature of soil and its relationship to the fungi that grow within it repays careful appraisal, moreover, because within this partnership all is not necessarily what it seems.

The soil is a blend of three types of matter. The most abundant is inorganic, mineral matter – matter that has never lived. In terms of particle size, this material is divided into sand $(0.06 - 2.0$ mm$)$, silt $(0.002 - 0.06$ mm$)$ and clay $(<0.002$ mm$)$. Thus, clay particles are commonly much less than the diameter of fungal hyphae and may be very much smaller than fungal spores. The relative proportions of sand, silt and clay particles in a soil define its texture; the degree to which they are aggregated together into crumbs defines, very largely, its structure. The greater is the aggregation of soil into crumbs, the greater will be the size of the pores between the crumbs, the greater the volume of air present within the soil, and the better draining is the soil. All these factors influence the types of fungi that thrive therein; those requiring a higher concentration of oxygen and having lower tolerance to the presence of free water, for instance, will be less likely to occur in a heavy, poorly structured clay. And, at the extremes, as will be described later, are fungi that live in the stagnant mud of pool bottoms, and those that can only survive in the mobile salt-laden sand of coastal dunes.

Not only does soil structure influence the types of fungi that can thrive in particular soils, but the fungi themselves, together with bacteria and other micro-organisms are major contributors to the processes of crumb

Phallus hadriani growing in a sand-dune

formation. They achieve this partly by producing chemicals that have adhesive properties and literally glue soil particles together, and partly because some of these substances have electrostatic charges: particles having opposite charge tend to be attracted to each other. Thus soil fungi, in large measure, actually help to shape the physical environment in which they live.

Although the soil provides fungi, as it does green plants, with small amounts of essential trace elements from slowly dissolving soil minerals, it is to the organic components of the soil (living matter, and matter once living but now dead) that they must turn for the major nutrients like carbon and nitrogen. The living component of the soil includes, of course, fungi themselves, in the shape of their mycelia, their spores or other perennating or survival bodies. It is from these soil-inhabiting mycelia that reproductive structures, including mushrooms and toadstools, arise. Fungi may arrive in the soil as spores or other structures carried through the air from some more distant fruit body or terrestrial mycelium, or as hyphae growing from a root or other organic base. In the process many spores, destined for a plant leaf, an animal's skin or some other potential food source, also arrive in the soil. Most of these fail to survive. The category of so-called soil-inhabiting fungi refers only to those that always spend at least part of their lives in the soil and are not inevitably degraded or devoured by other organisms. Nonetheless, it is important to appreciate

that some fungi, *apparently* growing in the soil are actually present in or on some body that happens to be there; a piece of buried twig or leaf, for instance. This distinction between the strictly and the not so strictly soil-inhabiting is more than one of mere semantics. Consider *Agrocybe cylindracea*. In this book, as in other field guides, this species is said, quite correctly, to occur on decaying wood. Evidently it requires some particular nutrient only obtainable there. Related and somewhat similar species, however, live in and on the soil, there exploiting more highly degraded organic matter. Yet many a field mycologist has been puzzled on occasion by finding such species as *A. cylindracea* growing on the ground and seemingly from the soil. A little further investigation, and a little excavation, would have revealed that the fruit body originated, in fact, from a length of buried branch or decaying root.

Agrocybe cylindracea in a cross-section of soil, showing its true substrate to be buried wood

273

Fungi share the soil with many other types of micro-organism. Most numerous are bacteria which are present in quite prodigious quantity – countless billions in every gram of soil. Their relationship with fungi is two-edged. In assisting the degradation of organic matter into forms more readily assimilable by fungi, they are positively beneficial. But bacteria also play a major role in the breakdown and degradation of fungi themselves: the gradual diminution, over a period of time (see p. 249), in the numbers of fungal spores surviving from an initial population is probably due as much to bacterial action as to anything else. Actinomycetes (in effect, mycelial bacteria) are also important in some soils; and all soils contain varying numbers of algal cells.

Among the members of other organism Kingdoms, protozoans and amoebae are major components of the micro-population in many soils and are important in being responsible for the degradation of soil-inhabiting spores and mycelia. In one particularly well studied example, giant (the term is used relatively) soil amoebae belonging to the appropriately named vampyrellid group have been observed actually causing large perforations in the spores of soil-inhabiting fungi preparatory to dining on their contents.

Presumably the relationship also operates in reverse, although, for obvious technical reasons, few observations of the degradation of protozoans and amoebae by fungi have been made. Among the animal kingdom, although relatively few soil-inhabiting creatures are actively parasitised or preyed on by fungi, there is probably no organism that, upon its death, is not degraded at least in part by fungal action (see p. 260); hence fungi will live not so much where these animals live as where they die. And as most animals, when dead, finish up on or in the soil, here is a further reason for fungi to be present therein.

But above all, it is the presence of plant material that provides the soil-

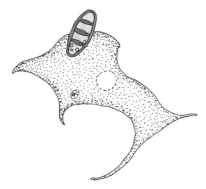

Vampyrellid amoebae perforating and consuming soil-inhabiting fungus spores

inhabiting fungus with its greatest nutrient source, be this the living plant material of roots and stems or the dead material comprising leaf litter, twigs and other debris. The range in these many substrates and the uses to which fungi put them will be discussed on pp. 278–282; but one particular zone of the soil has special importance and is appropriately mentioned here. The rhizosphere is the soil in the immediate vicinity of living plant roots, and it is possessed of some unique features. It is a region where fungi, bacteria and other micro-organisms make use of organic chemicals secreted or exuded from the roots as sources of carbon, nitrogen and other nutrients. There is little reciprocal benefit by the plant comparable with that derived from mycorrhizal growth, although there may be some small enhancement of mineral nutrients available to the roots. Thus in this rhizosphere region, almost uniquely within the soil, fungi grow not actually in contact with their nutrient source but within 'diffusing distance' of its origin.

One of the most fascinating yet mysterious of fungal appearances from the soil is the appealingly named fairy-ring. More or less circular groups of fruit bodies, especially of the aptly christened fairy-ring mushroom, *Marasmius oreades* (p. 79) are familiar both on natural grassland and, often to the chagrin of their

owners, on lawns too. This growth is an example of the pattern of growth of a fungal colony, as described on p. 253; but close examination will reveal that the ring is more than a mere collection of toadstools. Immediately outside the toadstools, and clearly visible even at times of the year when the fruit bodies themselves are absent, is a zone of darker-coloured grass; and within the fungal ring is very often a zone where grass growth is impoverished. The darker, richer-coloured grass is of the hue so beloved of gardeners and apparent after they have added nitrogenous fertiliser to a lawn. And so it is in the fairy-ring, for the advancing fungal mycelium at the periphery of the circular colony is actively breaking down organic matter in the soil to release simpler nutrients, among which nitrates are significant. A localised soil fertilising effect is taking place. By contrast, the inner ring represents a region where fungal growth is diminished because of the depleted nutrients; the mycelium gradually dies and forms an impervious mat, preventing the penetration of water into the soil and causing poor grass growth.

But if the fairy-ring presents the observer with an enigma and a puzzle, the so-called hypogeal fungi present him with a challenge. While many microscopic fungi not only grow but also sporulate below ground (producing their spore-bearing structures in the air-filled spaces between soil crumbs or in worms's or other animals' burrows, thence to be dispersed by members of the soil- inhabiting micro-fauna), relatively few macro-fungi are wholly subterranean. The problems they face in respect of spore dispersal have already been mentioned (p. 239), but the problems faced by the would-be collector appear insuperable. Although with experience, likely areas of woodland for the occurrence of truffles and other hypogeal fungi are fairly predictable, actually to locate individual fruit bodies several centimetres below ground-level conjures up comparisons with needles and haystacks. The equipment used by the dedicated truffle hunter includes large wooden rakes, trained truffle hounds and pigs on leads. Truffles will be mentioned again in the account of edible fungi, but meanwhile they serve to underline how elusive and still relatively unknown is the subterranean environment in which the greater proportion of the fungal growth of the world exists.

Reference has already been made to the factors necessary for the germination of spores and also to the fact that fungal spores in general, including those in soil, commonly pass through dormant or resting phases. The nature of the factors conferring dormancy or, perhaps more pertinently, of the factors necessary to break dormancy and stimulate germination to take place are imperfectly known. In some soils, however, a more widespread phenomenon has been observed in that there is clearly some, as yet unidentified but presumably chemical factor that prevents spores from germinating when they are actually in contact with soil particles. Remove the spores from the soil and germination proceeds. Sometimes, especially when such suppression of germination seems to apply only to specific types of spore, the expression suppressive soil is used to describe the phenomenon. Perhaps the best known example of this is the inability of the plant wilt diseases caused by species of the deuteromycete fungus *Fusarium* to develop in certain soils and on certain sites, even when large numbers of spores are added to the soil artificially. Another phenomenon clearly evident with many fungi in some soils is that their spores display survival curves; in other words, certain proportions of the initial spore population germinate at particular times and the gradual diminution of the total spore population displays a characteristic pattern that appears graphically as a gradual curve. Why and how this comes about is unknown but appears related both to maturity factors within the spores and also to external stimuli and/or suppressors in the soil itself.

Litter

Plant and animal remains that have fallen onto the soil surface are called litter; they provide a most fruitful feeding ground for fungi, and a fruitful substrate from which to collect specimens. The bulk of the litter to be found beneath a woodland canopy or a grassland sward is the remains of plants, of leaves especially, but with up to one third by volume of twigs and other woody material, fruits and seeds. Much of this will have been colonised by fungi before it fell to the ground and most of it is dead material, although seeds at least are living tissues. Almost all of it is present on the surface for a limited time only; some will be dragged into the ground by earthworms or other animals, there to be degraded by the fungal and other microbial activities already mentioned. Some will be carried or blown away to be deposited elsewhere. The remainder will be degraded in situ by micro-organisms, and ultimately take its place as an integral but temporary component of the soil itself. The fungal population in litter tends therefore to be a transient one of rapidly growing and fruiting species, and, among the agarics, generally of small and inconspicuous forms. When robust agarics like *Russula,* for instance, are found emerging through litter, close examination generally reveals that they originate from mycelia more deeply entrenched in the soil: indicating they are not efficient at degrading the substances that protect intact plant tissues in litter. On freshly fallen leaf litter, deuteromycetes like *Botrytis cinerea* and other micro-fungi tend to be predominant, although small ascomycetes like some *Dasyscyphus* species are common too. Generally, basidiomycetes are not found fruiting (although of course they may have been present as unseen mycelium) until leaf and conifer-needle litter is three or more years old. Then a whole range of species of *Clitocybe, Marasmius, Mycena* and others may be expected.

The woody material in litter can only be degraded by fungi able to break down its two most important chemical components, cellulose and lignin; this will be referred to in more detail in the account of wood in general as a substrate (p. 278).

Fallen fruits among the litter provide a substrate for a well defined ecological group of fungi; *Xylaria carpophila* on beech mast and *Hymenoscyphus fructigenus* on both beech-mast and oak acorns are two very well-known and common examples of such types among the ascomycetes.

Partly because animal remains are neither conspicuous nor numerous among litter, few fungi are known to be associated with them; genera such as *Cordyceps* (described in detail later, p. 283), that grow on dead caterpillars and other insects, tend to arise from carcasses buried just below the soil surface rather than in the litter itself. This may be indicative of a requirement for a particular level of moisture or aeration, or for more stable temperatures, than for any

A *Russula* species growing from soil through litter

Xylaria carpophila on beech-mast

Hymenoscyphus fructigena on an acorn

Onygena on cast antlers

Coprinus cinereus emerging in tufts from a strawy compost-heap

differences in the substrate itself. But if shed antlers can be considered a part of the litter of the woodland floor, then the species of the ascomycete genus *Onygena* that grow on them, on cow and sheep horns and hooves and, perhaps most significantly, on hair can be considered fairly common examples of fungi using the animal components of litter as substrates.

Although perhaps more familiarly grouped with dungs and manures, compost, in the shape of the contents of the garden compost-heap or bin, the straw stack and the leaf mould pile, does have much in common with litter, being the undigested remains of vegetation in varying states of decomposition. It was mentioned earlier that many heat-loving micro-fungi find a ready home in the elevated temperatures of the compost-heap; and among the macro-fungi likely to be collected there, as the compost breaks down and cools, especially if a large proportion of straw is present, are the toadstools of *Coprinus cinereus* and *Volvariella speciosa*.

Dung

Dung is the excrement of animals. Because the plant and animal matter from which it originates has passed through digestive tracts, its nutrient

content is very different from that of the raw material. But like all other organic materials, it provides fungi with a substrate and it attracts a clearly defined range of species able to exploit its particular chemistry. Animal dung can be divided into that of herbivores and that of carnivores, the chemistry of them, and hence the fungi associated with them, being generally different. Largely for reasons of availability, cow and horse dung has been most intensively studied; the desire of mycologists for pleasant working conditions may also have discouraged much investigation of carnivore excrement. One of the most celebrated British mycologists remarked some twenty years ago that relative fame, if not fortune, awaited the man who devoted his years to the intimate examination of decaying dog droppings. Understandably, few have risen (or sunk) to the challenge, and the fungal flora of carnivore dung remains relatively uncharted.

Some of the fungi of dung have already been mentioned in respect of the problems they face in spore dispersal (p. 239). Many dozens of ascomycete and basidiomycete species, as well as members of the microscopic groups, can exploit this particular substrate; and it is probably fungi rather than bacteria that are the major organisms bringing about the breakdown of dung in the environment at large. Among genera with many dung-inhabiting species are *Coprinus* and *Psilocybe* among the basidiomycetes and *Ascobolus, Ascophanus* and *Podospora* among ascomycetes. When fresh dung is collected and incubated artificially, a fairly well defined sequence of types of fungal fruit body appears but the biological significance of this sequence is not fully understood.

Stropharia merdaria on dung

Brown decay caused by the basidiomycete *Phaeolus schweinitzii*

White decay caused by the basidiomycete *Heterobasidion annosum*

Plant surfaces and plant tissues

As will already have become apparent, plants, both living and dead, provide the most important substrates for fungi. Although the various parts of plants have been mentioned as sites for parasitic fungal activity and as components of litter, it is now appropriate to consider the various parts and to appraise their importance as substrates.

First, however, a comment on the range of capabilities of fungi to bring about disintegration of plant tissues and to exploit the nutrients they contain. The methods of destruction adopted by fungi depend on their enzymic capabilities. Most have the ability to make use of sugars like glucose and sucrose and other carbohydrates like starch stored within plant tissues. Many can also digest proteins and various natural fats and oils. But for the fungus to gain access to these substances the tissues themselves must be broken down. Fungi with pectinolytic enzymes can bring about wholesale destruction of the tissues by removing the layers containing the chemical called pectin that helps join cells together. This produces the symptom of soft rot and, although many fungi can achieve this, it is an ability more generally associated with bacterial activity. The ability to degrade cellulose, the major component of plant cell walls and to break it down into its constitutent sugars is extremely widespread among the fungi and it produces, among wood-destroying species, a readily visible manifestation that distinguishes cellulose-destroying from lignin-destroying types. The basidiomycete fungi that degrade solely the cellulose component of wood give rise to a brown-coloured decay of the tissues, whereas the species of basidiomycete and ascomycete able to degrade not only cellulose but lignin also give rise to a white-coloured decay. A common example of a wood-destroying brown rot fungus is *Phaeolus schweinitzii* (p. 175) which causes the wood of affected trees to break into brown cubical blocks. By contrast, *Heterobasidion annosum* (p. 181) is a white rot species causing small, discrete pockets of white decay within the timber. While the fungi growing on leaf surfaces may be assumed to have some ability to degrade the waxy covering of the leaf tissues, those that use bark as a substrate must be able to some extent to degrade the complex substance called suberin which confers the corky texture to cork itself and to other barks.

Thus to consider the various plant parts in turn; and first the parts that exist largely unseen below ground: the roots – and, to a less well studied extent, bulbs, corms, tubers, rhizomes and similar structures. Reference has already been made to the rhizosphere, the region of soil adjacent to the root's surface. Here chemicals produced by the root diffuse into the soil where they can be used by fungi as nutrients; but the root tissues themselves, both on the root surface, the rhizoplane, and within the body of the root are also important. On the rhizoplane are accumulations of dead root cells, rather like the dead cells on the surface of an animal's skin and here a large population of saprotrophic micro-fungi develops. If the root dies, some of these fungi may well begin to invade the dead tissue and help bring about the degradation of the root

Decay of pea roots by a *Fusarium* species

itself. Certain rhizoplane fungi may also be biotrophic and able to use the rhizoplane to launch an invasion of living roots. Some of the root-infecting species of the deuteromycete genus *Fusarium* appear to act in this manner, subsequently causing decay of the roots and stem base and, ultimately, death of the host plant on whose tissues they may continue to live. Yet other root-infecting biotrophs may originate on fragments of plant material dispersed some distance away in the soil through which they grow to initiate infections. Honey fungus, the agaric *Armillaria mellea,* is the best known example of a fungus able to grow considerable distances through the soil to achieve this. It is, of course, virtually impossible for an obligately biotrophic fungus directly to invade root tissues from the soil and many, like root-infecting rusts, grow down into the roots after their spores landed first and germinated on some above-ground organ.

The most extensive above-ground plant organs are leaves and, just as the root surface is called the rhizoplane, so the leaf surface is called the phylloplane and bears a characteristic fungus flora. Virtually all of the phylloplane species in temperate climates are micro-fungi because, just as leaf litter is no substrate for a fungus that takes a long time to reach fruiting condition, so the leaf on the plant is very much a short-term prospect for rapidly-developing species. Rusts among biotrophic basidiomycetes, mildews among biotrophic ascomycetes, and the countless

deuteromycete genera like *Septoria* and *Coniothyrium* that produce leaf-spotting symptoms, are good examples. An exception to short-term growth may be found however, in some of the fungi that grow on or in the leaves of evergreens which, although not permanent, do tend to remain on the plant for longer than one season and thus give slightly more time for slower-growing fungi to mature. Species of *Lophodermium* (p. 208) on conifer needles illustrate this phenomenon well and in the tropics, there are many leaf inhabiting agarics.

Unlike roots, however, stable in position and buffered by the soil from sudden temperature fluctuations, the leaf is an exacting environment, in almost constant motion and subject to extremes of heat and cold, of drought and saturation. Leaf surfaces themselves, moreover, vary widely from the smooth glossiness of an evergreen

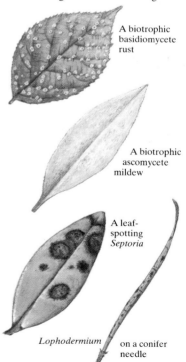

A biotrophic basidiomycete rust

A biotrophic ascomycete mildew

A leaf-spotting *Septoria*

Lophodermium on a conifer needle

279

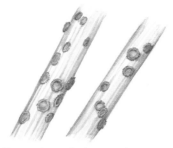

Dasyscyphus on herbaceous plant stems

such as laurel to the densely hairy texture such as that found on a holly-hock or a woundwort, and consequently offer to fungi widely differing micro-environments. Moreover, the leaf surface is constantly being showered with spores from the air, and there is a wide range of different species of fungi ostensibly seeking the same nutrient source. The ability, by very rapid growth or even by the production of some antagonistic chemical, to compete effectively with other species is a major attribute, therefore, for the leaf-dwelling fungus.

Green, non-lignified stems of herbaceous plants may be expected to have similar micro-ecological status to leaves, and certainly many of their micro-fungi appear to be the same, although some small species of basidiomycete and ascomycete can be found there too. Species of *Dasyscyphus* and related ascomycetes for instance are commonly associated with particular types of herbaceous plant stem.

Flowers have an even more ephemeral existence than leaves and only fast-growing micro-fungi are likely to occur there. But the flower can provide a fungus with the means of entry to the fruit and/or seeds; it is for this reason that gardeners and growers commonly spray strawberries and other crops with fungicide while the blossom is open, in order to prevent such fungi as *Botrytis cinerea* being able subsequently to bring about decay of the crop.

The occurrence of particular species of fungi on fallen fruits and seeds among litter has already been mentioned, but many can also be found growing on them while they are still attached to the plant. Although the attached fruit is living tissue, and only therefore able to provide nutrient for biotrophic species, slight wounding such as may be caused by insects or birds, can permit quite weak pathogens to enter, and, in turn, allow saprotrophic species to colonise the newly killed tissues. Most of the fungi concerned tend to be Zygomycetes like *Mucor* or deuteromycetes like *Monilia fructigena,* the cause of the very common brown rot disease of apples and other tree fruits. As the brown-rot affected fruit shrivels, however, and the nutrient supply for the fungus quite literally dries up, the apothecia of *Monilinia* the sexually-reproducing phase of *Monilia,* may arise, although these do not appear to occur in Britain. This provides a good illustration, nonetheless, of the general phenomenon among living things that sexual repro-

Brown rot developement in an apple

duction, the manifestation of a need to perpetuate the species, is very often a response to the depletion of the resources of the environment.

Wood is arguably the most important nutrient resource for fungi; even today, as much as one third of the earth's land surface is covered in forest of which woody material comprises over 90% of all the living matter above ground. Because of its importance, both in terms of size and in respect of the long-term economic value of trees, the degradation of wood, both by biotrophic and saprotrophic fungi has been studied intensively. And because of the inherently longer-lasting nature of the substrate, some of the general micro-ecological principles of invasion, colonisation and succession are best illustrated by reference to wood-attacking fungi. The relative importance of the abilities to degrade cellulose and lignin has already been mentioned, as has the fact that saprotrophic wood-destroying fungi, provided that by means of wounds or other entry points they can gain access to the non-living heartwood, can act effectively as biotrophs and cause significant damage to still living trees. But wood is a complex substrate, varying widely from species to species, from individual to individual tree, and from one part of a tree to another. It varies in the size of cells, the thickness and the amount of lignin present in the cell walls, in moisture and air content and other factors. Any field mycologist of even modest experience makes a bee-line for fallen tree-trunks and branches in a wood, in the sure knowledge that a wide range of interesting basidiomycetes and ascomycetes will be found there. He knows too that the species of fungi on the log will differ to some degree with the species of tree it came from, and especially with the time that it has lain on the ground. This variation in species of fungi is also true of those growing on standing trees, and of the position on the tree in which their fruit bodies occur. *Armillaria mellea* toadstools for instance will only be found at or a short distance above the

base of the trunk, reflecting the inability of the fungus to grow far up the trunk from the roots through which they first entered the tree, while another root-infecting basidiomycete *Heterobasidion annosum* typically produces its tough rubbery brackets actually at ground level where they are often hard to find among grass and other vegetation. By contrast, the fruit bodies of those fungi like *Pleurotus ostreatus* that invade the tree through broken branches or other wounds may be found emerging from the trunk many metres above the ground. Further examples of the types of fungi associated with particular types of tree will be given in the accounts of woodland habitats.

When a tree with wounds to its trunk and/or fungal fruit bodies on it is felled and sawn lengthwise, distinct zones of discolouration and decay will be seen extending from the wound into the timber; careful microscopic and cultural studies have revealed that the mycelia of different species of fungi occur in different parts of the

Armillaria mellea growing at the base of a tree-trunk; *Pleurotus ostreatus* growing higher up the tree

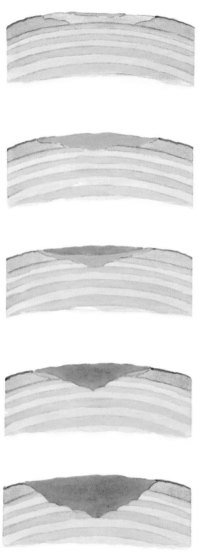

Cross-section of part of a tree branch showing the invasion of a wound in a branch by a canker fungus (yellow), followed by another species of micro-fungus (brown) which traps it and eliminates it from the lesion; the whole process has taken five years.

affected tissues. Although there is still dispute among mycologists over the correct interpretation of these observations, it seems likely that non-basidiomycete fungi and bacteria are usually the first to invade the wounds on standing trees, and perhaps render innocuous certain toxic chemicals produced by the tree as defence mechanisms, thus permitting wood-decaying basidiomycetes to follow in succession. Comparable studies have revealed characteristic fungal species patterns in the colonisation of fallen logs. But nowhere is the micro-ecological battle-ground better exemplified than in some canker lesions on tree branches, where the canker-causing fungus spreads outwards from the initial point of entry (p. 264) and vacates the central part of the lesion as it exhausts the supply of its required nutrients and kills the bark. It is followed by several other species of micro-fungi that colonise the dead bark and in turn also spread outwards. Ultimately, some of these succeeding 'waves' of invaders, growing faster than the canker fungus itself, 'trap' it against the live tissues which it is unable to penetrate sufficiently quickly. If these invading fungi possess, as many do, the ability to secrete a substance toxic to the canker fungus, they may eliminate it from the lesion that it has formed.

It is appropriate to mention here those fungi that use other fungi as a substrate and nutrient source. Reference has already been made in passing to those among the lower fungi, like some Plasmodiophoromycetes, that parasitise other lower fungi, and also the deuteromycete and Zygomycete moulds that occur on mushrooms and other large fruit bodies. To find macro-fungi using other macro-fungi as a food source is a less expected phenomenon, but there are two particularly common examples. *Asterophora lycoperdoides* (p. 73) occurs on the rotting caps of *Russula nigricans* and its close relative *A. parasitica* (p. 73) on many different types of *Russula* and *Lactarius* toadstools.

Asterophora lycoperdoides on *Russula nigricans*

Asterophora parasitica on a *Lactarius* species

Animal surface and animal tissues
It has already been mentioned that animals are much less important in general than plants as hosts for biotrophic fungi. Equally, they are less significant in providing substrates for saprotrophic species. This is partly due to the simple fact that animal carcasses are much less frequent in the world than are dead plants, for fungi do almost invariably occur on animal remains. It must be said, however, that almost all are microscopic species, unlikely to be encountered without careful scientific detection. Among the best known exceptions are species of the ascomycete genus *Cordyceps* (p. 205) that parasitise insects, especially caterpillars, and whose fruit bodies will be found emerging from the dead insects in the soil. And although the species is microscopic, the presence of the Zygomycete *Entomophthora* in dead flies is often revealed by the halo of discharged spores that commonly surrounds dead insects on window panes. A notable exception to the micro-fungi is the agaric *Hebeloma,* the ghoul fungus, of which some species grow on carcasses.

Although unseen, the ability of fungi to colonise and grow on a wide variety of animal substrates should not go unappreciated, for just as there are fungi able to degrade most of the chemical constituents of plant tissues, so it is with animal matter. Many fungi, especially among the ascomycetes, have the ability to degrade chitin (the complex substance that makes up much of the exoskeleton of insects and other arthropods), glyco-

gen (the important carbohydrate that is present in many animal tissues), and keratin (the chemically complex protein that is the major constituent of hair, fur, feathers, nails, hoofs and horns). The coats of mammals, the feathers of birds (and, indeed, the feathers, fur and hair used to line bird's nests), human finger-nails and cows' horns, and many other animal substrates all have a characteristic micro-flora of fungi which range from partly biotrophic to purely saprotrophic.

The fruit body of a *Cordyceps* species emerging from the body of a dead insect

A halo of *Entomophthora* spores round a dead fly on a window-pane

FUNGAL HABITATS

It will already be apparent that, to a greater or lesser extent, fungi have the ability to exploit most of the natural raw materials of the world as nutrient sources, and to tolerate most of the environmental variables that the earth can offer. There is almost no natural habitat, able to support life of any type, that is not inhabited by some species of fungi. The habitats to be encountered world-wide are of course extremely numerous, but many are confined to specific regions; to consider termite mounds on the African savannah, Mexican bat caves or Saharan oases, rich as they are in fungi, would be superfluous in this book. Detailed consideration will only be accorded those habitats most commonly encountered in western Europe.

While many general of basidiomycete and ascomycete are quite definitely fungi of one type of habitat rather than any other, few can be said to be wholly characteristic of individual types of woodland, grassland or other community. Nonetheless, there are certainly some fungal species, and more pertinently associations of several species, that do give to each habitat a characteristic fungal flora. *Amanita, Lactarius* and *Russula* for example, which are mycorrhizal associates of trees, are predominantly woodland genera, while *Leptonia* and especially *Hygrocybe* are usually found in grassland. The mycologist, given a species list including *Russula xerampelina, Lactarius acerrimus, Peniophora quercina* and *Boletus porosporus* will conjure up visions of an oakwood, much as a list comprising bluebells, bracken, dog's-mercury and holly conveys a similar image to the botanist.

Fungi on a birch growing in low, wet ground, and on a beech growing higher up

Woodland

Mushroom and toadstool collectors are drawn to woodlands as moths to a lamp, and almost every organised fungus foray includes a stretch of woodland among the habitats to be visited. The reason is quite simply that a greater number of species of macro-fungi is to be found there than anywhere else. The woodland offers to a fungus the availability of a rich and continuing nutrient source, a wide range of micro-habitats, from the leaves and twigs of tree-tops to the roots many centimetres below the surface, a soil environment reasonably well buffered against extremes of temperature, and a fairly moist environment at all times of the year. Woodlands are conveniently divided into the major categories of coniferous, broad-leaved and mixed, with additional habitats provided by the woodland edges and by open, grassy areas within the wood itself. Copses and hedgerows are also specialised types of woodland habitat. Within these broad divisions, further- more, there is a vast range of environ- ments. The category of broad-leaved woodland alone for instance embraces: the pure beech-wood of the chalk downs with a free-draining soil and dry floor bare of almost all plant life; the wet, water-laden birch-wood, its ground flora dominated by *Sphagnum;* and even the alder carr, where the field mycologist ventures only when well shod with rubber boots. Each woodland type will be considered briefly in turn as a habitat for fungi.

In Britain there are only three native conifers, Scots pine (*Pinus sylvestris*), juniper (*Juniperus communis*) and yew (*Taxus baccata*); but natural woodland dominated by these species is all-but extinct, and the coniferous woodland of Britain today is very largely that planted over the past two centuries. It includes some Scots pine, but exotic species – especially of other pines like Corsican and Austrian (varieties of *Pinus nigra*), larch (*Larix* spp.), Norway and Sitka spruce (*Picea abies* and *P. sitchensis*), Douglas fir (*Pseudostuga menziesii*), hemlock (*Tsuga* spp.), western red cedar (*Thuja plicata*), and firs (*Abies* spp.) – predominate. Native woodland and forest of some of these species occurs extensively in other parts of western Europe, but the remainder are north American introductions. The fungal flora of British coniferous woodland and plantation forest comprises those native fungal species that have adapted to the new environment, and those that have presumably been introduced along with their associated tree species. Thus, such fungi as the larch canker-causing ascomycete, *Lachnellula willkommii* (p. 211) or the larch bolete *Suillus grevillei* (p. 49), an obligate mycorrhizal companion of the genus *Larix*, could not have existed in Britain before the introduction of larch in the mid- seventeenth century. The dense shade cast by many conifers that inhibits so much plant life on the ground has, of course, no direct effect on fungi: they are often highly conspicuous on the more or less bare needle litter of the woodland floor. Conversely, the paucity of plant species associated with the pure stand of Sitka spruce in particular means that there is likely to be a general paucity of fungal species too. Indeed the spruce plantation offers a poorer hunting ground for fungi than almost any other British plant habitat.

No large genus of woodland fungi is exclusively associated with conifers, but among the terrestrial basidio- mycetes, *Cortinarius* (including the exceedingly poisonous *C. specio- sissimus* (p. 133)) and *Suillus*, are particularly well represented, either in coniferous woods or associated with conifers in mixed stands. Notable individual species include *Tricholo- mopsis rutilans* (p. 67) on conifer stumps, *Auriscalpium vulgare* (p. 160) and other small species emerging from buried pine cones, and *Chroogomphus rutilus* (p. 54) under pines. The only member of the important edible fungi of the genus *Agaricus* restricted to coniferous woods is the fairly uncommon *A. silvaticus* (p. 146). Wood-destroying

bracket fungi are more frequently specific to particular types of trees and the most important example affecting a wide range of conifers is *Heterobasidion annosum* (p. 181). One of the few fungi attacking yew, although it does occur on deciduous trees too, is the beautiful yellow bracket *Laetiporus sulphureus* (p. 183).

Over much of Britain, mixed deciduous woodland, containing greater or lesser numbers of oaks (*Quercus* spp.), beech (*Fagus sylvatica*), limes (*Tilia* spp.) hornbeam (*Carpinus betulus*), elms (*Ulmus* spp.), birches (*Betula* spp.), ash (*Fraxinus excelsior*) and alder (*Alnus glutinosa*), is the native vegetation type. Many fungi are associated with particular types of deciduous tree, and some tend to occur only in more or less pure woodland of individual species; *Boletus satanas* (p. 51), the beautiful, uncommon and poisonous bolete, for instance, occurs almost exclusively in beech woods on chalky soils.

Others, like *Leccinum scabrum* (p. 48), which is always found associated with birch, noticeably goes wherever the tree goes, be it in pure or mixed woodland, in copses or even as isolated individuals in parkland. Birch woodland and birch trees in general have a quite characteristic fungal flora, and there are perhaps more common species invariably associated with birch than with almost any other single British tree species. Yet other fungi are found in company with any of a range of deciduous trees. Many species, for instance, occur commonly with either beech or oak; old deciduous woodland, such as that in the New Forest, containing both these types of tree, probably supports the richest diversity of fungal species to be found in any British habitat. Among innumerable basidio-

mycete species invariably associated with beech wherever it grows are *Pholiota adiposa* (p. 140), *Oudemansiella mucida* (p. 77) and *Russula olivacea* (p. 107).

More local and restricted types of wood are those occurring predominantly on wetlands, in particular copses and riverside plantations of poplar and willow, and the most characteristic of all wetland woods, the alder carr. The characteristic fungi with willows and poplars tend to be small or microscopic leaf-infecting biotrophs, and few large basidiomycetes occur with these species and nowhere else. Some of the typical fungi of the alder carr may be found with willows in similar habitats, such as species of the genus *Naucoria* (p. 128), as well as *Pholiota alnicola* (p. 141) and *Uloporus lividus* (p. 53); all commonly found in such situations.

A hedgerow may be thought of as a long, narrow wood subject to fairly rigorous management. Although most of the tree species found in woodland proper can also occur in hedgerows, along with at least some of their

Laetiporus sulphureus on a yew tree

Tricholomopsis rutilans on a conifer stump

Auriscalpium vulgare emerging from buried pine-cones

Pleurotus cornucopiae (right) and *Peziza micropus* on felled elm logs

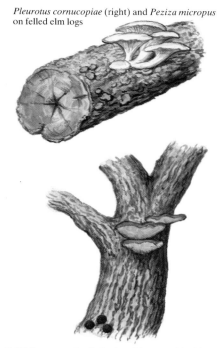

Daldinia concentrica (below) and *Inonotus hispidus* on an ash tree

associated fungi, certain trees have come to be thought of as predominantly hedgerow species. The various species of elm fell into this category until the recent activities of *Cerotocystis ulmi* (p. 206) removed them from the landscape. Interestingly the elms killed by Dutch elm disease and the numerous stacks of logs that are a consequence of felling operations have resulted in the proliferation of some fungi, previously less common. *Pleurotus cornucopiae* (p. 111) is one, and the large apothecial ascomycete *Peziza micropus* (p. 218) is another. Ash is also very much a tree of the hedgerow over most of Britain, and two fungi in particular are very commonly, although not obligately, associated with it, the ascomycete *Daldinia concentrica* (p. 207) and the wood-destroying basidiomycete *Inonotus hispidus* (p. 175).

Grassland

Grasslands in Britain today are entirely artificial habitats, created very largely on areas cleared in historic times of the ancient forest and used for grazing animals. Some grasslands are essentially short-term environments, lasting for one or a few years as breaks from other crops being grown in rotation on arable farmland. As habitats for macro-fungi these are almost sterile, for no large basidiomycete has enough time to be able to build up a mature mycelium in the soil before it is disturbed by ploughing. Such grasslands also tend to be subject, either directly or indirectly, to the fertilisers and crop-protection chemicals that form such an integral part of modern farming and which do little to create an encouraging environment for fungi. Indeed, apart from the biotrophic fungi that cause disease problems on crop plants, and the few species like *Cyathus olla* (p. 197) to be found on cereal stubble, the modern farm environment is scarcely worthy of much attention by the field mycologist.

Very different, however, are established grasslands, meadows and commons, and the grass of that curious artificial environment, created towards the end of the eighteenth century, the parkland. Here are habitats where the soil is fairly undisturbed although the grass itself is grazed or mown. The soil temperature is relatively uniform, protected by the grass sward, but prone to drying out in summer. Among major

Cyathus olla on cereal stubble

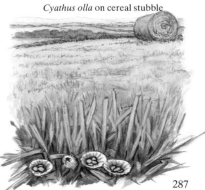

Typical fungus communities (bottom to top) of water-meadow in a valley bottom, poorer upland grassland, and short downland turf

basidiomycete genera, *Agaricus* (p. 145), *Clitocybe* (p. 63) and *Hygrocybe* (p. 91) are especially frequent on these grasslands; indeed, representatives of all groups not obligately mycorrhizal with trees or dependent on wood as a nutrient source, may be expected. The subdivision of grasslands is less straightforward than that of woodlands; although certain well defined types can be recognised, there are less obviously characteristic fungal floras in each.

The rich lowland pastures of water-meadows and valley bottoms, the rough and poorer hill grasslands and the fine downland pastures overlying chalk all include species of the major grassland genera. In the first, *Agaricus macrosporus* (p. 148), *A. arvensis* (p. 148) and *A. campestris* (p. 147) occur typically with *Psilocybe semilanceata* (p. 150) and many of the common dung fungi. On the poorer uplands areas will be found the majority of the brightly coloured species of *Hygrocybe* (p. 91) and *Cystoderma amianthinum* (p. 57), while the short downland turf reveals more *Agaricus* species, hygrocybes and, very frequently the St George's mushroom *Tricholoma gambosum*

(p. 71), one of the best of the Spring edible species. The fairy-ring mushroom, *Marasmius oreades* (p. 79) is also common on short grazed or mown turf, and it has been established through careful measurement that some of the fairy-rings on undisturbed downland pastures may be one hundred or more years old.

The fairy-ring mushroom also occurs on established lawns, along with several small fungi, known in 'the trade' as 'little brown jobs'; species that tend to pass unremarked in grosser environments but which thrust themselves conspicuously at the owner of manicured garden turf. These include species of *Coprinus* (p. 151), *Nolanea* (p. 119), *Panaeolina* (p. 156), *Panaeolus* (p. 156), and *Psathyrella* (p. 158).

Fairy-ring on a lawn

Gardens and urban environments

The garden, like the farm, is not in general a good habitat for fungi (apart perhaps from ascomycete mildews, *Diplocarpon rosae*, and *Plasmodiophora brassicae* p. 226) as the soil, other than on lawns, is too frequently disturbed. Nonetheless, there are a few species tolerant of the moderate disturbance that prevails in herbaceous borders and shrubberies, and none more so than the shaggy ink-cap, *Coprinus comatus* (p. 151) and the stink horn, *Phallus impudicus* (p. 198). The former species is one of the commonest culprits in raising tarmac from paths and pavements and is so much a species of disturbed ground that its presence can be predicted with a high degree of certainty within two or three years of new roadside verges being laid.

The neglected compost heap can be a fruitful environment for many small ascomycetes and even, if undisturbed for sufficiently long, for the characteristic toadstools mentioned on p. 277.

Few house owners would expect fungi to follow them from the garden indoors, but the fungi of the dwelling-place make a fascinating ecological group. The highly undesirable presence of *Serpula lacrimans* (p. 170) the dry rot fungus has already been mentioned; and few old houses will be without some growth of *Coniophora puteana* (p. 165), the commonest cause of wet rot in structural timbers, or of the deuteromycete *Cladosporium* (p. 223), one of the commonest of the black moulds that grow on damp plaster. Cellars are always a good source of interesting fungi, of which the commonest is perhaps the large apothecial ascomycete *Peziza cerea* (p. 217) which occurs on the damp mortar of cellar floors. Given the ease of examination, moreover, domestic substrates like cheese, jam, bread, fruit and vegetables all provide an excellent opportunity for close acquaintance with the many species of Zygomycete and deuteromycete mould which may pale into insignificance and pass unremarked in the environment at large.

A shaggy ink-cap growing at the junction of a herbaceous border and a tarmac path, which it is raising

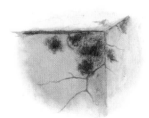

Wet rot

Black mould on plaster

Peziza cerea on a cellar floor

Marasmius androsaceus on a dead heather stem

Omphalina ericetorum in a lichen-like association with algal cells

Heaths, moors and mountains

Heaths and moors are habitats where, even more than in coniferous woodland, the environment is shaped by an acid soil. The dominant plants are not trees nor grasses, but largely members of the heather family. More than in any other British plant habitat, moreover, fungi in the shape of the fungal components of lichens may approach a dominant role in some areas. As a habitat for fungi, the high soil acidity presents a challenge, but moisture content remains generally high and the plant life relatively undisturbed for long spells, interrupted only by the limited grazing of sheep or deer and by periodic burning, either accidental or deliberate (see below). One of the commonest small basidiomycetes of moorland is *Marasmius androsaceus* (p. 78), the descriptively named horse-hair toadstool which grows on dead heather stems and is at least partially responsible for their demise. *Omphalina ericetorum* (p. 61), a member of a genus that includes several fungi growing on and amongst mosses, is also frequent on moorlands. In common with related *Omphalina* species, it forms a loose, lichen-like association with algal cells living in the same ecological niche. *Hypholoma ericaeum* (p. 150) and *Hygrocybe* spp. (p. 91) are other common moorland and mountain fungi, while in communities containing the dwarf willows like *Salix repens* and *S. herbacea*, mycorrhizal fungi representative of such familiar woodland genera as *Russula* and *Lactarius* also occur frequently at high altitudes.

Fire sites

Moorland is periodically burned, either as a result of accidents, of lightning strikes or of deliberate actions designed to stimulate regeneration of the heather. In some parts of Europe and even more so in other parts of the world, naturally-started fires play an important ecological role in maintaining the long-term vigour of the plant community. As mentioned in the account of spore germination (p. 250), fire can play an important part in fungal biology too. Not only does it stimulate some types of spore to germinate, but it also clears the affected area of potentially competing organisms. Fire sites have their own characteristic fungal flora, therefore. In woodlands, the tree pathogen *Rhizina undulata* (p. 217) presents such a serious threat that even the lighting of fires by foresters for the brewing of tea is strictly prohibited. Among the commonest fungi of burned ground generally are *Pholiota highlandensis* (p. 140), *Hebeloma anthracophilum* (p. 127) and two similar species of *Tephrocybe*, *T. anthracophila* and *T. atrata* (p. 73). Among several types of ascomycete, the appropriately named genus *Anthracobia* (p. 221) is especially frequent on burned areas in woods and hedgerows.

Burned ground colonised by *Rhizina undulata*, the cause of group-dying disease of conifers

Bogs, marshes and other wetland sites
Some of the woodland habitats discussed already (the birch woodland
and alder carr for instance) are essentially wetlands. Other habitats not
dominated by trees may also present
fungi with a moist, fairly uniform
environment. For soil-inhabiting
fungi, the major feature to which their
mycelium must adapt is that of poor
aeration, together with the possibility
of high concentrations of sulphurous
gases unable to escape into the
atmosphere. Such is the environment
of bogs on acid peat soils, fens on less
acid peats, and marshes on silty soils.
Bogs may occur at both high and low
altitudes, grading from moorland in
the former where rainfall is high and
drainage impeded. Fens occur
typically in the upper parts of certain
old river estuaries. In all such
communities, mosses form an
important component, and it tends to
be the fungi that grow in close association with moss that make up the most
characteristic species. *Omphalina*
(p. 61), *Galerina* (p. 136), *Pholiota*
(p. 139) and *Hypholoma* (p. 149) are
among the genera of generally small,
brownish, inconspicuous (and often
difficult to identify) basidiomycete
species encountered most frequently.
Some of these tiny toadstools have
markedly elongated stems to facilitate
the dispersal of their spores clear of
the vegetation. Many small ascomycetes are common too on the stems
of herbaceous plants and these, as a
group, form one of the most under-
studied of ecological types among
British fungi. Like so many small
ascomycetes, some of the species are
exceedingly beautiful, and this habitat
is one that repays particularly well any
careful study.

The open water is also a fungal
habitat, not only the fresh water of
lakes, ponds and rivers, but also the
brackish water of estuaries and the
salt water of the sea. Within it, fungi
use substrates comparable with those
on dry land: dead plant and animal
matter as well as the living aquatic
plants and animals that form the hosts
of biotrophic species. Clearly such
fungi have adapted, as have other,
aquatic organisms, to obtaining their
oxygen supply from the water rather
than the air. But, judging by the
numbers of species presently known,
fungi have recolonised (or have never
left) what is presumed to be their
ancestral home far less extensively
than have, for instance, the algae.
There are no known large aquatic
basidiomycetes comparable with conventional mushrooms and toadstools,
because their method of spore dispersal clearly does not lend itself to
functioning in water. Sub-aqua forays
have an improbable future, therefore.
Nonetheless, aquatic species of
basidiomycete and of ascomycete do
occur, although they seem to have
abandoned (or never perfected)
active spore discharge mechanisms,
and rely on the passive removal of
their spores by water currents. But
not surprisingly, a large proportion of
zoospore-forming members of the
'lower' fungi predominate, together
with a number of so-called aero-
aquatic deuteromycetes which grow
on submerged substrates like twigs
and wood, but which produce their
conidia on elongated hyphae which
raise them into the air.

A *Galerina* species growing in wet
conditions in association
with *Sphagnum* moss

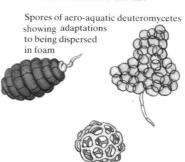

Spores of aero-aquatic deuteromycetes
showing adaptations
to being dispersed
in foam

Cut-away in sand to show (left to right) *Agaricus devoniensis*, *Psathyrella ammophila* and *Agaricus bernardii*

Dunes and salt marshes

Sand-dunes seem a most improbable habitat for fungi, apparently lacking nutrient and being in a state of permanent movement. Nonetheless, the more stable areas of dunes do have a small but highly characteristic range of species; they are a difficult group to collect, because some of the most interesting, like *Agaricus devoniensis* (p. 146) remain coyly below the surface with only the top of the cap protruding above the sand. Many of the species like *Psathyrella ammophila* (p. 158), have a very long stem that enables them either to reach down to moisture supplies at depth or to grow in association with the roots of dune plants such as marram grass. Among other basidiomycete species likely to be found are *Conocybe dunensis* (p. 143), *Inocybe devoniensis* (p. 124) and, less frequently, the stink horn *Phallus hadriani* (p. 198). *Agaricus bernardii* (p. 146) is among the most exciting of those dune fungi that occur also on salt marshes and other coastal habitats subject to salt spray. As with bogs and marshes, the ascomycetes of saline habitats are a poorly studied group and would repay detailed and careful collection.

REPRODUCTION IN THE FUNGI

There is but one objective behind the production of all of the fungal structures that occur in the diverse habitats and ecological niches described: reproduction. (The goal of every field mycologist, just like the goal of the field botanist, is the same; all are seeking reproductive structures.) Basidiomycete mushrooms and toadstools, the cups and flasks of the ascomycetes and the multifarious organs formed by micro-fungi, are all designed for the production and dispersal of spores. The biology and structure of the spores themselves, and the ways in which they disperse, have been described at length. It is now appropriate to consider the stages and processes that precede their appearance and presage the emergence of the fruit bodies above ground, through the bark of twigs and branches, or from any of numerous other substrates.

Fungal sex

It has been stressed that fungal spores may be produced either sexually or asexually. It is important to try to appreciate the meaning of sex in the context of fungal biology. The subject is extremely complex: the pathway to understanding is obstructed not only by the extreme biological diversity of fungi, but also because observation and experimentation are generally very difficult to perform. What follows is an extreme simplification, intended to give an indication of what happens before the visual manifestations of reproduction become apparent.

The notion of sex, certainly when considered in relation to animals, conjures up images of maleness and femaleness. All higher animals have two separate sexes. Among lower or less evolutionarily advanced groups of animals, hermaphroditism is quite widespread, both male and female sexual organs being borne on the same individual, although with varying degrees of self-fertility. Slugs, for example, are hermaphrodite; but one individual still needs to mate with another, for male cells are unable to fertilise the female cells produced on the same animal. Comparable sexual systems occur among plants; but they are visually less obvious because plants do not mate, and because plants' reproductive structures, flowers, display such a vast range of form that it is often far from evident which contain male organs, which female organs, and which both. Among plants, the variation in sexual arrangement comprises species in which each individual has only male flowers, those that have only female flowers, those with both male and female flowers, and those with bisexual flowers. Varying degrees of cross- and self-fertility also occur. The range of sexual systems found among plants is found among fungi too, but with some rather different and unexpected additions – to the extent that it is sometimes said that the fungi possess *several* sexes.

By widely accepted definition, the female of a species produces the cell that ultimately develops into the new individual and it does so after that cell has fused with or been fertilised by another cell carried from or delivered by the male. Among the fungi, however it is possible to see variation in the manifestations of maleness and femaleness: in some groups the sexes can better be described as different states or strains.

The onset of dikaryosis by the fusion of motile cells in lower fungi

Time-lapse of the fusion of gametangia to form a zygospore in Zygomycetes

In most organisms, the female cell is a larger, relatively sedentary body compared with the male. But only in one group among the lower fungi are motile sex cells produced that differ slightly in size. In other 'lower' groups such as the Plasmodiophoromycetes and Chytridiomycetes, for example, the cells that fuse, even when they can be recognised for what they are, are almost always structurally indistinguishable. Both are motile and apparently fuse outside the structure that produced them. They also display a pheonomenon quite widespread among the fungi at large, but unusual outside the group, in that fusion of the nuclei within the cells does not always follow immediately after fusion of the cells themselves. This condition is known as dikaryosis and will be referred to again when fungal life cycles are described.

The fusion of oogonium and antheridium in the oomycete *Saprolegnia*

oogonium

The fusion of antheridia and oogonia in the oomycete *Achlya*

male   female

Within the Zygomycetes, events are much more easily seen – the sexual organs in the group are swollen hyphal branches called gametangia, each gametangium growing towards one from an adjacent hypha either of the same (if the organism is self-fertile) or of another colony. The two gametangia and their entire contents then fuse. The result of the fusion is the formation of a zygospore (p. 230). Nonetheless, in almost all cases, the two gametangia appear identical and are said to be produced by + and − strains of the organism, rather than by male and female colonies.

When the Oomycetes are considered, however, differences between the fusing structures are very clearly marked; it is now with some confidence that one colony, producing a relatively large 'egg'-containing body, the oogonium, can be called a female and the other, forming hyphal branches called antheridia that grow towards and fuse with it, can be designated a male. The contents of the male antheridium pass into the oogonium, rather than there being total fusion between the two and as a result of the fertilisation, oospores are formed from the 'eggs'.

It is within the Oomycetes, moreover, that the greatest diversities in fungal sexual behaviour occur. Patterns of interaction have been discovered that, for curious but perhaps understandable reasons, have caught the imagination of those people who might otherwise be unlikely to accord mycology more than a passing thought. Most notable among these trends is that displayed by the aquatic genus *Achlya*, where sex is not constant, either within individual colonies or even from one part to another of

the same hypha. In other words, the same colony or hypha can sometimes function as a male, sometimes as a female, and sometimes as a hermaphrodite. And the change from one state to another can be influenced both by physical and chemical factors in the environmenmt, and sometimes by the proximity of other fungal colonies. Thus, in the appropriately named species *A. ambisexualis* and *A. bisexualis*, some strains can behave either as male or as female depending on the partner with which they are associated, while others (designated sexually strong) remain constant irrespective of their pairing.

In the largest fungal grouping, the ascomycetes, types exist both with and without distinct sexual organs. In many species, the fusion that is the prelude to nuclear fusion takes place between morphologically identical hyphae. In others, a coiled female hypha fuses either with very slender male hyphal branches called antheridia, or with very small spore-like bodies called spermatia. Following some cytological gymnastics, the familiar tube-shaped ascus then arises, typically containing eight ascospores.

Sexual reproduction in the basidiomycetes results in the formation of basidiospores, but as in some other fungal groups (see p. 294), spore formation takes place some time after sexual fusion, and the mycelium from which the familiar toadstool or other fruit body arises is dikaryotic (p. 294). There are often no clearly defined sex organs, and the necessary fusion to bring nuclei together occurs simply between the hyphae of two appropriate colonies. 'Appropriate' does not necessarily mean simply of opposite sex or strain, for some basidiomycetes are self-fertile, whereas in others there are complex requirements for successful pairings that involve more than one opposing factor in the two partners. In the rust fungi, for instance, where fusion occurs not between simple hyphae but between 'male' spermatia (see above) and 'female' receptive hyphae, the two must be of opposing strains

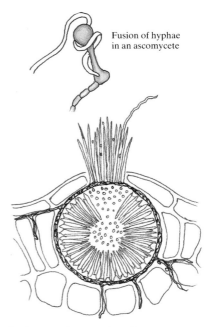

Fusion of hyphae in an ascomycete

Section through the pycnium of a rust fungus within which spermatia are formed

before a successful pairing can occur. Superficially such a system, which entails a much greater element of chance for two appropriate colonies to meet, might be thought likely to be biologically inefficient. The success of the rust fungi overall provides good evidence against this.

Sexual and asexual reproduction
Reference has been made to the existence among the fungi of sexually- and asexually-produced spores. It is perhaps unfortunate that the two should appear superficially so similar and both be given the name spore, for biologically, genetically and in the manner of their formation they are almost as different as seeds from bulbs. It has been pointed out that the ecological roles of sexually- and asexually-produced spores differ from group to group, and it is now pertinent to examine briefly the relative significance of the two states in the lives of the fungi at large.

An important concept should first be mentioned. It would be easy to consider the mushroom- and toadstool-forming basidiomycetes, point to their almost total absence of asexually-formed spores, and state that the asexual mode of life has no significance in their biology. But this would mislead by placing too great an emphasis upon the spore itself. Rather, the asexual spore should be considered merely a specialised type of hypha intended as a dispersal or survival body, and the relative importance of normal 'asexual' mycelia should be compared with that of dikaryotic or 'sexual' mycelia. Then it will be seen that some basidiomycetes do indeed live for long periods solely in an asexual state. (In passing, and to underline the complexities of the subject, it must be said that some would argue that *all* mycelium is, in fact sexual, for it is potentially able either to form sexual spores or to form or to act as sexual organs).

Among some other basidiomycetes, the rusts especially, the unequivocally asexual state is important, playing a part in size and longevity at least as great as that of the sexual state, and indeed acting as an equally efficient obligate biotroph in both. Among ascomycetes, the asexual state (the deuteromycete condition) is generally much more self-evident, and there are probably very few ascomycetes that do not have an asexual form (see p. 15). Where there has been a reduction in biological proclivity in the group, it appears to have been in the opposite direction: there are several deuteromycetes that seem able to form only rudimentary sexual structures. And certainly when looked at from the point of their importance in human affairs, there are probably equal numbers of ascomycetes that act as important plant pathogens in the asexual or the sexual state, and a few that do so in both. Some of the relative roles played by sexual and asexual phases among fungi are evident from the illustrations of life cycles (p. 234).

Fungal genetics and fungal life cycles

Although genetics, especially modern genetical science, is a highly complex subject involving mathematics and statistics, a few comments on the genetics and the cytogenetics of fungi are called for, partly as an explanation and an apology for the imperfect understanding of the subject that still prevails, and partly to mention an important and unique genetic phenomenon that the fungi display.

Genetics can be defined loosely as the study of inheritance; it explains, *inter alia*, why bald fathers may have bald sons and why the characters of two parents, be they plants, animals or fungi, may not appear in the next but in subsequent generations. Ultimately, the basis of such phenomena lies with what is popularly called 'the genetic material', DNA, carried in the genes, sub-microscopic structures invisible through conventional microscopes, but capable of being visualised with electron optics. The genes are borne on the chromosomes, larger (but still microscopic) bodies within cell nuclei, and it is the rearrangement of chromosomes (occurring after the nuclear fusion characteristic of sexual reproduction) that is responsible for the mixing and rearranging of parental characters in their offspring. The examination and counting of chromosomes under the microscope has long been a major *modus operandi* of geneticists. Unfortunately, fungal chromosomes are generally very small and at the limit of resolution of the light microscope. They also tend to be unresponsive to many of the conventional microscopic stains and tests. Largely as a consequence of these and other technical problems, the genetics of only a mere handful of fungi have been examined at all thoroughly. The majority of these are ascomycetes and one species in particular, *Neurospora crassa* has been investigated comprehensively. Indeed, because of its general amenability to study, this is almost the only fungus to have taken a place alongside the fruit fly *Drosophila* and the guinea pig as a routine genetic tool.

The pigmented and non-pigmented ascospores of *Neurospora* provide valuable markers in genetic experiments.

With the proviso that the evidence is based on relatively few species, it appears that in general the nuclear fusion, chromosome rearrangements and cell divisions (meiosis) that are associated with sexual reproduction in fungi are similar to the same processes in other organisms. It is in the nuclear and cell divisions that accompany normal vegetative growth (mitosis), however, that some fungi display curious aberrations. In particular, mention must be made of a phenomenon called parasexuality. This is manifest as the occurrence of genetically different nuclei in the same cell cytoplasm. These nuclei may fuse and undergo chromosome rearrangement not during meiosis but during mitosis. In other words, many fungal species have the facility for rearrangement of genetic material and hence for generating variability in the progeny without sexual reproduction. As a normal, natural phenomenon, this is unique to the fungi and it may occur in those that display conventional sexual reproduction too.

One manifestation of fungal genetic variability should be mentioned for its practical importance in the biology of plant disease. Some plant-pathogenic fungi exist not only as the species and varieties described on p. 260, but also in states called physiologic races. Briefly, a physiologic race is one of a group of forms of a fungal species that differ from other groups in the spec-trum of their pathogenicity. In other words, one physiologic race of, say, a rust fungus is able to cause successful infection of some cultivars or varieties of a host plant, but not of others. The ability or inability to infect is dependent on the presence of certain genes in the fungus and certain genes in the plant, which complement each other in rather complex ways. One practical consequence is that fairly small mutations or other genetic changes in the fungus, so forming a new physiologic race, can render it able to infect host plants that previously it could not. For the breeder of cereals and other crops, this can mean a constant struggle, by juggling with the genes of the plant, to stay one step ahead of the pathogen.

The time sequence in which particular fungal species produce sexual and asexual spores, pass through dormant or resting phases, and grow on or in different substrates and habitats, constitutes their life cycles. The range in life cycle type is considerable, but the few examples illustrated show something of the variation of which fungi are capable. At its most complex, in the rusts like *Puccinia graminis*, the whole seems designed for inefficiency, necessitating the formation of five different types of spore, requiring two separate and botanically unrelated host plants, and the wherewithal to pass unscathed through the rigours of a north temperate winter as well as needing the chance meeting in a leaf of male and female organs of opposing mating type. As has been mentioned already, it is one of nature's ironies that such fungi are among the most successful of plant pathogens.

Fungal fruit bodies
Micro-fungi bear their spores in many different ways, almost always on structures scarcely apparent to the naked eye. Such structures range from barely modified hyphae and simple hyphal branches, through various and often extremely complex hyphal branches, to small, balloon-like bodies, flasks and many other types. A range of some of these often

very beautiful creations is illustrated. The macro-fungi that comprise many of the ascomycetes and most of the basidiomycetes differ from the micro-fungi in that the spores, and the variously modified hyphae bearing them, are massed together in some larger organ termed a fruit body. Some reference to such fruit bodies as the cup- and dish-shaped forms among the ascomycetes, and the umbrella and bracket shapes of the basidiomycetes, has already been made in the account of spore dispersal. It is now apppropriate to consider fruit body form in a little more detail.

The ascomycetes were formerly divided into three taxonomic groups on the basis of their fruit body type: the 'Plectomycetes' with an enclosed spherical structure, the 'Pyreno-mycetes' with a flask-shaped form, and the 'Discomycetes' with an open cup- or dish-like body. For the field mycologist these are useful categories, and they have been used in this book for this reason; but the names are given within quotation marks to indicate that, taxonomically, they are no longer tenable, for they do not entirely reflect the true relationships of these fungi. Today, the most important structural feature in ascomycete classification and taxonomy is considered to be the structure of the ascus itself, and reference has already been made to the nature of the wall surrounding the ascus and the form of the opening through which the spores escape, in the identification of species (p. 43).

When reference was made in the account of spore biology to the form of the bodies containing the separate

A range of ascomycete fruit bodies

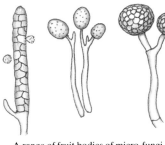

A range of fruit bodies of micro-fungi

asci, they were described as individual structures; and it may be supposed that when ascomycete fruit bodies are collected from the field, these are the objects being seen. In some instances, this is true. The cup-shaped fruit body of a *Peziza* or a *Lachnellula*, different as they are in size, are both single apothecia. Similarly, such genera as *Ceratocystis* have separate flask-shaped perithecia containing masses of individual asci. Nonetheless, these do not represent the sum total of ascomycete fruit body form, for many other species produce fruit bodies that comprise aggregates of apothecia, perithecia or other ascus-containing bodies embedded in a mass of hyphal 'tissue' called a stroma. The hard black fruit bodies of *Daldinia concentrica* (p. 207), for instance have the individual perithecia buried in surrounding tissue with their openings at the fruit body surface. Similarly, the depressions on the surface of a *Morchella* fruit body can be interpreted as numerous individual apothecia grouped over the surface of a common stroma.

As with the ascomycetes, so with the basidiomycetes. The gross form of the fruit body is now given much less significance than formerly as an indicator of relationships in the group; microscopic details of basidium

Peziza badia

Lachnellula willkomii

Ceratocystis ulmi

Daldinia concentrica

Morchella conica

Polyporus brumalis

Hedgehog fungus

Boletus lanatus

Cantharellus friesii

Lentinellus tridentinus

A range of basidiomycete fruit bodies

Auriscalpium vulgare

from the antler- and horn-like Clavariaceae through the brackets and resupinates to the cauliflower-like *Sparassis* (p. 185). Nonetheless, it is with the Gasteromycetes that basidiomycete fruit body form displays its most bewildering and often extremely beautiful variety, which incudes the more or less spherical structures among the puff-balls, earth-balls and star-like Geastraceae (all with the basidia and basidiospores initially enclosed within hollow globes), bird's-nests in the Nidulariaceae – and finally, repulsive, bizarre or beautiful, depending on your inclinations, the variously ornamented phalluses and other structures of the Phallaceae with the spores at first enclosed but then thrust outwards to cover the fruit body surface.

morphology and hyphal structures within the fruit body are considered more important. One consequence of current research and thinking is that the pore-bearing toadstools like *Boletus* are now considered to be closely related to the gill-bearing toadstools, rather than with other pore-bearing fungi like *Polyporus*. The toadstool form appears also in the Aphyllophorales in the shape of the hedgehog fungi of the Hydnaceae (p. 173), the fold-bearing fungi like *Cantharellus* (p. 161) whose true taxonomic status is under seemingly constant review, in *Auriscalpium* (p. 160), *Lentinellus* (p. 160) and a few other species.

While all gill-bearing fungi are considered to be closely related to each other, however, the non-stalked poroid basidiomycetes belong to a highly disparate group that also includes some flattened or resupinate types like those in the family Corticiaceae and its numerous relatives. The resupinate habit has been adopted by other fungi within the basidiomycetes, most notably by *Stereum* and its allies in the Stereaceae and related families. There are no really resupinate gilled species, although the genus *Pleurotus* in particular has gilled fungi with a bracket-like fruit body.

The fungi placed in the Aphyllophorales display an enormous overall variety in fruit body form, ranging

A range of Aphyllophorales

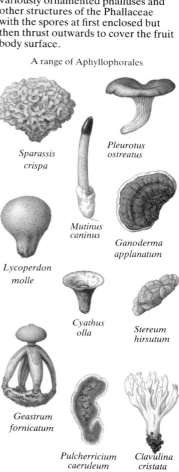

Sparassis crispa

Pleurotus ostreatus

Mutinus caninus

Ganoderma applanatum

Lycoperdon molle

Cyathus olla

Stereum hirsutum

Geastrum fornicatum

Pulcherricium caeruleum

Clavulina cristata

EDIBLE AND POISONOUS FUNGI

The fungi as a group include some of the most delectable gastronomic delicacies, sought with enthusiasm, devoured with relish and, in some instances, sold at quite prodigious prices. But by one of nature's ironies, some of them contain the most notorious among naturally occurring poisons. It is the toxic propensities of one species that have imbued certain peoples of the world (the British notably) with a desire to keep all fungi at arm's length and thus to deny themselves the culinary delights that other more enlightened races enjoy. That species is *Amanita phalloides* (p. 55). It is likely to be fatally poisonous to a healthy adult, and it is fairly readily identifiable. It certainly bears very little resemblance to the best edible species. Nonetheless, if lethal toxicity is limited to few species, there is undeniably a range of other physiological disturbances that fungi can inflict on humans. These range from mere unpleasant tastes, to include mild or severe gastric upsets and vomiting, headaches, allergic reactions of several kinds, to the various hallucinatory effects that have endowed the collecting of certain genera with an interest among some sections of the community that has little to do with academic mycology. These differing responses are brought about by a quite wide range of biochemical properties.

The fungi that can be considered truly dangerous, and sometimes lethal, to healthy adults in Europe can be counted on the fingers of two hands. This is not to minimise the fact that to children, and to elderly and weak individuals, rather more can have serious effects if eaten in certain quantities. Here, a brief summary will be given only of the types of toxic reaction caused by those macro-fungi found in the area covered by the book. Similar and other effects may be brought about by exotic species; and some micro-fungi can render

foodstuffs more or less toxic as a result of their growth in or on them.

The toxically active compounds produced by *Amanita phalloides* and by *Amanita virosa* (p. 56) are called amanitoxins and phallotoxins. They induce actual cell damage within the body, especially within the liver; a range of symptoms including abdominal pains, nausea and vomiting arises after about eight hours, with death commonly ensuing within three days. Among other fungi containing greater or lesser amounts of similar chemicals are some small *Lepiota* species including *L. hetieri* (p. 58) and *L. castanea* (p. 59), *Galerina unicolor* (p. 136) and *Concocybe filaris* (p. 144). Other toxic

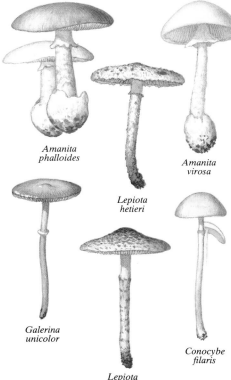

Amanita
phalloides

Amanita
virosa

Lepiota
hetieri

Galerina
unicolor

Conocybe
filaris

Lepiota
castanea

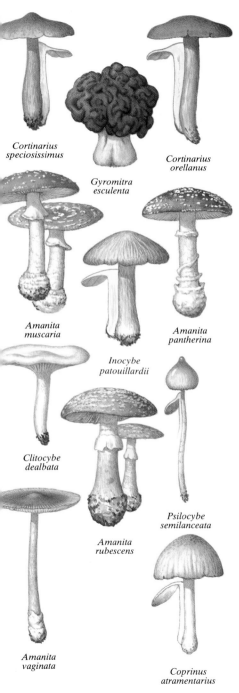

Cortinarius
speciosissimus

Cortinarius
orellanus

Gyromitra
esculenta

Amanita
muscaria

Amanita
pantherina

Inocybe
patouillardii

Clitocybe
dealbata

Amanita
rubescens

Psilocybe
semilanceata

Amanita
vaginata

Coprinus
atramentarius

substances with somewhat similar tissue destroying effects, usually resulting in severe kidney damage, are those known collectively as orellanin and produced by some *Cortinarius* species, especially *C. speciosissimus* (p. 133) and *C. orellanus* (p. 133). Despite its appetising name, *Gyromitra esculenta* (p. 216) also produces a substance that is converted to a tissue-destroying toxin when eaten.

Some *Amanita* species, especially *A. muscaria* (p. 55) and *A. pantherina* (p. 55), produce different toxins. One of these, muscimol, induces mildly hallucinatory effects, although it can render individuals comatose, while muscarine, which is also formed by certain *Inocybe* species, most notably *I. patouillardii* (p. 121) and by some small species of *Clitocybe* including *C. dealbata* (p. 64), results in a range of unpleasant effects including vomiting, intense sweating and salivation. The production of muscarine, once used to aid the control of flies, gave *Amanita muscaria* its common name of the fly agaric. More important than muscimol as an inducer of hallucinations is psilocybin and related compounds, produced typically by species of *Psilocybe*, but by related genera too. It is these fungi and this substance that have been used extensively for what is euphemistically called 'recreational purposes'. It is not only among modern society that such attractions have arisen; the extensive use of 'magic mushrooms' among ancient cultures, especially in Central America, has resulted in an entire field of mycological endeavour, ethnomycology, being devoted to their study.

Various other toxic substances are produced by other types of fungi. Many cause gastro-intestinal disorders, although a form of anaemia can result from eating uncooked *Amanita rubescens* or *A. vaginata*. Special mention should be made of two other unrelated effects, however. A few species, most notably *Coprinus atramentarius* induce an antabuse-like effect in some individuals if they are consumed with alcohol. One species

301

from among the micro-fungi, the ascomycete *Claviceps purpurea* (p. 205) must be mentioned as having been responsible for probably the most wide-scale fungal poisoning in history. *Claviceps* is a pathogen of grasses, including rye, and when rye-flour was used extensively in the past, the sclerotia or 'ergots' were sometimes ground in with the grain, resulting in contaminated bread that, when eaten, produced not only hallucinations but uncontrollable convulsions and sometimes death. The whole syndrome was known as St Anthony's fire, and a village in France was affected as recently as some thirty years ago.

It is pertinent to ask why fungi should produce such profoundly effective mammalian or even broad-spectrum toxins. The obvious explanation is as a defence mechanism but if so, it is one adopted by a very few species belonging to taxonomically very diverse groups. Moreover, slugs and some insect larvae are quite unaffected by them and devour large quantities of potentially lethal material. It may be that the toxic properties are merely incidental to some other, undetermined role that the various substances have in fungal functioning.

It must be mentioned that not all fungal products and by-products should be shunned, for fungi can be used for many different beneficial purposes. They have served as sources of drugs (even the toxic principle from *Claviceps* has a medical role as, *inter alia*, a treatment for migraine), of antibiotics (penicillin, probably the most famous antibiotic of all, is of fungal origin) and, of course, like the ascomycete bakers' yeast, *Saccharomyces* and the naturally occurring yeasts on grape skins, as fermenting agents. And although it falls beyond the scope of this book, relating little if at all to fungal biology, it may be mentioned in passing that fungi have been put to a wide range of other uses by man – as tinder, as razor strops and as sources of dyes, to mention only three examples.

As food, it is unlikely that at the present time fungi form a substantial part of human diet anywhere, although in times of hardship they have provided a welcome addition: during the American Civil War, a local mycologist (*the* local mycologist) claimed to be able to feed his family for long periods on fungi alone. Nutritionally, the family undoubtedly fell short of having a wholly satisfactory diet: while fungi contain most of the important human food requirements, apart from Vitamin A, these are present in such small amounts that a very large volume of material must be eaten. For instance, fresh edible mushroom contains about 92% water and about 1.8% protein, by weight; the corresponding values for potato are 80% and 1.4%, but per unit volume potatoes yield about twelve times as much energy. Nonetheless, for thousands of years, men have found the flavours of fungi both unique and appealing; it is curious that, despite the wide discrepancies in national tastes, mushrooms in general seem to have fairly universal appeal, although it must be said that the flavours of, say, the most popular Oriental species are somewhat different from those of Western Europe.

The most widely eaten edible fungus is *Agaricus bisporus* (p. 145), but this is simply because it is the most widely cultivated (see below). There are regular taxonomic arguments over the choice of name for the cultivated two-spored *Agaricus* species and although *Agaricus bisporus* is used here, it is accepted that the cultivated

Claviceps purpurea

Agaricus bisporus

Agaricus campestris

all edible and different species are collected enthusiastically in all parts of the world; *Boletus edulis* (p. 51) is perhaps the overall favourite although others are preferred locally.

Other fungi with more regional devotees, generally reflecting relative local abundances are *Cantharellus cibarius* (especially in parts of France) (p. 161), some of the subterranean truffles (especially the non-British species of *Tuber, T. melanosporum* and *T. magnatum* in France and Italy) (p. 219), morels (*Morchella* spp., especially in parts of the United States, Michigan most notably) (p. 215), *Lepista* spp. (p. 65), a few of the larger species of *Lepiota* (p. 58) and a few species of gilled bracket fungi.

For those in Britain, accustomed to thinking of mushroom collection as a small-time, weekend pursuit by the devoted amateur and to expressing surprise at occasionally finding blewits (*Lepista* spp.) offered for sale in provincial markets, the scale of the operation in other countries is astonishing. For in many parts of south and central Europe, of the Far East and other areas of the world, the systematic collecting of wild fungi for sale is indeed a flourishing activity. Although having perhaps declined in recent years, it is still possible to find several dozens of different species offered for sale in the markets of Italy, Poland and other mycophilic nations.

But just as man began, some 10 – 15,000 years ago to replace the collecting and gathering approach to obtaining food plants with that of the cultivator, so different races, at different times, have sought ingenious ways of subjecting fungi to the demands of domestication. Success has been extremely limited, and only a few species can be considered to have been adapted to cultivation on a truly commercial scale. Of these, two alone, *Agaricus bisporus* and *Lentinula edodes* are produced in quantities that can be measured in thousands of tonnes. (At the present time, the relative world annual production of them is about 950,000 and

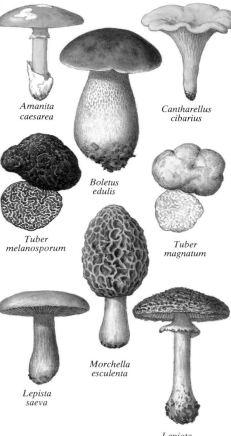

Amanita caesarea

Cantharellus cibarius

Boletus edulis

Tuber melanosporum

Tuber magnatum

Morchella esculenta

Lepista saeva

Lepiota friesii

form does differ in some respects from the wild species. Wild species of *Agaricus* are among the most popular edible fungi in many parts of the world: *Agaricus campestris* is probably the commonest of the good edible species in Britain, and many other species are equally sought after in areas where they are more frequent. *Amanita*, in addition to the most poisonous species, also includes one of the most desirable edible fungi in *A. caesarea* (p. 55), which is collected avidly in countries as far apart as Italy and Japan although it has never been found in Britain.

The boletes as a group are almost

Lentinula edodes

Interior of a modern mushroom production unit

190,000 tonnes respectively.) To some extent, success has only come with better understanding of fungal physiology and biology, for it was learned long ago that 'planting' fungi in the way that plants are planted was no way forward. The species longest in cultivation is almost certainly the non-European gilled bracket *Lentinula edodes*, known also as Shi-itake, which grows naturally on the fallen logs of deciduous trees in many parts of Asia. It is the most popular edible fungus in Japan, China and other Oriental countries and has been 'cultivated', or at least encouraged to grow, probably for at least two thousand years. At its crudest, the system employed is merely to soak in water logs cut from trees susceptible to *Lentinula* and place them in the proximity of naturally affected trees. This system is still used extensively, especially in China, although in Japan the logs are inoculated artificially with a culture of fungus. After about six or eight months of being stacked in the open in forest sites, the logs are transferred to more shaded locations where the fruit bodies begin to appear a few months later and continue to arise for several years. The fungus can be eaten fresh, although most is dried before sale. *Lentinula edodes* does not occur in Europe, and the genus is largely one of warm climates, although it was once considered to be related to *Lentinus lepideus* and *L. tigrinus* which are found occasionally in Britain. In some parts of the world, *Lentinus* species are important biotrophs, causing serious damage to standing trees.

Agaricus bisporus cultivation was a much later development. The fungus was encouraged to grow in the open, much as it does naturally, at least as early as the first part of the seventeenth century. By the early nineteenth century, methods had been developed for its culture in underground caverns that enabled it to be produced fresh all year round. As has been mentioned earlier, the use of underground sites really had nothing to do with the exclusion of light, but rather exploited the fairly high humidity and uniform temperatures. Nowadays, most large commercial mushroom production is carried on above ground in specially built sheds. The modern mushroom production unit is a highly sophisticated enterprise, the results of much research being embodied in the formulation of the compost within which the mushrooms are cultured, and with careful control of environmental variables, pests and diseases. Indeed, not only has mechanical harvesting of the crop been introduced, but also it is now possible to adjust production to ensure that the caps emerge and mature on certain days in order for the maximum numbers to be available for the pre-weekend supermarket trade.

The basis of mushroom compost in stable manure has origins that can be traced to the prevalence of several wild species of *Agaricus* in well-manured pastures; indeed, *A. arvensis* is still known as the horse mushroom. Fresh manure is wetted and stacked for one to two weeks, during which it is colonised by an

ecological succession of micro-fungi which bring about some decomposition of the straw and other substrates present, and cause a rise in temperature. Subsequently, the compost is turned in a composting machine and, as the temperature rises to around 60°C, thermophilic fungi predominate (see p. 255); it is of interest that other species of fungi provide the mushroom mycelium with certain of its required nutrients. Later, the compost is placed in trays or on shelves and pasteurised by raising the surrounding air temperature, usually with steam. Subsequently, the compost is allowed to cool and then inoculated with artificially-cultured mycelium, known as spawn, which grows rapidly through the substrate (in a process known as running) which takes about two weeks. Usually the compost tray is covered at the end of this period with a casing material of soil or, at the present time, more usually of a peat and chalk mixture. The purpose of the casing is to increase fruit body production, although the ways in which it achieves this are still imperfectly understood. Nonetheless, it seems to help regulate the moisture content, aeration and carbon dioxide content, pH and other features of the compost. After the fruit bodies first begin to appear, cropping normally continues for up to about ten weeks, after which the whole is sterilised. It is apparent, therefore, that modern commercial mushroom production embodies very evidently a thorough understanding not only of fungal nutrition and

physiology, but also of ecology, pathological and other organism interactions, the effects of environmental variables and, indeed, in the selection of the most productive strains, and of genetics and variability too.

No other artificial culture of edible fungi approaches that of *Lentinula edodes* or *Agaricus bisporus* although *Volvariella volvacea*, the padi straw mushroom, a species with relatives among European fungi, is cultured in the Far East using similar but much smaller scale processes to those for *Agaricus*. It is in Oriental countries that most progress has been made in the cultivation of other fungi and effective, if modest production of *Flammulina velutipes* (p. 88) in large culture jars, of *Pleurotus ostreatus* (p. 122) and of *Auricularia* spp. (p. 191) on naturally attacked logs is practised quite widely.

Although scarcely comparable with the mushroom culture described, the Perigord truffle (*Tuber melanosporum*) has not surprisingly attracted the attention of the commercial market. But attempts to induce true culture have failed, and the process used for many years is little more than the planting of oak trees on sites which experience suggests might support *Tuber* mycelium in the soil.

And finally, it is appropriate to mention if only in passing the extensive and important 'industrial' culture of micro-fungi like *Penicillium* (p. 223) and the yeast *Saccharomyces* in large vats of liquid nutrient for subsequent use in fermentation and other processes.

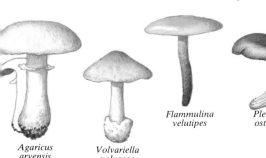

Agaricus arvensis

Volvariella volvacea

Flammulina velutipes

Pleurotus ostreatus

Auricularia auricula-judae

EPILOGUE

I hope sincerely that those who have started at the beginning and survived to this end will now be a little wiser about the ways of the fungi. I hope they can now distinguish a fungus from a plant and realise that they will never find a fly agaric beneath a lime tree. But I am saddened that I have been able to progress so little towards explaining why a fungus has evolved differently from a sunflower, why fungi have never developed chlorophyll and what it is about a lime tree that distinguishes it from the birch to which the fly agaric is so inexorably drawn. Not until you begin close encounters with the fungal world do you appreciate how greatly indebted the evolutionist is to the fossil record and how anyone seeking to explain the origins of fungi is condemned forever to grope in a museum of half facts, of 'might have beens' and 'just possibles'.

Yet if we cannot turn back the evolutionary clock, modern biology has at least given us some of the tools to make more meaningful our speculation on events past and our understanding of happenings present. From the biochemical laboratory have come, for instance, such techniques as nucleic acid analysis that suggest relationships between organisms from the examination of their most fundamental chemical units. Yet there is much of enormous fascination that it is still beyond our wit to explain. By what process of natural selection has the situation arisen of the wheat rust fungus that not only produces five different types of spore and infects two quite unrelated host plants in order to complete its life cycle, but also exists in more than one strain and more than one mating type which must meet in the appropriate combinations in the correct host tissues before they can reproduce? And by what quirk of natural fate is that fungus, so apparently disadvantaged, one of the most successful of all plant pathogens, causing countless economic losses to cereal food crops across the world?

Unrelated biologically they may be, yet fungi on the one hand and plants and animals on the other have clearly co-existed on an essential level almost since the dawn of time. It seems probable that fungi emerged from a primaeval aquatic habitat inside plant tissues, and many have stayed close by ever since, sometimes to mutual benefit, sometimes to the plant host's disadvantage. In so many aspects of plant and animal ecology, it is a fungal hand that rests on the driving wheel, gently influencing the course of events – the breakdown of dead organic matter into its constituent parts, the aiding of plant nutrition through mycorrhizal action, the tipping of the ecological balance from one plant to another by dint of its susceptibility to fungal infection. In the biological world, fungi have begun to grow up, to be recognised not as inexplicable conundrums but as crucial components of the life and death of habitats and environments everywhere.

GLOSSARY

abruptly bulbous (stem): with swollen (bulbous) base narrowed sharply above: p. 34.

absorptive nutrition: method of obtaining nutrient by absorbing pre-digested matter (*cf*, holozoic): p. 258.

acervulus (acervuli): a cushion-like hyphal mass bearing conidiophores and conidia: p. 44.

actinomycete: a member of the Actinomycetales, sometimes called mycelial bacteria: p. 274.

adherent (volva): closely attached to the stem base: pp. 34, 35.

adnate (gill attachment): joined to the stem for the whole of the gill width: p. 32.

adnexed (gill attachment): joined to the stem for less than the full gill width: p. 32.

aeciospore: a type of asexually-formed spore produced by fungi of the Order Uredinales: pp. 228, 234.

aecium (aecia): a cup-like body within which aeciospores are formed by fungi of the Order Uredinales: p. 234.

agaric: popular name for fungi of the Order Agaricales, including most of those generally called mushrooms and toadstools: p. 16.

agaricoid: of superficially agaric-like form: p. 16.

alga (algae): unicellular or multicellular, more or less ribbon-like plants containing chlorophyll and having relatively complex internal organisation.

amanitoxin: one of group of cyclic octapeptide fungal toxins: p. 300.

amoeba (amoebae): single-celled, semi-fluid animals of constantly changing shape, feeding with the aid of enveloping protrusions from their surfaces.

amyloid (response). turning blue with iodine because starch is present: p. 36.

annulus: ring- or bracelet-like structure on the stem of agaric fungi: p. 34.

antheridium (antheridia): a male sex organ: pp. 294, 295.

apical: occuring at the apex (tip).

aplanospore: asexually-formed non-motile spore, especially in zygomycete fungi: p. 230.

apothecium (apothecia): cup- or bowl-like fruit body in which ascospores are borne in "Discomycete' fungi: pp. 42, 242.

arachnoid (veil): cobweb-like: pp. 34, 35.

ascomycete: popular name for a fungus in the Sub-Division Ascomycotina, reproducing sexually by the formation of ascospores borne in an enclosed ascus.

ascospore: a sexually-formed spore borne in an ascus in fungi of the Sub-Division Ascomycotina: p. 235.

ascus (asci): enclosed structure within which ascospores are formed in fungi of the Sub-Division Ascomycotina: pp. 42, 235, 241.

aseptate: lacking septa (cross-walls or divisions): p. 252.

asexual (reproduction): not involving sexual fusion: p. 228.

attached (ring): tightly adhering to the stem: pp. 34, 35.

autoluminescence: glowing visibly without any external source of illumination: p. 257.

autotrophic: independent of outside sources of organic nutrient for provision of its own organic constituents which can be manufactured from inorganic material: p. 258.

bacterium (bacteria): unicellular or multicellular microscopic organism, lacking chlorophyll, containing a simple nucleus and usually multiplying by simple fission.

basidiole: a basidium-like but sterile structure in the spore-bearing surface of fungi of the Sub-Division Basidiomycotina: p. 38.

basidiospore: sexually-formed spore of fungi in the Sub-Division Basidiomycotina: pp. 228-231.

basidium (basidia): microscopic structure bearing basidiospores: p. 232.

binding (hypha): thick-walled, much branched, aseptate, interwoven, narrow hyphae: p. 40.

biotrophic: form of nutrition using only living cells as a nutrient source: pp. 258, 260.

bird's-nest fungus: fungus of the Order Nidulariales.

bisexual: bearing both male and female sex organs: p. 293.

bitunicate (ascus): having a double-layered wall structure: p. 42.

blewit: colloquial name for certain edible fungi in genus *Lepista*, especially *L. saeva*

bolete: colloquial name for a fungus of the family Boletaceae: p. 16.

bracket fungus: a fungus, especially of the Order Aphyllophorales have a bracket or shelf-like fruit body.

cambium: meristematic tissue that produces increase in girth of stems and roots in higher plants by producing additional xylem and phloem: p. 264.

campanulate (cap): bell-like: p. 30

canker: a disease of a woody plant in which there is death of part of the cambium, producing a sharply defined necrotic stem or branch lesion.

capillitium (capillitia): a mass of sterile, thread-like tubes or fibres among the spores of fungi of the Class Gasteromycetes.

carbohydrate: one of a large group of organic chemical compounds containing carbon, hydrogen and oxygen and having the general formula $C_m(H_2O)_n$.

carnivore: a flesh-eating mammal, especially of the Order Carnivora.

carr: an area of wet, boggy woodland especially containing alder and willow: p. 286.

cell: the smallest unit of an organism that is able to function independently, containing a nucleus surrounded by cytoplasm and other organelles: p. 227.

cellular (tissues): comprising cells: p. 38.

cellulose: a polysaccharide chemical containing long unbranched chains of glucose units: p. 228.

chitin: a complex polysaccharide chemical having a structural role in the hyphal walls of many fungi: p. 228.

chlamydospore: a thick-walled conidium formed by the rounding up of a cell or cells.

chlorophyll: the green pigment of plants that traps the energy of sunlight for photosynthesis, existing in several forms of which the commonest has the formula $C_{55}H_{72}O_5N_4Mg$: p. 258.

chloroplast: a sub-cellular structure containing chlorophyll: p. 252.

chromosome: a microscopic structure that appears in a cell nucleus especially during cell division, comprising nucleoprotein arranged into discrete units (genes).

chytridiomycete: fungus of the Class Chytridiomycetes: p. 226.

clavate (stem): club-shaped: p. 34.

cleistothecium (cleistothecia): flask-shaped structure bearing ascospores: p. 42.

clump: a cluster.

coelomycete: one of the group of deuteromycetes that bear conidia in pycnidia or on acervuli: p. 44.

coenocyte: a multinucleate structure analagous in function to a cell: p. 252.

commensalism: two different species of organism living in close association without being interdependent: p. 267.

concentric: having a common centre: p. 34.

conducting tissues: tissues within which water, dissolved nutrients and other substances are moved from one part of an organism to another.

conic (cap): cone-shaped: p. 30.

conidioma (conidiomata): conidia-bearing structures.

conidiophore: modified hypha on which conidia are borne.

conidium (conidia): an asexually-formed fungal spore: p. 230.

convex (cap): curving or bulging outwards (upwards): p. 30.

cortex: unspecialised tissue, especially that in higher plants lying between the conducting tissue and the epidermis: p. 267.

crossa-fertility: fertilisation between male and female cells of different individuals of the same species: p. 293.

culture: artificial controlled growth of fungi especially in a synthetic nutrient: p. 25.

cup fungus: one of the "Discomycete" group of ascomycetes: pp. 235, 242.

cutaneous: relating to the skin: p. 263.

cuticle: the protective layer covering the epidermis of higher plants: p. 262.

cyanophilous: staining blue with cotton blue reagent: p. 38.

cystidium (cystidia): sterile structures formed by the ends of hyphae, especially among the basidia on the spore-bearing surface of basidiomycete fungi: pp. 37, 38.

cytogenetics: that branch of genetics that correlates the structure of chromosomes with heredity and variation: p. 296.

cytological: pertaining to cell form, formation and structure.

cytoplasm: the protoplasm that occurs within the cell membrane and contains the nucleus and other organelles: p. 227.

decurrent (gill attachment): tapering downwards to merge smoothly with the stem: p. 32.

deep-seated: embedded well below the surface: p. 263.

deliquescence: the state of becoming liquid after maturing: p. 32.

depressed (cap): having a depression in the centre: p. 30.

depressed (tube attachment): having a depression close to the junction with the stem: p. 38, 39.

deuteromycete: a fungus of the Sub-Division Deuteromycotina, having no known method of sexual reproduction.

dikaryosis: the state in which the hyphae or cells each contain pairs of haploid nuclei: pp. 293, 294.

dimitic (hyphal system): containing generative and skeletal hyphae: p. 40.

discomycete: colloquial name for those ascomycetes bearing their asci in apothecia.

discontinuous (fruit body): occurring in more or less separated parts on the surface of the substrate: pp. 40, 41.

distant (gill spacing): having a wide gap between adjacent gills: p. 33.

domed (cap): curving or bulging markedly and uniformly upwards: p. 30.

dormant: not in active growth.

double (ring): comprising two visually distinct rings, one above the other: pp. 34, 35.

earth-ball: a fungus of the family Sclerodermataceae.

eccentric: having the stem arising not centrally from the cap or bracket: p. 33.

ectomycorrhiza: a mycorrhizal growth more or less confined to the outside of the host plant root: p. 267.

effused (fruit body): stretched out flat in a film-like growth: p. 39.

effuso-reflexed (fruit body): stretched out flat but with the margins curled upwards: p. 39.

ellipsoid: a geometric surface, symmetrical about the three coordinate axes and whose plane sections are ellipses or circles.

emarginate (gill attachment): having a notch at the point of attachment to the stem: p. 32.

embryo: an undeveloped or rudimentary state of an organism, incapable of independent existence: p. 227.

endomycorrhiza: a mycorrhizal growth with extensive development within the host plant tissues: p. 268.

entire (fruit body): complete, unbroken, not fragmented: pp. 40, 41.

entire (margin): complete, not indented, notched or otherwise disrupted: p. 31

enzyme: a protein that acts as a catalyst in specific biochemical reactions.

ephemeral: short-lived.

epidermis: the outer protective layer of cells of a plant.

epiphytic: growing on a plant: p. 265.

ergot: a fungus of the genus Claviceps, its sclerotium, or the plant disease caused by it: p. 254.

eroded (margin): irregularly wavy or indented: p. 31.

everted: turned outwards or inside out.

exudate: an exuded substance: p. 250.

fibril: a fine fibre: p. 34.

filamentous (tissues): having fibrous rather than rounded, cellular components: p. 38.

fimbriate (gill margin): fringed: pp. 32, 33.

flagellum: whip-like microscopic propulsion organ of spores and cells, having a complex internal structure: p. 229.

flat (cap): neither curved upwards nor downwards, plate-like: p. 30.

flattened: becoming flat, usually after having commenced with some other shape: p. 33.

free (gill attachment): having a gap between the inner end of the gills and the stem: p. 32.

free (volva): not attached closely to the stem, bag-like: pp. 34, 35.

fruit body: the overall spore-containing reproductive structure in fungi, often clearly visible to the naked eye: p. 298.

fusion: the merging of separate structures by the integration of their protoplasms: p. 294.

gall: an abnormal, swollen tissue growth on a plant, often brought about as a result of a fungal infection.

gametangium: an organ or cell in which gametes are produced: p. 294.

gamete: a haploid germ cell that fuses with another germ cell during fertilisation: p. 234.

gasteromycete: colloquial name for a fungus of the Class Gasteromycetes.

gene: a hereditary unit comprising DNA, occupying a fixed position on a chromosome.

generative (hypha): thin-walled, branched, usually septate hyphae: p. 40.

genetics: the study of heredity: p. 296.

geotropism: a directional growth stimulated by the influence of gravity: p. 257.

germination: the sprouting of a seed, spore or other organ to form new tissues following an increase in metabolism: p. 249.

germ tube: the first hypha to emerge from a spore on germination: p. 250.

gill: a plate-like structure on which basidia are produced. characteristically borne on the underside of the cap of agarics: pp. 32, 240.

gleba: the spore-bearing tissue of fungi of the Class Gasteromycetes and Order Tuberales.

glume: a dry, membranous bract, especially of a grass flower.

growing point: the apex of a stem of a higher plant at which extension growth takes place: p. 254.

haustorium (haustoria): a modified hypha that grows within the living cell of another organism: p. 262.

herbaceous: a plant not depending on woody tissue for support: p. 268.

herbarium: a collection of preserved material of plants or fungi: p. 25.

herbivore: a plant-eating animal.

hermaphrodite: bearing both male and female reproductive organs: p. 293.

heterotrophic: using complex organic compounds to manufacture their own organic constituents: pp. 8, 258.

holozoic: obtaining nourishment by eating other organisms: p. 258.

hypha (hyphae): one of the filamentous structures that constitute the mycelium of a fungus: pp. 232, 251.

hyphal system: a designation of the types of hyphae present in a fungus: p. 40.

Hyphomycete: a sub-grouping of the deuteromycetes that possess no well-defined enclosed fruit body: p. 44.

hypogeal: underground: p. 275.

imbricate (fruit body): overlapping, like the tiles on a roof: p. 39.

indigenous: originating or occurring naturally in a particular place: p. 268.

inferior (ring): positioned below half-way on the stem: pp. 34, 35.

inflorescence: the part of a flowering plant that comprises the flower-bearing stalks.

inoperculate (ascus): lacking an operculum or lid: pp. 42, 241.

inrolled: curled inwards upon itself.

internodal: occurring or arising between nodes or branching points.

irregular (fruit body): of non-uniform shape such that it is impossible to give a precise diameter: p. 40.

lamellulae: short gills occurring between the normal length gills on an agaric: p. 32.

lateral: pertaining to or arising from the side: p. 33.

lesion: a structural change in a body arising from a wound or disease: p. 264.

lichen: an organism comprising a symbiotic association between a fungus and an alga: p. 270.

lignin: a complex polymer of plant cells, its pesence giving rise to woody tissue.

litter: fallen leaves, twigs and other plant and animal debris lying on the surface of the soil: p. 276.

'lower' fungus: loosely applied to any fungus not an ascomycete, basidiomycete or deuteromycete.

luciferin: a substance occurring in autoluminescent organisms that undergoes an enzyme-catalysed oxidation and emits light on decaying to its ground state: p. 257.

macrocyclic: a fungus of the Order Uredinales having a long life cycle that involves five different types of spore: p. 234.

macro-fungus: any fungus that produces a relatively large fruit body whose details are readily visible to the naked eye.

macroscopic: capable of being seen without a microscope.

marginate (gill margin): of different colour from the remainder of the gill: pp. 32, 33.

marginate bulbous (stem): with swollen (bulbous) base bearing a marked, raised rim on the upper edge: p. 34.

meiosis: a type of cell division in which each nucleus divides into four daughter nuclei, each containing half the chromosome number (the haploid state) of the parent nucleus; characteristic of sexual reproduction:, p. 297.

melanin: one of a group of dark brown pigments occurring in plants, animals and fungi: p. 228.

membranous (veil) of fine, filmy, skin-like texture: pp. 34, 35.

meristem: plant tissue responsible for growth and whose cells divide and differentiate to produce the organs of the plant: p. 253.

micaceous: glistening, as if particles of mica: p. 31.

microcyclic: a fungus of the Order Uredinales having a short life cycle and producing less than five different types of spore: p. 234.

micro-fungus: loosely applied to any fungus of which structural details are visible only with a microscope.

micrometer eye-piece: a microscope eye-piece lens that incorporates a measuring scale: p. 26.

micrometre (μ**m**): a measure of length equal to one millionth of a metre (formerly called a micron).

microscopic: capable of being seen only with the aid of a microscope.

mildew: applied loosely to any fungal growth but more strictly to a fungus (or the disease caused by it) of either the family Erysiphaceae (powdery mildew) or the family Peronosporaceae (downy mildew).

mitosis: a method of cell division in which the nucleus divides into daughter nuclei, each containing the same number of chromosomes as the parent nucleus: p. 297.

monomitic (hyphal system): containing only generative hyphae: p. 40.

morel: an edible fungus of or closely related to the genus *Morchella*.

morphological: relating to the form and structure of an organism.

motile: capable of independent locomotion.

mould: loosely applied to any fungal growth.

movable (ring): not fixed, but capable of being moved to some extent up and down the stem: pp. 34, 35.

mucilage: a complex glutinous carbohydrate.

muscarine: an alkaloid type of fungal toxin: p. 301.

mushroom: loosely applied to many umbrella-shaped agarics, especially to edible forms.

mutualism: another name for symbiosis: p. 267.

mycelium (mycelia): the vegetative body of most fungi; a mass of hyphae: pp. 251, 253.

mycorrhiza: an association of a fungus and the roots of a higher plant in which the fungus lives on or within the roots, generally in a symbiotic relationship: p. 267.

necrotrophic: feeding on dead organisms: p. 258.

nematode: an unsegmented worm of the Class Nematoda.

non-obligate: not feeding or living necessarily in any particularly defined manner: p. 259.

non-parasite: an organism living and feeding without detriment to another living organism.

non-septate: lacking septa or cross-walls: p. 43.

nucleus (nuclei): that part of a cell, bounded by a membrane, that contains the chromosomes and associated molecules and organelles that control the characteristics and growth of the cell: p. 227.

nutrient: food.

nutrition: feeding.

obligate: feeding or living necessarily in a particularly defined manner.

oidium (oidia): (1) spore-like male sex cells in certain basidiomycete fungi or (2) conidia formed in chains by the breaking up of a hypha: p. 232.

oil-immersion objective: a high-magnification objective lens for a microscope that depends for its functioning on a droplet of oil being placed to form a continuum between the glass of the lens and the microscope slide: p. 26.

oogonium (oogonia): female sex organ of some fungi, especially in the Class Oomycetes: p. 294.

oomycete: fungus of the Class Oomycetes.

oospore: a thick-walled, sexually-formed spore, especially in fungi of the Class Oomycetes: p. 230.

operculate (ascus): having a well defined operculum (lid): pp. 42, 241.

orellanin: one of a group of fungal toxins, comprising orellanine, grzymaline, cortinarine and two benzonines: p. 301.

organelle: discrete microscopic or sub-microscopic structure within a cell: p. 227.

osmotic: relating to the process of osmosis: p. 256.

ovoid: egg-shaped.

ovum (ova): an unfertilised female gamete or egg cell: p. 228.

papilla: a small protruberance.

parabolic (cap): having, in vertical section, the form of a parabola: p. 30.

paraphysis (paraphyses): a sterile hypha occurring among spore-bearing hyphae or structures, especially in ascomycete fungi: pp. 42, 43.

parasexuality: a state in which recombination of hereditary material is based not on meiosis and sexual reproduction but on mitosis: p. 297.

parasite: an organism that lives on or in another organism and obtains nutrient from it, usually to the host organism's detriment: pp. 13, 258.

parenchyma: soft, simple, thin-walled tissue: p. 253.

partial (veil): a layer of tissue that joins the cap edge to the stem in agarics during maturation of the fruit body: pp. 34, 35.

pathogen: an organism that causes disease in another.

pectinolytic: capable of breaking down the structure of the chemicals known as pectins: p. 278.

perennation: survival from year to year: p. 248.

peridiole: a discrete part of the gleba in fungi of the Order Nidulariales that functions as a unit for distribution: p. 238.

peridium (peridia): the wall or other limiting membrane

GLOSSARY

of a fruit body.

periphery: the outermost boundary or surface.

perithecium (perithecia): a flask -shaped, ascus-bearing fruit body: p. 42.

permeable: capable of being permeated, especially by liquids: p. 256.

phallotoxin: one of several cyclic heptapeptide fungal toxins: p. 300.

photosynthesis: the combination of carbon dioxide and water to form carbohydrates in green plants using the energy of sunlight trapped by the green pigment chlorophyll: p. 258.

phototropism: directed growth movement stimulated by light: p. 242.

phylloplane: the surfaces of leaves: p. 279.

physiologic race: one of a group of fungi, generally alike in morphology but differing in their spectrum of pathogenicity to different host plants: p. 297.

pin mould: colloquial name for some fungi in the Order Mucorales, especially species of *Mucor*: p. 230.

plasmodium (plasmodia): amoeboid mass of protoplasm containing many nuclei.

plasmodiophoromycete: a fungus of the Class Plasmodiophoromycetes.

polypore: any fungus of the Sub-Division Basidiomycotina (apart from the boletes) that discharges its spores through pores: p. 16.

pore: a small hole, especially (in fungi) one through which spores are discharged: p. 39.

poroid: bearing pores.

protozoan: usually applied loosely to any microscopic invertebrate of the Phylum Protozoa.

pseudo-amyloid (response): an effect superficially similar to an amyloid response: p. 36.

pseudo-parenchyma: superficially resembling parenchyma tissue in form or function: p. 253.

pseudo-tissues: superficially resembling tissues in form or function: p. 253.

psilocybin: one of a group of indole-type fungal toxins: p. 301.

pubescent: finely hairy: p. 32.

puff-ball: colloquially, a fungus of the Order Lycoperdales or its fruit body.

pustule: a small, cushion-like growth, especially a fruit body: p. 232.

pycnidium (pycnidia): a microscopic, flask-like, conidiabearing fruit body: p. 44.

pyrenomycete: colloquial term for most of the ascomycetes bearing asci in flask-like fruit bodies.

radial lines: lines running radially inwards from the edge on the surface of an agaric cap: p. 31.

reagent: a substance used in a chemical reaction, especially in an analytical test: p. 26.

remote (gill attachment): of gills having a large gap between their ends and the fruit body stem: p. 32.

resting sporangium (sporangia): dormant, perennating body that on germination produces **spores**.

resting spore: a spore whose primary function is to facilitate a fungus's survival through adverse conditions: p. 229.

resupinate (fruit body): flattened against the substrate: p. 39.

reticulated: net-like: p. 39.

rhizoid: a root-like structure of a fungus or lower plant: p. 267.

rhizomorph: a root-like aggregation of mycelium: p. 254.

rhizoplane: the surfaces of roots: p. 278.

rhizosphere: the micro-environment very close to the root surface and influenced by chemicals produced by the root: pp. 274, 278.

ring: (1) the remains of the partial veil as manifest on the stem of an agaric, (2) a group of fungi, especially of agarics, occurring in a circular pattern on soil: pp. 34, 35.

rooting: of a fungal stem that penetrates deeply into the soil in a taproot-like manner: pp. 28, 29.

rust: a fungus of the Order Uredinales or the symptoms that it causes on a host plant.

saprophyte: an organism that feeds on dead plant mate-

rial: p. 258.

saprotrophic: feeding on dead organic matter: pp. 258, 264.

scab: a hard, crusty lesion formed on host plants by some pathogenic fungi.

sclerotium (sclerotia): a firm, often rounded, darkly pigmented mass of hyphae serving a perennating function: p. 254.

secretion: a substance that is released from a cell: p. 262.

self-fertility: the state in which an organism is able to fertilise its own female cells with its own male cells: p. 293.

septate: having septa or cross-walls: p. 252.

septum (septa): a cross wall, especially in a hypha or spore: pp. 231, 235, 252.

serrate (gill margin): toothed: pp. 32, 33.

sessile (fruit body): lacking a stem: p. 39.

seta (setae): a minute bristle-like hair.

sexual: relating to or characterised by sex: pp. 228, 293.

sinuate (gill attachment): having a sharp notch or wave at the lower edge where they join the stem: p. 32.

skeletal hypha: thick-walled, branched or unbranched, septate, straight or slightly wavy hyphae having thin-walled apices: p. 40.

smut: colloquially, a fungus of the Order Ustilaginales or the disease symptoms that it causes on a host plant.

sorus: a fruit body in certain fungi, especially of the Orders Uredinales and Ustilaginales.

spawn: colloquially, fungal mycelium, especially when used to initiate artificial growth of edible mushrooms: p. 305.

specificity: exclusiveness of the association between two organisms: p. 268.

sperm: male reproductive cells: p. 228.

spermatium (spermatia): a sex cell in certain groups of fungi, generally having a male function: pp. 228, 234, 295

spikelet: a small spike, especially the inflorescence of certain grasses.

split (margin): having pronounced radial splits: p. 31.

sporangium (sporangia): a spore-bearing body: p. 230.

spore: a microscopic reproductive body, lacking an embryo and generally unicellular: p. 227.

spore print: the pattern produced on paper or other surface when the spores are allowed to be discharged from a fungal fruit body: p. 35.

spore sac: an ascus or similar enclosed spore-bearing structure.

spore trap: an instrument that samples the air and enables estimates to be obtained of the numbers and types of spores present in it: p. 245.

sporulation: the act of producing spores: p. 263.

sterigma (sterigmata): minute peg-like structure on a basidium and to which each basidiospore is attached: p. 232.

stoma (stomata): pore on the surface of higher plant organs, especially leaves, through which gaseous exchange takes place: p. 260.

strand: a root-like aggregation of mycelium: p. 254.

stroma: a mass or matrix of vegetative hyphae in or on which spores are produced: p. 298.

stuffed (stem): having a hollow interior loosely filled with mycelium: p. 298.

sub- (prefix): under, not fully: p. 37.

sub-cutaneous: under the skin: p. 263.

suberin: fatty or waxy substance(s) present in cork cells: p. 278.

substrate: the surface on which a fungus grows and feeds: pp. 28, 271.

succession: the chronological sequence of different organisms colonising a particular substrate: p. 271.

superior (ring): present on the upper half of the stem: pp. 34, 35.

suppressor: a substance or organism that limits the growth of another organism: p. 275.

symbiosis: a close association of two organisms that are dependent on one another: p. 266.

systemic infection: an infection that permeates the tissues of the host organism: p. 263.

telium (telia): a structure in or on which teliospores are

produced.

teliospore: a sexually-formed spore produced by fungi of the Orders Ustilaginales and Uredinales and that, on germination, gives rise to basidiospores: pp. 228, 232.

thallus: the undifferentiated vegetative body of fungi, algae and lichens.

thermophilic: heat-loving: p. 255.

tissue: part of an organism comprising cells having a similar structure and function: p. 253.

toadstool: colloquial name for some larger fungi, especially some agarics.

toxin: poison.

trama: the layer of hyphae in the central part of an agaric gill: p. 38.

trimitic (hyphal system): having generative, skeletal and binding hyphae: p. 40.

troop: a group of fungal fruit bodies on the same substrate, occurring close together but physically separate: pp. 28, 29.

truffle: a subterranean fungus or its fruit body of the Order Tuberales.

tube: a tubular structure in the fruit body of many basidiomycetes and in which the spores (*cf.* gill): pp. 38, 240.

tuft: a group of fungal fruit bodies arising from a common base: p. 29.

turgor: the normal rigid state of a cell caused by the pessure of its contents against the cell wall: p. 252.

umbilicate (cap): having a depression on the surface in the centre of which is a small bump: p. 30.

umbo: a bump in the centre of an agaric cap.

umbonate (cap): having an umbo: p. 30.

unicellular: comprising one cell only.

unitunicate (ascus): having a single-layered wall: p. 42.

universal (veil): a membranous tissue that envelops the entire developing fruit body of some agarics, sometimes persisting in the mature body as a volva and fragments on the cap: pp 34, 35.

uplifted (cap): having upward curling margins: p. 30.

uredinium (uredinia): structure in which urediniospores are produced in a fungus of the Order Uredinales.

urediniospore: one of the types of asexually formed spores of a fungus of the Order Uredinales, borne in a uredinium: pp. 228, 234.

vascular: having or relating to cells that conduct liquids: p. 264.

veil: a form of membranous covering to the developing fruit body of an agaric: pp. 34, 35.

volva: a more or less bag-like structure enveloping the stem base of some agarics and representing part of the remains of a universal veil: pp. 34, 35.

water-mould: colloquial name for fungi of the Class Oomycetes: p. 230.

wavy (cap margin): having an irregular, undulating appearance: p. 31.

wavy (gill margin): having an irregular, undulating appearance: pp. 32, 33.

wilt: a disease of higher plants characterised by obstruction of the vascular tissue and a restriction of the water supply to the leaves: p. 264.

yeast: a single-celled state adopted by fungi of more normally filamentous groups, especially of the ascomycete genus *Saccharomyces*: p. 255.

zoospore: a motile asexually-formed spore: p. 229.

zygomycete: a fungus of the Class Zygomycetes.

zygospore: an asexually-formed resting spore produced by fungi of the Class Zygomycetes: pp. 230, 294.

INDEX

This index is restricted to the names of species. Figures in **bold** refer to the main entry in the DIRECTORY.

312

RUSSULA spore ornamentation

MILK, *see p. 94.*

OOSPORE, μm, *see p. 230*

PARAPHYSIS (PARAPHYSES), μm, *see p. 43.*

PERITHECIUM (PERITHECIA), cm, *see p. 42.*

PLASMODIUM (PLASMODIA), μm, *see Glossary.*

PORE, number/mm, *see p. 39.*

PORE SURFACE, *see pp. 39-40.*

PYCNIDIUM (PYCNIDIA), cm, *see p. 44.*

RESTING SPORANGIUM (SPORANGIA), μm, *see Glossary.*

RESTING SPORE, μm, *see p. 229.*

SCLEROTIUM (SCLEROTIA), cm, *see p. 254.*

SETA (SETAE), μm, *see Glossary.*

SMELL: The smell of some species is distinctive, and is described as far as possible in relation to familiar objects (see p. 31), e.g.

mealy

but taste is very rarely an important diagnostic criterion, and collectors should be discouraged from tasting species belonging to unknown genera. Nonetheless, for a very few groups, like *Russula* and *Lactarius,* it is important for specific identification (*see p. 31*).

SORUS, cm, *see Glossary.*

SPINES, cm, *see p. 40.*

SPINE SURFACE, *see p. 40.*

SPORE (without further designation means basidiospore), μm, *see p. 36.*

Microscopic details are given at the end of each account. All microscopic measurements are in μm; details of how to measure are given on *pp. 26-27.* The descriptions of the surface characteristics of spores are usually self-evident; but for *Russula* and *Lactarius* species reference should be made to the rather special patterns shown here:

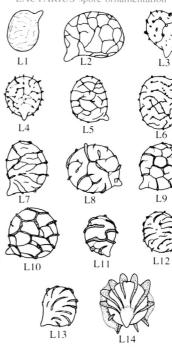

LACTARIUS spore ornamentation

In a few instances, microscopic chemical tests are indicated (*see p. 38*). A typical entry for microscopic details, therefore, is

SPORES elongated-ellipsoid, smooth, 4-5 x 7-8, non-amyloid. Gill face cystidia flask-shaped with long neck. Cap cuticle cells rounded.

SPORE BALLS, μm, *see p. 199.*

SPORE-BEARING SURFACE, *see p. 40.*

SPORE PRINT: The colour of the spore print, obtained as described on p. 35, is given for each species, and is usually self-evident; but with *Russula* species the distinction between shades of cream, white and yellow is critical, and reference should be made to the accompanying colour-chart:

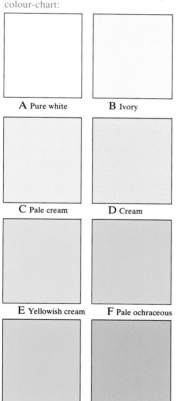

A Pure white	B Ivory
C Pale cream	D Cream
E Yellowish cream	F Pale ochraceous
G Ochraceous	H Ochre

SPORE SAC, μm, *see Glossary.*

STEM: The range in stem height is given in centimetres, measured as explained on *p. 33*, e.g.

4-6

Stem thickness is not expressed numerically, but indicated with reference to its length; shape is generally an indication of how far the whole varies from cylindrical or equal-sided, although special mention is made of the form of the stem base, and surface texture is described similarly to that of the cap (*see p. 31*), e.g.

equal or tapering slightly upwards from bulbous white woolly base, slender, apex slightly floury, fibrous, often twisted.

SYMPTOMS, *see p. 41.*

TASTE, *see p. 31, and see* SMELL

TELIUM (TELIA), cm, *see Glossary.*

TELIOSPORE, μm, *see p. 232.*

THALLUS, cm, *see Glossary.*

TUBES, cm, *see p. 38.*

UREDINIUM (UREDINIA), μm, *see Glossary.*

UREDINIOSPORE, μm, *see p. 234.*

ZOOSPORE, μm, *see p. 229.*

ZYGOSPORE, μm, *see p. 230*

Distribution is very difficult to indicate precisely, because so little study has been made of the subject, and so little mapping done. Nonetheless, an attempt at indicating the distribution throughout Europe is made, together with the frequency of recording in Britain for those species occurring here, e.g.

Widespread, predominantly southern. Uncommon.

No attempt is made to give details of fungal gastronomy, but a distinction is made between edible, inedible, poisonous and deadly poisonous species. Where published details seem to conflict or be ambiguous, the erring has been on the side of caution.